Mrs Ritter

PRENTICE HALL

MIDDLE GRADES Mathematics

An Interactive Approach

Suzanne H. **Chapin**

Mark **Illingworth**

Marsha **Landau**

Joanna O. **Masingila**

Leah **McCracken**

PRENTICE HALL

MIDDLE GRADES Mathematics

An Interactive Approach

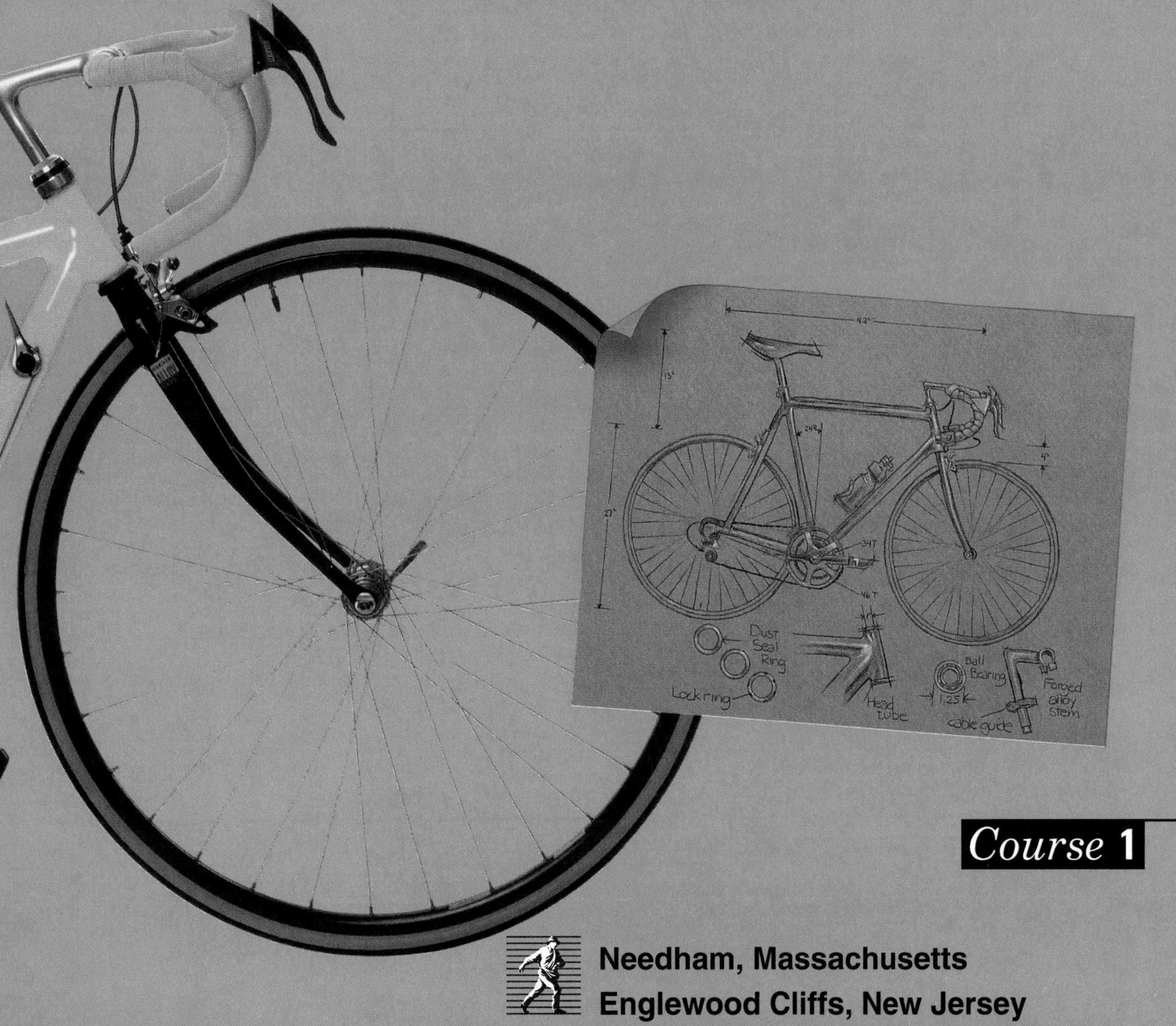

Course 1

Needham, Massachusetts
Englewood Cliffs, New Jersey

The authors and consulting authors on *Prentice Hall Mathematics: An Interactive Approach* team worked with Prentice Hall to develop an instructional approach that addresses the needs of middle grades students with a variety of ability levels and learning styles. Authors also prepared manuscript for strands across the three levels of Middle Grades Mathematics. Consulting authors worked alongside authors throughout program planning and all stages of manuscript development offering advice and suggestions for improving the program.

Authors

Suzanne Chapin, *Ed. D., Boston University, Boston MA;* Statistics and Probability strands

Mark Illingworth, *Hollis Public Schools, Hollis, NH;* Graphing strand

Marsha S. Landau, *Ph. D., National Louis University, Evanston, IL;* Algebra, Functions, and Computation strands

Joanna Masingila, *Ph. D., Syracuse University, Syracuse, NY;* Geometry strand

Leah McCracken, *Lockwood Junior High, Billings, MT;* Data Analysis strand

Consulting Authors

Sadie Bragg, Ed. D., Borough of Manhatten Community College, The City University of New York, New York, NY

Vincent O'Connor, Milwaukee Public Schools, Milwaukee, WI

ISBN 0-13-031105-7

Printed in the United States of America

1 2 3 4 5 98 97 96 95 94

Reviewers

All Levels

Ann Bouie, Ph. D., Multicultural Reviewer, Oakland, CA
Mary Lester, Dallas Public Schools, Dallas, TX
Dorothy S. Strong, Ph. D., Chicago Public Schools, Chicago, IL

Course 1

Darla Agajanian, Sierra Vista School, Canyon Country , CA
Rhonda Bird, Grand Haven Area Schools, Grand Haven, MI
Leroy Dupee, Bridgeport Public Schools, Bridgeport, CT
Jose Lalas, California State University, Dominguez Hills, CA
Richard Lavers, Fitchburg High School, Fitchburg, MA

Course 2

Raylene Bryson, Alexander Middle School, Huntersville, NC
Sheila Cunningham, Klein Independent School District, Klein, TX
Natarsha Mathis, Hart Junior High School, Washington, DC
Jean Patton, Sharp Middle School, Covington, GA
Judy Trowell, Little Rock School District, Little Rock, AR

We are grateful to our reviewers who read manuscript at all stages of development and provided invaluable feedback, ideas, and constructive criticism to help make this program one that meets the needs of middle grades teachers and students.

Course 3

Michaelle F. Chappell, Ph. D., University of South Florida, Tampa, FL
Bettye Hall, Math Consultant, Houston, TX
Joaquin Hernandez, Shennandoah Middle School, Miami, FL
Dana Luterman, Lincoln Middle School, Kansas City, MO
Loretta Rector, Leonardo da Vinci School, Sacramento, CA
Anthony C. Terceira, Providence School Department, Providence, RI

Staff Credits

Editorial: Carolyn Artin, Alison Birch, Judith D. Buice, Kathleen J. Carter, Linda Coffey, Noralie V. Cox, Edward DeLeon, Audra Floyd, Mimi Jigarjian, John A. Nelson, Lynn H. Raisman
Marketing: Michael D. Buckley, Bridget A. Hadley
Production: Jo Ann Connolly, Gabriella Della Corte, David Graham, Virginia Shine
Electronic Publishing: Will Hirschowitz, Pearl Weinstein
Manufacturing: Roger Powers
Design: Betty Fiora, Russell Lappa, L. Christopher Valente, Stuart Wallace

Prentice Hall dedicates this interactive mathematics series to all middle level mathematics educators and their students.

TABLE OF CONTENTS

CHAPTER 1 Representing Data

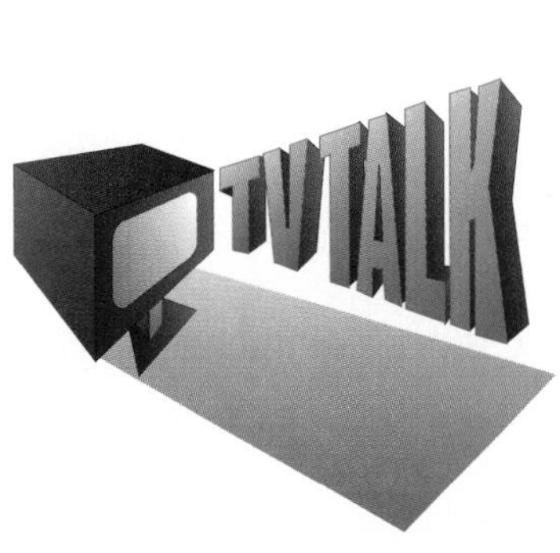

Look for photos with captions that bring math to life in every chapter!

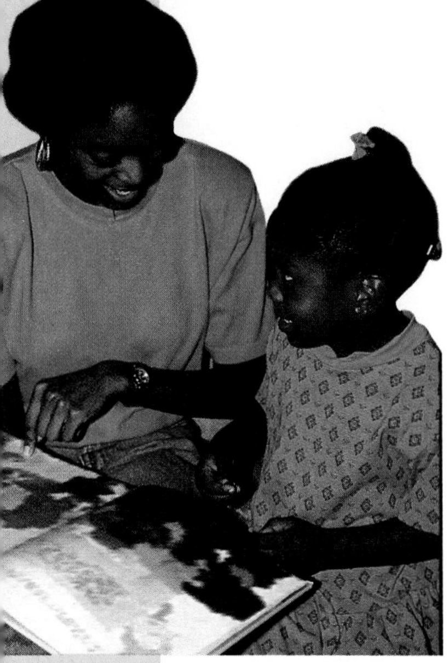

Aja Henderson has a collection of over 1,000 books! Aja lends them out to neighborhood kids who can't get to the public library.

✱ ***Hot Page Lesson***

CHAPTER 2 Geometry Concepts

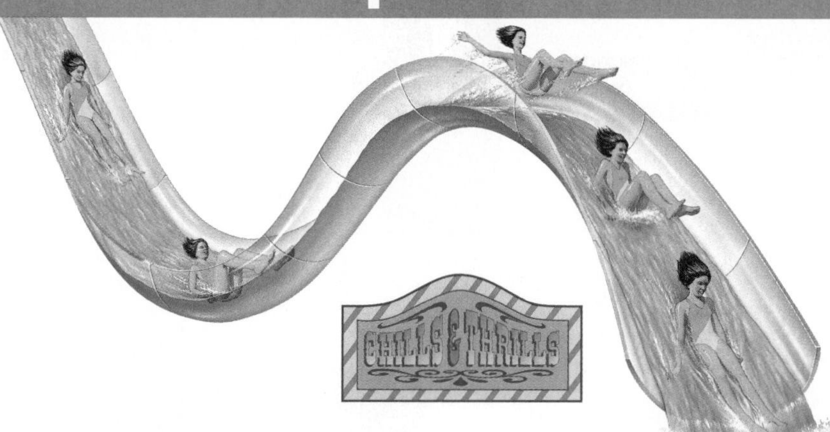

Look for the Who?, What?, Why?, Where?, When?, and How? features in every chapter!

WHAT? A harlequin was a quick-witted clown from the Italian theater. He wore a suit of bright silk diamonds, sometimes with lace and ruffles. He also carried a "wand" which he used to signal the change of scene.

Source: *The Oxford Companion to the Theater*

✱ ***Hot Page Lesson***

CHAPTER 3

Adding and Subtracting Decimals

Look for newspaper clippings that bring math to life in every chapter!

Light Years Away

The brightest star in the sky is Sirius, which is about 8.7 light years from Earth. The stars Alpha Centauri A and B are each about 4.37 light years from Earth. Proxima Centauri is about 4.28 light years away. Other star neighbors are 61 Cygni B, about 11.09 light years away, and Procyon B, about 11.4 light years away.

If you could drive to Alpha Centauri at 55 mi/h, the trip would take about 52 million years!

✳ ***Hot Page Lesson***

CHAPTER 4

Multiplying and Dividing Decimals

MEASURING UP

Look for photos with captions that bring math to life in every chapter!

Earth's crust continually moves, causing earthquakes, forming mountains, and separating continents.

Look for relevant quotations in every chapter!

> *Mathematics, rightly viewed, possesses not only truth but also supreme beauty — a beauty . . . like that of sculpture.*
>
> —Bertrand Russell (1872-1970)

✱ ***Hot Page Lesson***

CHAPTER 5 Patterns, Functions, and Equations

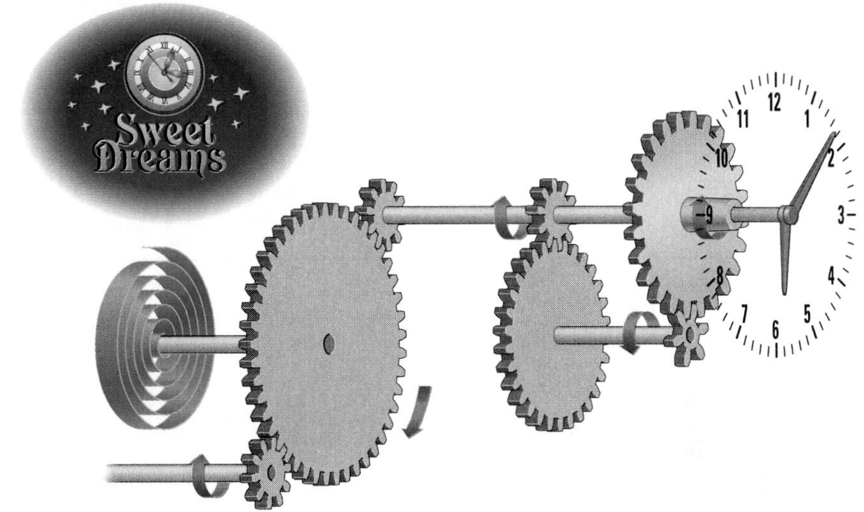

Look for the Flashback (just-in-time review) features in every chapter!

FLASHBACK

A number in standard form is separated into groups of three digits by commas.

Look for the Mixed Review in every lesson to maintain problem solving and computational skills!

Mixed REVIEW

Round to the nearest tenth.

1. 44.68
2. 8.146

Find each answer.

3. $59.36 ÷ $7.42
4. $189.32 + $33.79

Write each decimal in words.

5. 0.73
6. 386.908

7. Maria spent $35 on a pair of jeans and $18 on a shirt. She has $24 left. How much money did she start with?

✷ *Hot Page Lesson*

CHAPTER 6

Measurement

Pedal POWER

Look for the Who?, What?, Why?, Where?, When?, and How? features in every chapter!

The Great Wall of China spans 2,971 km. The wall is 14 m high and 7 m thick in some places. **If you traveled along the wall at 10 km/h, how long would it take you to travel its length?**

Source: *A Ride Along the Great Wall*

✷ ***Hot Page Lesson***

CHAPTER 7

Fraction Concepts

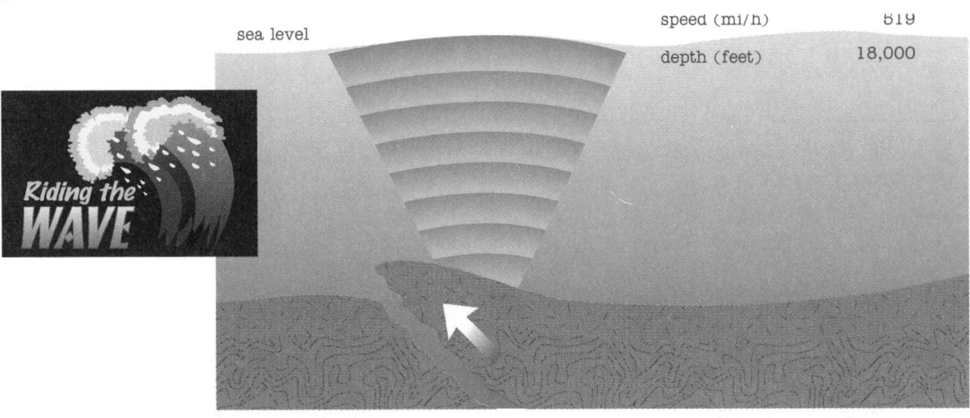

Look for Problem Solving Hints in every chapter!

Problem Solving Hint

Make an organized list.

Look for long term investigations in every chapter!

Mission: Make a list of objects you could use to represent whole numbers 0 through 9. Anyone looking at an object should easily understand the number it represents. Decide how to use the objects to represent the numbers 10 through 20. Make a poster displaying your own personalized numeration system.

✷ ***Hot Page Lesson***

CHAPTER 8

Fraction Operations

✱ ***Hot Page Lesson***

Look for photos with captions that bring math to life in every chapter!

The National Wheelchair Athletic Association *was founded in 1957 and has about 1,500 members.*

CHAPTER 9

Ratio, Proportion, and Percent

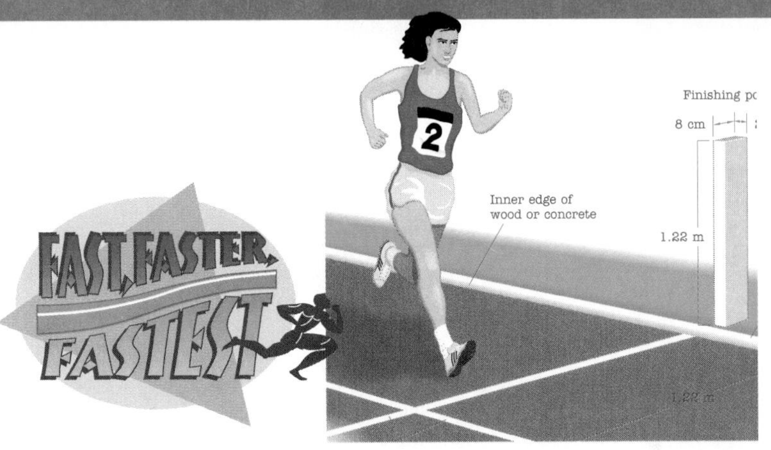

Look for frequent use of real data in every chapter!

Kids' Top Ten Foods

Pizza	82%
Chicken nuggets	51%
Hot dog	45%
Cheeseburger	42%
Macaroni & Cheese	42%
Hamburger	38%
Spaghetti & Meatballs	37%
Fried chicken	37%
Tacos	32%
Grilled cheese	22%

Source: *Gallup Organization*

✱ ***Hot Page Lesson***

CHAPTER 10 Probability

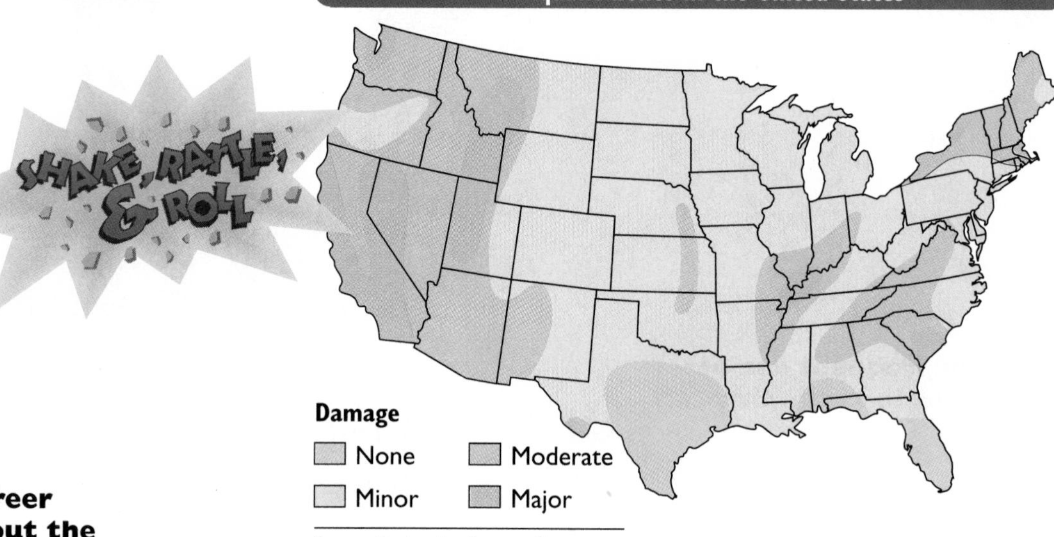

Look for Great Expectations career letters throughout the book!

GREAT EXPECTATIONS

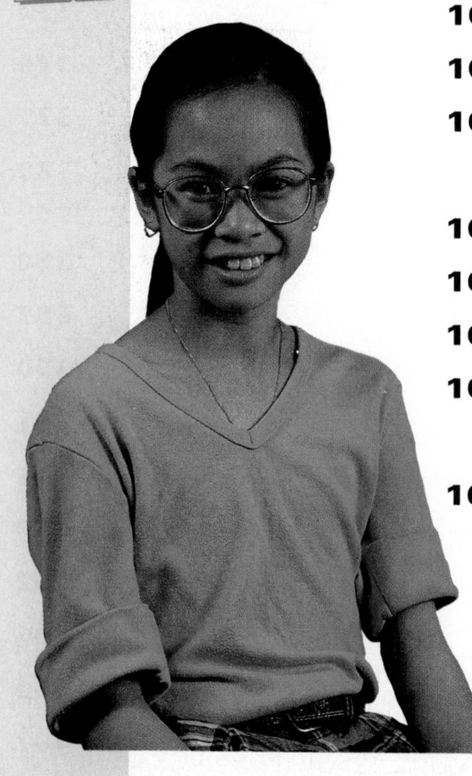

✱ ***Hot Page Lesson***

CHAPTER 11

Integers and Coordinate Graphing

✱ ***Hot Page Lesson***

Look for What You'll Need materials lists in every chapter!

WHAT YOU'LL NEED

✓ Geoboard 

✓ Rubber bands 

Look for the World View feature in every Data File!

Hawaii is moving *toward* Japan at a rate of over 4 in. per year. North America and Europe are moving *apart* at a rate of about 1 in. per year.

CHAPTER 1

Representing Data

Data File 1

Today 98% of United States households own at least one TV. More than half the households surveyed reported they watch between 7 h and 21 h of TV each week. Look at the chart below and decide into which group you fit.

How Much TV Do We Watch?

Hours Per Week	Percent
Less than 7	17
7 to 14	29
15 to 21	22
22 to 28	12
29 to 35	9
36 to 42	4
43 to 49	2
50 to 70	3
71 or more	1
No response	1

Source: *TV Guide*

How Many Own Televisions?

Homes with:	Number
Color sets	90,258,000
Black and white sets	1,842,000
2 or more sets	59,865,000
1 set	32,235,000
Cable	56,235,340
Any type of set	92,100,000

Sources: *1993 Information Please Almanac; World Almanac, 1993; Nielsen Media Research.*

How an Interactive Network Might Work

3 Satellite receives data, transmits it to an office for processing, and then receives further instructions.

2 Ground based receiver gets data and sends it to a satellite.

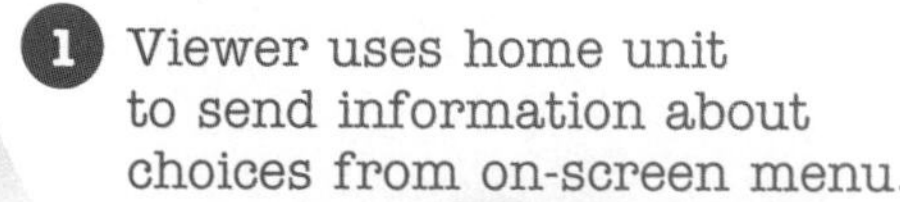

1 Viewer uses home unit to send information about choices from on-screen menu.

WHAT YOU WILL LEARN

- how to gather data and display it in a graph
- how to find and use mean, median, and mode
- how to use technology to analyze data
- how to solve problems by making a table

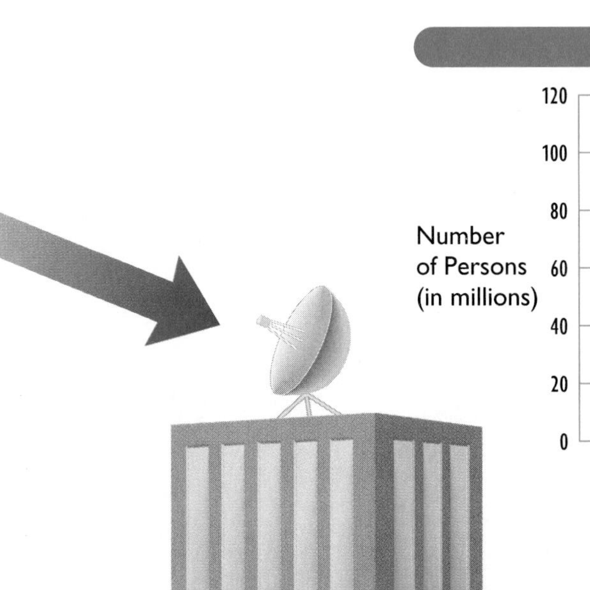

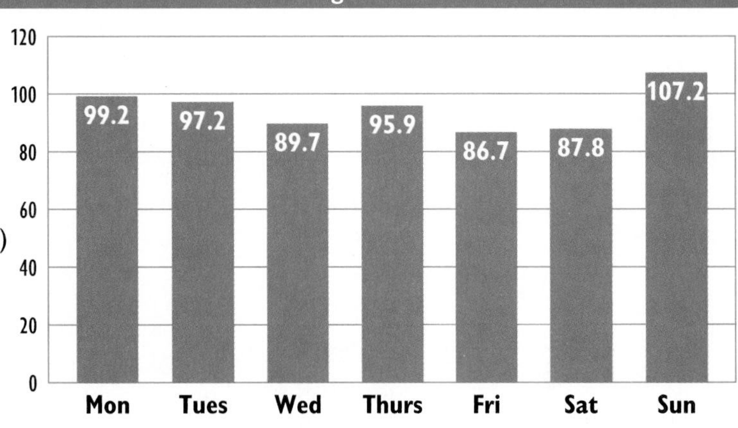

Prime time is 8-11 P.M. (EST) Mon–Sat and 7-11 P.M. on Sun.

The Japanese government spends $17.71 per person on public television. The Canadians spends $32.15 and the United States spends only $1.06.

4 Office receives data and sends information to next station.

5 Store or other agency receives and fulfills requests and prepares billing.

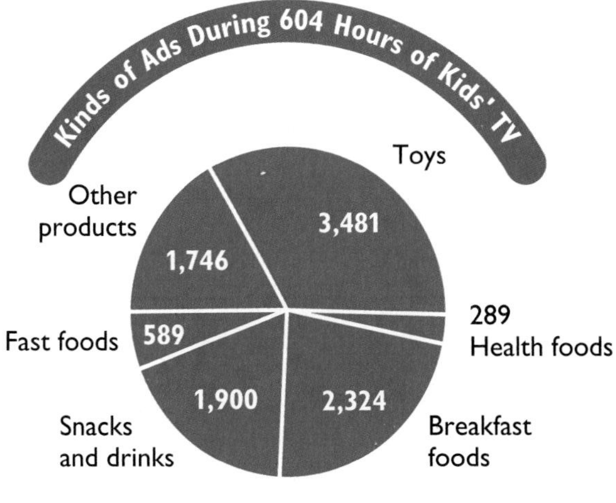

Total Ads: 10,329

Source: *Dynamath*

investigation

Project File

Memo

The human heart may be the world's most amazing machine. It weighs only about half a pound, yet it can pump blood through some 12,000 mi of bloodways in the human body. It never rests or stops for repairs. In a single year your heart pumps around a million gallons of blood through your body. In an average person's lifetime a heart beats more than 2 billion times.

Mission: Find the pulse rates (beats per minute) of your classmates. Then make a poster displaying your results. Describe how you conducted your investigation and tell how you interpreted the results.

- ✓ For how many students should you find the pulse rate?
- ✓ How many times should you take each student's pulse?
- ✓ What kind of information about pulse rates should you display on your poster?

What's Ahead

- Organizing data in frequency tables and line plots

1-1 Frequency Tables and Line Plots

THINK AND DISCUSS

You can make any color paint by mixing the colors blue, red, and yellow. These colors are the *primary colors.* An art teacher asked students in her class to name their favorite primary color. She organized their responses in the *frequency table* below. A **frequency table** shows the number of times each piece of data occurs.

Favorite Primary Color	Tally	Frequency
blue	𝍸 ||||	9
red	𝍸 𝍸	10
yellow	|	1

Blue is the favorite color of most Americans. In order, the next favorite colors are red, green, white, pink, purple, orange, and yellow.

Source: *3-2-1 Contact*

1. What does each tally mark, or |, represent?
2. How is the frequency in the third column determined?
3. **Discussion** How many students are in the class? Describe two ways you can find this number.

A *line plot* is another way you can organize data. A **line plot** displays data on a horizontal line.

Heights of Students in a Math Class (in.)

						×				
		×		×	×	×		×		
	×	×	×	×	×	×	×	×		
×	×	×	×	×	×	×	×	×	×	×
55	56	57	58	59	60	61	62	63	64	65

4. What does each × represent?
5. **Discussion** How many students are in the math class? Explain how you found this number.

Mixed REVIEW

Find each answer.

1. 243 + 43 + 817 + 36
2. 96 + 17 + 89 + 16
3. 23,427 − 4,798
4. 592 − 418

5. Vivian has six coins that total 52¢. What coins, and how many of each, does she have?

WORK TOGETHER

- Make a frequency table in which you can record the birth months of the students in your math class.
- Have each student in your class tell in what month he or she was born. Fill in your frequency table with the responses.
- Display the results in a line plot.
- Work with a partner to write a short paragraph describing the results.

The **range** of a set of data is the difference between the greatest value and the least value in a set of numerical data.

6. In 1852, surveyors made these six measurements of Mt. Everest to determine the height of the mountain.

28,990 ft	28,992 ft	28,999 ft
29,002 ft	29,005 ft	29,026 ft

a. What was the greatest height measured? the least height measured?

b. Find the range of the measurements.

ON YOUR OWN

7. Social Studies There is a town in Wales named Llanfair-pwllgwyngyllgogerychwyrndrobwllllantysiliogogogoch.

Letter	Tally	Frequency
a	|||	3
e	■	■
i	■	■
o	■	■
u	■	■

a. Copy and complete the frequency table at the left using the name of the Wales town.

b. Describe the data recorded in your frequency table.

8. Literature The number of letters in each of the first twenty-five words of the book *The Story of Amelia Earhart* are shown below. Make a frequency table.

6 3 4 2 3 5 3 7 3 4 3 3 4
3 3 3 6 6 3 5 3 2 3 7 5

9. Calculator NASA requires that an astronaut be at least 58.5 in. and at most 76 in. tall. Find the height range.

10. **a.** What information is displayed in the line plot?

b. How many test grades are recorded in the line plot?

c. How many students received a grade of C or better?

Science Test Grades

	×			
	×			
×	×			
×	×	×		
×	×	×	×	
×	×	×	×	×
A	B	C	D	F

11. **Writing** How are frequency tables and line plots alike? How are they different?

12. **Sports** The ticket prices available for a Milwaukee Brewers' baseball game are \$14, \$12, \$4, \$15, \$8, \$7, and \$11. Find the range.

13. **Social Studies** The birth states of the 42 Presidents of the United States are shown below.

<table>
<tr><th colspan="6">Presidential Birth States</th></tr>
<tr><th>State</th><th>Tally</th><th>State</th><th>Tally</th><th>State</th><th>Tally</th></tr>
<tr><td>VA</td><td>𝍸 |||</td><td>KY</td><td>|</td><td>CA</td><td>|</td></tr>
<tr><td>MA</td><td>||||</td><td>OH</td><td>𝍸 ||</td><td>NE</td><td>|</td></tr>
<tr><td>SC</td><td>|</td><td>VT</td><td>||</td><td>GA</td><td>|</td></tr>
<tr><td>NY</td><td>||||</td><td>NJ</td><td>||</td><td>IL</td><td>|</td></tr>
<tr><td>NC</td><td>||</td><td>IA</td><td>|</td><td>AR</td><td>|</td></tr>
<tr><td>NH</td><td>|</td><td>MO</td><td>|</td><td></td><td></td></tr>
<tr><td>PA</td><td>|</td><td>TX</td><td>||</td><td></td><td></td></tr>
</table>

a. Make a line plot of the data.

b. In what four states were the most presidents born?

c. Is it possible to find the range for these data? Explain.

***Franklin D. Roosevelt** was born in New York and was President longer than any other person. He was elected four times and served more than twelve years.*

14. **Activity** There are 8 states that begin with the letter M.

a. Ask 20 people who are not in your math class to name as many states that begin with the letter M as they can. Record the states that each person correctly names in a frequency table.

b. Display your results in a line plot.

c. **Writing** Describe the results of your survey. What state was most often missed?

15. **Investigation (p. 4)** Collect data on the number of times 10 people blink their eyes in one minute. Display your results in a frequency table.

PROBLEM SOLVING

What's Ahead

- Solving problems by making a table

1-2 Make a Table

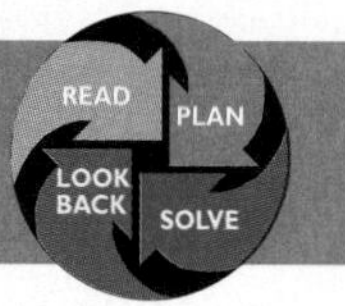

Mr. Mon E. Bags has a pocket full of coins. He says that he can show you all possible ways to make 18¢. How many ways should you expect Mr. Mon E. Bags to show you if what he says is true?

READ

Read and understand the given information. Summarize the problem.

Think about the information you are given and what you are asked to find.

1. What does the problem ask you to find?

2. What type of coins must Mr. Mon E. Bags have in his pocket? What is the value of each of these coins?

PLAN

Decide on a strategy to solve the problem.

You can make a table to help you organize the possible ways to make 18¢.

3. a. Mr. Mon E. Bags puts 1 dime on the table. How many pennies must he put on the table to make 18¢?

b. What is another way that Mr. Mon E. Bags could make 18¢ after putting 1 dime on the table?

4. Mr. Mon E. Bags uses only pennies to show you 18¢. How many pennies are on the table?

SOLVE

Try out the strategy.

Make a table like the one below to form an organized list of all possible ways to make 18¢.

Dimes	Nickels	Pennies
1	0	8
:	:	:
:	:	:
0	0	18

5. Copy and complete the table above.

The most popular coin is the Lincoln head penny. Since 1909 over 250 billion pennies have been minted. If stacked, they could reach from Earth to the moon.

Source: *Guinness Book of Records*

6. Why does the number 2 not appear in the column labeled *dimes*?

7. **Discussion** Why is it easier to determine first the number of dimes needed rather than the number of pennies? Use an example to support your answer.

8. Count the number of ways that Mr. Mon E. Bags can make 18¢.

You can use the table you made to answer many other questions.

LOOK BACK

Think about how you solved this problem.

9. **Discussion** Are there any patterns in the numbers that appear in your table? If so, describe the patterns.

10. To make 18¢, what is the minimum number of coins needed? the maximum number of coins needed?

11. Ten coins total 18¢. What types of coins are they?

TRY THESE

Make a table to solve each problem.

12. How many possible ways are there to make 28¢?

13. There are 16¢ in a bag. There are more nickels than pennies.
    a. What types of coins are in the bag?
    b. How many of each type of coin are in the bag?

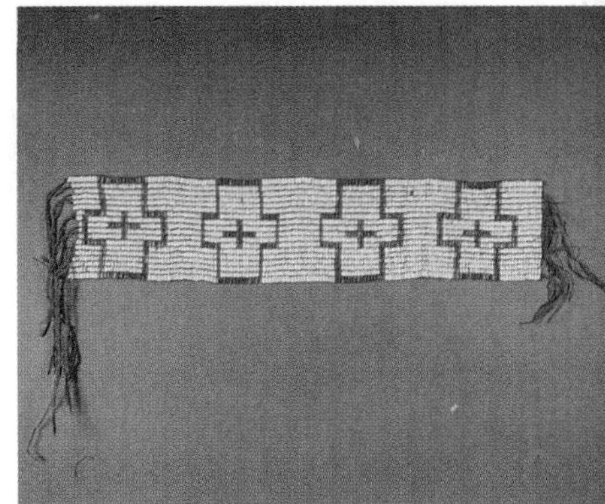

***Wampum belts** made of beads were used by Native Americans as money. They traded wampum with American settlers for goods. Five purple beads equaled one English penny.*

Source: *Reader's Digest Book of Facts*

ON YOUR OWN

Use any strategy to solve each problem. Show all your work.

14. Michael has a paper route. He earns 15¢ for each daily paper and 35¢ for each Sunday paper he delivers. Michael delivers twice as many daily papers each week as Sunday papers. How many of each type of paper does he deliver if he earns $13 each week?

WHO? Caitrin McKiernan wrote and produced a TV news report on homeless children when she was just ten years old. She hopes to become a broadcast journalist when she gets older.

Source: *National Geographic World*

15. Yasmine, Fiona, and Carmen graduated from college. They have degrees in engineering, nursing, and law. Yasmine and the engineer plan to share an apartment. The nurse helps Carmen pack. Fiona's law firm specializes in corporate law. Who is the engineer?

16. Mr. Odina's class is sponsoring an auction to raise money for the homeless. Each class member is assigned to make tags. Chen's task is to make three-digit number tags using the digits 3, 7, and 8. How many number tags can Chen make using each digit exactly once on each tag?

17. How many triangles are contained in the floor tile below?

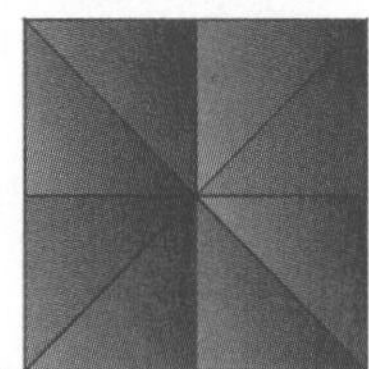

18. Find the smallest number that meets all these conditions.
    - When you divide the number by 7, there is 1 left over.
    - When you divide the number by 9, there is 7 left over.
    - When you divide the number by 11, there is 10 left over.

19. A printer uses 121 pieces of type to number the pages of a book. The first page is numbered one. How many numbered pages are in the book?

20. Thelma and her brother Otis visit their grandmother and uncle each Friday. From their apartment they walk three blocks north and four blocks west to their grandmother's. They then continue one block south and nine blocks east to their uncle's. What are three ways Thelma and Otis can return home by walking a total of seven blocks?

21. Buses leave Boston for New York every 40 min. The first bus leaves at 5:10 A.M. What is the departure time closest to 12.55 P.M.?

22. The carnival has two types of rides for children. Each race car seats 4 children and each tug boat seats 6 children. Altogether there are 28 race cars and tug boats that seat a total of 136 children. How many of each are there?

Mixed REVIEW

Use the data for Exercises 1–3. Student heights (in.): 53, 55, 60, 53, 57, 55, 52, 54, 53, 55

1. Make a frequency table.
2. Make a line plot.
3. Find the range.
4. Andrés is starting a book-trading group. He is the only member now, but he plans to have each member find an additional 3 new members each month. How many members does Andrés expect to have after 6 months?

What's Ahead

- Finding mean, median, and mode
- Deciding which average is most appropriate for a given situation

1-3 Three Kinds of Averages

WHAT YOU'LL NEED

✓ Graph paper 

✓ Scissors

WORK TOGETHER

- Write the names of the students in your group on strips of graph paper like the sample shown below.

L	I	S	A						
A	N	T	O	N	I	O			
I	A	N							
C	H	R	I	S	T	I	N	A	
A	L	E	X	A	N	D	E	R	

- Find the average length of the names of the students in your group. Describe how your group found this number.
- Compare your work with other groups. Did everyone find the average length of the names the same way? Explain.

THINK AND DISCUSS

You can make general statements about data using the averages *mean, median,* and *mode.* The **mean** of a set of data is the sum of the data divided by the number of pieces of data.

Math In the World

Country	Minutes in Math Class Each Week
South Korea	179
Switzerland	251
Taiwan	204
Jordan	180
United States	228
France	230

Example 1 Find the mean number of minutes students spend in math class each week.

- Find the sum of the data.

179 + 251 + 204 + 180 + 228 + 230 = 1272

- Divide the sum by the number of pieces of data.

1272 ÷ 6 = 212

Students spend about 212 min in math class each week.

You can also describe data by finding the *median.* The **median** is the middle number in a set of ordered data.

Example 2 The average daily temperatures (°F) for one week are 86, 78, 92, 79, 87, 91, and 77. Find the median.

Order the data and choose the middle number.

77 78 79 (86) 87 91 92

The median temperature is 86°F.

You can find the median when there is an even number of data items by adding the two middle numbers and dividing by 2.

Average Monthly Temperatures (°F) for St. Louis, MO					
29	34	43	56	66	75
79	77	70	58	45	34

1. The average monthly temperatures (°F) for St. Louis, Missouri, are shown at the left.
   a. Find the mean and median.
   b. **Discussion** Which average better describes the temperatures in St. Louis over a year? Explain.

Data can also be described by the *mode.* The **mode** is the data item that appears most often. The mode is especially helpful when the data are not numerical.

Example 3 The line plot shows the items collected by a group of students. Find the mode.

Collectibles

Coins	Cards	Stamps	Comic Books	Other
× × × ×	× × × × ×	× ×	× × ×	×

The mode is cards because it appears most often.

A set of data can have more than one mode. There is no mode when all the data items are listed the same number of times.

Aja Henderson has a collection of over 1,000 books! Aja lends them out to neighborhood kids who can't get to the public library.

2. Suppose a student who collects stamps collects coins instead. Find the mode.

3. **Discussion** Describe the line plot if the data has no mode.

TRY THESE

Find the mean, median, and mode of each set of data.

4. 15 12 20 13 17 19
5. 95 80 92 91 98 94 94

6. **Sports** In professional baseball, a baseball is used for a mean average of five pitches. What are seven numbers that have a mean of 5?

7. Which average would best describe the favorite subject of students in your math class? Explain.

Lengths of 20 Comedy Movies (min)				
102	111	105	100	100
99	107	104	101	89
101	90	92	87	96
92	95	101	110	98

ON YOUR OWN

8. a. **Entertainment** Describe the average length of a comedy movie using mean, median, and mode.
   b. **Activity** Visit a nearby video store. Record the lengths in minutes of 20 science fiction movies. Analyze your data using mean, median, and mode.
   c. **Writing** Use mean, median, and mode to compare the lengths of science fiction and comedy movies.

9. **Music** The line plot shows the number of songs on 27 recently released rock CDs.

Number of Songs on Rock CDs

			x			
		x	x			
		x	x			
	x	x	x			
	x	x	x			
	x	x	x			
x	x	x	x	x	x	
x	x	x	x	x	x	x
9	10	11	12	13	14	15

   a. Find the median and mode.
   b. What average do you think best reflects the number of songs on a rock CD? Explain.
   c. **Critical Thinking** Would it make sense to use the mean to describe this data? Why or why not?

Mixed REVIEW

Find each answer.

1. 718 + 46
2. 2,057 − 569
3. 114 × 12
4. 248 ÷ 8
5. At one point on a mountain road, the elevation is 4,000 ft. Two miles up the road, the elevation is 5,200 ft. If this pattern continues, what will the elevation be six miles up the road from the starting point?

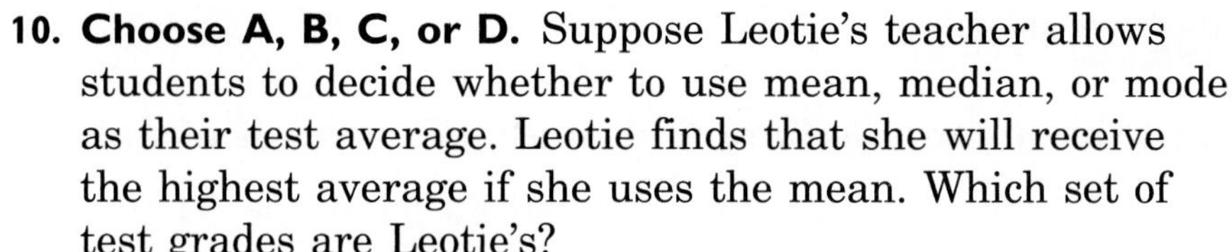

10. **Choose A, B, C, or D.** Suppose Leotie's teacher allows students to decide whether to use mean, median, or mode as their test average. Leotie finds that she will receive the highest average if she uses the mean. Which set of test grades are Leotie's?

    A. 74, 80, 92, 82, 92 **B.** 74, 80, 74, 82, 85
    C. 74, 80, 92, 85, 74 **D.** 74, 80, 70, 71, 80

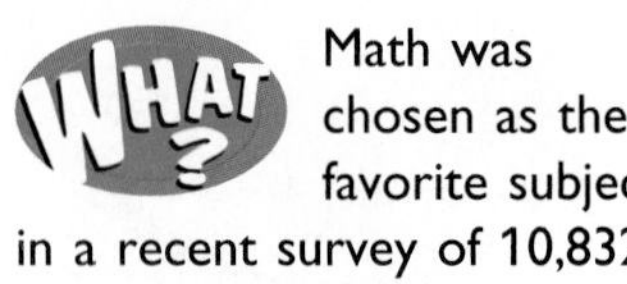

Math was chosen as the favorite subject in a recent survey of 10,832 junior high students.

Source: *Scholastic Math*

Critical Thinking **What average is most appropriate for each situation? Explain.**

11. the favorite subject of students in your grade
12. the snowfall for the month of December in Lansing, MI
13. the cost of houses in your community
14. Data File 1 (pp. 2–3) Use a calculator to find the mean number of people viewing TV during prime time Monday through Friday.
15. Writing Describe a situation that would be most appropriately described by each average: mean, median, and mode.

16. Investigation (p. 4) Collect data on the number of times ten people blink in one minute. Find the mean, median, and mode of your results.

Sport	Players on a Team
American Football	11
Volleyball	6
Basketball	5
Soccer	11
Ultimate Frisbee	7
Ice Hockey	6
Softball	9
Field Hockey	11
Speedball	11
Baseball	9

CHECKPOINT

Use the following data for Questions 1 and 2.

Grams of fat per serving for 25 popular breakfast cereals:
0, 1, 1, 3, 1, 1, 2, 2, 0, 3, 1, 3, 2, 0, 1, 0, 2, 1, 1, 0, 0, 0, 2, 1, 0

1. Make a frequency table. 2. Make a line plot.

Use the table at the left for Questions 3 through 6.

3. Calculator Find the mean number of players.
4. Find the median. 5. Find the mode.
6. Which average best describes the number of players on a sports team? Explain.

Problem Solving Practice

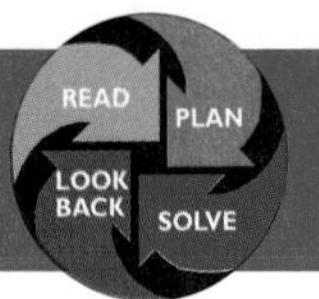

PROBLEM SOLVING STRATEGIES

Make a Table
Use Logical Reasoning
Solve a Simpler Problem
Too Much or Too Little Information
Look for a Pattern
Make a Model
Work Backward
Draw a Diagram
Guess and Test
Simulate a Problem
Use Multiple Strategies

Solve. The list at the left shows some possible strategies you can use.

1. You have been given five single gold links. A jeweler charges $1 to cut and mend a link. What is the minimum cost the jeweler will charge to make the five links into a single gold chain?

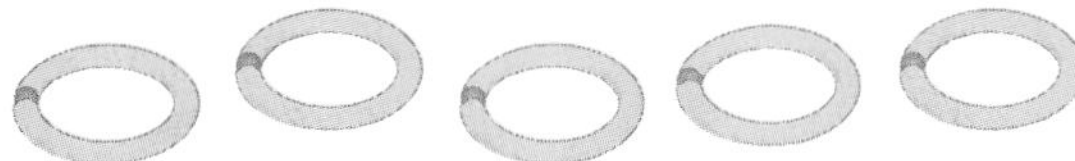

2. Solve this riddle: "I think of a number, add 6, multiply by 4, divide by 8, and subtract 3. The answer is 2." What is the original number?

3. There are two children in the Jackson family. The sum of their ages is 15, and their product is 54. How old are each of the children?

4. Zahur's favorite game uses a velcro board, like the one below, and three velcro darts. When a dart lands on a line, the higher value is counted. What possible scores can Zahur get if all three darts hit the board?

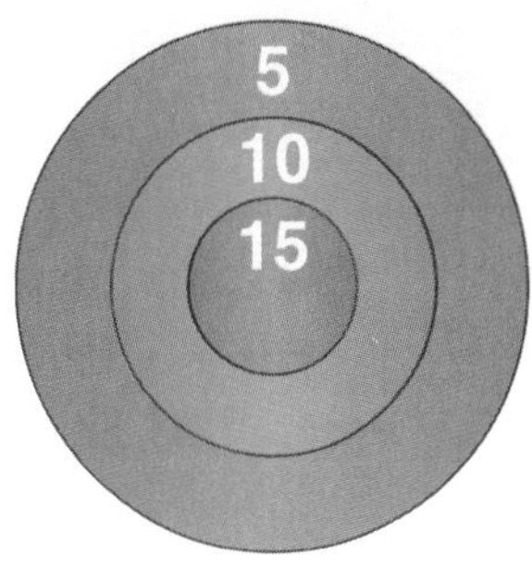

Velcro was invented by Georges de Mestral, a Swiss engineer. He got his idea from nature after examining how burrs stuck so well to his woolen socks.

Source: *How in the World?*

5. Calculator Divide 3 by 11. What number would be in the 50th decimal place?

6. Six apples weigh the same as two oranges and two kiwi. An orange weighs the same as eight kiwi. How many kiwi equal the weight of an apple?

TECHNOLOGY

1-4 Computer Spreadsheets

What's Ahead

- Organizing data in a spreadsheet
- Using spreadsheets to explore averages

WHAT YOU'LL NEED

✓ **Computer** 

✓ **Spreadsheet software** 

THINK AND DISCUSS

A compact disk can hold nearly 80 min of music. Do your CDs have room for more songs? Do some types of CDs contain more music than other types?

The *spreadsheet* below shows the length of 20 CDs from five different musical categories. You can use a **spreadsheet** to organize and analyze data.

	A	B	C	D	E	F
1	Music Type	Disk 1 (min)	Disk 2 (min)	Disk 3 (min)	Disk 4 (min)	Mean Length (min)
2	Rock/Pop	40	44	45	47	
3	Rap	47	53	55	41	
4	Country	32	34	30	36	
5	Classical	45	73	51	59	
6	Jazz	41	58	44	77	

***A compact disk** holds 3 mi of playing track. CDs can never get scratched because no needle ever touches the surface.*

Data are arranged in a spreadsheet in columns and rows.

1. **a.** How are columns identified in a spreadsheet?
   b. How are rows identified in a spreadsheet?

A **cell** is the box where a row and column meet. For example, the box where column E and row 3 meet is called cell E3. The value in cell E3 is 41.

2. **a.** What value is in cell D4? What does this number mean?
   b. What cells are in row 2?
   c. What cells are in column C?

3. **a.** Which cell contains the greatest value? the least value?
   b. What type of music is on the CD which contains the greatest amount of music? the least amount of music?

WORK TOGETHER

A spreadsheet program can save you a lot of time and effort. For example, the computer can automatically fill in the values for an entire column of your spreadsheet if you tell it what calculations to do. A **formula** is a set of instructions that tells the computer what to do.

Work with a partner to answer each question.

4. a. **Writing** Cell F2 displays the mean length of the four rock/pop CDs. Describe how you would calculate this value without using a computer.
   b. **Discussion** With a spreadsheet program you can enter the formula =(B2+C2+D2+E2)/4 into cell F2. How is this formula like the description you wrote? How is it different?
   c. **Computer** Set up a spreadsheet like the one on the previous page. Enter the formulas for cells F2 through F6. What are the mean lengths for each of the five types of music?

5. **Critical Thinking** Determine what will happen to the value in F4 if each of the following occurs.
   a. the value in cell C4 gets larger
   b. the value in cell B4 gets smaller
   c. the value in cell B3 gets larger

6. **Discussion** How would the formulas that are now in column F change if there were five disks representing each type of music instead of four?

7. **Computer** Suppose the length of the first classical CD was entered incorrectly. Change the value in cell B5 to 65. How did the spreadsheet change when you made this correction?

8. **Computer** Add a row 7 to your spreadsheet.
   a. Include these data about four CDs that hold movie soundtracks: 31 min, 48 min, 32 min, 49 min.
   b. What formula did you put in cell F7?
   c. What is the mean length of the movie soundtrack CDs?

The word *cell* comes from the Latin word *cella,* meaning "room."

Source: *The Oxford Dictionary of English Etymology*

Problem Solving Hint

You can substitute appropriate values into each cell to see what happens to the value in cell F4.

ON YOUR OWN

Use the information below for Exercises 9–12.

Tamara works part-time at Rad Sounds music store, where she gets paid \$6 per hour. She set up a spreadsheet to keep track of the time she works and the money she earns. The spreadsheet below shows a typical schedule for a week.

	A	B	C	D	E
1	Day	Time in (PM)	Time Out (PM)	Hours Worked	Amount Earned
2	Monday	3	5	■	■
3	Wednesday	4	6	■	■
4	Friday	3	6	■	■
5	Saturday	1	6	■	■
6			Total:	■	■
			Average:	■	■

9. How can you calculate the value of cell D2? cell E2?

10. a. **Computer** Make a spreadsheet like Tamara's. Use your answer to Exercise 9 to write formulas in columns D and E.
    b. How many hours does Tamara work in a typical week?
    c. What is the average number of hours Tamara works each shift?
    d. How much does Tamara earn in a typical week?
    e. What is the average amount Tamara earns each shift?

11. a. Would your formula for cell D2 still work if Tamara arrived at the store at 11 A.M. and left at 1 P.M.? Why or why not?
    b. **Critical Thinking** How would you change your spreadsheet so it could handle morning and afternoon hours?

12. **Computer** Determine Tamara's weekly earnings if she has the same schedule except that she receives a \$2 per hour raise.

In Denmark, *Tamara would earn about 42 kroner per hour.* ***How many kroner equal one dollar?***

Use the information below for Exercises 13–18.

It's music video month in Ms. Houston's class. Each group of students creates a video and receives three scores from 0 to 100 for originality, effort, and technical quality. Ms. Houston entered all the scores on a spreadsheet, but a "bug" in her computer erased some of the data.

	A	B	C	D	E	F
1	Group	Originality	Effort	Quality	Total	Mean Score
2	Red	90	■	80	■	85
3	Orange	90	90	■	■	80
4	Yellow	95	100	75	■	■
5	Green	■	80	80	■	75
6	Blue	85	■	85	■	85

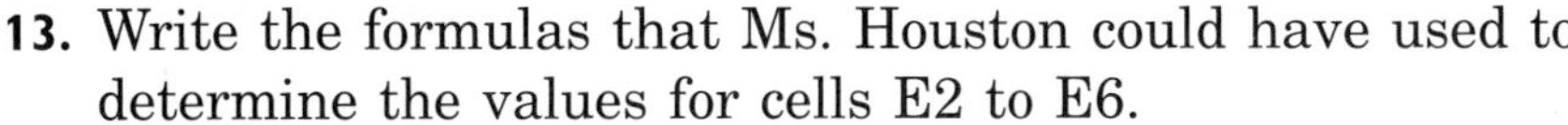

13. Write the formulas that Ms. Houston could have used to determine the values for cells E2 to E6.

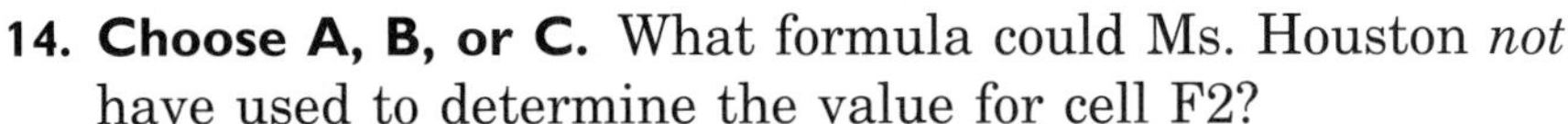

14. **Choose A, B, or C.** What formula could Ms. Houston *not* have used to determine the value for cell F2?

A. =E2/3

B. =(B2+B3+B4)/3

C. =(B2+C2+D2)/3

15. Was it necessary for Ms. Houston to include column E in her spreadsheet to determine the mean score for each group? Explain.

16. **Writing** Explain how you can find the value in cell D3.

17. **a.** **Calculator** Copy and complete the spreadsheet above.

b. Which group created the most original video?

c. Which group put the least effort into creating their video?

d. Which group did the best job overall on their video project? Explain.

18. **Critical Thinking** Why does the value in cell B5 have to be less than 80?

Rear Admiral Grace Hopper (1907–1992) was the first person to use the phrase "computer bug" to describe computer errors.

Source: *The Book of Women*

Mixed REVIEW

Use the data: 37, 11, 15, 16, 19, 11, 13, 20, 11

1. Find the range.

2. Find the mean.

3. Find the median.

4. Find the mode.

5. At 9:00 P.M. the temperature was 42°F. Between 9:00 P.M. and midnight, the temperature dropped 8°. Between midnight and 10:00 A.M., the temperature rose 15°. What was the temperature at 10:00 A.M.?

What's Ahead

- Reading graphs for information
- Determining the most appropriate graph to represent data

1-5 Reading and Understanding Graphs

THINK AND DISCUSS

You can display data in many different ways. The type of graph you choose depends on the type of data you have collected as well as the idea you want to communicate. A **bar graph** is used to compare amounts.

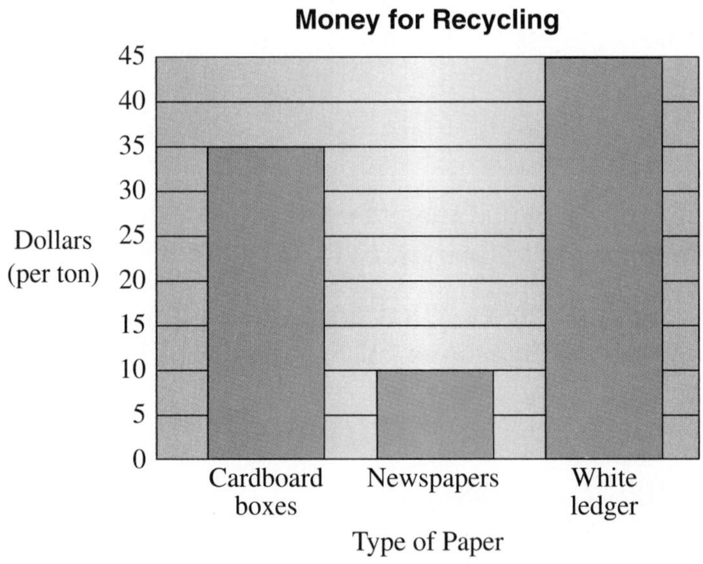

WHEN? Paper has been made from recycled materials throughout history. The Chinese invented paper in 105 A.D., using discarded rags and fishing nets. Trees were not cut down for paper-making until the 1850s.

Source: *Origins of Everything Under, and Including, the Sun*

1. What information does the bottom of the graph show?
2. What do the numbers on the left side of the graph represent?
3. a. Without finding the dollar amounts, order the types of paper from highest to lowest dollar amount per ton.
   b. **Discussion** How does the bar graph allow you to make these comparisons quickly?
   c. Describe the relationship between the heights of the bars and the dollars per ton of paper.
4. a. How much is each type of paper worth?
   b. The Neighborhood Club collects 15 t of newspaper. About how much money will they receive?

You can also display data in a *line graph.* A **line graph** shows how an amount changes over time.

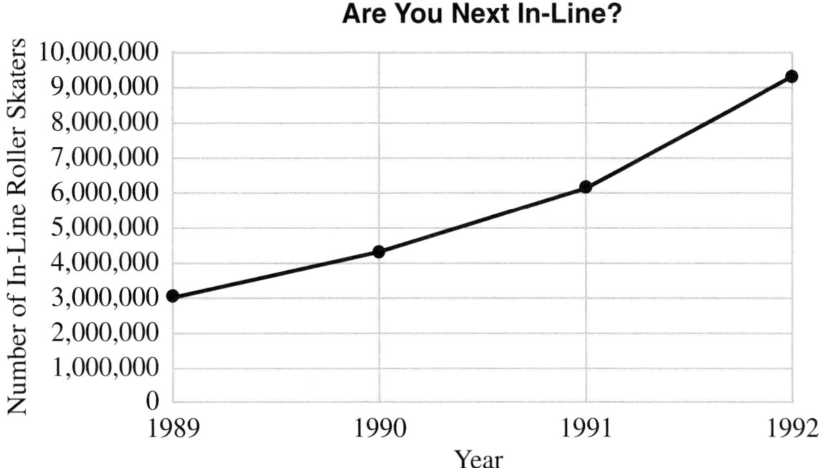

5. a. What trend does the line graph above show?
   b. How does the line graph visually display this trend?
6. **Discussion** Why might someone find the line graph more helpful than a table of data?
7. **Estimation** About how many skaters were there in 1991?
8. Between what two years was there the greatest increase? How can you tell without calculating?

A circle graph compares parts to a whole. The entire circle represents the whole. Each wedge in the circle graph represents a part of the whole.

9. On what type of surface do the most mountain biking accidents occur?
10. On what type of surface do the fewest mountain biking accidents occur?
11. Describe the relationship between the size of the wedges and the number of accidents in each category.

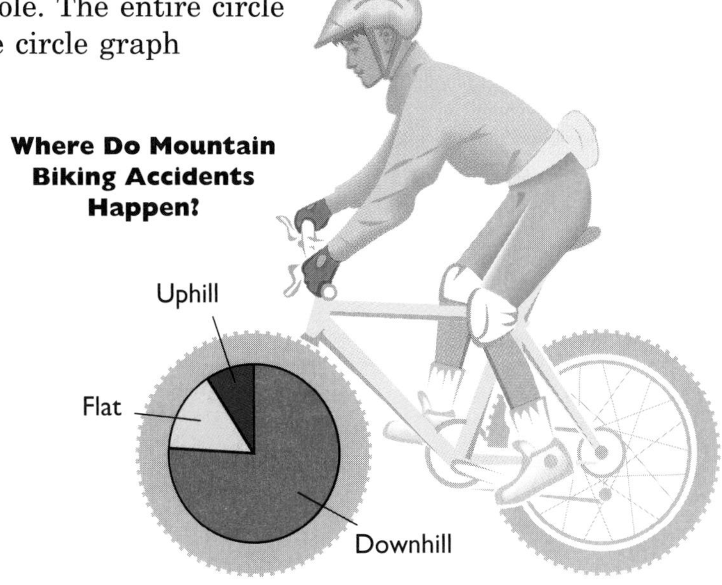

WORK TOGETHER

Work with a partner.

12. Choose the most appropriate graph to display each set of data. Support your answer.
    a. the students from each grade that are in the chorus
    b. the school enrollment for each year from 1980-present
    c. the heights of the ten highest waterfalls in the world

13. Describe two situations that would best be displayed in each type of graph. Ask your partner to identify the most appropriate graph for each situation.
    a. bar graph   b. line graph   c. circle graph

WHAT? Angel Falls is the highest waterfall in the world. It is located in Venezuela and is 1,000 m high.

Source: *The Information Please Almanac*

ON YOUR OWN

Go for the Gold!

Beginning in 1994, Olympic winners will receive money as well as medals. The amount will be based on the type of medal won. The U.S. Olympic Committee says the awards will provide "a way to pay for training, to stay in the sport longer."

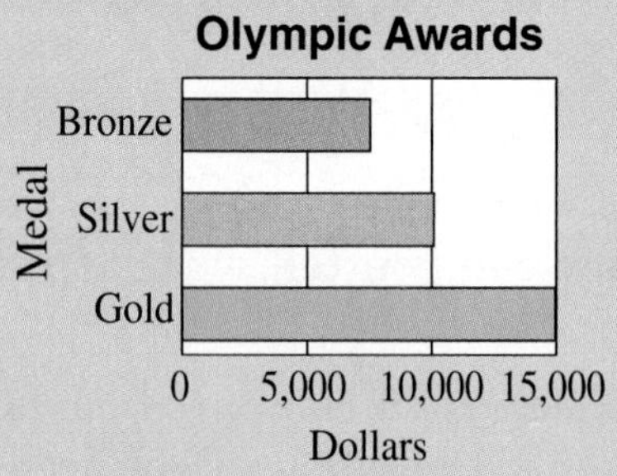

Olympic Awards

Medal: Bronze, Silver, Gold

0 5,000 10,000 15,000

Dollars

Sports **Use the article above for Questions 14–16.**

14. How much money will an Olympic gold medalist receive? a silver medalist? a bronze medalist?

15. **Writing** Would a line graph also be appropriate for displaying this data? Why or why not?

16. Describe the relationship between the length of the bar and the dollar amount for each type of Olympic medal.

Mixed REVIEW

Complete.

1. A table made on a computer is known as a ■.
2. A box where a row and column meet in a spreadsheet is a ■.
3. A ■ is a set of instructions that tells the computer what to do.
4. The mean average of three test scores is 85. Is it possible that the test scores are 92, 77, and 86? Why or why not?

Sports **Use the line graph below.**

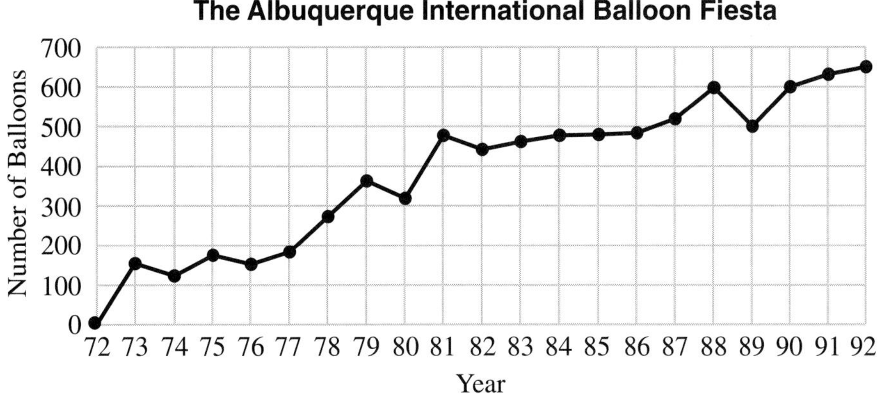

The Albuquerque International Balloon Fiesta draws entries from more than 15 countries.

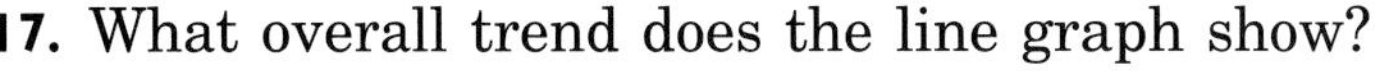

17. What overall trend does the line graph show?

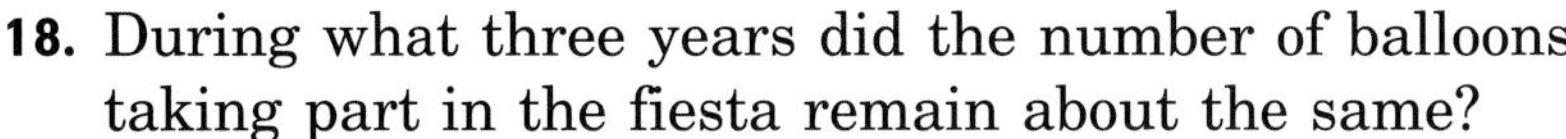

18. During what three years did the number of balloons taking part in the fiesta remain about the same?

19. During what years did the number of balloons taking part in the fiesta increase the most?

20. About how many balloons took part in the fiesta in 1992?

Education **Use the circle graph at the right.**

21. How many teachers do most middle grade students have?

22. Do about the same number of middle grade students have one teacher as four teachers? Explain.

Number of Teachers for the Typical Middle Grade Student

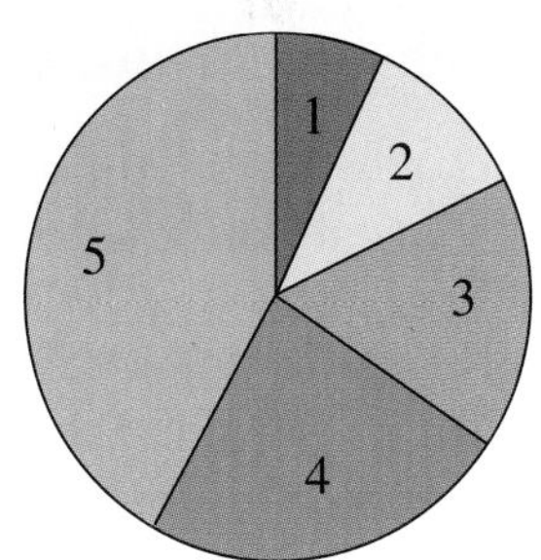

Choose the most appropriate graph to display each set of data. Support your answer.

23. the number of left-handed students and the number of right-handed students in your math class

24. the number of cases of measles in the United States for the years 1930, 1940, 1950, 1960, 1970, 1980, and 1990

25. the life spans of selected animals

26. the average temperature of Earth for each year from 1980 to the present

27. **Data File 1 (pp. 2–3)** What kind of ad appears most frequently during kid's TV?

Practice

Use the data in the table at the right.

1. Make a line plot.
2. Find the median and mode.
3. Find the range.

Ten Fastest Laps of the Daytona 500 (mi/h)

196	196	199	202	205
205	210	197	197	196

Make a frequency table for each set of data.

4. \$125, \$122, \$138, \$135, \$125, \$122, \$122
5. 800, 900, 700, 700, 800, 800, 800, 800

Find the mean, median, and mode.

6. 85, 73, 93, 74, 71, 101, 71, 90, 98
7. 1,216; 4,891; 2,098; 3,662; 5,748

Name the type of graph most appropriate for each situation. Support your answer.

8. average cost of lunch at six restaurants
9. change in taxes paid from 1950 to 2000
10. number of senior citizens, adults, and children visiting Paramount Parks in one day

Use the bar graph at the right.

11. Which New England state has the greatest amount of land? the least amount of land?
12. Which New England states have about the same amount of land?
13. Compare the amount of land in Maine to the amount of land in Vermont.

Area of New England States

Make a table to solve.

14. Mr. Humphrey has 14 animals in his barnyard. Some are chickens, and some are goats. Simone counted 38 legs in all. How many of the animals are chickens? goats?

What's Ahead

- Constructing bar and line graphs

1-6 Constructing Bar and Line Graphs

THINK AND DISCUSS

Many animals face the danger of disappearing forever. Environmental changes, such as climate and geology, are the main causes. However, human activities like hunting, pollution, and land clearing also contribute. The table shows the number of animals endangered in the United States.

U.S. Endangered Animals

Type of Animal	Number Endangered
Mammals	36
Birds	53
Reptiles	18
Amphibians	10
Fish	70

Example 1 Draw a bar graph to display the data at the left.

- Draw the horizontal and vertical axes. Put the name of each type of endangered animal on the horizontal axis.
- Choose a scale for the vertical axis. The data go from 10 to 70. Draw and label a scale from 0 to 70, using intervals of 10.
- Draw a bar to show the number of each type of endangered animal.
- Label the horizontal and vertical axes. Give your bar graph a title.

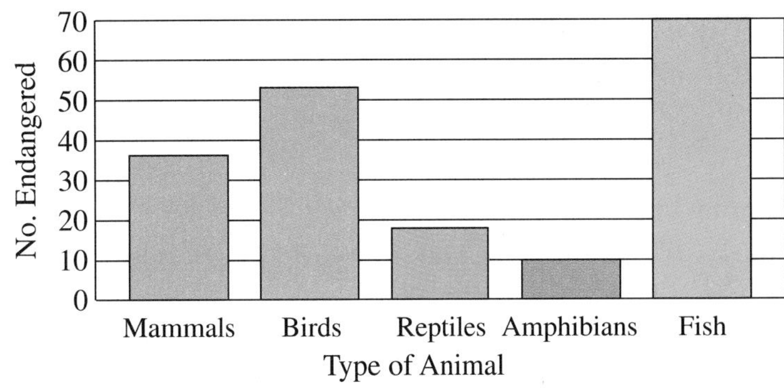

1. **Discussion** How would you display this data in a bar graph where the bars are horizontal?
2. Suppose the graph was drawn using intervals of 5. What are the advantages and disadvantages of using intervals of 5, instead of 10?

> *The long fight to save wild beauty represents democracy at its best. It requires citizens to practice the hardest of virtues—self-restraint.*
>
> —Edwin Way Teale (1899–1980)

The table shows the United States population per square mile for selected years from 1930.

United States Population Per Square Mile	
Year	Population
1930	35
1940	37
1950	43
1960	51
1970	58
1980	64
1990	70

Example 2 Draw a line graph to display the data at the left.

- Draw the axes. Then write the years on evenly spaced intervals on the horizontal axis.
- Choose a scale for the vertical axis. The data go from 35 to 70. Draw and label a scale from 0 to 70, using intervals of 10.
- Place a point on the graph for the population for each year. Connect the points.
- Label the horizontal and vertical axes. Give your line graph a title.

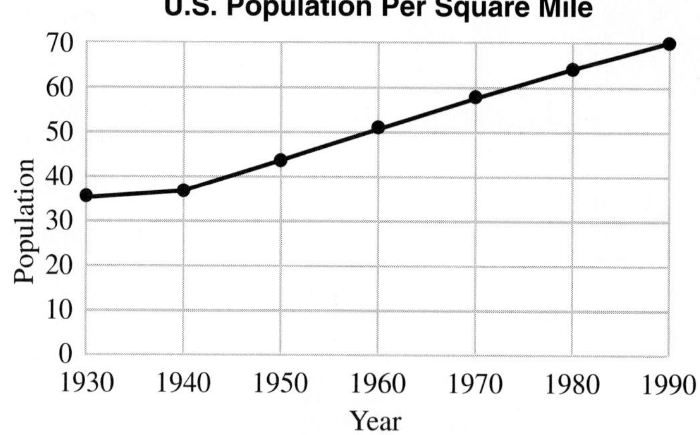

3. **a.** What trend does the line graph show?

b. Would changing the intervals on the vertical axis affect the trend? Explain.

TRY THESE

Sailboats Built in the United States	
Year	Number
1988	14,510
1989	11,790
1990	11,709
1991	8,672
1992	11,264

4. Suppose the average speeds of five animals range from 25 mi/h to 60 mi/h.

a. What scale would you use to display the data in a horizontal bar graph? Why?

b. How would you label the horizontal and vertical axes?

5. Display the data at the left in a line graph.

ON YOUR OWN

Architecture **Use the table below for Exercises 6–8.**

Five Highest Buildings in New York City		
Building	Stories	Height (ft)
World Trade Center (North)	110	1,368
World Trade Center (South)	110	1,362
Empire State Building	102	1,250
Chrysler Building	77	1,046
American International Building	67	950

6. What intervals would you use to construct a bar graph displaying the number of stories in each building?

7. What intervals would you use to construct a bar graph displaying the heights of the buildings?

8. Construct a bar graph displaying the number of stories in New York City's five highest buildings.

Social Studies **Use the table below for Exercises 9 and 10.**

Population of Ohio Cities		
Year	Cleveland	Columbus
1950	914,808	375,901
1960	876,050	471,316
1970	751,000	540,000
1980	574,000	565,000
1990	505,616	632,958

9. Construct a line graph for the population of Cleveland. What trend does your line graph show?

10. a. **Writing** How is the data for the population of Cleveland different from the data for the population of Columbus?

b. **Writing** How would this difference be displayed on a line graph?

For Exercises 1–3, name the type of graph that would be most appropriate.

1. frequency with which students in your class rent movie videos

2. average monthly rainfall in Seattle, Washington

3. change in home prices from 1980 to the present

4. Find two consecutive numbers whose product is 462.

Ohio is situated between Lake Erie and the Ohio River. The state's name comes from an Iroquois word meaning "great river."

Source: *Encyclopedia Americana*

Cost of a College Education

School Year	Public ($)	Private ($)
1984–1985	3,682	8,451
1986–1987	4,138	10,039
1988–1989	4,678	11,474
1990–1991	5,243	13,237
1992–1993	6,125	15,255

11. **Education** Use the table at the left.
    a. Construct a line graph displaying the cost of a public college education.
    b. Construct a line graph displaying the cost of a private college education. Use the same intervals as the ones you used to construct a line graph in part (a).
    c. Describe the trend(s) shown in your line graphs.
    d. Which type of college education has increased at a higher rate?
    e. How is this shown on the graph?

12. **Investigation (p. 4)** Collect data on the number of times 10 people open and close their fists in one minute. Choose the most appropriate graph to display your data.

CHECKPOINT

Use the spreadsheet below.

	A	B	C	D	E	F
1	Student	Test 1	Test 2	Test 3	Test 4	Mean Score
2	Justin	80	78	94	88	■
3	Elizabeth	64	78	82	80	■
4	Naomi	94	84	88	82	

1. **Choose A, B, or C.** What formula could you use to determine the value for the cell that the cursor is in?
   A. =(B2+B3+B4)/3
   B. =(A4+B4+C4+D4+E4)/5
   C. =(B4+C4+D4+E4)/4

2. Construct a bar graph displaying the mean scores for the students listed in the spreadsheet.

Use the circle graph at the left.

Medals of Honor Awarded for Service in Vietnam

Marines 57
Air Force 12
Navy 14
Army 155

3. Which branch received the most medals of honor for service in the Vietnam War?

4. How many medals of honor were awarded for service in the Vietnam War?

1-7 Analyzing Graphs

What's Ahead

- Analyzing the effect of different scales and intervals on graphs
- Recognizing misleading graphs

THINK AND DISCUSS

You can represent data in many different ways. Companies often display data in a way that presents their best image and persuades you to see things their way. The table at the left shows the basic monthly rate for Quality Cable Company.

Quality Cable Company

Year	Monthly Charge
1960	$5
1965	$5
1970	$6
1975	$7
1980	$8
1985	$10
1990	$18

1. Suppose Quality Cable Company wants to raise the monthly charge.
   a. What graph might the cable company use to persuade you that an increase is justified? Explain.
   b. What graph might the customers use to argue that an increase is not justified? Explain.

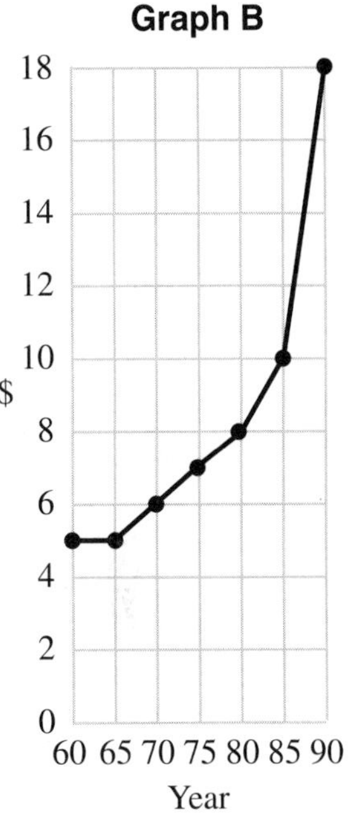

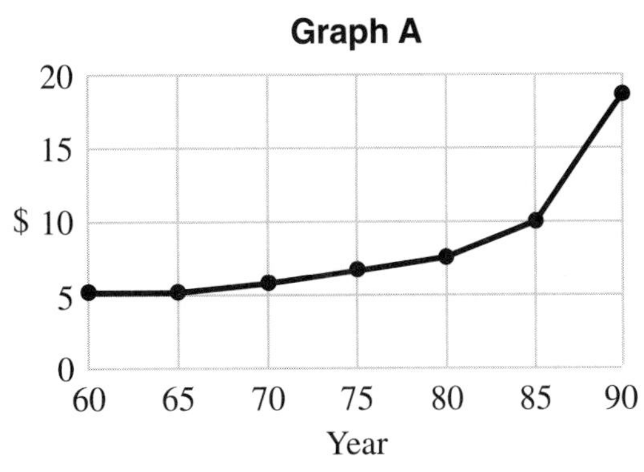

2. a. How does the appearance of a set of data displayed in a line graph change as the intervals on the vertical scale decrease?
   b. **Discussion** How would the appearance of a set of data displayed in a vertical bar graph change as the intervals on the vertical scale increase?

3. How does the appearance of a set of data displayed in a line graph change as the data items on the horizontal scale are spaced farther apart?

The American Tour de Sol *is an annual pollution-free car race. Its purpose is to educate the public about non-polluting alternatives to gasoline-fed automobiles.*

Source: *AAA World*

WORK TOGETHER

A car dealership claims that it has dramatically increased its business over the past three months. One of their advertisements shows the graph at the right.

4. Do you agree or disagree with their claim? Explain.

5. a. There is a gap in the scale, which begins at 77 instead of 0. How is this gap represented?

b. How does a gap affect the appearance of the data?

6. Suppose the company wants to show that car sales have been constant over the past three months. Draw a bar graph to support this claim.

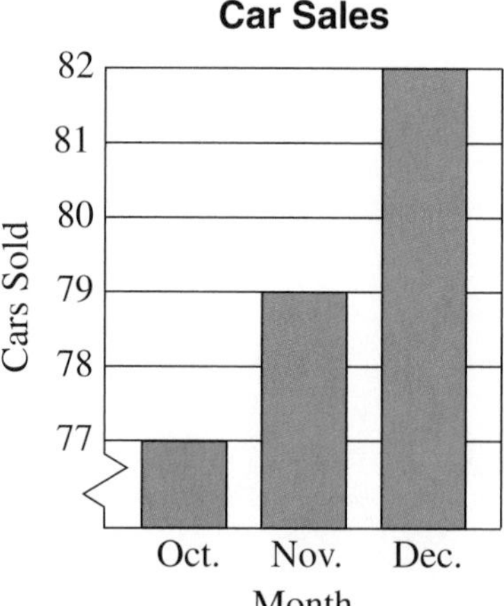

DECISION MAKING

Polling Your Peers

COLLECT DATA

Collect data about the favorite pastimes of 25 of your classmates. You may want to limit the choices to seven or eight different pastimes. Some choices may include reading, exercising, shopping, and dancing.

1. What other choices could you include in your survey?

2. a. Describe how you will organize the responses of the 25 classmates.

b. Is there more than one way that you could organize the responses? Explain.

ANALYZE DATA

3. What was chosen as the favorite pastime of your classmates?

ON YOUR OWN

Use the table below.

Money Raised in a National Telethon			
Year	Dollars	Year	Dollars
1983	30,691,627	1988	41,132,113
1984	32,074,566	1989	42,209,727
1985	33,181,652	1990	44,172,186
1986	34,096,773	1991	45,071,857
1987	39,021,723	1992	45,759,368

7. Draw a line graph showing that the money raised increased dramatically each year.
8. Draw a line graph showing that the money raised increased at a fairly slow rate.
9. **Writing** Explain how you constructed the graphs in Exercises 7 and 8 to achieve the desired results.

Mixed REVIEW

1. Draw a bar graph to display the data below.

City	Average Snowfall
Albany, NY	65.5 in.
Boston, MA	41.8 in.
Juneau, AK	102.8 in.
Omaha, NE	31.1 in.

2. Sumi earns $4.50 an hour baby-sitting. She is saving to buy a tape player that costs $89.95. For how many hours will she have to baby-sit to earn enough money to buy the tape player?

---

4. Was any one pastime a lot more popular than the others? If so, which one? Why do you think so?
5. Order the pastimes according to popularity.

MAKE DECISIONS

6. What type of graph would be most appropriate to display your data? Explain.
7. Suppose you have to make a presentation to the school principal about the favorite pastimes of your classmates.
   a. Draw a bar graph showing that there is a wide variety in the pastimes of your classmates.
   b. Draw a bar graph showing that all pastimes are liked about the same by your classmates.
   c. Explain how you constructed each graph to achieve the desired results.

***Listening to music** is a favorite pastime for people of all ages.*

CHAPTER 1

Wrap up

Frequency Tables and Line Plots 1-1

A ***frequency table*** lists data and uses a tally system to show the number of times each response or item occurs. A ***line plot*** displays data above a horizontal line.

1. Make a frequency table showing the number of times each vowel appears in the paragraph above.

2. Make a line plot showing the number of times the words *the, and, a,* and *are* appear in the paragraph above.

Make a Table 1-2

You can make a table to organize the possible solutions to a problem.

3. In how many ways can you make 21¢?

4. In how many ways can you make $1.00 using only dimes, quarters, and half-dollars?

Three Kinds of Averages 1-3

The ***mean*** is a number around which the numbers in a set seem to cluster. The ***median*** is the middle number in a set of data. The ***mode*** is the data item that appears most often.

Find the mean, median, and mode of each set of data.

5. scores: 34, 49, 63, 43, 50, 50, 26

6. rainfall in centimeters: 3, 7, 1, 9, 9, 5, 8

Technology: Computer Spreadsheets 1-4

A ***spreadsheet*** is an electronic table. A ***cell*** is the box where a row and column meet. Cells can hold data or formulas.

	A	B	C	D	E
1	Date	Kite Sales ($)	String Sales ($)	Book Sales ($)	Total Sales ($)
2	9/9/93	500	85	145	■
3	9/10/93	750	65	125	■

7. What does the number in cell C3 mean?

8. How can you calculate the value of cell E2?

9. What is the value of cell E3?

Bar Graphs and Line Graphs 1-5, 1-6, 1-7

We use ***bar graphs*** to show numerical data that captures a moment in time. We use ***line graphs*** to show data that changes over time. The intervals you use on the graph's scales can affect the graph's appearance.

Choose the most appropriate graph to display each set of data. Support your answer.

10. the distance from your town to the best colleges in your state

11. your height on each birthday from birth to the present

12. the sales of different types of lunches in the cafeteria

Graph each data set using the most appropriate graph.

13. the data you compiled in the frequency table in Exercise 1

14. the cost of tickets showing a dramatic price increase

15. the cost of tickets showing a slight price increase

Year	Ticket Cost
1970	10.00
1975	15.00
1980	20.00
1985	25.00
1990	30.00

GETTING READY FOR CHAPTER 2

Geometric shapes are all around us. Many everyday objects rely on geometry for good design.

Identify each plane figure.

1. 

2. 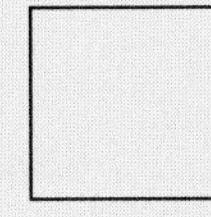

3. 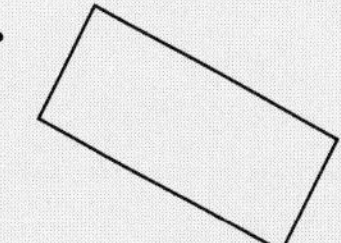

4. 

Name an object that has the given geometric shape.

5. triangle
6. square
7. circle
8. rectangle

Follow Up

The problems preceded by the magnifying glass (p. 7, # 15; p. 14, # 16; and p. 28, # 12) will help you complete the investigation.

Have a Heart

In this chapter you learned ways to analyze and display data. Look back at the poster you made to display the results of your pulse-rate survey. How could you better analyze the data? How could you display your results in a more meaningful way? Revise your poster using what you have learned. You may want to use the following suggestions to improve your poster.

- ✓ Use a frequency table.
- ✓ Use averages.
- ✓ Use an appropriate graph.

The blood that your heart pumps throughout your body is rich in oxygen from your lungs. The better your physical condition the more efficiently your heart and lungs work together to process and transport oxygen. Would you expect a professional athlete to have a higher or lower pulse rate than that of the average person?

Excursion: When is your pulse rate higher than average? When is it lower? Sketch a graph showing your estimated pulse rates over a 24-hour period. The graph should begin when you wake up and extend to the same hour the next day.

"And the winner is..."

Take a survey. Ask 20 students in your school to name their favorite musical group. Organize the results of your survey onto a graph, table, or line plot. Write a brief summary explaining the results of your survey. Tell why you chose to display your data the way you did.

DATA DUELS

- Collect examples of bar graphs, line graphs, circle graphs, and tables from newspapers and magazines.
- Select one bar graph, one line graph, one circle graph, and one table from your collection.
- Write several math problems that can be solved by using the data represented in each graph or table. Challenge others to solve your problems.

UPS & DOWNS

Record the high and low temperatures each day for one week. The information can be obtained from radio broadcasts or newspapers. Use your data to construct a line graph with two lines. One line will show the high temperatures and another will show the low temperatures. Explain your graph to a friend.

measuring UP

Try this with your group.

- *Use a ruler or yardstick to measure the height of each member of your group.*
- *Record your data and display it on a horizontal bar graph.*
- *Find the average height of the members of your group. Draw a vertical line down the graph, showing the average height.*

CHAPTER 1

Assessment

1. The sizes of 15 families living on Pike Road are 1, 3, 2, 1, 3, 1, 2, 6, 2, 3, 3, 4, 3, 4, and 5.
   a. Make a frequency table.
   b. Make a line plot.

2. Find the mean, median, mode, and range of each set of data.
   a. 12, 7, 8, 6, 9, 7, 10, 8, 11, 8
   b. \$31, \$45, \$20, \$22, \$31, \$48, \$27

3. Elena packs black shorts, jeans, and red pants. She adds a yellow T-shirt, a green tank top, and a white blouse. For shoes, she packs sneakers and sandals. How many different outfits will she have for her trip?

4. **Choose A, B, or C.** If all the numbers in a set of data occur the same number of times, then the set has no ■.
   A. median **B.** mean **C.** mode

5. Use the circle graph below.

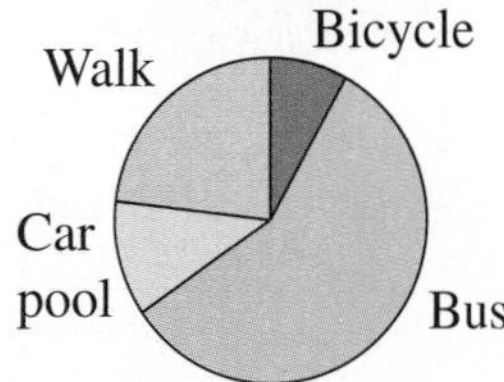

   a. What method do students use *most* to commute to school? *least?*
   b. **Writing** Would a bar graph have been appropriate for displaying this data? Explain.

6. **Writing** The ages of students at a school dance are 14, 13, 12, 12, 13, 12, 15, 16, 14, 13, 13, and 14. Which average would best describe this data: mean, median, or mode? Explain.

7. The table below shows the colonial population from 1700 to 1740. Display the data in a line graph.

1700	1710	1720	1730	1740
250,900	331,700	466,200	629,400	905,600

8. Average daily temperatures (°F) for one week are 60, 59, 58, 61, 63, 59, and 64. Find the median.

9. List a set of data with six numbers in which the mean is 40, the median is 41, and the range is 18.

10. Use the bar graph below.

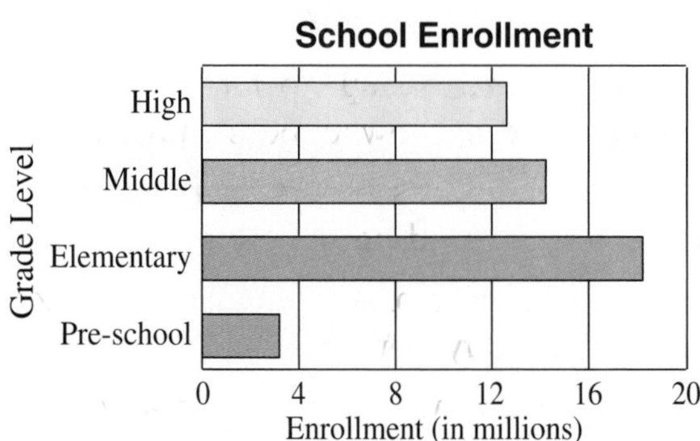

   a. Which grade level has the least number of students enrolled?
   b. Estimate the mean.
   c. Estimate the median.
   d. Estimate the range.

Cumulative Review

Choose A, B, C, or D.

1. Which average is the greatest for the data: 81, 70, 95, 73, 74, 91, 86, 74?

   A. mean B. median
   C. mode D. range

2. When a number is divided by 13, the quotient is 15 and the remainder is less than 4. Which could be the number?

   A. 198 B. 200 C. 190 D. 206

3. What information does the bar graph shown *not* give you?

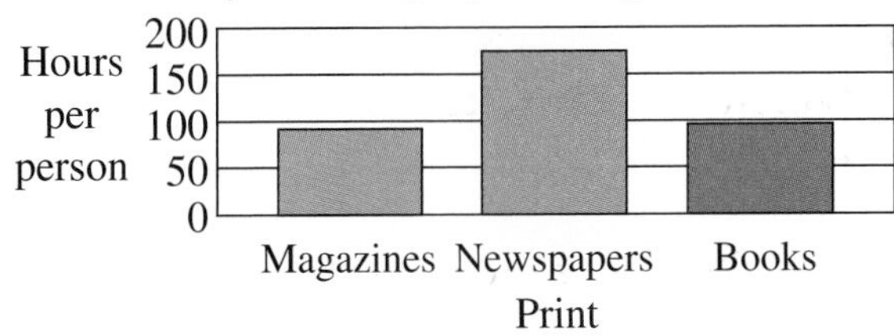

   A. Americans spend more time reading newspapers than books.
   B. Americans spend about the same time reading magazines as books.
   C. Majority of Americans read the Sunday newspaper.
   D. Americans spend twice as much time reading newspapers as books.

4. Which product gives the best estimate of the product 519×36?

   A. 500×30 B. 550×40
   C. 500×40 D. 550×30

5. In one store boom boxes sell for $90, $109, $79, and $60. Find the range.

   A. $60 B. $109 C. $49 D. $19

6. The mean of three numbers is 19 and the median is 22. What do you know about the other two numbers?

   A. They are both between 19 and 22.
   B. The numbers must be 17 and 18.
   C. At least one of the numbers is between 19 and 22.
   D. If one number is 24, the other must be 11.

Use the line graph for Questions 7–8.

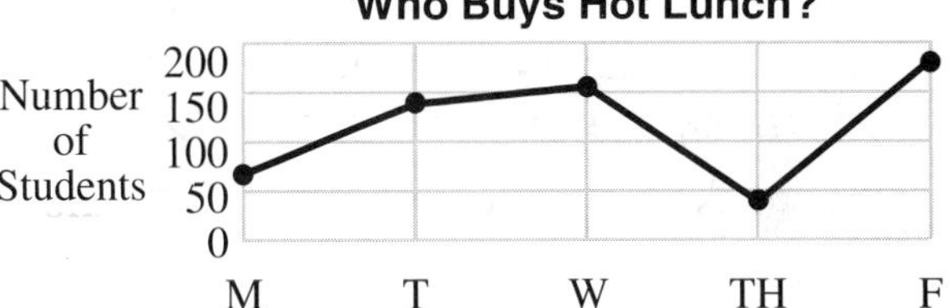

7. Estimate the median number of students buying hot lunch.

   A. 70 B. 140 C. 150 D. 120

8. How could you redraw the graph so it appears that about the same number of students buy lunch each day?

   A. Begin the vertical scale at 50.
   B. Use intervals of 10, instead of 50.
   C. Use intervals of 100, instead of 50.
   D. Display the data in a circle graph.

CHAPTER 2

Geometry Concepts

CHILLS & THRILLS

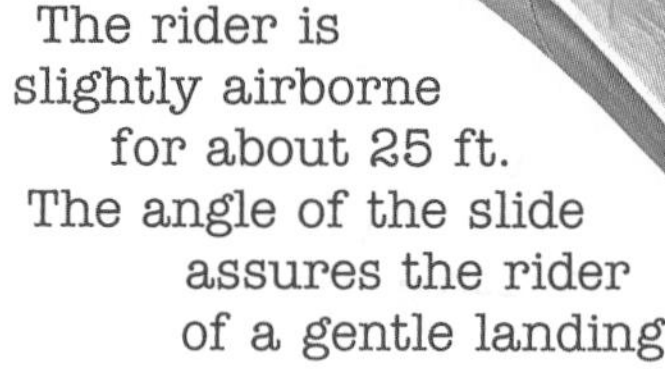

The rider is slightly airborne for about 25 ft. The angle of the slide assures the rider of a gentle landing.

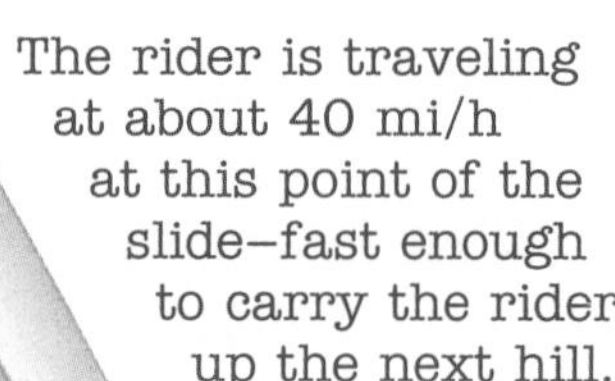

The rider is traveling at about 40 mi/h at this point of the slide–fast enough to carry the rider up the next hill.

The Waimea in Salt Lake City, Utah, is the first water ride with a hill. The whole ride takes only 15 s. At one point you drop 50 ft and then head up a hill. At the top of the hill you are actually airborne. When you hit the water again you're still going about 25 mi/h.

Source: 3•2•1 Contact

The rider sees only sky on the way up the hill. This makes the ride more scary.

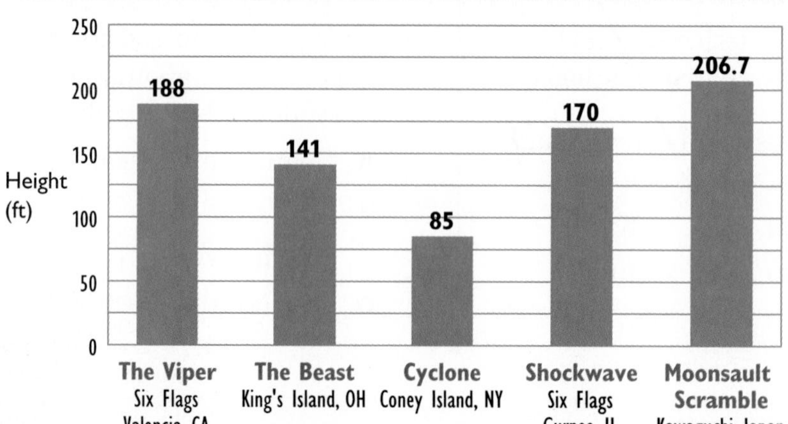

WHAT YOU WILL LEARN

- how to recognize geometric figures
- how to use tools to draw geometric figures
- how to use technology to explore geometry
- how to solve problems by using logic

Favorite Amusement Park Rides

Park (annual attendance)	**Admission**	**Ride**	**Wait Time (min)**	**Ride Time (min)**
Walt Disney World	Adult: $32.75	Space Mountain	45:14	2:36
Lake Buena Vista, FL.	Child: $26.40	Captain EO	14:29	16:47
(30 million)		For kids: Peter Pan	20:37	3:09
Knott's Berry Farm	Adult: $21.00	XK-1	2:30	1:30
Buena Park, CA.	Child: $16.00	Timber Mountain Log	9:22	4:25
(4 million)		Montezooma's Revenge	1:30	0:37
		For kids: Red Baron	0:55	2:00
Kings Island	Adult: $20.95	The Beast	45:00	4:30
Kings Island, OH	Child: $10.45	Vortex	30:00	2:30
(3.2 million)		The Racer	15:00	2:15
		For kids: Beastie	10:00	1:30
Cedar Point	Adult: $19.95	Demon Drop	30:00	0:15
Sandusky, OH	Child: $10.95	Cedar Downs	5:00	2:30
(3.2 million)		For kids: Sir Rub-a-Dub's Tubs	15:00	3:00

Source: *Money*

On the final hilltop, the rider rises from one inch to six inches off the slide in a state of near weightlessness.

In 1851 London hosted the first international fair in the Crystal Palace. The exhibition attracted 6,039,195 people.

The rider travels at 40 mi/h down the last hill before a gentle landing in a breaking pool.

investigation

Project File

Memo

When a figure is repeated in a design, a *visual pattern* results. Patterns in designs are all around you. The design shown here consists of a flower repeated again and again. The Canadian flag design consists of two halves, each the reverse of the other. If the flag is folded along the dotted line, the two halves match each other. The logo for the Data Processing Corporation consists of two **d**'s. The second **d** is turned upside-down to form a **p**. Each of these designs displays a pattern.

Mission: Find examples of patterns in visual designs. Some patterns you can find simply by looking around your classroom. Others you can find by looking in books and magazines and by brainstorming with your group. Study the designs. Then create a design for a flag for your class or school. Your design should display a visual pattern.

LeADS tO FOLLow

- ✓ Which designs do you like best? Which are the most memorable? What can you do to create a likable, memorable design for your flag?
- ✓ What would you like to say about your class or school that you can represent in a design?

What's Ahead

- Identifying and working with points, lines, segments, and rays

2-1 Points, Lines, and Planes

THINK AND DISCUSS

What geometric figures do the following everyday items suggest: a straight road? a tabletop? a pencil? a sunbeam?

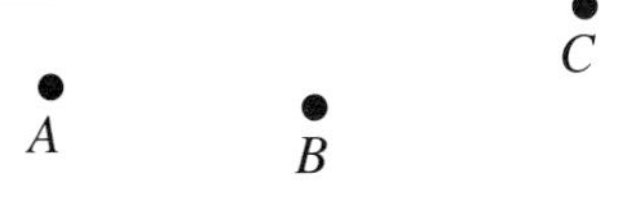

A **point** has no size, only location. A very small dot made by a pencil tip can represent a point. You can name points by a capital letter. Points A, B, and C are shown.

1. Name something else that could be a physical model of a point.

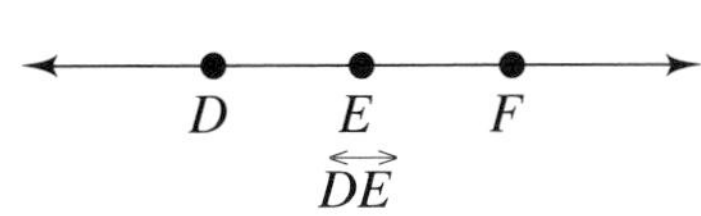

A **line** continues without end in opposite directions. It has no thickness. You can name a line by using two points on the line. For example, one name for this line is $\overleftrightarrow{DE}$ (read as "line DE").

2. What are some other names for the line?
3. Name something that could be a physical model of a line.

A **plane** is a flat surface that extends indefinitely in four directions. It has no thickness.

4. Name something that could be a physical model of a plane.

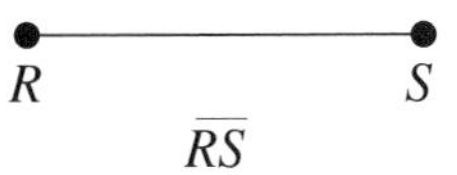

A **segment** is part of a line. It is made up of two points and all the points of the line that are between the two points. You name a segment by the two *endpoints*. This is $\overline{RS}$ (read as "segment RS").

5. Give another name for $\overline{RS}$.
6. Name something that could be a physical model of a segment.
7. Draw a line and label several points on it. Name four different segments.

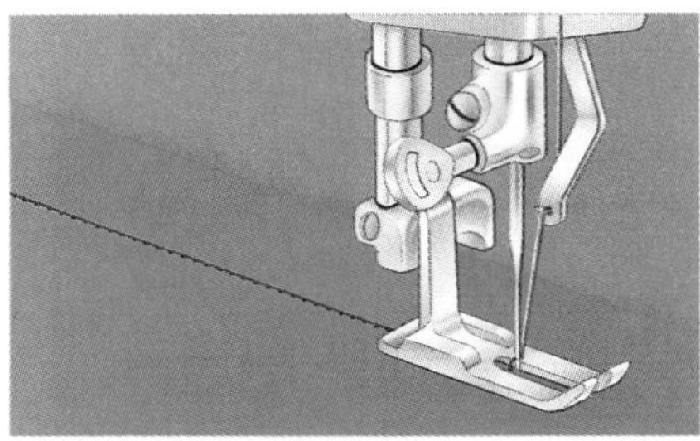

What geometric term does the stitching represent?

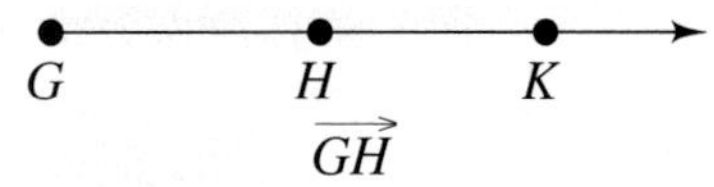

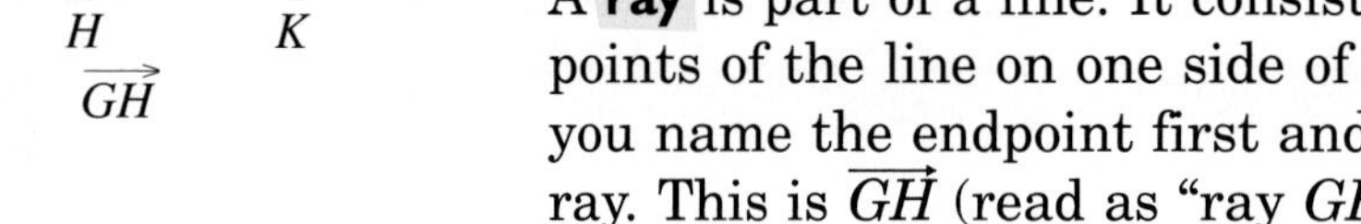

A **ray** is part of a line. It consists of one *endpoint* and all the points of the line on one side of the endpoint. To name a ray, you name the endpoint first and then any other point on the ray. This is $\overrightarrow{GH}$ (read as "ray *GH*").

8. If possible, give another name for $\overrightarrow{GH}$.

9. Name something that could be a physical model of a ray.

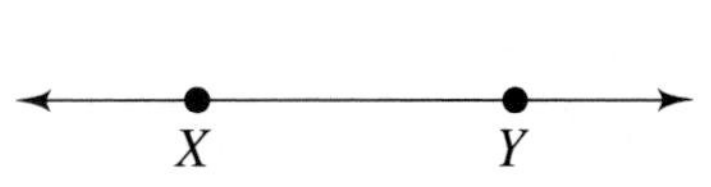

10. Describe $\overrightarrow{YX}$. How is $\overrightarrow{YX}$ different from $\overrightarrow{XY}$? What part of $\overleftrightarrow{XY}$ do $\overrightarrow{YX}$ and $\overrightarrow{XY}$ have in common?

If there is a line that goes through a set of points, the points are **collinear.** If there is no line that goes through all the points, the points are **noncollinear.**

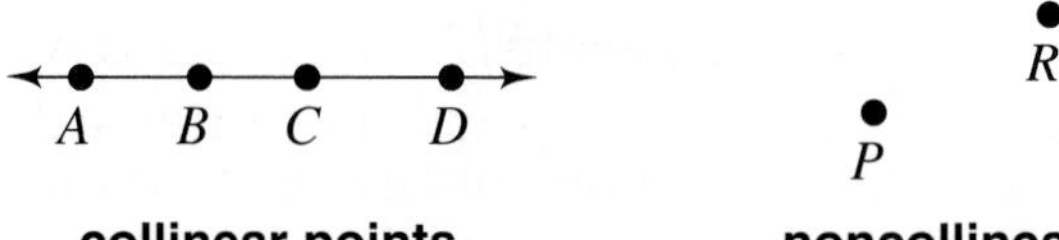

collinear points **noncollinear points**

11. a. Draw two points. Then draw all the lines that go through both points.

b. If you have two points, how many lines go through the points?

12. a. Draw three points. Then draw all the lines that go through two of the points. Is there a different way to arrange the three points so that you get a different number of lines?

b. If you have three points, how many lines go through at least two of the points?

13. a. Arrange four points in as many different positions as you can. Draw the lines that go through at least two of the points.

b. If you have four points, how many lines go through at least two of the points?

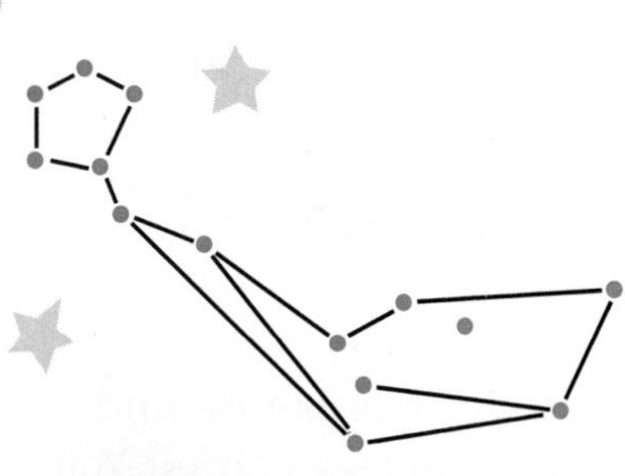

The stars that form the constellation Cetus can be represented by points. These points are connected here with segments to help you identify the shape that is suggested by the constellation's Latin name. **What shape do you see?**

Source: *Encyclopedia Americana*

There are two possible relationships between two lines that lie in a plane: either they intersect or they are parallel. **Parallel lines** are lines in the same plane that do not intersect. **Parallel segments** are segments that lie in parallel lines.

Example Is each pair of lines parallel or intersecting?

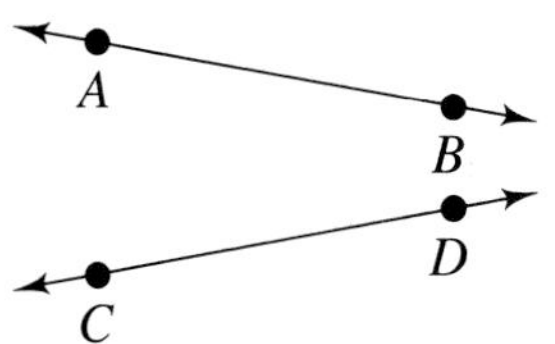

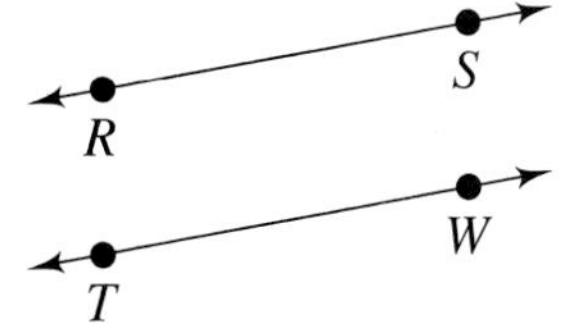

- $\overleftrightarrow{AB}$ and $\overleftrightarrow{CD}$ are intersecting lines, even though the point of intersection is not shown.
- $\overleftrightarrow{RS}$ and $\overleftrightarrow{TW}$ are parallel. No matter how much you extend them, they will not intersect.

***Parallel bars** are an event in men's gymnastics. They are a model for parallel segments.*

TRY THESE

Match each figure with its name.

14. E F | **a.** $\overleftrightarrow{EF}$

15. E F | **b.** $\overrightarrow{EF}$

16. E F | **c.** $\overline{FE}$

17. E F | **d.** $\overline{\mathrm{EF}}$

18. Name the line in several different ways.

19. Name four different rays.

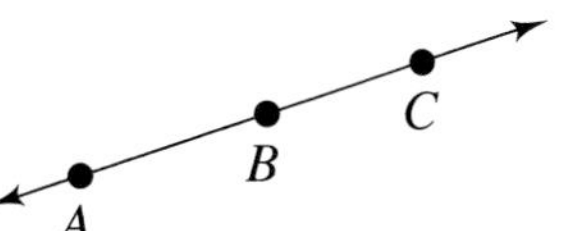

Use the article at the right to answer each question.

20. a. How could you describe geometrically the position of the moon, Earth, and sun during a solar eclipse?

b. **Critical Thinking** Why is it that we can think of heavenly bodies as large as these as points?

Eclipses

Earth is about 248,550 mi from the moon and an amazing 93,000,000 mi from the sun. The diameters of Earth and the moon are about 7,910 mi and 2,200 mi, respectively. The diameter of the sun is about 865,400 mi. A solar eclipse occurs when the moon comes between the sun and Earth.

Mixed REVIEW

Use mental math.

1. 24×5
2. $160 \div 8$

Use the data: 50, 39, 46, 68, 53, 59, 49.

3. Find the mean.
4. Find the median.

5. Forty-six members of the hiking club are going camping. Each tent can hold 4 people. How many tents do they need to take with them?

ON YOUR OWN

Name each of the following.

21. three collinear points
22. three noncollinear points
23. three segments
24. three rays
25. two lines that appear to be parallel
26. two pairs of intersecting lines

Name the segments that appear to be parallel.

27.

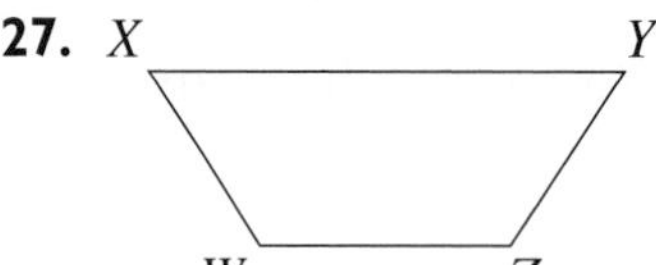

28.

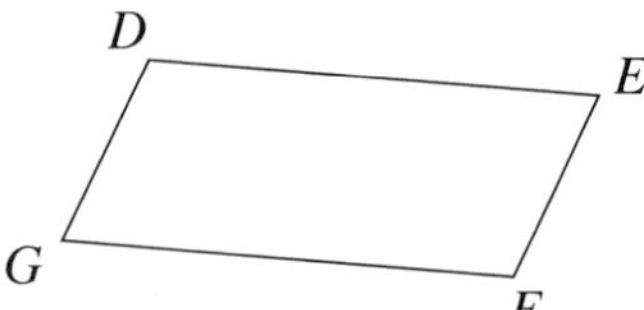

29. Draw five collinear points.
30. Draw three noncollinear points.

Complete each sentence with *sometimes, always,* or *never.*

31. Two points are ■ collinear.
32. Two parallel lines are ■ intersecting.
33. Four points are ■ collinear.
34. A segment ■ has two endpoints.
35. A ray ■ has two endpoints.
36. A line ■ has two endpoints.

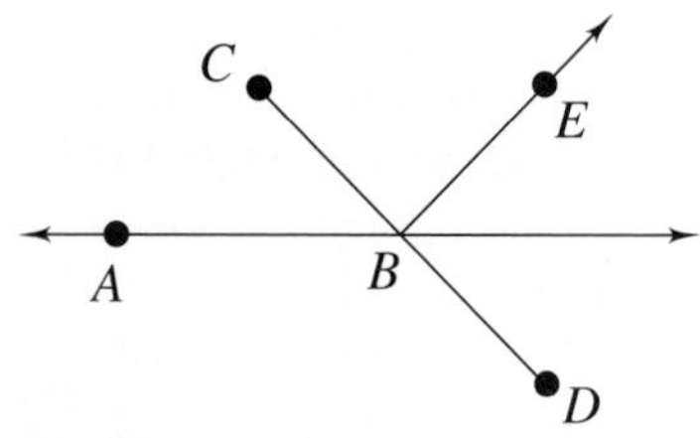

37. **Writing** Write a description of the figure shown at the left that would help someone draw a figure like this one.
38. **Critical Thinking** In how many ways can three lines that lie on one plane be related? Draw sketches to show all the ways that the lines can intersect or be parallel.

What's Ahead

- Estimating, measuring, and drawing angles
- Classifying angles as acute, right, obtuse, or straight

WHAT YOU'LL NEED

✓ Protractor 

2-2 Exploring Angles

THINK AND DISCUSS

More than 3,000 years ago the Babylonians discovered that it took about 360 days for the sun to travel in a circular path in the sky. As a result of this discovery, the Babylonians divided the circle into 360 equal parts. We now call each of these parts a *degree.*

You measure *angles* in degrees. An **angle** is made up of two rays with a common endpoint, called the *vertex* of the angle. The rays are the *sides* of the angle.

1. a. Name the vertex and sides of the angle.
   b. One name for the angle is $\angle YXZ$. Describe what the three letters represent.
   c. Can you use three letters to give a different name for the angle?

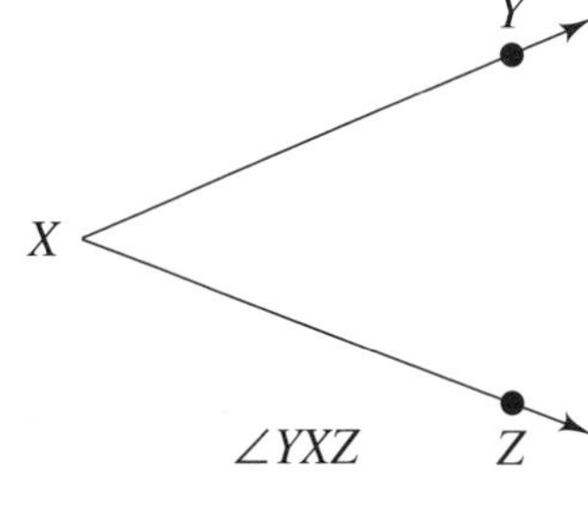

2. Sometimes you can name an angle with a number, like $\angle 1$, or by a single letter. What one-letter name would you use for $\angle YXZ$? Why?

3. a. How many angles are shown? Name them.
   b. Why can't you use a single letter to name any of the angles?

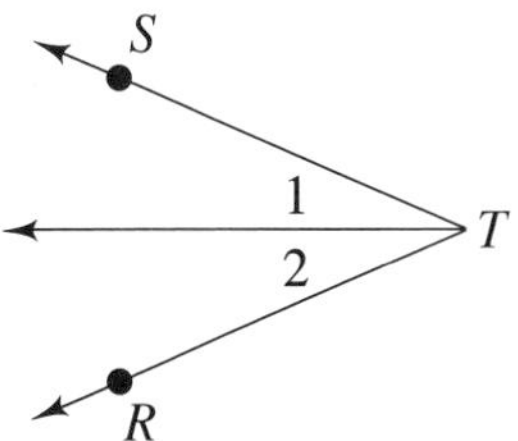

You can use a *protractor* to measure the size of an angle in degrees, as shown on the next page.

The Babylonians used a number system based on the number 60. **How do we use Babylonian ideas to measure time?**

Source: *Historical Topics for the Mathematics Classroom*

WHY? Birds fly in a V formation because it helps them to conserve energy. The bird in front reduces the wind for the other birds. When the lead bird gets tired, another bird takes over.

Source: *The Information Please Kids' Almanac*

4. a. Draw a large angle. To find the measure of the angle, place the center point of your protractor on the vertex of the angle. Make sure that one side of the angle passes through zero on the protractor scale.

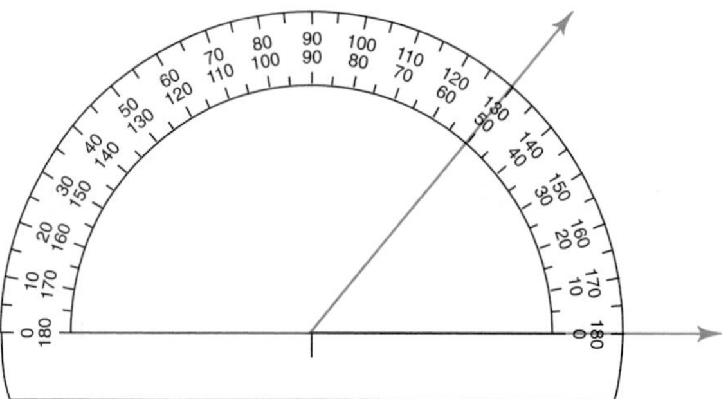

b. To find the measure of the angle, you read the scale where it intersects the second side of the angle. Most protractors have two scales. How do you decide which number to read?

c. Find the angle measure.

5. How would you measure an angle with sides that don't extend to the scale of the protractor?

6. Use a protractor to measure each angle.

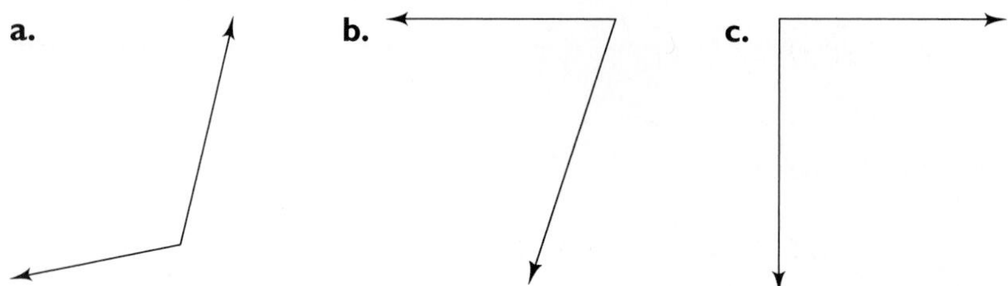

You can classify angles according to their measures.

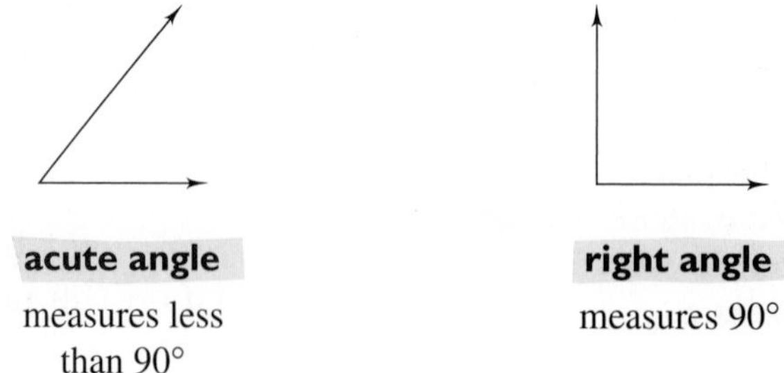

acute angle
measures less than 90°

right angle
measures 90°

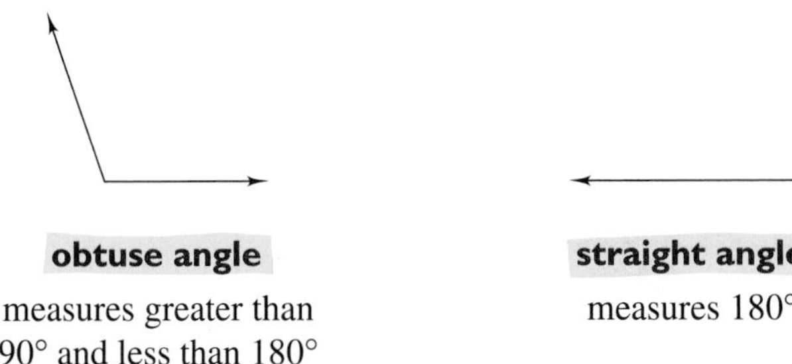

obtuse angle
measures greater than 90° and less than 180°

straight angle
measures 180°

7. Classify the angles in Question 6 as acute, right, obtuse, or straight.

8. You also can use a protractor to draw angles. Describe how you would use your protractor to draw a 110° angle.

Lines that intersect to form right angles are **perpendicular.** You can use the symbol ⌉ to indicate that lines are perpendicular or that an angle is a right angle.

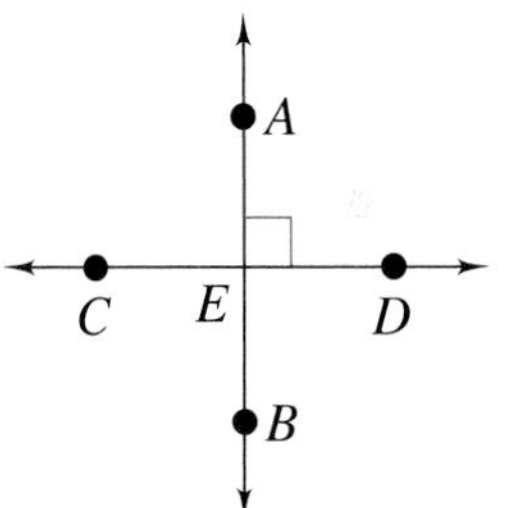

9. Name all the right angles formed by the perpendicular lines, $\overleftrightarrow{AB}$ and $\overleftrightarrow{CD}$, shown.

10. Find examples of perpendicular lines in your classroom.

WORK TOGETHER

Being able to visualize certain angles will help you estimate angle measures.

- Use a protractor to draw angles with the following measures, but do not draw the angles in the order listed.

  30° 45° 60° 90° 120° 135° 150°

- Exchange papers with a partner.
- Without using a protractor to measure, write the measure of each angle next to the angle.

Did you have more trouble identifying some angles than other angles? If you did, try drawing angles with those measures without using a protractor. Then use your protractor to check how close you got.

A 50 mm camera lens has a 45° viewing angle. **What kind of angle is this?**

Source: *How in the World?*

ON YOUR OWN

11. a. Name three rays.
    b. Name three angles. Classify each angle as acute, right, obtuse, or straight.

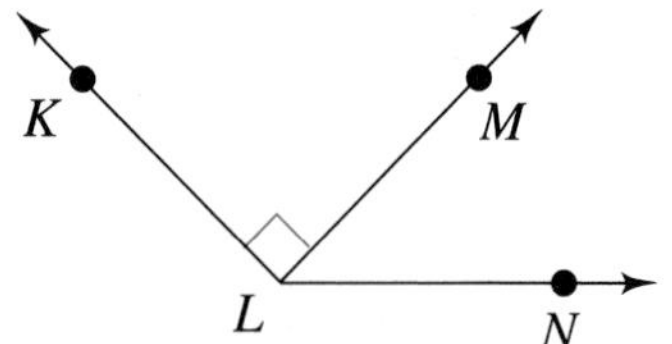

12. a. Draw two perpendicular lines, $\overleftrightarrow{RS}$ and $\overleftrightarrow{TW}$.
    b. How many right angles are formed?

13. Draw an obtuse $\angle DEF$ and an acute $\angle NOP$.

14. Without using your protractor, try to draw a 45° angle.

15. Are there any angles you can draw accurately without using a protractor? Explain.

Without using your protractor, estimate the measure of each angle. Choose the best estimate from 30°, 60°, 90°, 120°, 150°.

16. 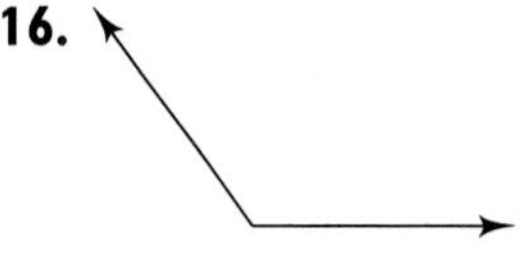

17. 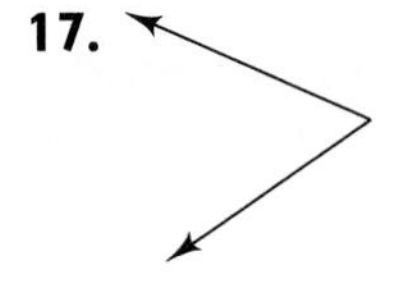

18. 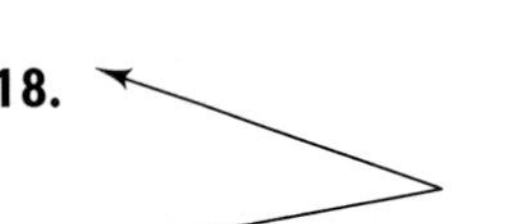

19. 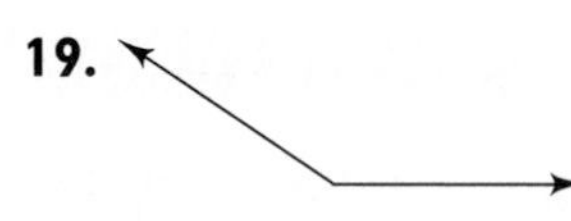

Estimate the measure of each angle. Then use a protractor to find the measure. Classify each angle.

20. 21. 22.

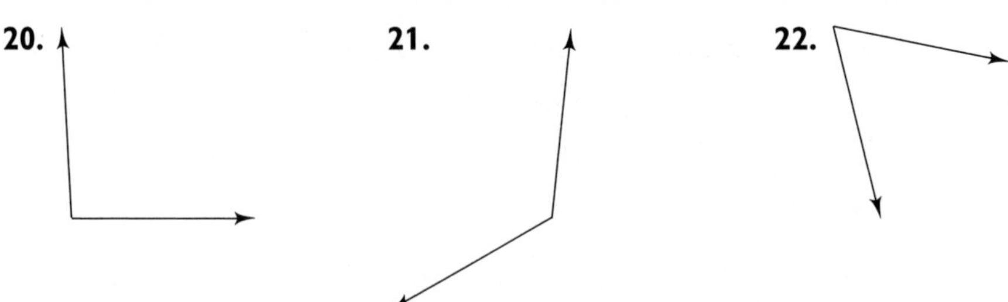

Use a protractor to draw an angle with each measure.

23. 125° 24. 75° 25. 82° 26. 154°

Find each answer.

1. 918 + 79
2. 2,076 − 582
3. Tell whether mean, median, or mode would best describe the favorite pizza topping of the students in your class.

Use the diagram below for Exercises 4 and 5.

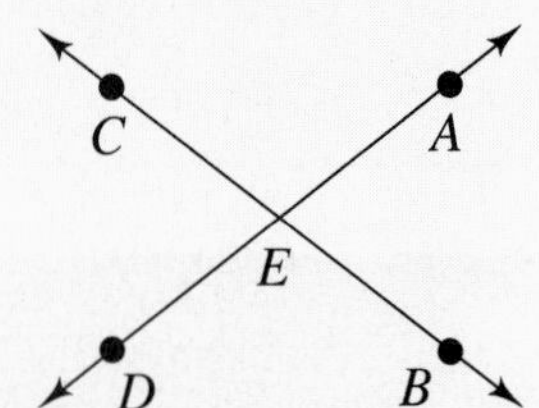

4. Name three noncollinear points.
5. Name two rays on $\overleftrightarrow{BC}$.
6. A bookstore advertised the following sale: *Buy 3 books, get 1 book free!* How many books do you have to buy to get 4 free books?

27. What angle does the Tyrannosaurus rex make with the ground in this drawing?

28. a. Data File 1 (pp. 2–3) What product was advertised in about one fourth of the commercials during kids' TV shows?

b. What two categories together accounted for about half of the commercials?

29. **Choose A, B, C, or D.** Which measure is not a measure of one of the angles shown at the right?

A. 60°   B. 90°

C. 120°   D. 150°

30. Writing Must two acute angles have the same measure? Must two right angles? two obtuse angles? two straight angles? Explain.

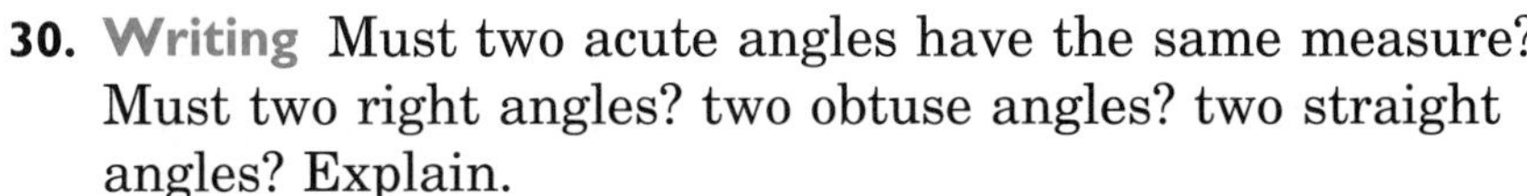

31. Find the measure of each angle.

a. $\angle AGF$ b. $\angle DGB$ c. $\angle BGE$ d. $\angle EGC$

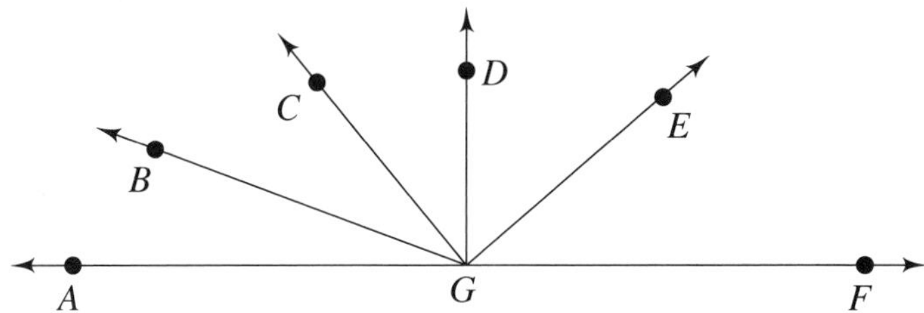

e. List all the obtuse angles shown.

f. List all the right angles shown.

g. List all the straight angles shown.

T. Rex on the Prowl

Many museum models of Tyrannosaurus rex show the dinosaur in an upright, tail-dragging position. Scientists now believe that Tyrannosaurus rex actually walked at an angle, using its tail for balance.

Problem Solving Practice

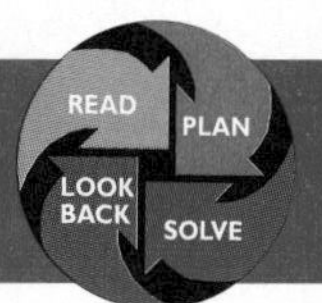

PROBLEM SOLVING STRATEGIES

Make a Table
Use Logical Reasoning
Solve a Simpler Problem
Too Much or Too Little Information
Look for a Pattern
Make a Model
Work Backward
Draw a Diagram
Guess and Test
Simulate a Problem
Use Multiple Strategies

Use any strategy to solve each problem. Show all your work.

1. Under which letter in the chart would you find the number 45? 101?

A	B	C	D	E	F
1	2	3	4	5	6
7	8	9	10	11	12
13	14	15	16	17	18

2. What are the different amounts of money you can make by using any of the following coins: three pennies, two nickels, one dime?

3. Ewa is selling magazine subscriptions for her class fund raiser. She is trying to sell 26 subscriptions in order to win 10 movie tickets. She has already sold 7 subscriptions. If she is able to sell 3 subscriptions each day, how many days will it take her to reach her goal?

4. There are 20 students on the intramural tennis team. Eight students play only singles and 8 students play both singles and doubles. How many students play only doubles?

5. Draw one diagram that contains all the following geometric figures. Read through the list first and draw the minimum number of lines to fulfill all the requirements.
   - at least three segments not all on the same line
   - at least three lines that intersect in one point
   - at least two parallel lines
   - at least three noncollinear points

6. Kyle mowed several lawns after school on Friday. He mowed for 2 h and finished at 5:30 P.M. He did his homework for 50 min before he mowed. At what time did he begin to work on his homework?

The widest lawnmower in the world is 60 ft wide and weighs 5.6 t. The "Big Green Machine" mows an acre in 60 s.

Source: *Guinness Book of Records*

2-3 Constructing Segments and Angles

What's Ahead

- Constructing a segment congruent to a given segment
- Constructing an angle congruent to a given angle

WHAT YOU'LL NEED

✓ Ruler 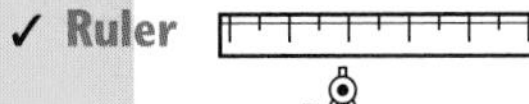

✓ Compass 

✓ Straightedge 

✓ Protractor 

THINK AND DISCUSS

Do you think that $\overline{UV}$ or $\overline{XY}$ is longer?

Check your answer by using a ruler to measure the length of each segment. Although $\overline{UV}$ appears to be longer, $\overline{UV}$ and $\overline{XY}$ are actually the same length. Segments that have the same length are **congruent segments.** You can *construct* a segment that is congruent to another segment by using two geometric tools: a compass and a straightedge.

A **compass** is a tool that you can use to draw circles or parts of circles called *arcs*. A **straightedge** is like a ruler but does not have marks that show measurement. You can use a ruler as a straightedge if you ignore the markings.

1. Draw $\overline{AB}$ about as long as shown here. Then follow the steps below to construct a segment congruent to $\overline{AB}$.

Step 1 Use your straightedge to draw a ray. Label the endpoint of the ray as C.

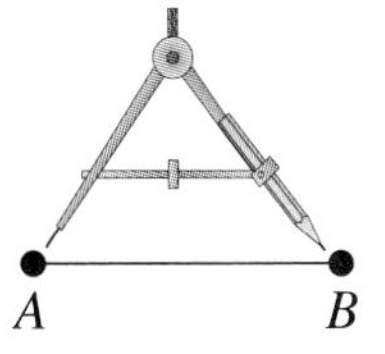

Step 2 Put the tip of the compass at A and open the compass wide enough so that you could draw an arc through B.

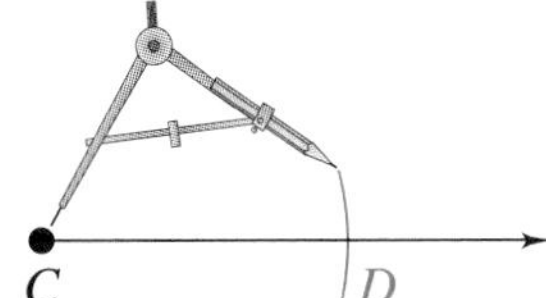

Step 3 Keeping the compass open to the same width, put the tip at C and draw an arc intersecting the ray. Label the point of intersection as D.

You now have constructed a segment, $\overline{CD}$, that is congruent to $\overline{AB}$.

Angles that have the same measure are **congruent angles.** You can use a compass and straightedge to construct an angle congruent to a given angle.

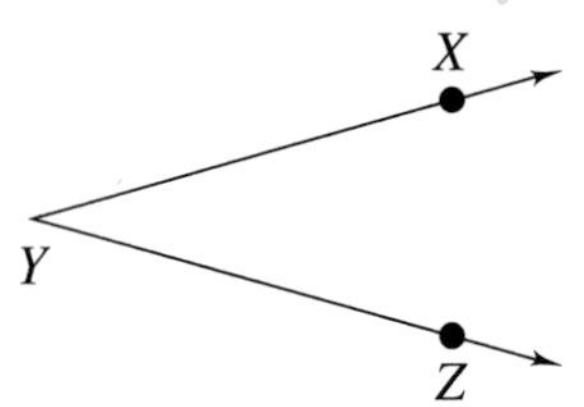

2. Draw an acute angle, $\angle XYZ$. Then follow the steps below to construct an angle congruent to $\angle XYZ$.

Step 1 Draw a ray. Label the endpoint as S.

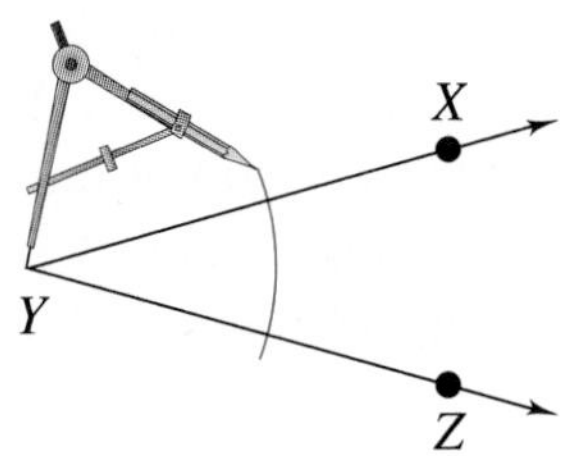

Step 2 Put the compass tip at Y and draw an arc that intersects both $\overrightarrow{YX}$ and $\overrightarrow{YZ}$.

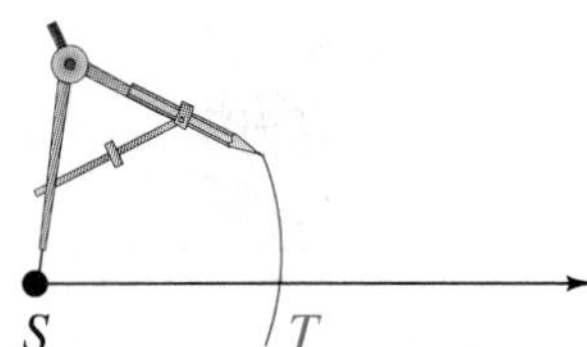

Step 3 Keeping the compass open to the same width, put the tip at S. Draw an arc intersecting the ray at a point you label as T.

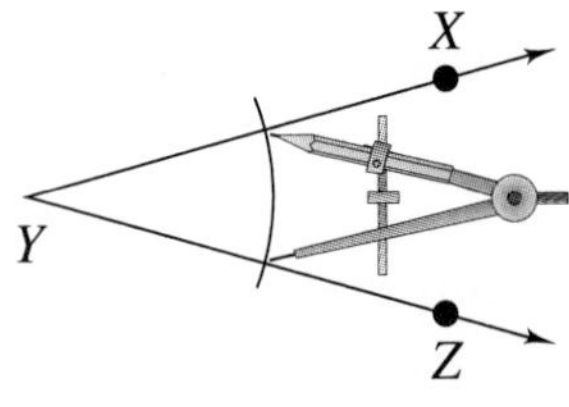

Step 4 Adjust the compass width so that the tip and the pencil are at the points where the arc intersects $\overrightarrow{YX}$ and $\overrightarrow{YZ}$.

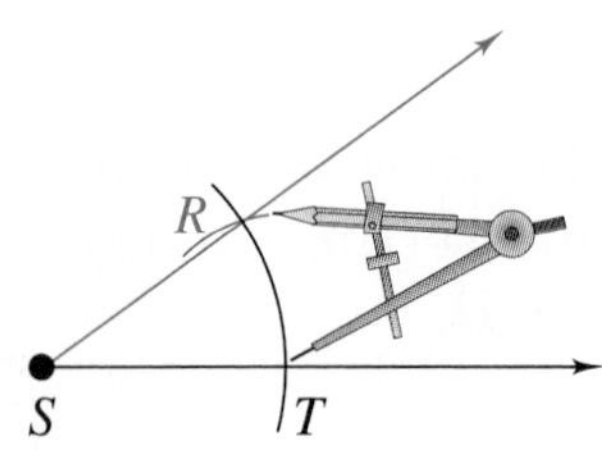

Step 5 Keeping the same compass width, put the tip at T and draw an arc that intersects the first arc. Label the point of intersection as R. Draw $\overrightarrow{SR}$.

You just constructed an angle, $\angle RST$, that is congruent to $\angle XYZ$.

3. Draw an obtuse $\angle G$. Then construct an angle, $\angle K$, congruent to $\angle G$.

4. Use a protractor to measure your $\angle XYZ$, $\angle RST$, $\angle G$, and $\angle K$. Did you get the same measure for $\angle XYZ$ and $\angle RST$? for $\angle G$ and $\angle K$? What might account for any differences?

5. Do you need to know the length of a segment or measure of an angle to construct a congruent segment or angle? Why or why not?

WORK TOGETHER

- Use a straightedge to draw a segment. Label it as $\overline{AB}$.
- Open your compass so the tip is on point A and the pencil point is on B. Draw a circle.
- Keeping the compass open to the same width, put the tip at B. Draw an arc that intersects the circle at one point. Label the point of intersection as point C.
- Draw $\overline{AC}$ and $\overline{BC}$. Describe the figure formed by $\overline{AB}$, $\overline{BC}$, and $\overline{AC}$.
- Use a protractor to measure $\angle A$, $\angle B$, and $\angle C$. Compare your results with those of your group. Make a conjecture.

ON YOUR OWN

6. Draw a segment and label it as $\overline{KL}$. Construct a segment congruent to $\overline{KL}$.

7. Draw an acute $\angle A$. Construct an angle congruent to $\angle A$.

8. Draw an obtuse $\angle B$. Construct an angle congruent to $\angle B$.

9. Draw a segment, $\overline{GH}$. Construct a segment three times as long as $\overline{GH}$.

10. Draw an angle like $\angle C$. Then construct an angle with measure twice the measure of $\angle C$.

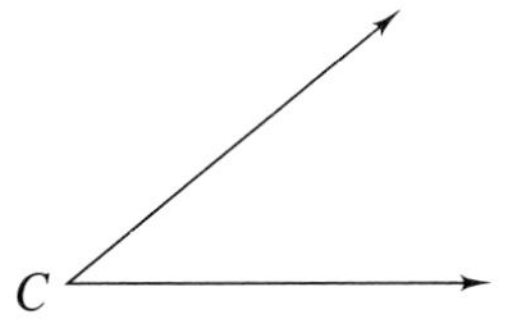

11. **Writing** Describe how to construct an angle with measure three times the measure of $\angle C$.

Mixed REVIEW

Complete with <, >, or =.

1. 13 × 7 ■ 120 − 27
2. 237 + 338 ■ 25 × 23

Use the data: 2, 4, 4, 0, 3, 1, 2, 3, 1, 0.

3. Make a frequency table.
4. Find the range.

Use the diagram below for Exercises 5 and 6.

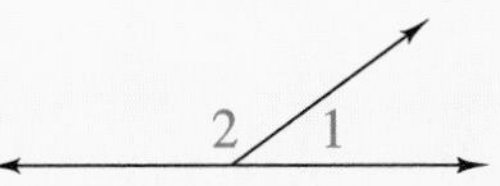

5. Name an acute angle.
6. If the measure of $\angle 1$ is 35°, find the measure of $\angle 2$.

7. A mountain climber starts at an altitude of 2,830 ft and climbs 4,920 ft. The next day, she climbs another 3,130 ft. What is her final altitude?

What's Ahead

- Identifying triangles by their angles
- Identifying triangles by their sides

WHAT YOU'LL NEED

✓ Geoboard

✓ Rubber bands

✓ Dot paper

2-4 Exploring Triangles

WORK TOGETHER

Work in groups. On geoboards form as many of the triangles described below as you can. If possible, try to form two triangles with different shapes that fit each description. Record each triangle on dot paper.

a. a triangle with three acute angles

b. a triangle with one right angle

c. a triangle with one obtuse angle

d. a triangle with one right angle and one obtuse angle

e. a triangle with no sides congruent

f. a triangle with exactly two congruent sides

THINK AND DISCUSS

You can classify triangles by angle measures or by the number of congruent sides.

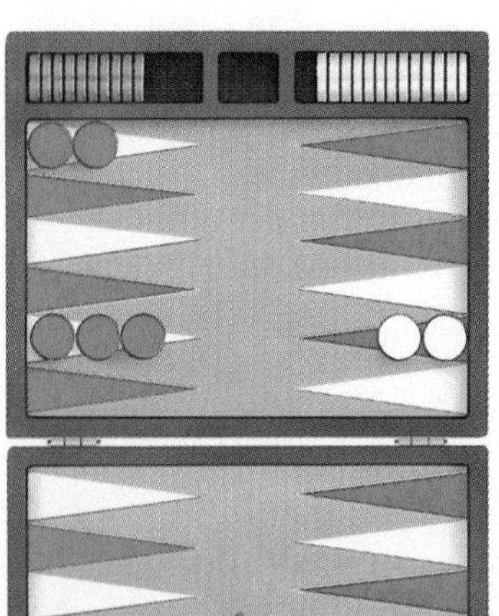

A backgammon board *contains many triangles.* ***How would you classify the triangles?***

Classifying by Angles

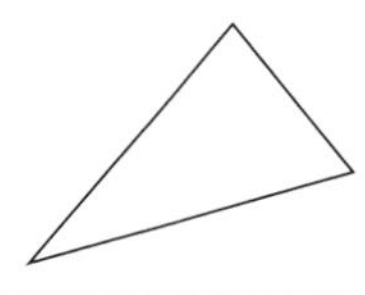

acute triangle
three acute angles

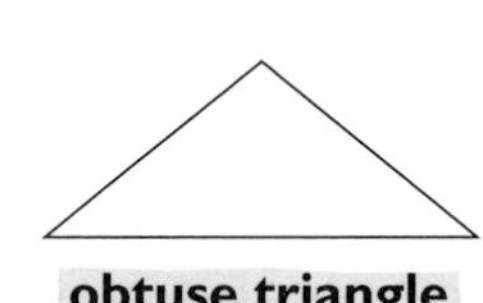

obtuse triangle
one obtuse angle

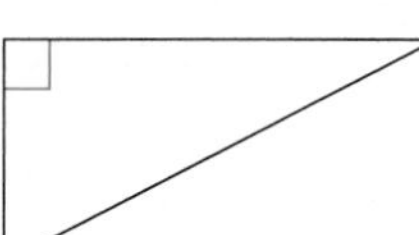

right triangle
one right angle

Classifying by Sides

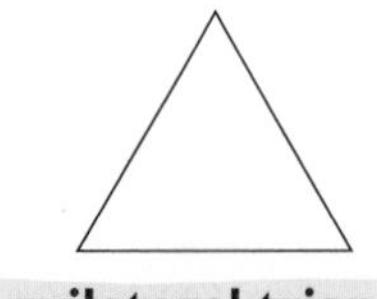

equilateral triangle
three congruent sides

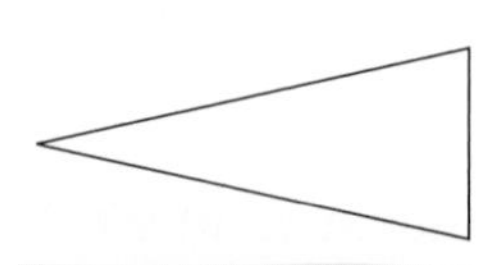

isosceles triangle
at least two congruent sides

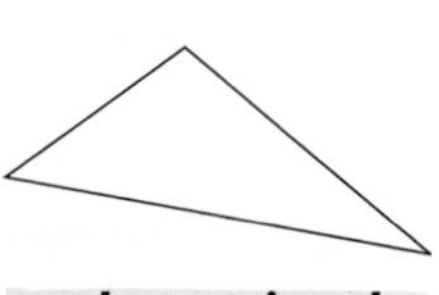

scalene triangle
no congruent sides

1. Which triangle or triangles described in the Work Together activity could you *not* form on your geoboard? Why do you think that you were unable to form them?

2. Can an isosceles triangle be an acute triangle? a right triangle? an obtuse triangle?

3. Can a scalene triangle be an acute triangle? a right triangle? an obtuse triangle?

4. Can an equilateral triangle be an acute triangle? a right triangle? an obtuse triangle?

5. Suppose a triangle is both isosceles and obtuse. What is the best name for it?

A lateen, or triangular sail, allows a boat to sail in any direction—even into the wind.

Example Judging by appearance, give all the names you can for the triangle. What is the best name?

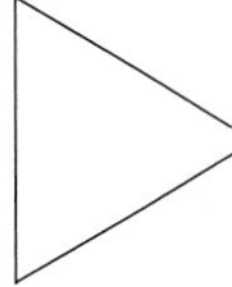

- The triangle is acute, equilateral, and isosceles.
- The best name is equilateral, because every equilateral triangle is acute and isosceles.

TRY THESE

Judging by appearance, name all the triangles that fit each description.

6. equilateral triangle
7. isosceles triangle
8. scalene triangle
9. acute triangle
10. right triangle
11. obtuse triangle

a.

b.

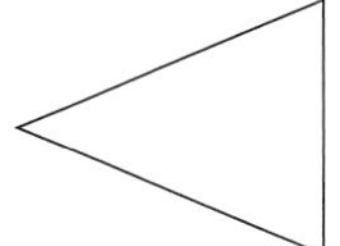

c.

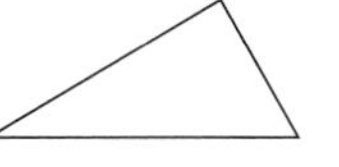

d.

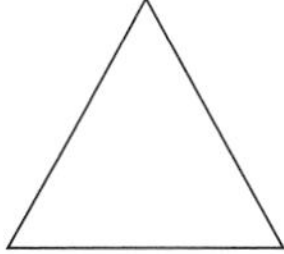

e.

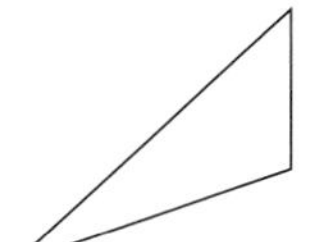

f.

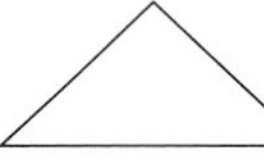

Mixed REVIEW

1. Order the following numbers from greatest to least: 3,201; 2,684; 978; 2,852; 4,527; and 3,097.

2. Data File 1 (pp. 2–3) About how many more people own color sets than black and white sets?

Complete.

3. The two geometric tools you use in constructions are the ■ and straightedge.

4. Angles that have the same measure are ■ angles.

5. In how many ways can you have coins that total 15¢?

ON YOUR OWN

12. Use a centimeter ruler and protractor to measure the sides and angles of each triangle. Classify each triangle according to its angle measures and side lengths. Then choose the best name for each triangle.

a. 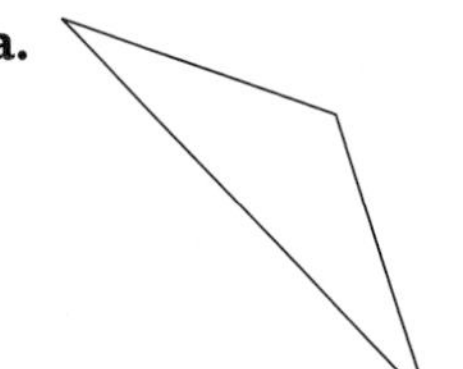

b. 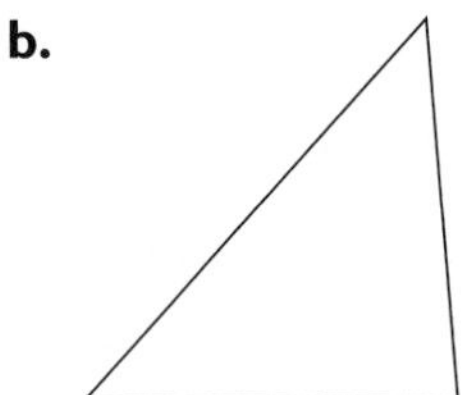

c. 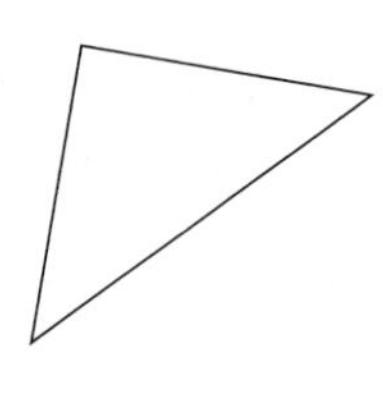

Classify the triangle described as scalene, isosceles, or equilateral.

13. The side lengths are 6, 8, and 6.

14. The side lengths are 12, 7, and 9.

15. The side lengths are 11, 11, and 11.

Classify the triangle described as acute, right, or obtuse.

16. The angle measures are 100°, 37°, and 43°.

17. The angle measures are 56°, 88°, and 36°.

18. The angle measures are 50°, 90°, and 40°.

19. **Writing** Must an equilateral triangle be an isosceles triangle? Why or why not? Must an isosceles triangle be an equilateral triangle? Why or why not?

20. **Critical Thinking** Use a centimeter ruler and protractor to measure the sides and angles of each triangle. Classify each of the triangles by side lengths. Then make a conjecture.

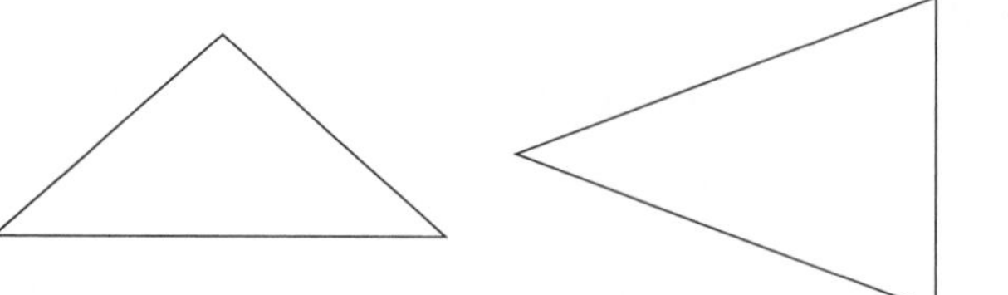

If possible, sketch each triangle. If you can't sketch a triangle, explain why.

21. an acute isosceles triangle
22. an obtuse scalene triangle
23. a right isosceles triangle
24. an obtuse equilateral triangle
25. an acute scalene triangle
26. a right scalene triangle
27. an obtuse isosceles triangle
28. a right equilateral triangle
29. an acute obtuse triangle

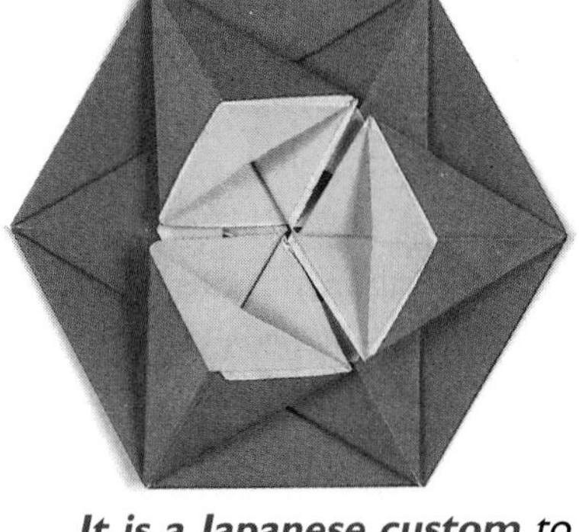

***It is a Japanese custom** to decorate gifts with noshi cases. These paper decorations symbolize good fortune.*

CHECKPOINT

Use the figure at the right to name each of the following.

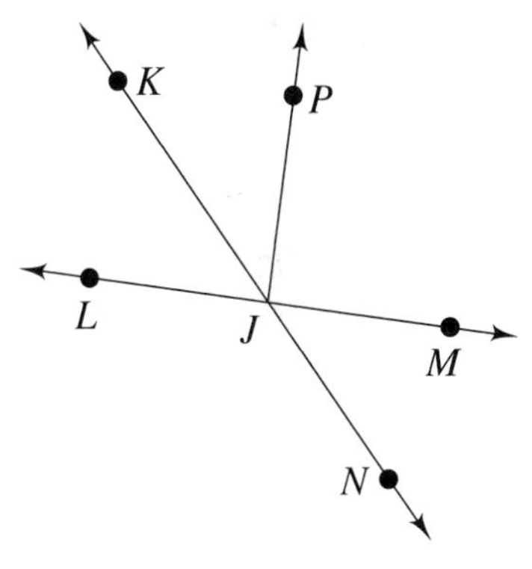

1. two lines
2. three rays
3. three segments
4. an acute angle
5. an obtuse angle
6. a right angle
7. a straight angle
8. three collinear points
9. three noncollinear points
10. Use a protractor to measure $\angle LJK$.
11. Use a protractor to draw an angle with measure 105°.
12. Draw an obtuse $\angle E$. Then construct an angle congruent to $\angle E$.
13. **Choose A, B, C, or D.** Judging by appearance, classify the triangle.
    A. right scalene
    B. acute isosceles
    C. equilateral
    D. obtuse isosceles

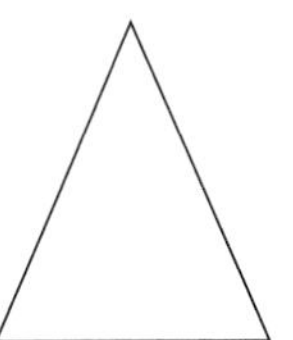

14. Give examples of three ways triangles might be used in real life.

What's Ahead

- Determining if a figure is a polygon
- Identifying triangles, quadrilaterals, pentagons, hexagons, octagons, and decagons

2-5 Exploring Polygons

WORK TOGETHER

Some of the figures shown are *polygons.* The others are not polygons. Work with your group to answer the following questions.

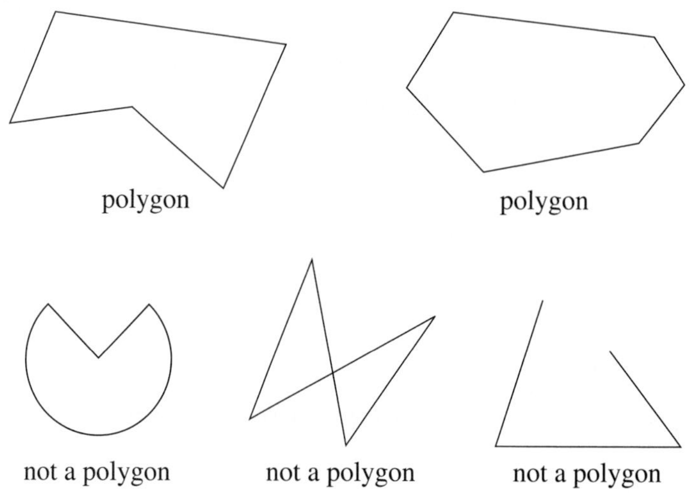

1. a. What characteristics do the polygons share?
   b. How do the polygons differ from the figures that are not polygons?
   c. **Writing** Formulate a definition for a polygon. Be prepared to share your definition with the class.

2. Use your definition to tell which of these figures are polygons. Does your definition work? If not, how would you change it?

a. 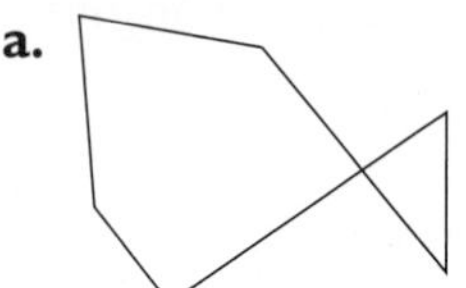
b. 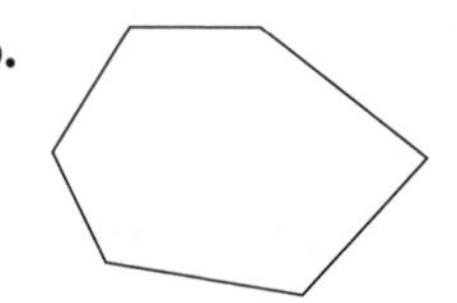
c. 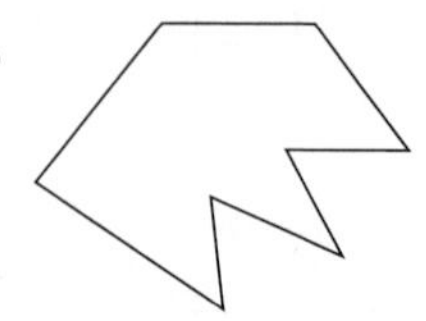
d. 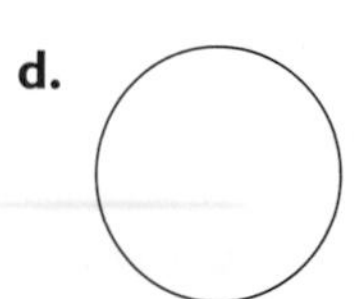
e. 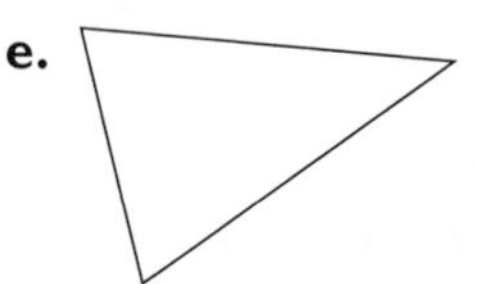
f. 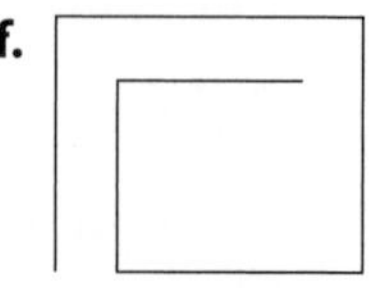

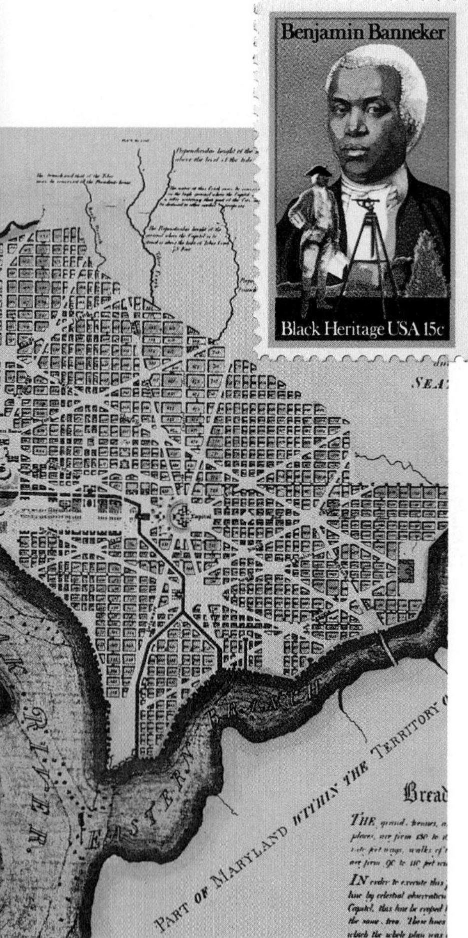

Benjamin Banneker helped design the city of Washington, D.C. The map shows the use of geometry in his design.

THINK AND DISCUSS

Polygons are named for the number of their sides. Some common names are shown below.

Polygon	Number of Sides	Polygon	Number of Sides
Triangle	3	Hexagon	6
Quadrilateral	4	Octagon	8
Pentagon	5	Decagon	10

3. Classify each polygon as a triangle, quadrilateral, pentagon, hexagon, octagon, or decagon.

a. 

b. 

c. 

d. 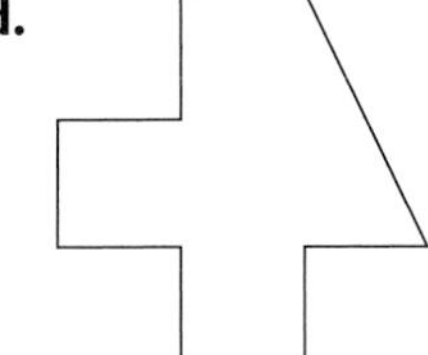

e. 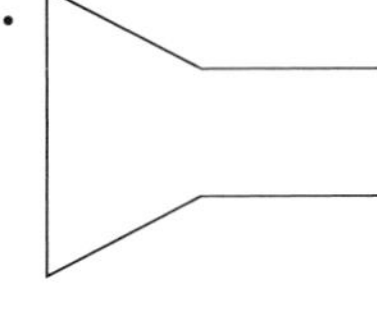

f. 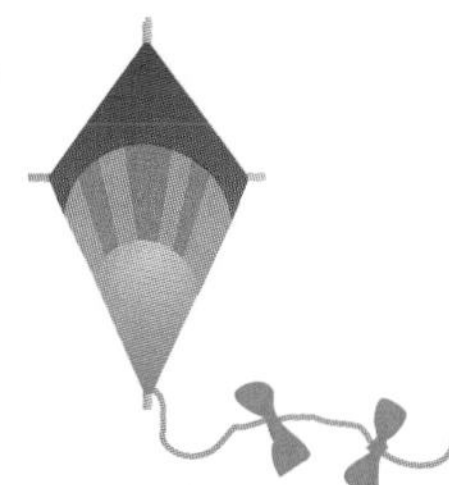

You can see polygons in a cluster of bubbles. ***What kinds of polygons do you see in the photo?***

You can think of a **convex** polygon as one that a rubber band could fit around snugly, without any gaps. The polygon shown is not convex because the red band does not fit snugly.

not convex

4. Are any nonconvex polygons shown in Question 3?

5. **Critical Thinking** How many right angles does the blue polygon appear to have? Does it make sense to talk about the angles of this polygon?

When we talk about a polygon, we will mean a convex polygon.

Octos is a bicycle built for eight. The bicycle is 7 ft wide and can reach a speed of 50 mi/h with strong pedalers. **Why do you think the bicycle was named *Octos*?**

Source: *3-2-1 Contact*

ON YOUR OWN

Classify each polygon.

6. 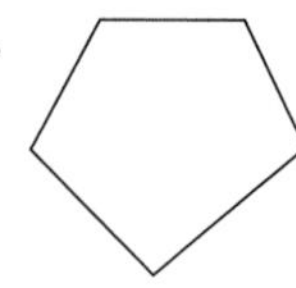

7. 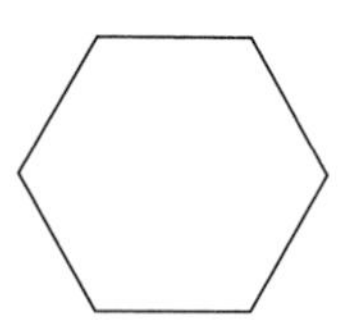

8. 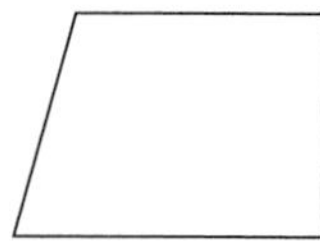

9. 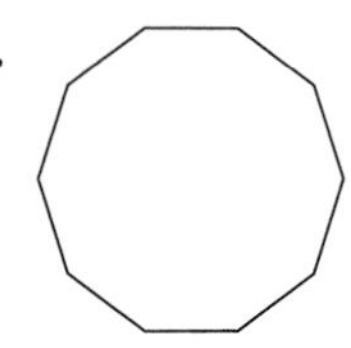

10. 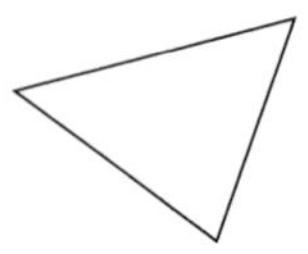

11. 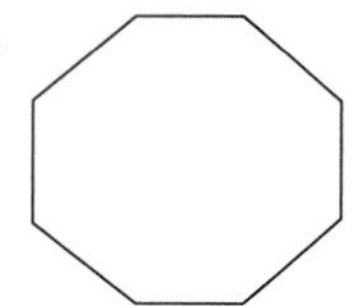

12. Draw a triangle, quadrilateral, pentagon, hexagon, octagon, and decagon on dot paper.

- **a.** How many angles does each polygon have?
- **b.** **Writing** What is the relationship between the number of sides and the number of angles in a polygon? Why does this relationship exist?

13. **a.** What do the triangles shown have in common?

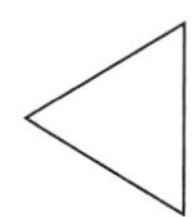  

b. What do the quadrilaterals shown have in common?

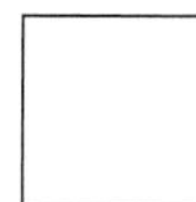 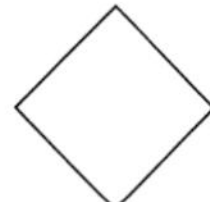 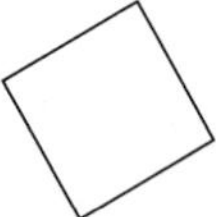

c. What do the pentagons shown have in common?

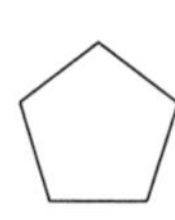 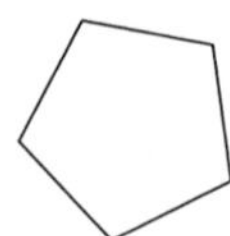 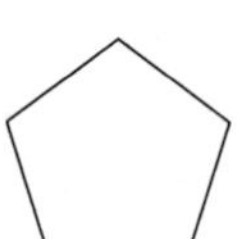

d. **Critical Thinking** What characteristics do the triangles, quadrilaterals, and pentagons share?

14. **Language** List three words, besides triangle, that begin with the prefix *tri-*.

Mixed REVIEW

Use mental math.

1. 23×10

2. $1500 \div 100$

Classify each triangle as acute, right, or obtuse.

3. The angle measures are 48°, 53°, and 79°.

4. The angle measures are 42°, 104°, and 34°.

5. Paper cups come in packages of 50. There are 576 students and teachers at Memorial Middle School. How many packages of paper cups should be purchased for the school picnic?

15. **Language** List three words, besides quadrilateral, that begin with the prefix *quad-*.

Use dot paper to draw each polygon.

16. a quadrilateral with exactly two right angles

17. a quadrilateral with no right angles

18. a pentagon with three right angles

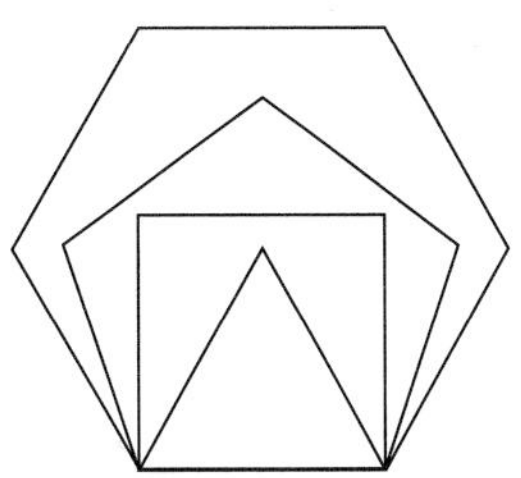

19. **Choose A, B, C, or D.** For which polygon shown is the measure of each angle 120°?

A. triangle **B.** quadrilateral

C. pentagon **D.** hexagon

The Raft of the Treetops

If you've ever climbed a tree, then you know how much fun it is to reach the top. Imagine walking across treetops that are more than 100 ft off the ground! That's what botanist Francis Hallé and his team are doing with the help of their Raft of the Treetops. This "raft" allows the scientists to investigate the top of the rain forest—something only expert tree climbers could do before.

The inflatable platform weighs about 1,650 lb and has an area of about 6,500 ft^2. That's about the size of two tennis courts. The platform looks like a six-sided inner-tube with sausage cross-links and a circus net bottom. Even though the raft sounds heavy, it can spread across the treetops while hardly breaking a twig!

20. **a.** What shape is the platform?

b. Draw a polygon shaped like the platform. Instead of dividing it into six triangles, divide it into four triangles.

c. Draw a polygon shaped like the platform. Divide it into a quadrilateral and two triangles.

d. Why do you think that Francis Hallé designed the platform the way he did?

What's Ahead

- Identifying and classifying special quadrilaterals

2-6 Special Quadrilaterals

THINK AND DISCUSS

WHAT YOU'LL NEED

✓ Tangrams 

Certain quadrilaterals have special names because they have characteristics that distinguish them from other quadrilaterals.

A **parallelogram** is a quadrilateral with both pairs of opposite sides parallel.

A **rectangle** is a parallelogram with four right angles.

1. Find several examples of rectangles in your classroom.

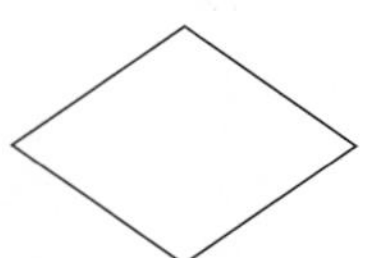

A **rhombus** is a parallelogram with four congruent sides.

2. Can a rhombus be a rectangle? Why or why not?

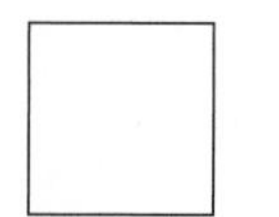

A **square** is a parallelogram with four right angles and four congruent sides.

3. **a.** Must a square be a rectangle? Must a rectangle be a square? Explain.
   b. Must a square be a rhombus? Must a rhombus be a square? Explain.
   c. What is the best name for a rhombus that is also a rectangle?

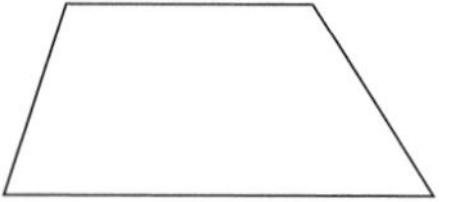

A **trapezoid** is a quadrilateral with exactly one pair of opposite sides parallel.

4. Can a trapezoid be a parallelogram? Why or why not?

Example Judging by appearance, give all the names that apply to the polygon. Then choose the best name.

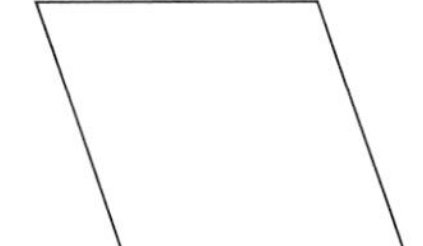

- It has four sides.
- Both pairs of opposite sides are parallel.
- The four sides are congruent.
- The polygon is a quadrilateral, parallelogram, and rhombus.
- The best name is rhombus, because every rhombus is a quadrilateral and a parallelogram.

WORK TOGETHER

You can use tangram pieces to form quadrilaterals. Two ways of forming a parallelogram are shown at the right.

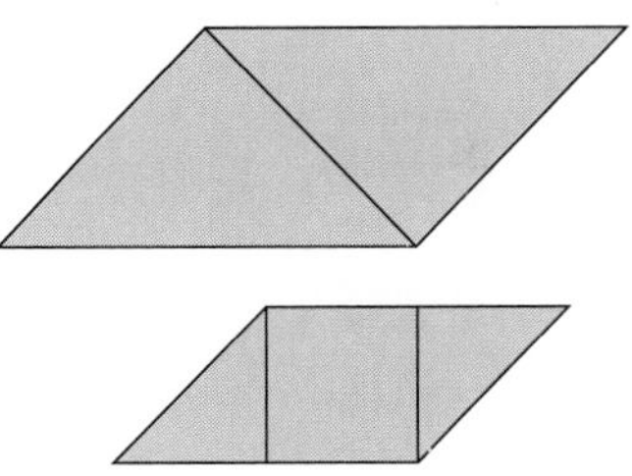

Work with a partner. Record all possible ways you can use tangram pieces to form a parallelogram, rectangle, rhombus, square, and trapezoid. Organize your results in a table. Compare your results with other groups.

TRY THESE

List the letters of all the polygons that have each name.

5. quadrilateral
6. parallelogram
7. rhombus
8. rectangle
9. square
10. trapezoid

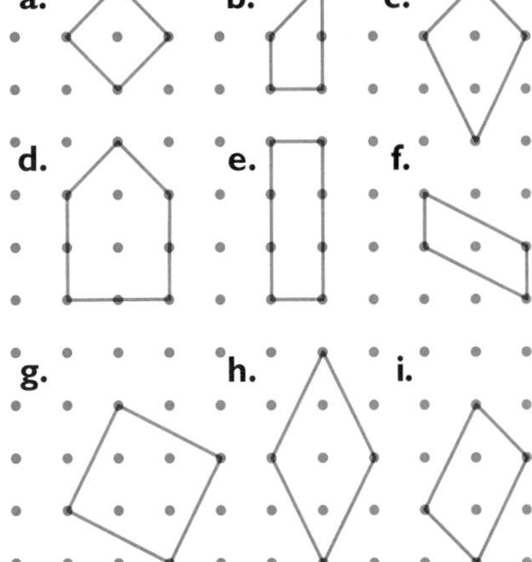

How many squares are shown in this textile pattern?

11. For each polygon shown, state the best name.

Find each answer.

1. 116 ÷ 4
2. 250 × 100

Name each polygon.

3. a polygon having 8 sides
4. a polygon having 5 sides

5. The measure of ∠A is twice the measure of ∠B. The measure of ∠B is three times the measure of ∠C. ∠A is a right angle. What is the measure of ∠C?

ON YOUR OWN

Sketch each quadrilateral.

12. a parallelogram **13.** a square **14.** a trapezoid

15. a rectangle that is not a square

16. a rhombus that is not a square

17. a quadrilateral that is not a trapezoid or parallelogram

List all the names that appear to apply to each quadrilateral. Choose from parallelogram, rectangle, rhombus, square, and trapezoid. Then circle the best name.

18. 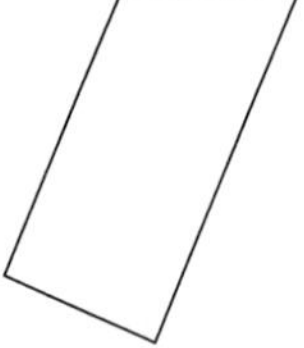

19. 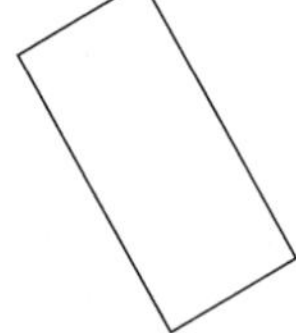

20. 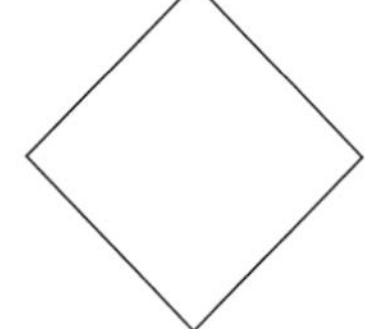

21. Data File 6 (pp. 226–227) What geometric shapes can you find on the bicycle?

22. Writing Explain the relationship between the following figures: rectangle, rhombus, and square.

23. a. Four trapezoids are shown below on dot paper. What do you notice about each pair of nonparallel sides?

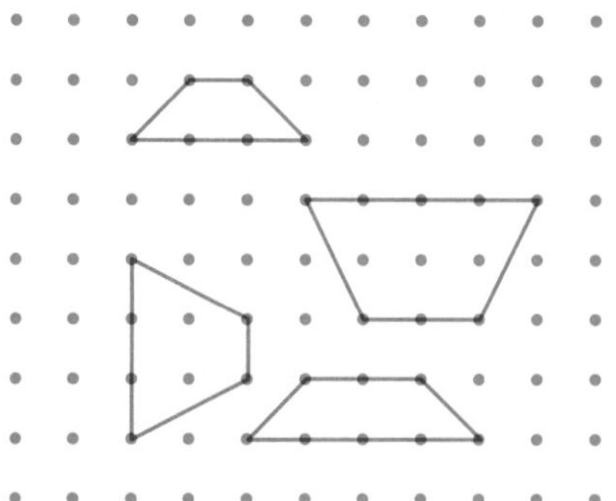

b. When sides of a triangle have this same characteristic, what special name do you give the triangle?

c. Critical Thinking What special name could you use for trapezoids like this? Why does this name fit?

24. Make three copies of the trapezoid on tracing paper.

a. Draw a line through one trapezoid that divides it into two trapezoids.

b. Draw a line through the second trapezoid that divides it into a parallelogram and a triangle.

c. Draw a line through the third trapezoid that divides it into a rhombus and a trapezoid.

Name all the types of quadrilaterals that fit each description.

25. at least two sides parallel

26. parallelogram with four right angles

27. parallelogram

28. parallelogram with four congruent sides

Complete each sentence with *All, Some,* or *No.*

29. ■ quadrilaterals are parallelograms.

30. ■ trapezoids are parallelograms.

31. ■ parallelograms are quadrilaterals.

32. ■ squares are rectangles.

33. ■ rhombuses are rectangles.

34. **Choose A, B, C, or D.** Which name does *not* appear to describe quadrilateral $RSTU$?

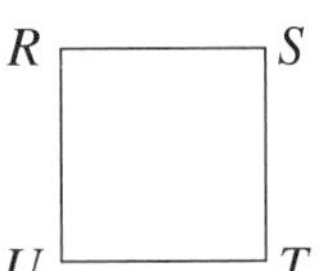

A. square **B.** rhombus

C. trapezoid **D.** parallelogram

35. **Investigation (p. 40)** Collect pictures of buildings. Include old buildings as well as new ones. What special quadrilaterals are commonly found in architecture?

A harlequin was a quick-witted clown from the Italian theater. He wore a suit of bright silk diamonds, sometimes with lace and ruffles. He also carried a "wand" which he used to signal the change of a scene.

Source: *The Oxford Companion to the Theater*

PROBLEM SOLVING

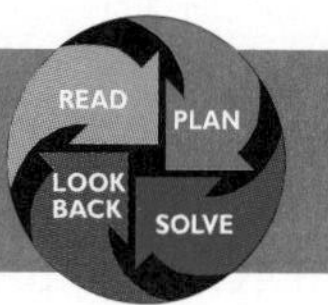

2-7 Use Logical Reasoning

What's Ahead

- Solving problems by using logical reasoning

You often can use logical reasoning to solve problems involving relationships among groups of objects or people.

The sixth grade class at Fairfield Middle School surveyed 130 seventh and eighth grade students to find out how they earn money. The survey showed that 45 students baby-sit, 32 have paper routes, 28 do yard work, and 12 have after school jobs at local businesses. Each student who works does only one kind of work except for 15 who baby-sit and do yard work. **How many students earn money by either baby-sitting or doing yard work (or both)? How many students do not earn money?**

READ

Read and understand the given information. Summarize the problem.

1. Think about the information you are given and what you are asked to find.
   a. How many students were surveyed? How did they earn money?
   b. How many students did two different kinds of work?
   c. What does the problem ask you to find?

PLAN

Decide on a strategy to solve the problem.

Logical reasoning is a good strategy to use here. You can draw a *Venn diagram* to show the relationships among the different ways students earn money. First draw a rectangle to represent all the seventh and eighth grade students.

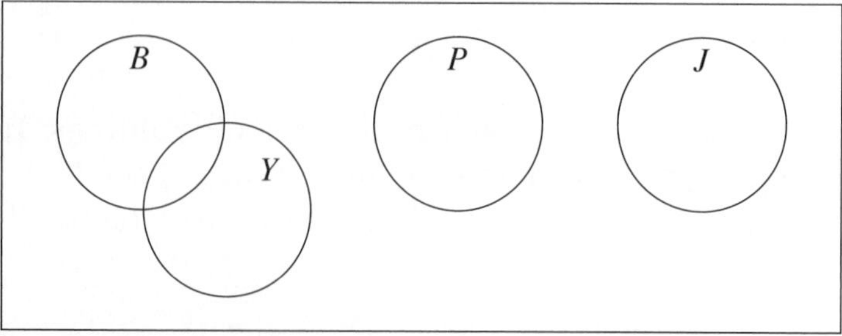

Then draw a circle, B, to represent the students who baby-sit. Draw another circle, P, to represent the students who have paper routes. Draw a circle, Y, that overlaps B to represent students who do yard work and a circle, J, to represent the students who have jobs at businesses.

2. Why should Y and B overlap?

3. Why do circles J and P not overlap any other circle?

Write 15 where B and Y overlap. Write 32 in P and 12 in J.

SOLVE

Try out the strategy.

4. Find the number of students who only earn money by baby-sitting. Write this number in the part of B that does not overlap Y.

5. Find the number of students who only earn money by doing yard work. Write this number in the part of Y that does not overlap B.

Use this information to answer the questions in the problem.

6. What numbers can you add to find the total number of students who earn money either by baby-sitting or doing yard work (or both)? What is the total number?

7. a. What does the sum of the five numbers in the Venn diagram circles represent?

   b. If you subtract the sum from 130, what does the result represent? Write that number inside the rectangle, but not inside a circle.

LOOK BACK

Think about how you solved this problem.

Look at your Venn diagram and see if all the numbers add up to 130. Make sure that you have stated clearly your answers to the questions in the problem.

You can use a Venn diagram to show the relationships among quadrilaterals, rectangles, parallelograms, squares, trapezoids, and rhombuses.

8. Draw a large Venn diagram like the one shown. Label it to show the relationships among types of quadrilaterals.

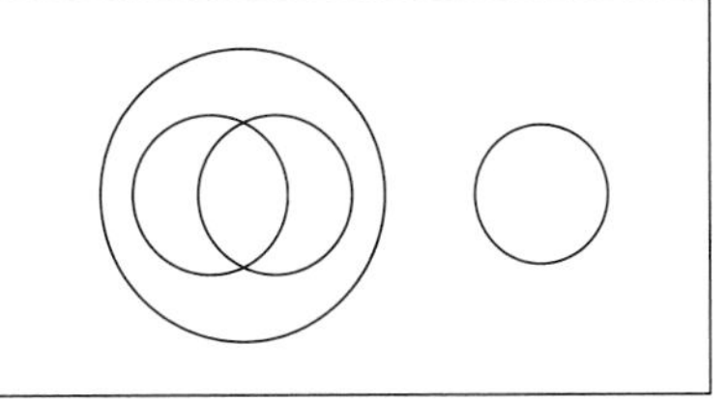

Mixed REVIEW

Use mental math.

1. 30 × 21
2. 20 × 19

Use the data: 8, 11, 9, 17, 18, 7, and 8.

3. Find the range.
4. Find the median.

State the best name for each figure.

5. 

6. 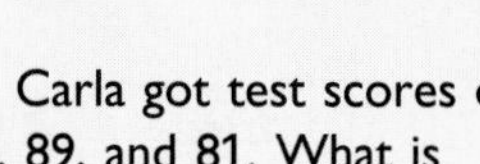

7. Carla got test scores of 76, 89, and 81. What is Carla's average?

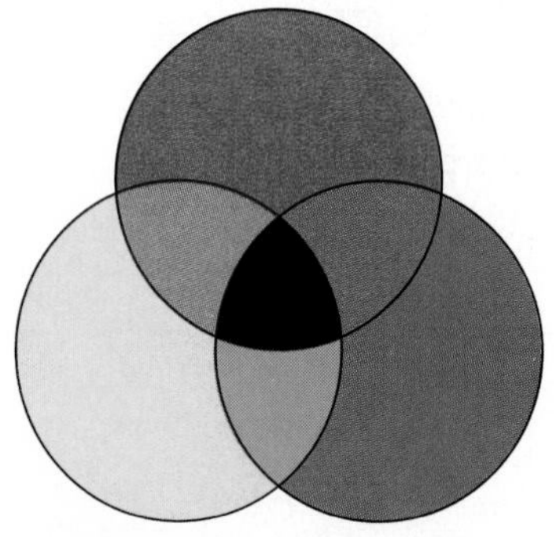

Red, yellow, and blue are the primary colors. ***What color do you get when you mix blue and red?***

TRY THESE

Solve using logical reasoning.

9. In a box of 39 buttons there are 25 that have four holes, 18 that are red, and 13 that have four holes and are also red. The rest of the buttons have two holes or are colors other than red.

a. How many buttons have four holes but are not red?

b. How many red buttons have two holes?

c. How many buttons do not have four holes and are not red?

ON YOUR OWN

Use any strategy to solve each problem. Show all your work.

10. If you have three pairs of pants, four sweaters, and five shirts, how many days can you wear an outfit consisting of a pair of pants, a sweater, and a shirt before you wear the same outfit again?

11. In a restaurant, 37 customers ordered lunch between 11:30 A.M. and 12:30 P.M. Twenty-five of the customers ordered soup with their lunch, 16 ordered salad with their lunch, and 8 ordered both soup and salad.

a. How many customers ordered soup but no salad with their lunch?

b. How many customers did not order soup or salad?

12. Suppose you have a baseball card collection and you decide to sort your cards. When you put your cards in piles of two, you have one left over. You also have one left over when you put the cards in piles of three or piles of four. But when you put them in piles of seven, you have none left over.

a. What is the least number of cards in your collection?

b. Name two other possibilities for the number of cards in your collection.

13. In what ways can you have coins that total exactly 17¢?

Practice

Name each of the following.

1. three collinear points
2. four noncollinear points
3. three segments
4. four rays
5. an acute angle
6. an obtuse angle

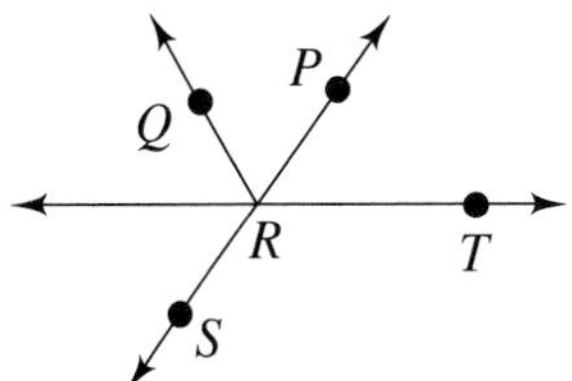

Use a protractor to find the measure of each angle.

7. $\angle KHL$
8. $\angle NHM$
9. $\angle KHN$
10. $\angle JHN$
11. $\angle LHM$
12. $\angle LHJ$

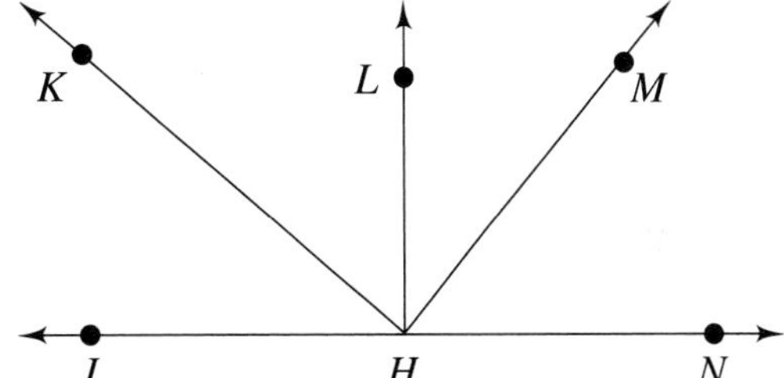

13. Use a protractor to draw a 115° angle.
14. Draw a segment, $\overline{GH}$. Construct a segment twice as long as $\overline{GH}$.
15. Draw an obtuse $\angle A$. Construct an angle congruent to $\angle A$.

Classify the triangle with the given side lengths as scalene, isosceles, or equilateral.

16. 6 cm, 6 cm, 6 cm
17. 6 in., 8 in., 6 in.
18. 17 m, 15 m, 8 m

Classify the triangle with the given angle measures as acute, obtuse, or right.

19. 60°, 90°, 30°
20. 40°, 100°, 40°
21. 60°, 70°, 50°

Sketch each of the following.

22. a pentagon
23. an octagon
24. a hexagon

True or False?

25. All squares are rectangles.
26. Some rectangles are parallelograms.
27. No rhombuses are trapezoids.
28. All rectangles are quadrilaterals.

What's Ahead

- Determining whether figures are congruent
- Determining whether figures are similar

WHAT YOU'LL NEED

✓ Dot paper

✓ Scissors

2-8 Congruent and Similar Figures

WORK TOGETHER

Work with a partner.

- Draw a triangle on dot paper.
- Draw three copies of the triangle on dot paper.
- Cut out the four triangles.
- Put the triangles on top of each other to check that they have the same size and shape.

1. a. Arrange the four triangles so that they form a larger triangle that has the same shape as the original triangle. None of the triangles should overlap.

b. Draw your arrangement on dot paper. Show how the four smaller triangles fit together to form the larger triangle. How do the lengths of the sides of the original triangle and the larger triangle compare?

2. Suppose you have nine triangles that have the same size and shape as your original triangle. On dot paper show how to arrange these triangles to form a larger triangle with the same shape. How do the lengths of the sides of the larger triangle compare to the lengths of the sides of the original triangle?

Why do you think it is important that parts produced on an assembly line be congruent?

THINK AND DISCUSS

Figures that have the same size and shape are **congruent.** As you saw in the Work Together activity, two figures can be congruent even if one of the figures is turned. Two figures also can be congruent even if one of them appears to be turned over.

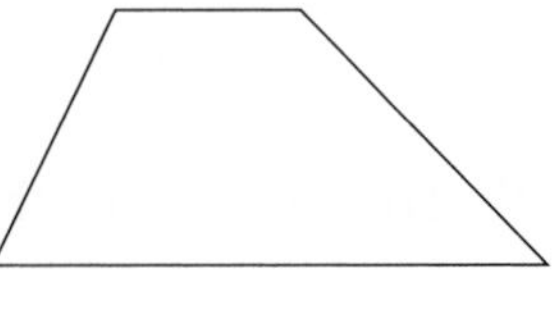

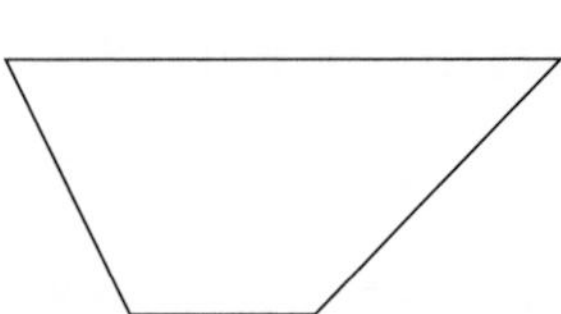

3. How could you check that the trapezoids shown are congruent?

4. Which triangles are congruent to the triangle at the right?

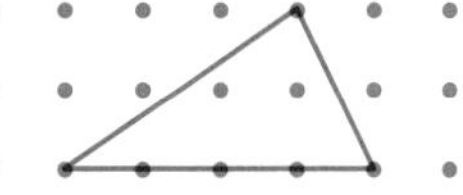

a. 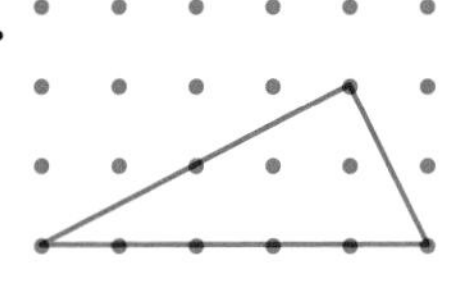 **b.** 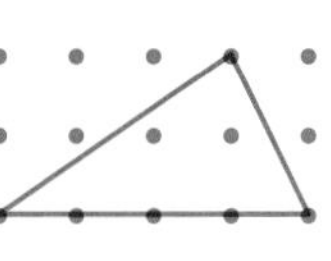 **c.** 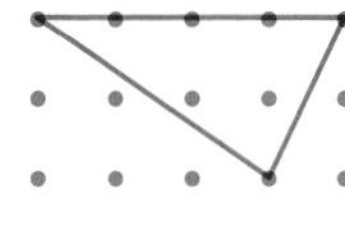

d. 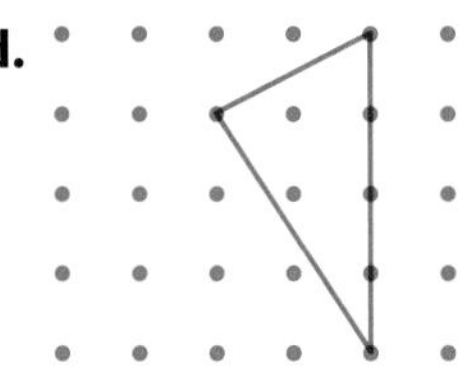 **e.** 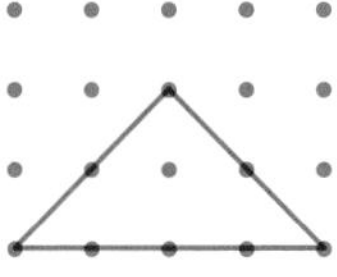 **f.** 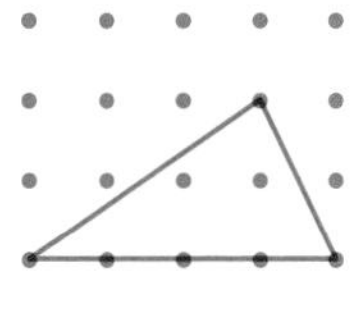

You can see congruent and similar triangles in Arizona's Navajo Bridge. The bridge crosses the Colorado River.

Figures that have the same shape are **similar.** Two figures can be similar even if one is turned or appears to be turned over. The larger triangles you formed in the Work Together activity are each similar to the original triangle. They also are similar to each other.

5. Must two congruent figures be similar? Why or why not?

6. Which triangles are similar to the triangle at the right?

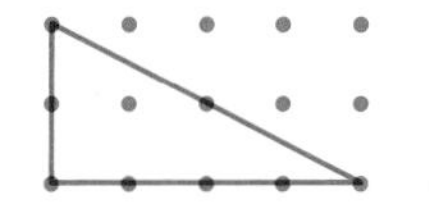

a. 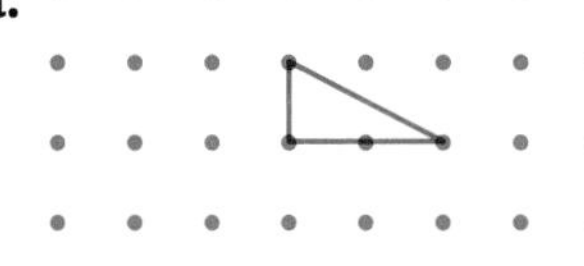 **b.** 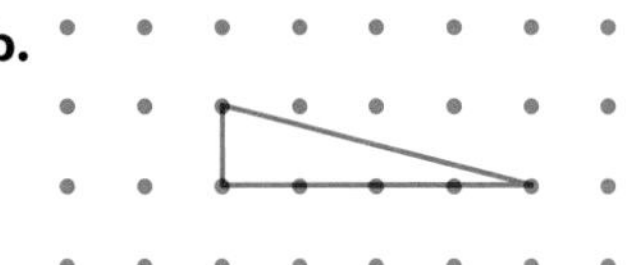

c. 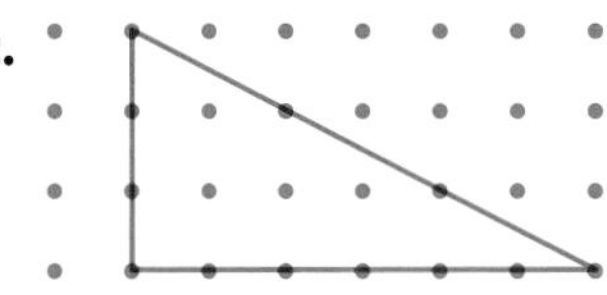 **d.** 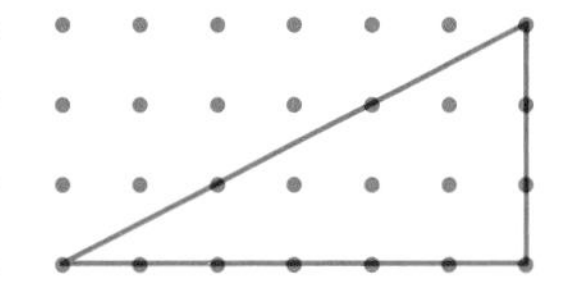

e. 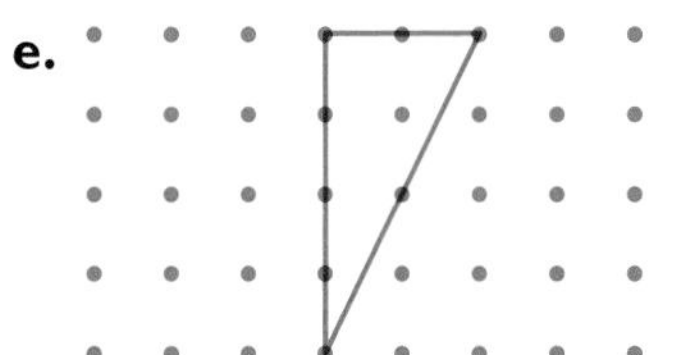 **f.** 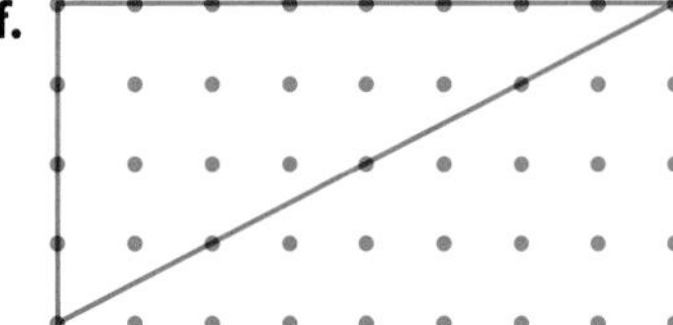

Mixed REVIEW

Complete with <, >, or =.

1. 24 × 5 ■ 600 ÷ 5
2. 1,100 ÷ 100 ■ 110 ÷ 10
3. Suppose you ask 100 people whether they prefer blueberry, raspberry, or vanilla yogurt. What type of graph would be appropriate to display your results? Explain.

Use the Venn diagram below for Exercises 4 and 5.

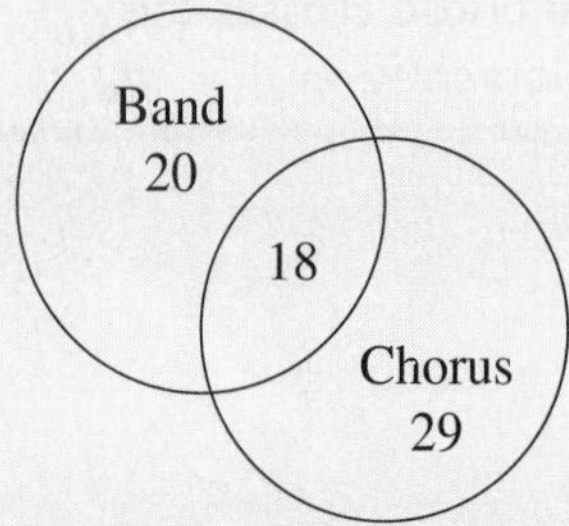

4. How many students play in the band?
5. How many students are in both the band and the chorus?

ON YOUR OWN

7. Which figures appear to be congruent to the trapezoid at the right?

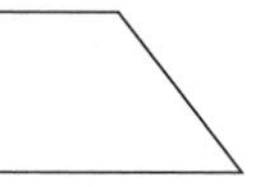

a. 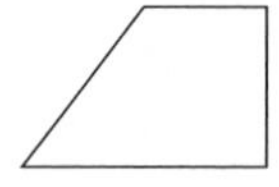 b. 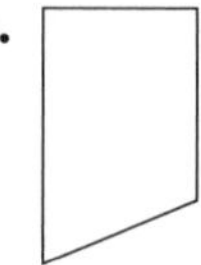 c. 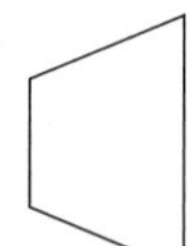 d. 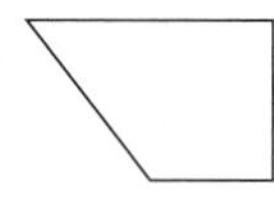

8. Which rectangles are similar to the rectangle at the right?

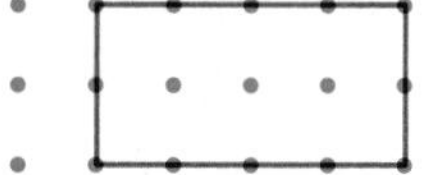

a. 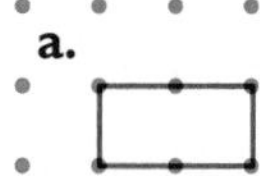 b. 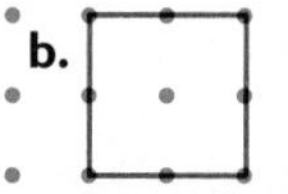 c. 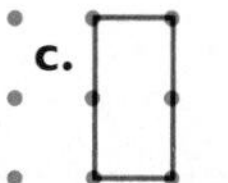 d. 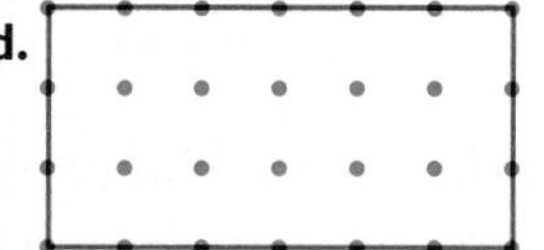

Tell whether the triangles appear to be congruent, similar, or neither.

9. 
10. 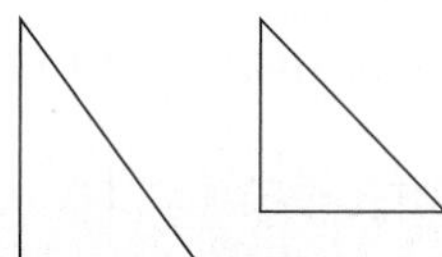
11. 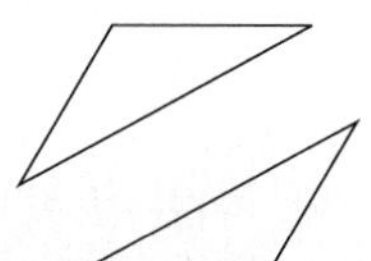

12. List the pairs of triangles that appear to be congruent.

a. 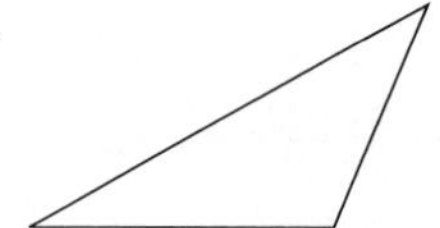 b. 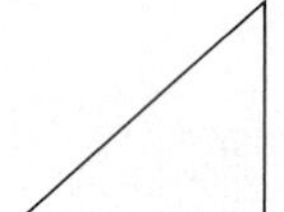 c. 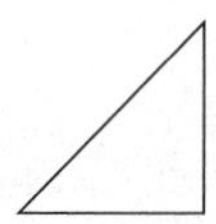

d. 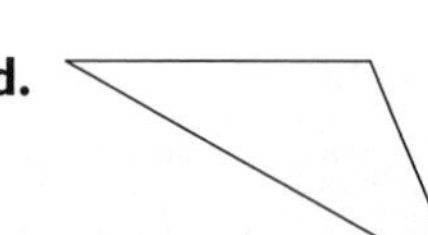 e. 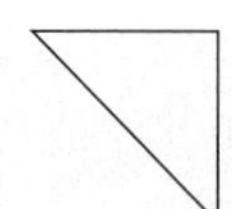 f. 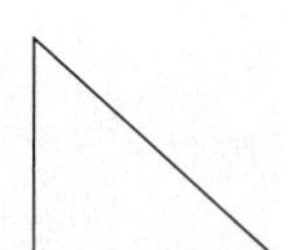

13. **Writing** Are congruent figures similar? Are similar figures congruent? Explain.
14. Use dot paper to draw four congruent triangles in different positions.
15. Suppose you are replacing a window. Should the replacement be congruent to or similar to the original? Explain your reasoning.

16. List the pairs of figures that appear to be similar.

a. **b.** **c.**

d. **e.** **f.**

g. **h.** **i.**

j. **k.** **l.**

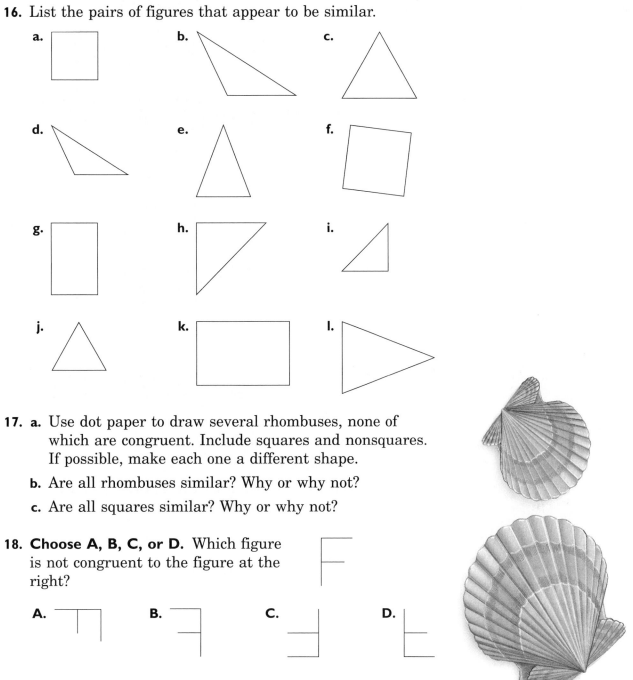

17. a. Use dot paper to draw several rhombuses, none of which are congruent. Include squares and nonsquares. If possible, make each one a different shape.

b. Are all rhombuses similar? Why or why not?

c. Are all squares similar? Why or why not?

18. Choose A, B, C, or D. Which figure is not congruent to the figure at the right?

A. **B.** **C.** **D.**

19. Use a protractor to draw a triangle with two angles measuring 45° and 60°. Then draw a second triangle that is not congruent to the first triangle, but that has angles measuring 45° and 60°. What appears to be true of the two triangles?

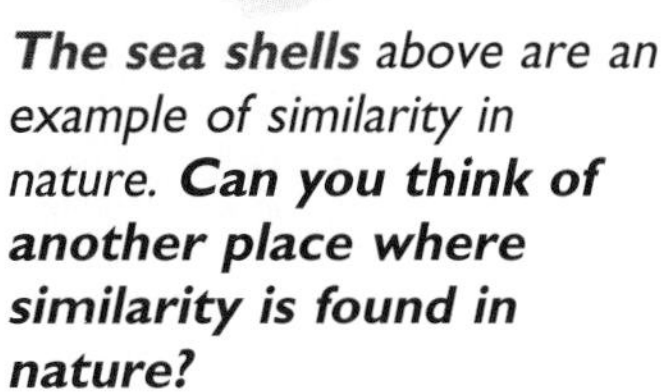

The sea shells** above are an example of similarity in nature. **Can you think of another place where similarity is found in nature?

What's Ahead

- Determining whether a figure has line symmetry

WHAT YOU'LL NEED

✓ Tracing paper

✓ Scissors

2-9 Exploring Symmetry

WORK TOGETHER

- Trace the equilateral triangle and the square. Then cut them out.

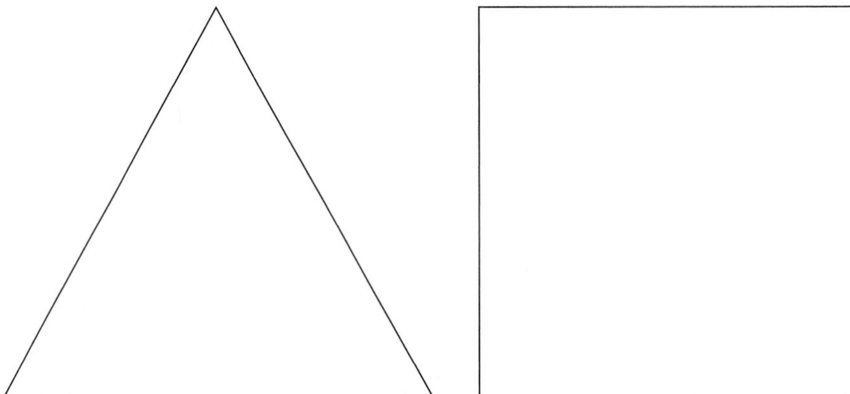

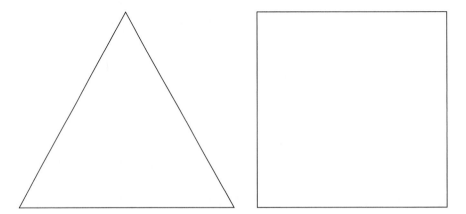

- Fold the triangle in as many ways as you can so that one half matches the other half.
- Repeat for the square.
- Compare your results with a partner's. In how many different ways can you fold each figure?

THINK AND DISCUSS

You often see symmetry in nature—in the human body, in flowers, insects, birds, and many other natural objects. Because symmetrical designs are appealing to the eye, they often are used in fabrics, flags, carvings, masks, weavings, and pottery.

A figure has **line symmetry** if there is a line that divides the figure into two congruent halves. The line is called a *line of symmetry.*

1. Does the butterfly have any lines of symmetry? How many?

2. How many lines of symmetry does an equilateral triangle have? Draw an equilateral triangle and sketch the lines of symmetry.

This is a** mask from Indonesia. **How many lines of symmetry does it have?

3. How many lines of symmetry does a square have? Draw a square and sketch the lines of symmetry.

4. How many lines of symmetry does each figure have? Describe each line of symmetry as horizontal, vertical, or neither.

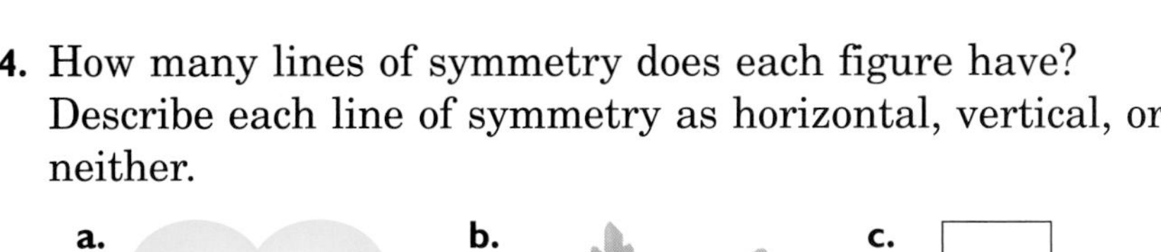

a.  **b.**  **c.** 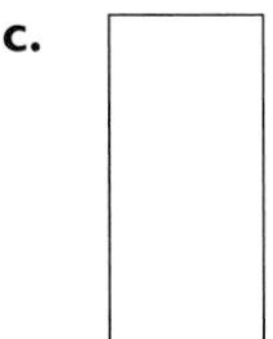

d. 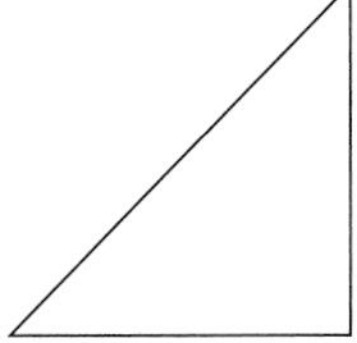 **e.** 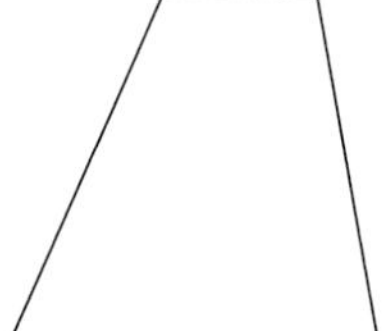 **f.** 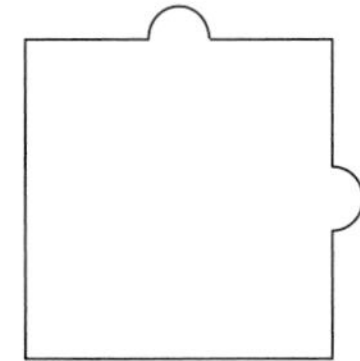

5. **Critical Thinking** How could you check whether a figure has line symmetry?

ON YOUR OWN

Does the figure have line symmetry? If it does, trace the figure and draw all the lines of symmetry.

6. 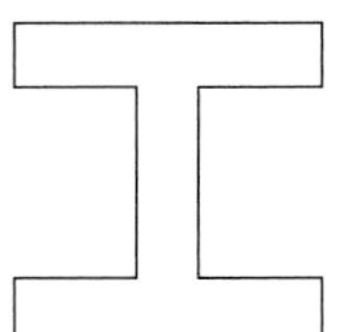 **7.** 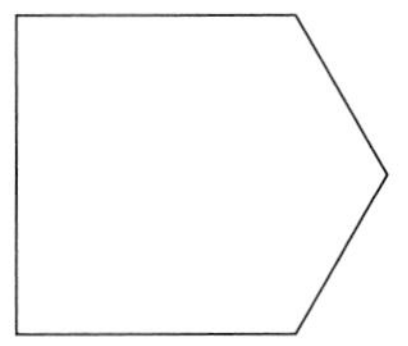 **8.** 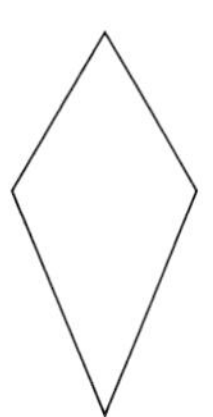

9. 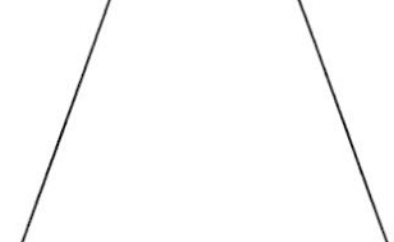 **10.** 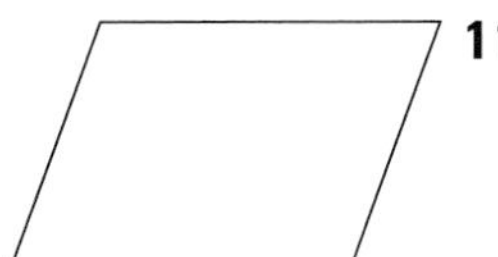 **11.** 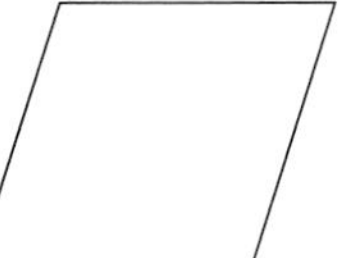

Mixed REVIEW

Use mental math.

1. 0 + 332
2. 332 ÷ 1

Classify each triangle as scalene, isosceles, or equilateral.

3. a triangle having side lengths of 8, 8, and 8
4. a triangle having side lengths of 9, 14, and 7

Use the figures below for Exercises 5 and 6.

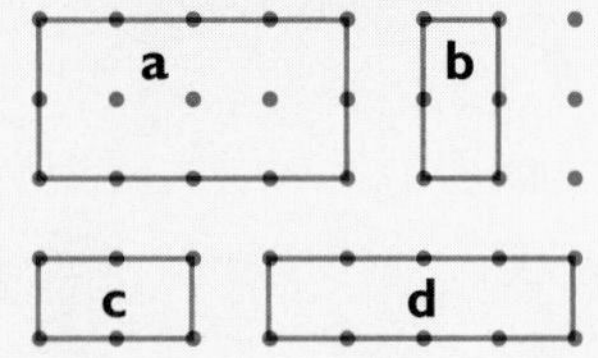

5. Which figures appear to be congruent?
6. Which figures appear to be similar?
7. The product of two whole numbers is 35. Their difference is 2. What are the two numbers?

Copy each figure on dot paper. Complete the figure so that the line is a line of symmetry.

12.

13.

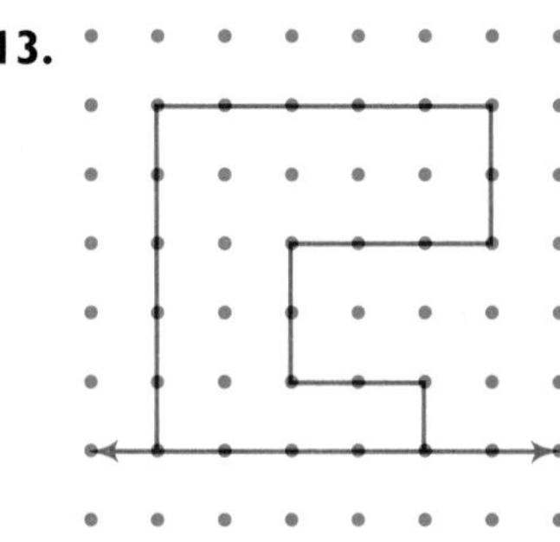

14. Trace the hexagon and draw all the lines of symmetry.

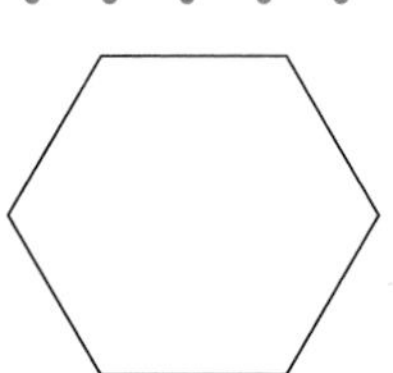

15. **a.** Draw three or more isosceles triangles like those shown below. Draw all the lines of symmetry for each triangle.

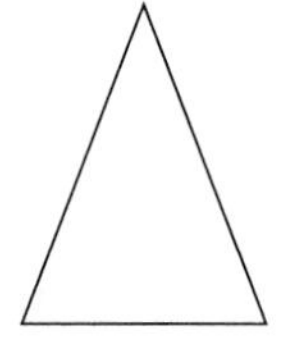

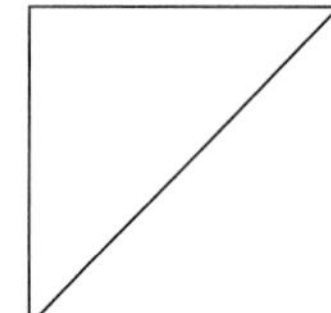

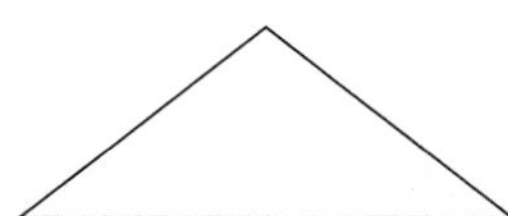

b. Draw three or more scalene triangles. Draw all the lines of symmetry for each triangle.

c. **Writing** Describe the lines of symmetry that scalene triangles, equilateral triangles, and isosceles triangles have.

16. Which letters of the alphabet, when printed in capital letters, have line symmetry?

A B C D E F G H I J K L M

N O P Q R S T U V W X Y Z

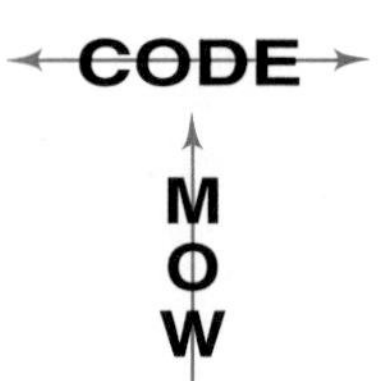

17. The word CODE has a horizontal line of symmetry. Find another word that has a horizontal line of symmetry.

18. When the word MOW is written in column form, it has a vertical line of symmetry. Find another word like that.

19. Many flags, such as the Canadian flag shown, have line symmetry.

   a. Design a flag that has line symmetry.

   b. Design a flag that has no line symmetry.

20. a. **Activity** Fold a sheet of paper. Cut out a shape that will have the foldline as a line of symmetry.

   b. Fold a sheet of paper into quarters. Cut out a shape that will have two perpendicular lines of symmetry.

***Canada's Maple Leaf** flag is a symbol of unity.*

CHECKPOINT

How many sides does each of the following polygons have?

1. a decagon
2. an octagon
3. a quadrilateral
4. **Writing** In your own words, define a square.
5. The Yummyum Cafe had 63 customers for dinner. Twenty of the customers ordered an appetizer with their dinner, 36 ordered dessert with their dinner, and 14 ordered both an appetizer and dessert.

   a. How many customers ordered an appetizer but no dessert with their dinner?

   b. How many customers did not order an appetizer or dessert with their dinner?

6. a. Which of the figures shown below appear to be congruent?

   b. Which figures appear to be similar?

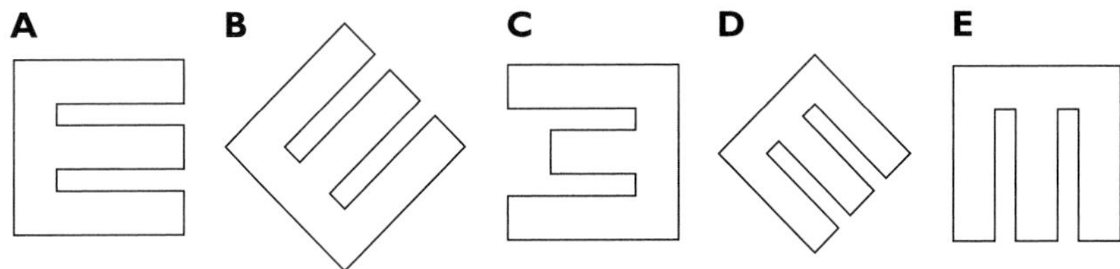

7. **Choose A, B, C, or D.** Which figure has the greatest number of lines of symmetry?

   A. a square
   B. a right isosceles triangle
   C. a scalene triangle
   D. an equilateral triangle

TECHNOLOGY

What's Ahead

- Identifying and working with parts of a circle

2-10 Exploring Circles

WHAT YOU'LL NEED

✓ Computer

✓ Software

✓ Compass

✓ Ruler

THINK AND DISCUSS

From factories to Ferris wheels, computers aid in design. Designers and engineers use geometric figures on the computer screen to model real objects. For example, you can model a Ferris wheel with a *circle* and segments inside the circle.

A **circle** is the set of points in a plane that are the same distance from a given point, the *center.* You name a circle by its center. This is circle O.

A **radius** is a segment that has one endpoint at the center and the other endpoint on the circle.

$\overline{OG}$ is a radius of circle O.

A **diameter** is a segment that passes through the center of a circle and has both endpoints on the circle.

$\overline{AE}$ is a diameter of circle O.

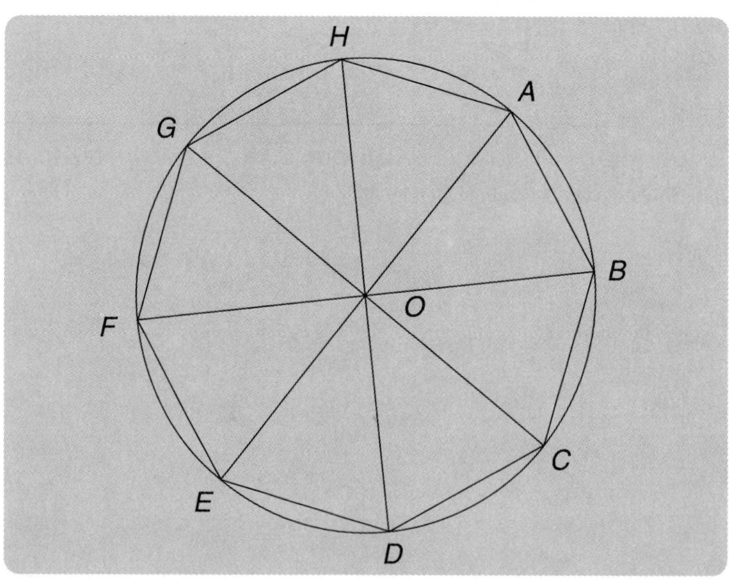

A **chord** is a segment that has both endpoints on the circle.

$\overline{ED}$ is a chord of circle O.

The space city *of the future may be built in a wheel shape or torus.*

Use a compass to draw a circle. Label the center as S.

1. a. Name a radius of circle O other than $\overline{OG}$.
   b. Draw a radius of your circle. Label it as $\overline{ST}$.
   c. Did everyone draw $\overline{ST}$ the same way?
   d. **Critical Thinking** The plural of radius is *radii.* How many different radii can a circle have?

2. a. Name two diameters of circle O other than $\overline{AE}$.
   b. Choose any point on your circle other than T. Label it as U. Draw diameter $\overline{UV}$. How many times longer is $\overline{UV}$ than $\overline{ST}$?
   c. Is the length of any radius of a circle always half the length of any diameter of that circle? Why or why not?

A circle may be small, yet it may be as mathematically beautiful and perfect as a large one.

—Isaac D'Israeli (1766–1848)

The length of a radius of a circle is *the radius* of the circle. The length of a diameter is *the diameter.*

3. a. If the diameter of circle O is 6 cm, what is the radius?
   b. Find the diameter and radius of circle S.

4. Draw $\overline{UT}$ in your circle. What do you call this type of segment?

5. Draw and measure several chords of circle S. What is the longest chord of a circle called?

6. A computer model of a 6-car Ferris wheel, like the one at the right, contains many angles. Some of the angles, like $\angle APB$, are *central angles.* Why do you think they have this name?

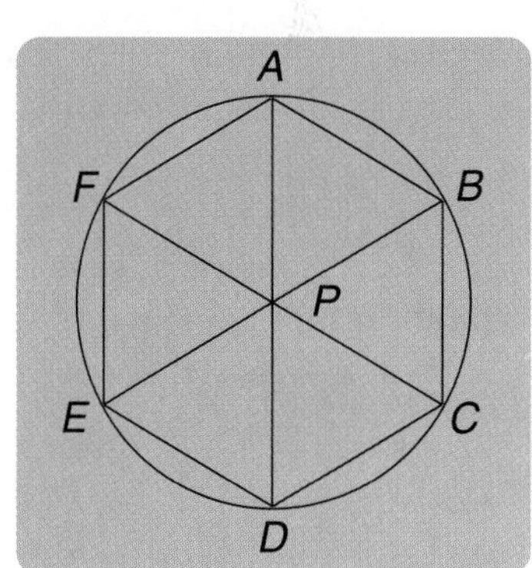

7. a. List the 6 acute central angles shown in circle P.
   b. What is the sum of their measures?
   c. These central angles are congruent. What is the measure of each angle?

8. a. Describe the triangles shown for circle O on the facing page.
   b. What is the measure of $\angle AOB$ of circle O?
   c. Judging by appearance, classify the triangles shown for circle P.

Mixed REVIEW

Compare using <, >, or =.

1. 750 ÷ 150 ■ 80 ÷ 16
2. 19 × 17 ■ 176 + 83

How many lines of symmetry does each figure have?

3. 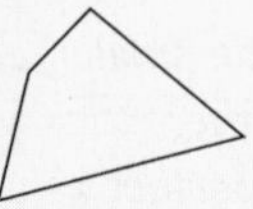

4. 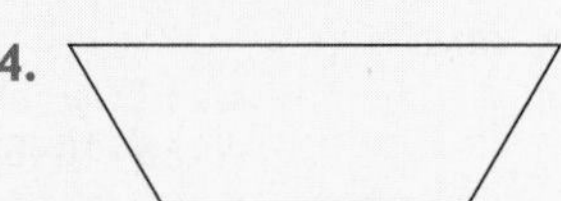

Use the figure below for Exercises 5 and 6.

5. How many parallelograms are shown?
6. How many rhombuses are shown?

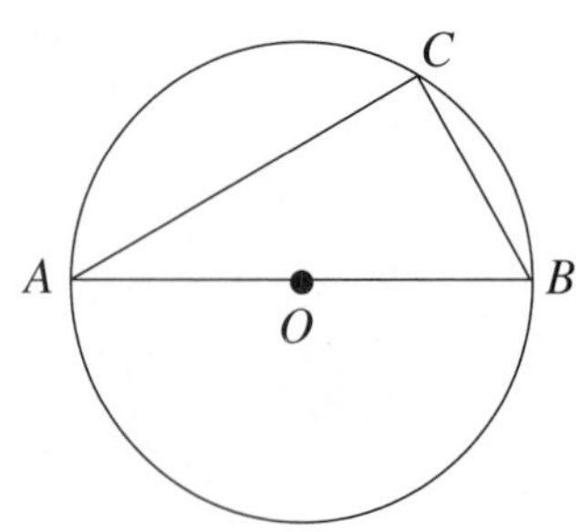

WORK TOGETHER

9. a. **Computer** Make a conjecture about the sum of the measures of the non-overlapping central angles in a circle. Test your conjecture by trying it with different circles and different central angles.

   b. **Critical Thinking** Suppose you are testing a conjecture on a computer and the sum of the measures of the angles is off by 1°. What could account for that?

ON YOUR OWN

Name each of the following for circle *O*.

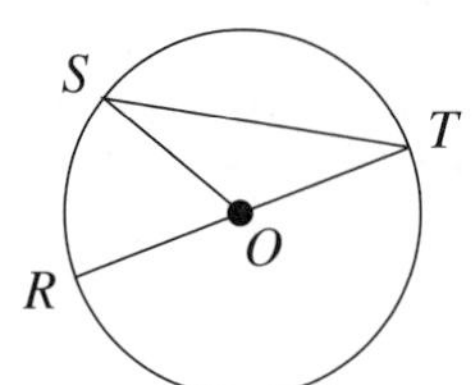

10. three radii
11. a diameter
12. two central angles
13. two chords
14. If the radius of a circle is 8 cm, what is the diameter?
15. If the diameter of a circle is 10 in., what is the radius?
16. A graphic designer used a computer to create the logo shown at the left. She wants to know what a friend in another city thinks of her design. The fax machine is broken, so she must describe the drawing in words.

    a. **Writing** Write a set of instructions that the graphic designer could give someone over the phone to help him to draw the logo. Use geometric terms like radius, diameter, and chord in your directions.

    b. Try out your instructions on a friend or family member. If necessary, revise the instructions.

17. **Computer** Draw a circle and several chords having different lengths. Measure the distance from the center of the circle to each chord. Describe the relationship between the length of the chords and the distances from the center of the circle.

18. **Choose A, B, C, or D.** The acute central angles of circle P are congruent. What is the measure of $\angle APC$?

A. 60° **B.** 120°

C. 150° **D.** 180°

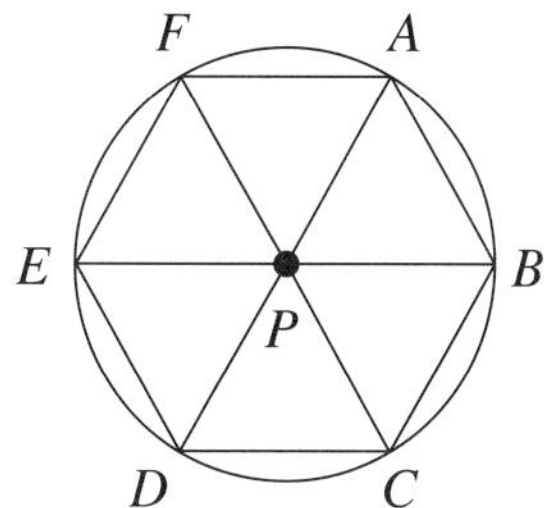

Riding in Circles

The Ferris wheel first appeared at the Chicago World's Fair in 1893, thanks to George Washington Ferris. This mechanical engineer dreamed of designing and building something "original, daring, and unique." Because of this dream, we enjoy his creation at fairs worldwide.

The first Ferris wheel was 265 ft high and had a diameter of 250 ft. That's almost the length of a football field! The 36 cars carried 2,160 passengers high above the crowd. And, unlike today, a single spin took 20 min. The cost of building this Ferris wheel was $385,000.

Use the article above to answer exercises 19 and 20.

19. What was the radius of the first Ferris wheel?

20. How many people could fit in one car?

21. **Computer** Design your own Ferris wheel using geometric figures. How many cars does it have? What is the measure of each central angle?

22. **Computer** Draw and label a circle. Then draw a central angle of your circle. If you increase or decrease the size of your circle, what happens to the measure of the central angle?

23. **Computer** Make and test a conjecture about what happens to $\angle ACB$ as point C moves around the circle. (Hint: What kind of angle is ACB?)

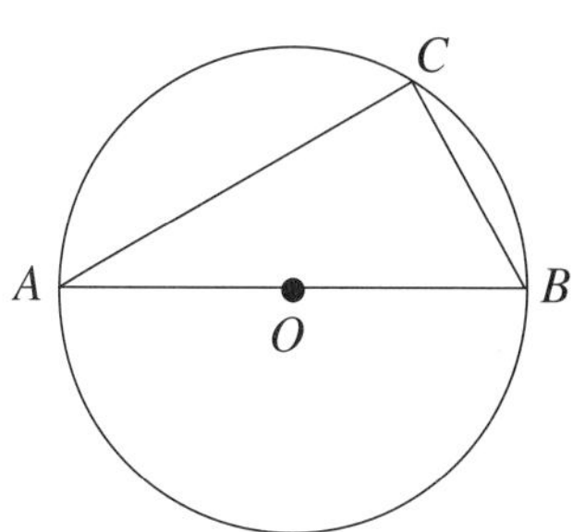

24. **Investigation (p. 40)** Use the computer to create a flag that has symmetry. Describe the symmetry of your flag.

MATH AND DESIGN

2-11 Exploring Tessellations

What's Ahead

- Drawing tessellations

WHAT YOU'LL NEED

✓ Protractor

✓ Dot paper

✓ Scissors

THINK AND DISCUSS

Tessellations are repeated geometric designs that cover a plane with no gaps and no overlaps. Tessellations have been used in designing and decorating buildings, streets, and walkways for a long time. For example, the Sumerians in the Mesopotamian Valley (about 4000 B.C.) decorated their homes and temples with mosaics in geometric patterns. Brick streets, tiled floors, and patios are just a few examples of modern tessellations.

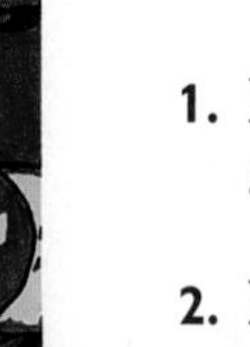

The title of this** art work is "Apple Core." **What two figures tessellate the plane?

1. Describe the polygons used to form the tessellations above.

2. Measure the angles of each polygon. For each tessellation what is the sum of the measures of angles that have the same vertex?

3. Describe how you could use a pattern for each polygon to draw the tessellation. Can you draw each of the three tessellations without turning the pattern?

4. Are any of the tessellations related? In what way?

WORK TOGETHER

5. Working with a partner, draw an acute scalene triangle and an obtuse scalene triangle on dot paper. Each of you should cut out several congruent copies of one of the triangles and use them to form a tessellation. Copy each tessellation on dot paper.

FLASHBACK

A scalene triangle has no congruent sides.

6. On dot paper draw a quadrilateral that has no congruent sides. Work with your partner.
   a. Cut out nine copies of the quadrilateral.
   b. Experiment to find out how to form a tessellation.
   c. Copy the tessellation on dot paper.
   d. What does your tessellation show about the sum of the measures of the angles of your quadrilateral? Explain your reasoning.

ON YOUR OWN

Trace each figure. Determine whether you can use the figure to form a tessellation.

7. 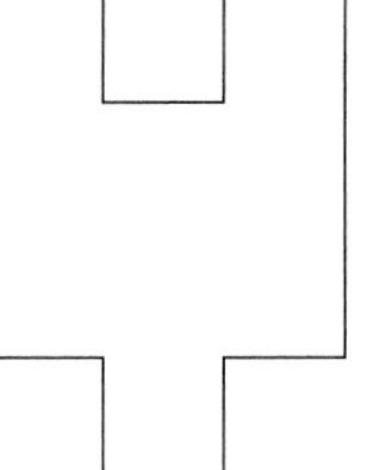

8. 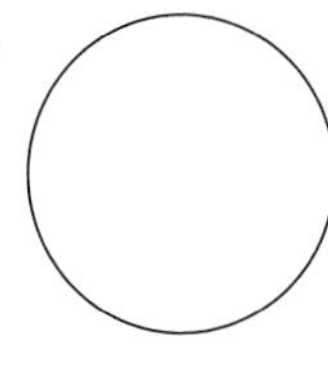

9. 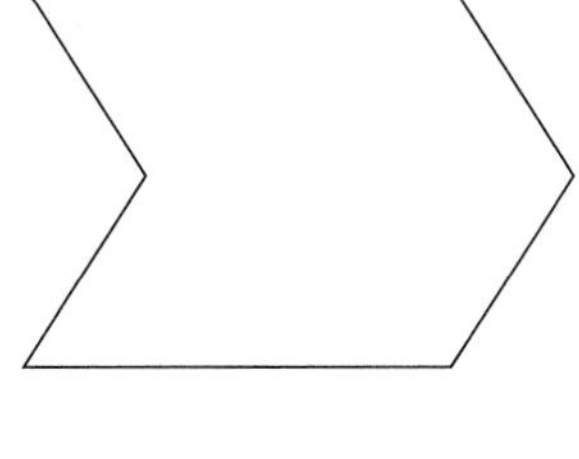

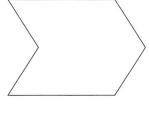

10. You can create your own tessellating figure. Start with a square and follow the steps below.
    a. Cut a shape out of one side of the square.
    b. Tape the shape on the opposite side of the square.
    c. Cut another shape from a different side and tape it to the opposite end.
    d. Trace the new figure repeatedly to form a tessellation.
    e. Writing Why does this procedure result in a figure that will form a tessellation?

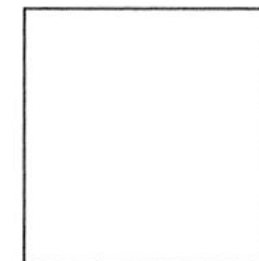

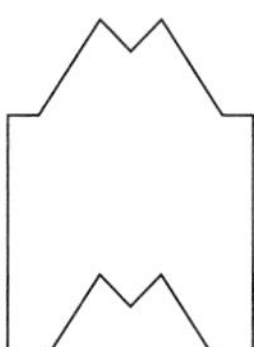

Mixed REVIEW

Find each answer.

1. 13,789 + 23,653
2. 34,567 − 27,488
3. How many more sides es an octagon have than ıuadrilateral?
4. How many fewer sides does a triangle have than a decagon?

Complete.

5. A diameter of a circle is ■ as long as a radius of the circle.
6. A ■ is the longest chord of a circle.

11. You can use more than one type of polygon to form a tessellation. By tracing, use two or more of the figures below to create a tessellation.

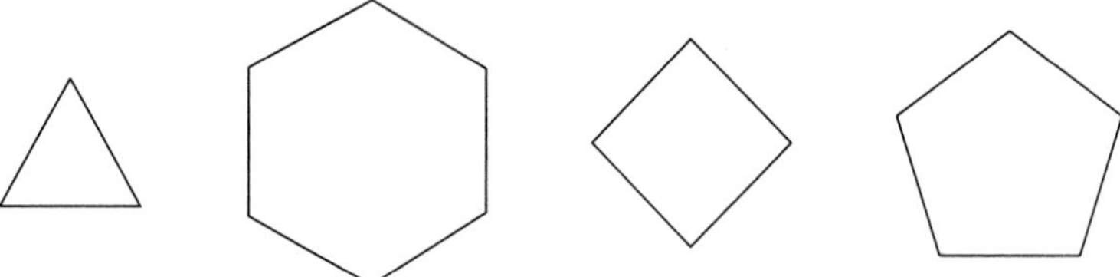

12. **Critical Thinking** Is it possible to use a figure with curves to form a tessellation? If you think it is possible, sketch an example. If you think it is not possible, explain your reasoning.

DECISION MAKING

COLLECT DATA

You can use square tiles to tile a floor. Or you can create a more interesting design by using more than one shape, like those shown below.

$5

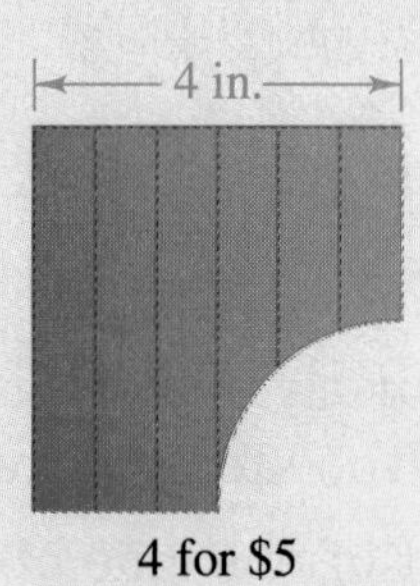

4 for $5

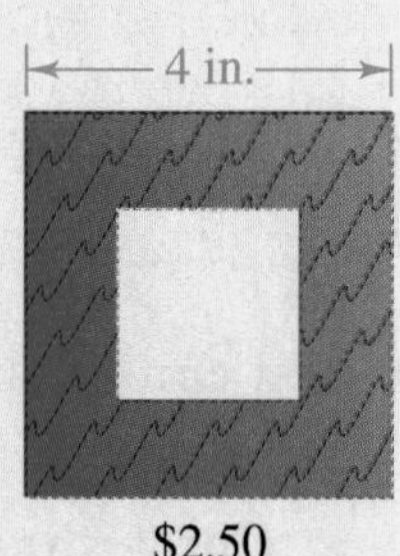

$2.50

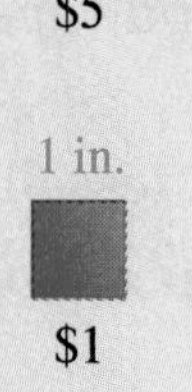

$1

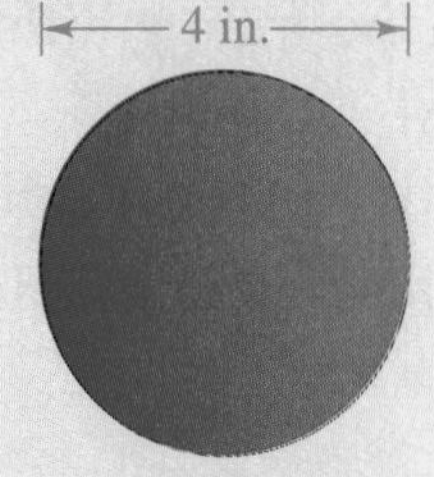

$7

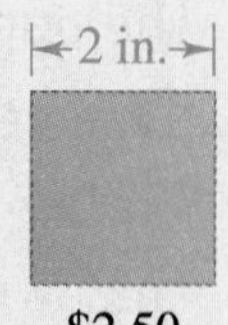

$2.50

13. **Choose A, B, C, or D.** Which of the following could you use to tessellate the plane?

A. 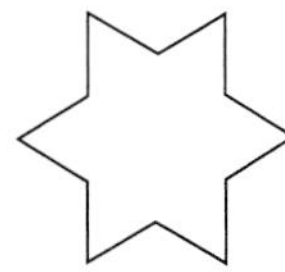

B.  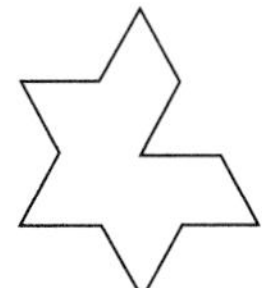

C. 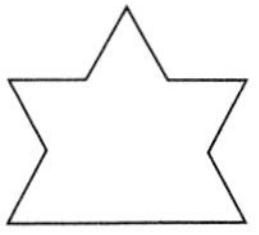

D. 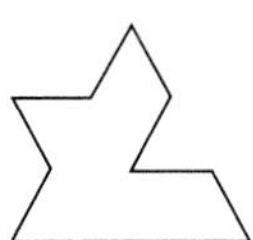

Problem Solving Hint

Trace the figures and draw a diagram.

14 Investigation (p. 40) You can design the letters C, S, and T to tessellate. Use graph paper to create a tessellation using each letter.

The 1-in. square comes in different colors. The circular tile and 2-in. square come in different designs.

ANALYZE DATA

1. Use tracing paper to draw three designs. For each design use two kinds of tile shown.
2. Suppose you are using each of your designs to tile an area 1 ft by 1 ft square.
   a. Which tiles, if any, must you cut?
   b. How many of each kind of tile will you need?

MAKE DECISIONS

3. You want to tile a 12 ft by 8 ft floor. Find the cost for each of your three designs. If you have to use any half or quarter tiles, assume that the cost is one half or one quarter that of a whole tile. Then choose one of your designs and explain why you made that choice.

The word tessellation *comes from the Latin tessellare. It means "to pave with tiles."* ***What figures tessellate in the photo?***

CHAPTER 2

Wrap Up

Points, Lines, Planes, and Angles 2-1, 2-2

You can represent ***points, lines,*** and ***planes*** by everyday objects.

A ***segment*** is a part of a line with two endpoints. A ***ray*** is a part of a line with one endpoint.

You can classify angles as ***acute, right, obtuse,*** or ***straight.***

1. Draw three noncollinear points A, B, and C.

2. Draw parallel lines $\overline{JK}$ and $\overline{MN}$.

3. How many segments are in the figure? how many rays? how many lines?

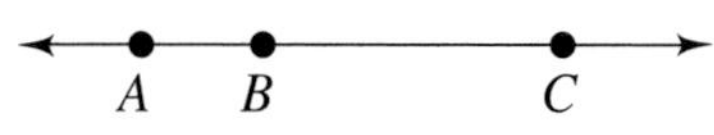

Classify each angle.

4. 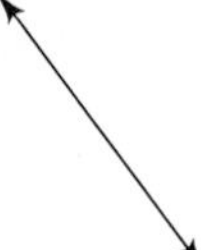

5. 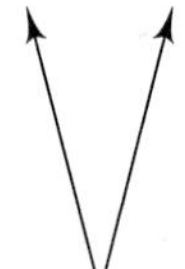

6. 

Circles 2-10

A ***radius*** has one endpoint at the center and one endpoint on the circle. A ***diameter*** has two endpoints on the circle and passes through the center. A ***chord*** has two endpoints on the circle.

Name the following for circle *O*.

7. three radii

8. a diameter

9. two central angles

10. three chords

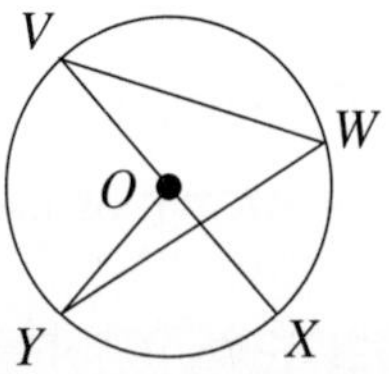

Construction 2-3

Figures that are the same size and shape are ***congruent.***

11. **Writing** Explain how to construct a segment congruent to a given segment.

12. Draw an acute $\angle Z$. Construct an angle congruent to $\angle Z$.

Polygons, Congruence, and Similarity 2-4, 2-5, 2-6, 2-8

You can classify triangles as ***acute, obtuse,*** or ***right*** and ***equilateral, isosceles,*** or ***scalene.***

We name polygons for the number of their sides.

Figures that have the same size and shape are ***congruent.*** Figures that have the same shape are ***similar.***

13. Choose A, B, C, or D. When $\overline{XZ}$ is drawn in parallelogram *WXYZ*, two congruent equilateral triangles are formed. What kind of figure is *WXYZ*?

A. rectangle **B.** rhombus **C.** trapezoid **D.** square

Do the triangles appear congruent, similar, or neither?

14. 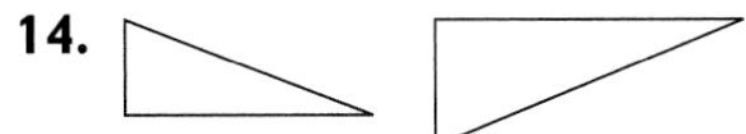

15. 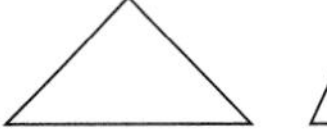

Symmetry and Tessellations 2-9, 2-11

A ***line of symmetry*** divides a figure into two congruent parts.

Tessellations are geometric figures that cover a plane with no gaps or overlaps.

16. How many lines of symmetry does a rhombus that is not a square have?

17. Draw a sketch to show how a parallelogram tessellates a plane.

Strategies and Applications 2-7

You often can use logical reasoning to solve problems.

18. Of 26 students, 3 read both "The Black Stallion," and "Island of the Blue Dolphin." Eleven read the first book, but not the second. Seven students read neither book. How many read only the second book?

GETTING READY FOR CHAPTER 3

In the number 254, 4 is the units' digit, 5 is the tens' digit, and 2 is the hundreds' digit.

1. In the number 4,908, 9 is the ■ digit.

2. Identify the thousands' digit in 36,158.

PUTTING IT ALL TOGETHER

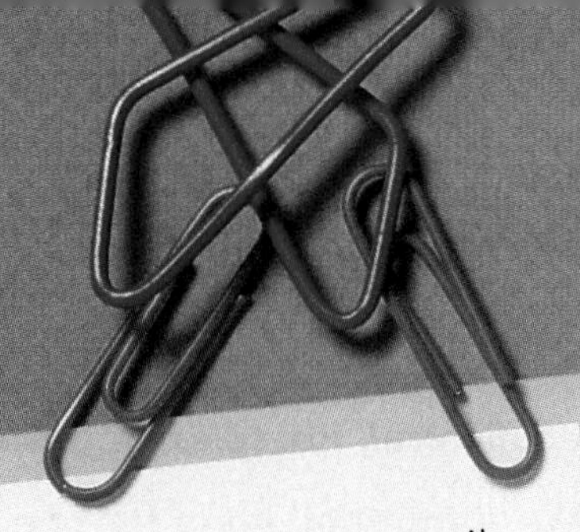

Pattern Hunt

At the beginning of this chapter, you and your group designed a flag. Now you have been invited to carry the flag in the parade at the annual Math Fair.

The Fair Committee has stated that the design of each flag must be geometrical and must display symmetry. Take a look at your flag. If it does not display symmetry, redesign it. When you are satisfied with your design, explain how it is geometrical. Do this in one of the following ways.

- ✓ Make an oral presentation to the committee.
- ✓ Write a letter to the committee.
- ✓ Write an article for the school paper.

The problems preceded by the magnifying glass (p. 65, # 35; p. 81, # 24; and p. 85, # 14) will help you complete the investigation.

Excursion: Redesign your flag so that the design is a tessellation.

Who to Talk To:

- an art teacher
- a graphic designer

SHAPE UP

Rules:

- Play with three or more people
- One player keeps time and assigns a shape to the other players, such as a square.
- Players are given 1 minute to look around the classroom and list as many objects as possible that are in that shape or have that shape in their design.

When time is up, players compare lists to see who was able to find the most objects. The player with the longest list assigns the next shape and serves as timekeeper for the next round of play.

WHAT'S YOUR ANGLE?

Look around your classroom and list as many objects as possible that contain right angles. Draw a picture of three of the objects and show the angles with colored pencil.

123 SYMMETRY

Use graph paper to draw the numbers 0 through 12. Make sure your numbers are all uniform in shape. Use your numbers to answer the following questions. Which one digit numbers have line symmetry? Which two digit numbers have line symmetry? Can you form a three digit number and a four digit number that have line symmetry?

Portrait of a Polygon

Draw a picture on a sheet of paper using at least six different polygons. Exchange papers with a classmate. Count the number of angles and the number of sides for each polygon. Identify any lines of symmetry for each polygon. Find any parallel sides for each polygon. You may wish to mark the angles blue, the lines of symmetry red, and the parallel sides green.

Assessment

1. Draw three noncollinear points and label them X, Y, and Z. Draw $\overleftrightarrow{XY}$. Then draw a line through Z that appears to be parallel to $\overleftrightarrow{XY}$.

2. **Estimation** The *best* estimate for the measure of $\angle PQR$ is:

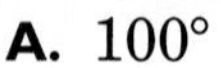

A. 100°

B. 80°

C. 135°

D. 150°

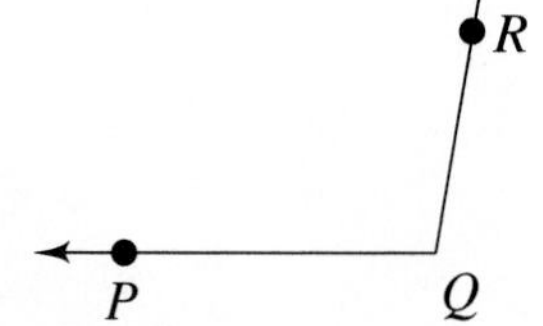

3. $\triangle ABC$ is isosceles. Copy the triangle and then use a straightedge and compass to construct a triangle congruent to $\triangle ABC$. (*Hint:* First construct an angle congruent to $\angle B$.)

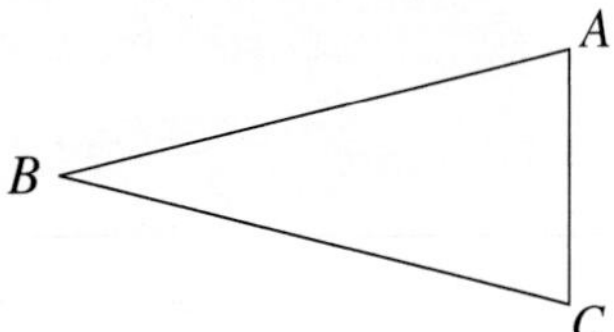

4. **Writing** In the polygons below, *diagonals* from one vertex are drawn. How many diagonals can you draw from one vertex of a hexagon? a 7-sided polygon? a 100-sided polygon? Explain your reasoning.

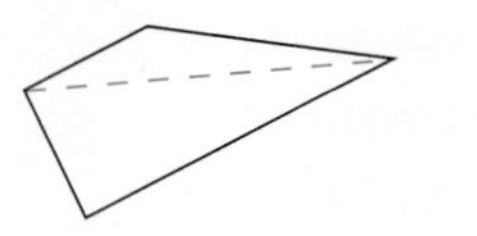

5. Draw a circle O and any chord $\overline{AB}$ that is not a diameter. Draw $\overline{OA}$, $\overline{OB}$, and the radius that is perpendicular to $\overline{AB}$. Make as many conjectures as you can about the angles, segments, and triangles in your diagram.

6. In order to conclude that $MNOP$ is a rhombus, you have to know that:

A. $\overline{MO} \perp \overline{NP}$

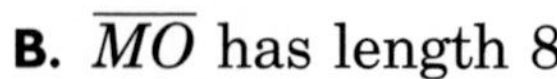

B. $\overline{MO}$ has length 8

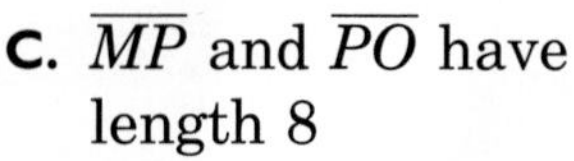

C. $\overline{MP}$ and $\overline{PO}$ have length 8

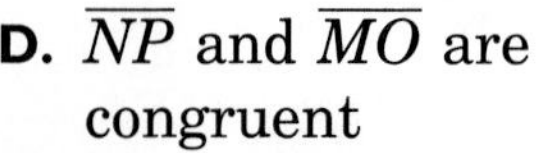

D. $\overline{NP}$ and $\overline{MO}$ are congruent

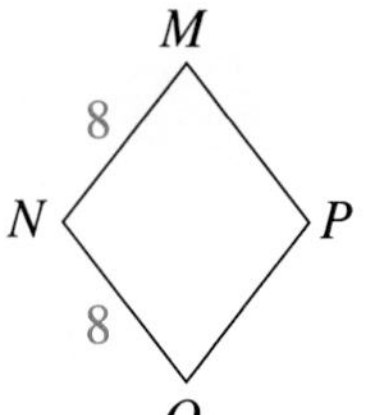

7. Of the 16 boys in Mrs. Stern's math class, 7 play soccer and 5 are in the band. Four play football but they do not participate in any other activity. Two students play soccer *and* play in the band. How many students participate in none of the three activities?

8. a. Name a pair of triangles that appear to be congruent.

   b. Name a pair of triangles that appear to be similar but not congruent.

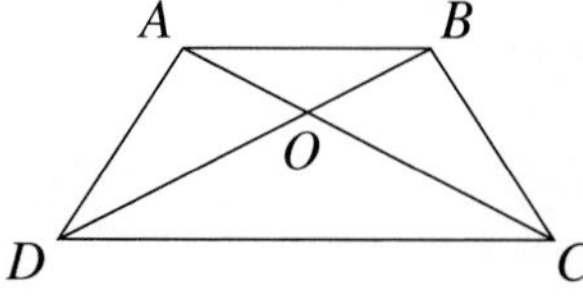

9. Draw a quadrilateral with the given number of symmetry lines.

   a. 0 b. 1 c. 2 d. 4

10. Copy the figure below and use it to create a tessellation of the plane.

Cumulative Review

Choose A, B, C, or D.

1. What can you conclude from the line plot?

   A. Most absences occurred on Monday and Friday.

   B. The mean number of absences per day was 2.5.

   C. Only one person was absent on Wednesday because of a field trip.

   D. At least one person was absent twice that week.

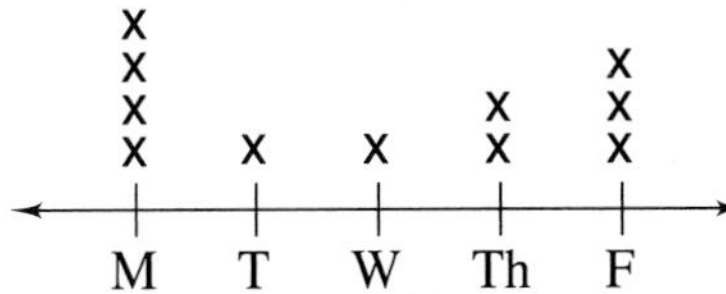

2. How many lines of symmetry does a rectangle that is not a square have?

   A. 0 B. 1 C. 2 D. 4

3. Which ray does NOT contain C?

   A. $\overrightarrow{DB}$ B. $\overrightarrow{BA}$

   C. $\overrightarrow{AD}$ D. $\overrightarrow{BD}$

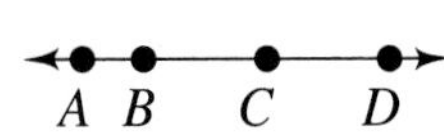

4. Estimate the sum of the measures of an obtuse angle and a right angle.

   A. less than 90° B. equal to 180°

   C. between 90° and 180°

   D. more than 180°

5. What kind of triangle is impossible to draw?

   A. right scalene B. acute isosceles

   C. obtuse isosceles

   D. obtuse equilateral

6. Find the mode of the following temperatures: 100°, 70°, 70°, 85°, 70°

   A. 70° B. 75° C. 77° D. 79°

7. Find the median of these test scores: 78, 90, 71, 85, 68, 77, 88, 96.

   A. 81.5 B. 78 C. 85 D. 82

8. If bagels cost \$2 per dozen, how would you find the cost of 5 bagels?

   A. $\$2 \times 5 \times 12$ B. $\$2 \div 12 \times 5$

   C. $\$2 \times 12 \div 5$ D. $\$2 \div 5 \times 12$

9. What information does the circle graph NOT tell you?

   A. Jen purchased lunch more often than she brought it from home.

   B. Jen purchased hot and cold lunches equally often.

   C. Jen brought lunch from home more often than she purchased cold lunch.

   D. Jen purchased hot lunch more often than she brought lunch from home.

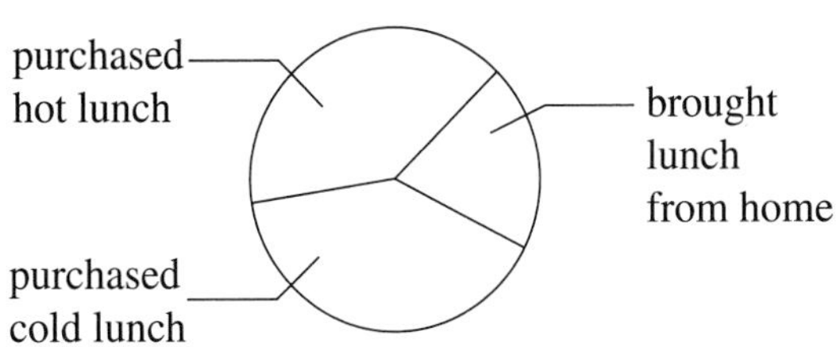

10. How many acute angles can you find in the figure?

    A. 3 B. 4

    C. 5 D. 6

CHAPTER 3

Adding and Subtracting Decimals

STAMPS

The enlarged stamp shows the possible parts of a postage stamp. The next time you use a postage stamp or open a letter, see how many of the parts you can find.

Source: *Usborne Guide to Stamps and Stamp Collecting*

This "stamp-on-stamp" was issued in 1950 to commemorate one hundred years of Spanish stamps. The small stamp in the upper left corner is a copy of the first Spanish stamp issued in 1850.

This 1980 stamp shows some bottles waiting to be picked up by a row boat near Ascension Island. This was the custom 300 years ago, because it was too dangerous for sailing ships to approach the rocky coast.

Source: *Stamps! A Young Collectors Guide*, Brenda Lewis

Data File 3

WHAT YOU WILL LEARN

- how to use and apply decimal concepts
- how to estimate decimal sums and differences
- how to use technology to apply decimal concepts
- how to solve problems using a simpler problem

The world's smallest stamps were issued in Bolivia from 1863 to 1866. They measured 0.31 in. by 0.37 in.

Valuable Baseball Cards

Player's Name	Year(s) Issued	Publisher	Value ($)
Honus Wagner	1909-11	T206	250,000
Napoleon "Larry" Lajoie	1933	Goudey	25,000
Eddie Plank	1909-11	T206	25,000
Mickey Mantle	1951	Bowman	24,000
Robin Roberts*	1951	Topps	15,000
Eddie Stanky*	1951	Topps	12,500
Jim Konstanty*	1951	Topps	12,500
Sherry Magie	1909-11	T206	12,000
Ty Cobb	1911	T3	5,000
Babe Ruth	1933	Goudey	4,500

*All Star card

Note: Cards with the initial "T" refer to cards manufactured by the American Tobacco Company.

Sources: *Baseball Card Price Guide*, Dr. James Beckett; *U.S. News and World Report*

BASEBALL CARDS

The most valuable baseball card is the 1909 Honus Wagner card printed by the American Tobacco Company. There are only six existing cards in excellent condition and about 40 of poorer quality. Few cards remain because Wagner, a nonsmoker, demanded that the American Tobacco Company remove his card from circulation.

Source: *U.S. News and World Report; The Saturday Evening Post*

investigation

Project File

Memo

The Music Club sells cassettes and CDs by mail. Currently the club is making the following offer to attract new members.

> **12 Cassettes**
> **For Only a Penny!**
>
> Send us a penny, we'll send you 12 great cassettes or CDs of your choosing. In return, you must agree to purchase 8 more items during the next two years at our regular prices (currently \$7.98 to \$11.98, plus \$1.79 shipping and handling).
>
> ***Don't delay! Join today!***

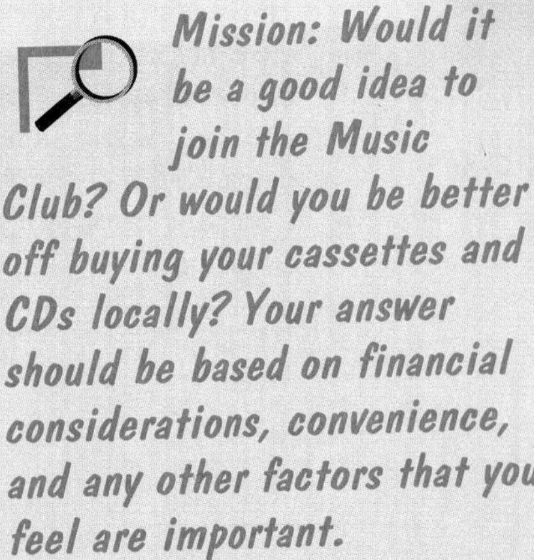

Mission: Would it be a good idea to join the Music Club? Or would you be better off buying your cassettes and CDs locally? Your answer should be based on financial considerations, convenience, and any other factors that you feel are important.

Leads to Follow

- ✓ How many cassettes or CDs are you likely to buy in the next two years?
- ✓ How much does the average cassette or CD cost in your town?
- ✓ How much will you spend to fulfill your obligation to the Music Club?

What's Ahead

- Exploring decimals with models

3-1 Exploring Tenths and Hundredths

THINK AND DISCUSS

WHAT YOU'LL NEED

✓ Graph paper

Suppose you are in charge of cutting a huge square birthday cake. There are 100 people that must be served. How would you cut the cake so that each person receives an equal-sized piece?

1. **Discussion** To model the cake, draw a square on a piece of graph paper. How big will you draw the square?

2. Cut the "cake" vertically into ten equal strips. On your model, draw a line for each cut.

Tenths' model

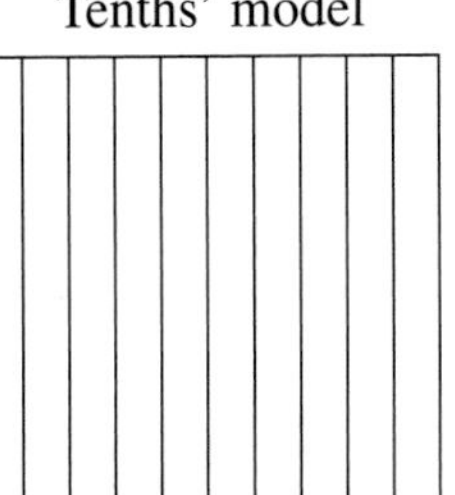

One strip is *one tenth* of the cake. You write one tenth as 0.1. Two strips is two tenths, or 0.2, of the cake.

3. a. How many strips is 0.8 of the cake?
   b. How many tenths is 0.3 of the cake?
   c. How many strips is all of the cake?
   d. Write a decimal that describes half the cake.
   e. Draw a model for nine tenths of the cake.

4. Now cut the "cake" horizontally so that each vertical strip is cut into 10 squares. On your model, draw a line for each cut. How many pieces of cake do you have?

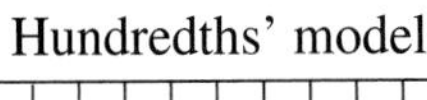

Hundredths' model

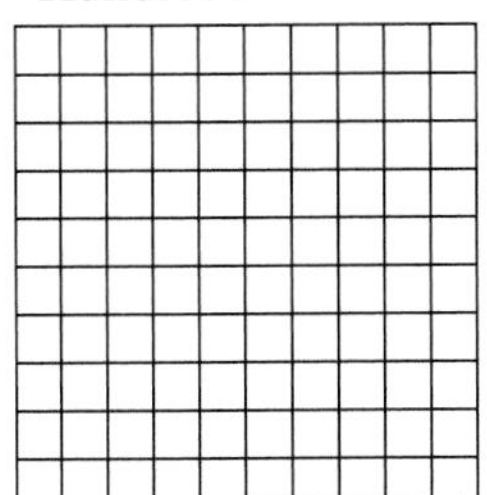

One piece is *one hundredth* of the cake. You write one hundredth as 0.01. Two pieces is two hundredths, or 0.02.

5. a. How many pieces is 0.07 of the cake?
   b. How many pieces is 0.43 of the cake?
   c. How many hundredths is 0.09 of the cake?
   d. How many hundredths is 0.90 of the cake?
   e. Write a decimal that describes half the cake.
   f. How many hundredths is one quarter of the cake?
   g. Draw a model for 0.11 of the cake.

On October 18, 1989 a huge cake in the shape of the state of Alabama was made to celebrate the 100th birthday of the town of Fort Payne. The cake weighed 128,238.5 lb, including 16,209 lb of icing. 100-year-old resident Ed Henderson made the first cut.

Source: *Guinness Book of Records*

Two different models for half the cake are shown below.

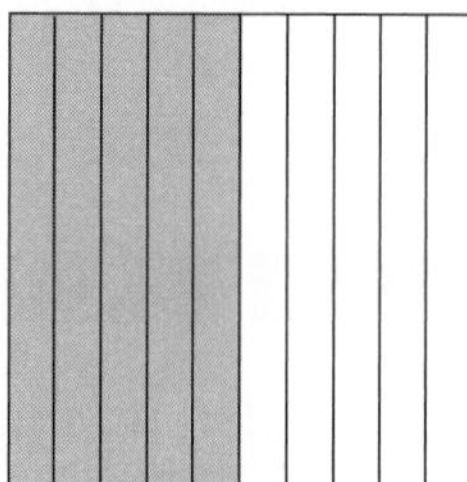

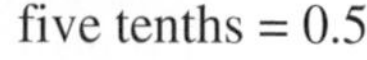

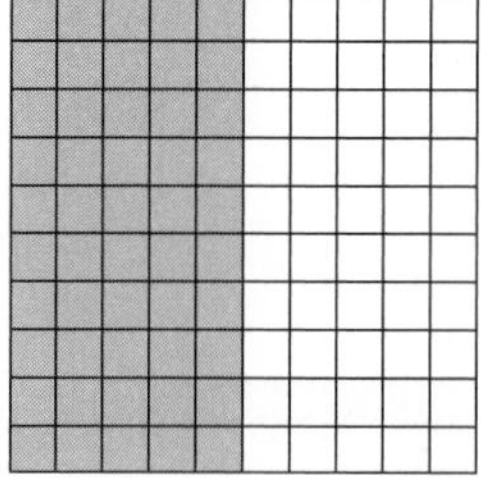

fifty hundredths = 0.50

6. Do the two models represent the same amount of cake?

Numbers that represent the same amount are **equivalent.** The decimals 0.5 and 0.50 are equivalent.

7. a. How many tenths describe the whole cake? How many hundredths describe the whole cake? Are the numbers equivalent? Why?

b. What whole number describes the whole cake?

8. How many hundredths is equivalent to seven tenths?

WORK TOGETHER

- Work with a partner. Suppose you have a dime and a penny. Are these coins tenths' or hundredths' of a dollar? Draw models for one dollar, one dime, and one penny. Write a decimal number for the value of each coin.
- Draw models for one nickel and one quarter. Write the decimal numbers for a nickel and a quarter.

ON YOUR OWN

Draw a model for each decimal.

9. 0.7 **10.** 0.36 **11.** three tenths **12.** four hundredths

Write each decimal in words.

13. 0.08 **14.** 0.2 **15.** 0.56 **16.** 0.30

17. Writing Sue thinks this model shows 0.4. Paul thinks it shows 0.40. Do you agree with Sue? with Paul? Explain.

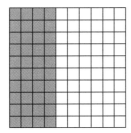

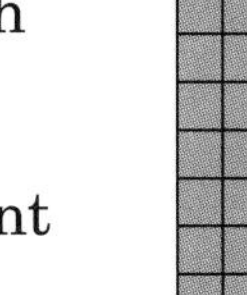

18. How many tenths is equivalent to sixty hundredths?

Write a decimal for the given words.

19. four tenths
20. ninety-six hundredths
21. six tenths
22. five hundredths

Write a decimal for each model.

23. 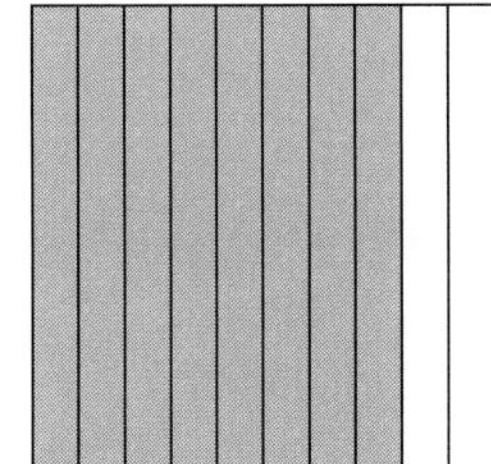

24. 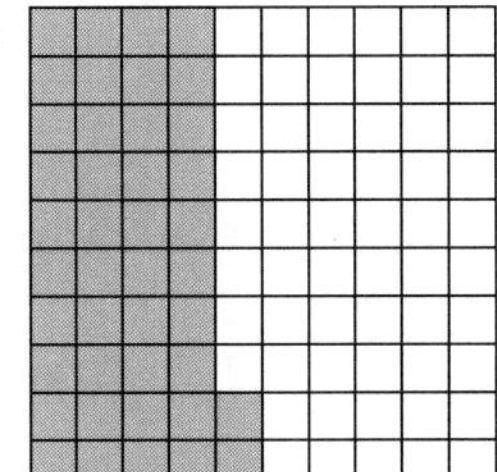

Estimation **Each square model represents 1. Write a decimal to estimate the amount shaded.**

25. 

26. 

27. Writing Imagine you are asked to introduce a new coin into the money system. How much would your coin be worth? Explain your choice and give the coin a name.

28. Critical Thinking Suppose you want to cut a square birthday cake into 10 equal pieces. A vertical strip will not fit on a party plate, so you decide on a different shape.
    a. Draw a model that shows how you will cut the cake.
    b. Write a decimal number to represent one piece of cake.

Mixed REVIEW

Find the mode.

1. 4, 5, 9, 2, 2, 3
2. 98, 95, 91, 98, 95, 95

Tell whether you could form a tessellation with each figure.

3. □ 4. ○

5. An ant can lift 50 times its own body weight. Suppose a student weighing 85 lb could do the same. How much could the student lift?

What's Ahead

- Writing decimals in standard and expanded forms
- Reading and writing decimals

WHAT YOU'LL NEED

✓ Graph paper

3-2 Understanding Place Value of Decimals

THINK AND DISCUSS

If you use a $1.00 bill to buy a snack for $.75, you get $.25 in change. To model $1.00, draw a hundredths' model.

1. For $.25 change, you might get 2 dimes and 5 pennies. Use graph paper to model this amount. Use tenths and hundredths to describe $.25.

2. Instead you might get 25 pennies! Use graph paper to model this amount. Use hundredths to describe $.25.

Two tenths and five hundredths is equivalent to twenty-five hundredths. They describe the same amount. One is expressed in *expanded form* and the other in *standard form*.

Expanded Form	=	Standard Form
0.2 + 0.05	=	0.25
two tenths and five hundredths		twenty-five hundredths

A number in **expanded form** shows the place and value of each digit. Look at 0.25 in the place value chart below.

Thousands	Hundreds	Tens	Ones		Tenths	Hundredths	Thousandths	Ten Thousandths	Hundred Thousandths	Millionths
			0	.	2	5				

The prefix *dec-* means *ten.*

3. In the number 0.25, the digit 2 is in the tenths' place. Its value is two tenths, or 0.2. What is the value of the 5?

4. **Discussion** As you move from left to right in the place value chart, how do the values increase or decrease?

When you use standard form to read or write a decimal number greater than or equal to 1, the word "and" tells you where to place the decimal point.

Example **a.** Read 1.897 as "one *and* eight hundred ninety-seven thousandths."

b. Write "three hundred twenty-seven and sixty-four hundredths" in standard form as 327.64.

WORK TOGETHER

Work with a partner. A *mill* is a very small unit of money that state governments sometimes use to calculate taxes. One mill is equivalent to one thousandth of a dollar ($.001). There is no coin to represent one mill.

5. **Money** Write each number of mills as part of a dollar. About how many cents is each number of mills worth?

a. 6 mills **b.** 207 mills **c.** 53 mills **d.** 328 mills

Gasoline prices are usually calculated to the *thousandths' place.* **How does this work when you pay for gasoline?**

TRY THESE

What is the value of the digit 4 in each number?

6. 0.4 **7.** 3.004 **8.** 1.285964 **9.** 42.39

Read each number in expanded form.

10. 352.3 **11.** 6.025 **12.** 11.2859 **13.** 70.009

Write each number in standard form.

14. four hundred seventy-five thousandths

15. four hundred and seventy-five thousandths

16. two and six hundred five ten-thousandths

17. $1 + 0.6 + 0.03$

18. **Work in pairs** Write a decimal number in standard form. Have your partner write the number in expanded form. Repeat several times, then switch roles.

Mixed REVIEW

Tell whether the angle is acute, obtuse, or right.

1. 67° 2. 45°

Write each decimal.

3. nine tenths
4. one and five hundredths

Write in words.

5. 0.35 6. 2.33

7. Evan saves two quarters and three nickels each day. At the end of 30 days how much has he saved?

ON YOUR OWN

19. a. Draw a model for twenty-two hundredths. Write this number in standard form.

b. In your model, how many tenths and hundredths did you shade? Write the number in expanded form.

Money **Write each amount as a decimal part of $1.00.**

20. 8 dimes **21.** 6 pennies **22.** 49 pennies **23.** 3 quarters

24. Data File 2 (pp. 38–39) Suppose you plan to take two rides on the Beast at Kings Island Amusement Park. How much waiting time should you expect?

What is the value of the digit 5 in each number?

25. 0.5 **26.** 4.0052 **27.** 3.004365 **28.** 530.34

29. Writing Explain how the value of the digit 2 changes in each place in the number 22.222.

Write the words for each number in standard form.

30. 342.5 **31.** 0.09 **32.** 41.283 **33.** 0.00001

Write each number in expanded form.

34. 4.133 **35.** 0.2498 **36.** sixteen and four tenths

37. Research The Earth revolves around the sun in 365.24 days. Find out what happens to the extra 0.24 day.

Biology **Write each measurement in standard form.**

38. A flea can jump six hundred forty-six thousandths' feet.

39. A goat makes four and seven tenths' pints of milk a day.

Bees don't really buzz. They flap their wings up to 250 times per second, which makes the familiar buzzing sound.

40. A tortoise moves seventeen hundredths' miles per hour.

41. It takes a housefly about one thousandth of a second to beat its wings once.

42. A bee's wing weighs five hundred-thousandths' gram.

43. Investigation (p. 94) Conduct a simple survey to see if people are interested in joining a music or book club.

What's Ahead

- Comparing and ordering decimals
- Graphing decimals on a number line

WHAT YOU'LL NEED

✓ Graph paper

3-3 Comparing and Ordering Decimals

THINK AND DISCUSS

Buenos Aires, Argentina, has an estimated population of 12.23 million people. Rio de Janeiro, Brazil, has an estimated population of 12.79 million. To compare the two populations, first look at the whole number parts, 12 and 12. They are the same. Now look at the decimal parts, 0.23 and 0.79.

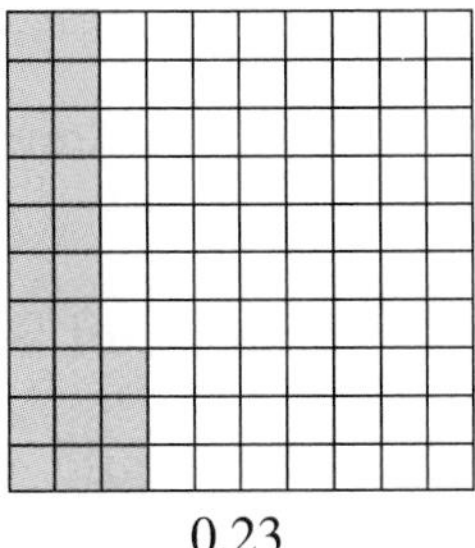

0.23

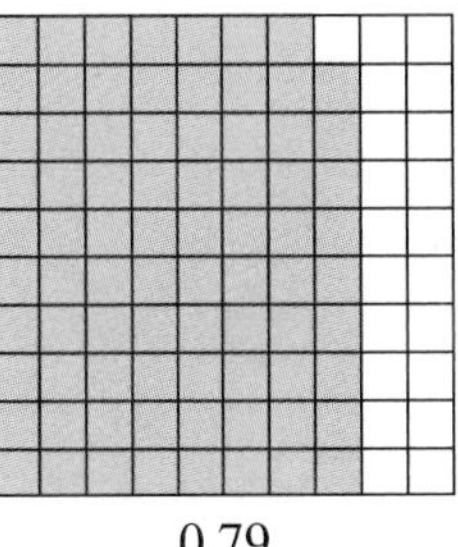

0.79

The model for 0.79 shows more shaded area than the model for 0.23. So 0.79 is greater than 0.23, and $12.79 > 12.23$.

FLASHBACK

To compare numbers, use these symbols.

$=$ is equal to

$>$ is greater than

$<$ is less than

1. **Social Studies** Which city has the greater estimated population, Buenos Aires or Rio de Janeiro?

2. Draw models for 0.7 and 0.72. Which number is greater?

You can graph decimals on a number line to compare them. Numbers are greater as you move to the right.

3. Use $=$, $<$, or $>$ to make true statements.

   a. 0.7 ■ 0.4 b. 0.4 ■ 0.7

4. a. What decimal numbers are at points A and B?

   b. Write two statements to compare the numbers.

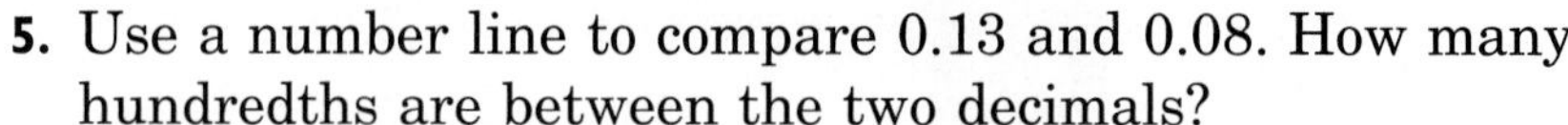

5. Use a number line to compare 0.13 and 0.08. How many hundredths are between the two decimals?

Salt per Liter in Major Bodies of Water	
Black Sea	0.018 kg
Caspian Sea	0.013 kg
Dead Sea	0.28 kg
Great Salt Lake	0.205 kg
Ocean (average)	0.035 kg

Source: *Natural Wonders of the World*

You can also use place value to compare decimal numbers. Start at the left and move right, one place at a time.

Example 1 Which body of salt water is saltier, the Dead Sea or the Great Salt Lake? Use the data at the left.

Compare 0.28 and 0.205. Line up decimal points.

0.28 **Compare digits in the ones' place.**
0.205 **They are the same.**

0.28 **Compare digits in the tenths' place.**
0.205 **They are the same.**

0.28 **Compare digits in the hundredths' place.**
0.205 **8 > 0, so 0.28 > 0.205.**

The Dead Sea is saltier than the Great Salt Lake.

LOOK BACK How could you use a model or number line to solve the problem?

6. **Discussion** Explain how you can use place value to compare 1.679 and 1.697.

***The Dead Sea** between the countries of Israel and Jordan is so salty a person would have no trouble floating in its waters.*

You compare decimals to place them in order.

Example 2 Order the bodies of water in the chart from most salty to least salty.

Compare 0.018, 0.013, 0.28, 0.205, and 0.035.

0.280 > 0.205 **Compare the numbers with the greatest tenths' digits.**

0.03 > 0.01 **Look at the hundredths' digits in the remaining numbers.**

0.018 > 0.013 **Compare the remaining numbers.**

The bodies of water from most salty to least salty are Dead Sea, Great Salt Lake, Ocean, Black Sea, and Caspian Sea.

FLASHBACK

The median is the middle value in a set of ordered data.

7. a. **Discussion** What must you do first to find the median of the five values given in the chart?
   b. Find the median of the five values.

WORK TOGETHER

Work in groups of three. Each member writes down any decimal number between 0 and 1 and draws a model for the number. Assign one of the tasks below to each member.

- Graph the numbers on a number line.
- Place the models in order from least to greatest.
- List the decimals in order from least to greatest.

Make sure your number line, models, and list agree! Repeat this activity until each member has done every task.

TRY THESE

8. **Discussion** Draw models for 0.45 and 0.55. How do the models show which number is greater?

Compare. Use >, <, or =.

9. 0.06 ■ 0.60 10. 3.968 ■ 4.007 11. 0.05 ■ 0.050

12. Graph 6.4, 6.04, 7.6, 6.59, and 7.2 on a number line.

ON YOUR OWN

Compare. Use >, <, or =.

13. 0.58 ■ 0.578 14. 5.7 ■ 5.70 15. 0.37 ■ 0.3651

16. 8.009 ■ 8.079 17. 6.6 ■ 6.2 18. 49.5 ■ 49.05

19. Graph 0.49, 0.34, 0.4, 0.3, and 0.38 on a number line.

20. **Choose A, B, C, or D.** Decimals x, y, and z are graphed on a number line. Read statements I–IV. Which two statements give exactly the same information?

I. $y < z$ and $z < x$ II. y is less than x and z
III. $y < x$ and $x < z$ IV. $y < z$ and $y < x$

A. I and II **B.** II and III **C.** II and IV **D.** III and IV

21. **Critical Thinking** Are there only 9 decimals between 0.4 and 0.5? Explain your reasoning.

Mixed REVIEW

Find the measure of a complementary angle for each given angle.

1. 22° 2. 59°

Find the value of the digit 3 in each number.

3. 108.39 4. 38.22

5. A large paving stone weighs 5 times as much as a small brick. Together they weigh 30 lb. What is the weight of the paving stone?

Light Years Away

The brightest star in the sky is Sirius, which is about 8.7 light years from Earth. The stars Alpha Centauri A and B are each about 4.37 light years from Earth. Proxima Centauri is about 4.28 light years away. Other star neighbors are 61 Cygni B, about 11.09 light years away, and Procyon B, about 11.4 light years away.

If you could drive to Alpha Centauri at 55 mi/h, the trip would take about 52 million years!

22. Data File 1 (pp. 2–3)

a. List the days of the week in order from most popular to least popular for watching prime-time TV.

b. Writing How does the bar graph model each number?

23. What decimal numbers do points A, B, and C represent?

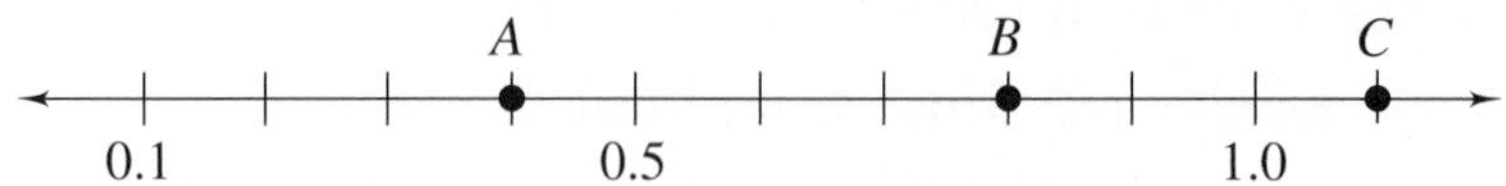

Astronomy Read the article at the left. Use the information in Exercises 24–26.

24. Which star is farthest from Earth? Which is closest to Earth?

25. Write the distances from Earth of the six stars in order from least to greatest.

26. Use <, >, and = to write three statements about the distances of any of these stars from Earth.

27. Research Look up the meaning of light year. Why do you think astronomers use this measure?

28. Investigation (p. 94) List the advantages and disadvantages of belonging to a music or book club. Order the entries from most important to least important.

CHECKPOINT

Write each decimal in words.

1. 0.9 **2.** 0.01 **3.** 0.73 **4.** 0.60

Write a decimal in standard form.

5. three tenths **6.** two hundredths **7.** 0.9 + 0.02

Find the value of the underlined digit.

8. $5.\underline{6}8$ **9.** $0.8\underline{7}0$ **10.** $\underline{8}.005$ **11.** $4.20\underline{3}$

Compare. Use >, <, or =.

12. 0.2 ■ 0.29 **13.** 32.07 ■ 32.070 **14.** 1.8 ■ 1.08

PROBLEM SOLVING

3-4 Solve a Simpler Problem

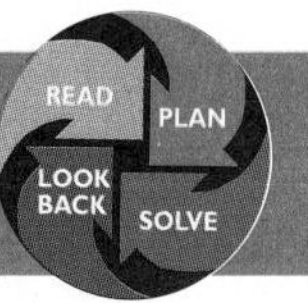

What's Ahead

- Solving problems by using a simpler problem

When solving a problem, you may find it helpful to solve a similar, simpler problem first.

Imagine you are playing the video game Treacherous Tunnel. You have two choices for entering the next level of the game. You have played before and don't want to use Choice 1, because it takes too long. Your goal is to use Choice 2 and follow the correct path within the time limit.

Treacherous Tunnel

Choose a path. Travel Time: 1 min

Choice 1 This path has diamonds in bunches of 2, 3, 4, and so on, to 100. You must collect all even-numbered bunches. The sum of the bunches instantly appears with each bunch you collect. If you miss any, or if you collect odd-numbered bunches, the game ends.

Choice 2 A three-headed creature guards the path. One of the numbers below is the total number of diamonds you can collect in Choice 1 and still go on to Choice 2. If you select the wrong sum, the creature will not let you pass, and the game ends.

3,129 5,050 4,201 2,550 1,201

READ

Read and understand the given information. Summarize the problem.

Think about the information you have and what you need to find.

1. Read Choices 1 and 2 carefully. What is your goal?
2. What numbers will you add to find the number of diamonds needed to get to Choice 2?
3. What numbers can you eliminate? Why?

PLAN

Decide on a strategy to solve the problem.

One strategy for finding the sum of all even numbers from 2 to 100 is to solve a simpler problem first. Start with all even numbers from 2 to 20: 2, 4, 6, 8, 10, 12, 14, 16, 18, 20. Look for shortcuts for finding this sum.

SOLVE

Try out the strategy.

4. Try adding pairs of numbers.

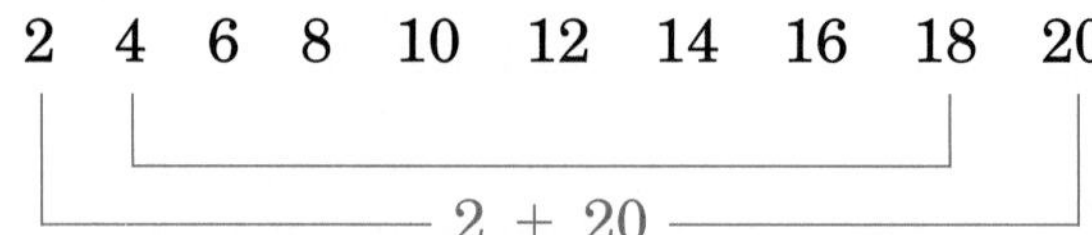

a. Continue to add pairs. What sum do you get each time?

b. How many even numbers did you start with?

c. How many pairs do you have?

d. How can you use the number of pairs to find the sum?

5. Look at the original problem and use the same procedure.

a. What are the first and last numbers you will add? What is the sum of these two numbers?

b. There are 50 even numbers from 2 to 100. How many pairs can you make?

c. Show with examples that each pair has the same sum.

d. What is the sum of all the even numbers from 2 to 100? This is the number you will select in the video game.

LOOK BACK

Think about how you solved this problem.

6. **a.** **Discussion** Explain how solving a simpler problem helped you find the answer to the original problem.

b. **Discussion** Is this strategy better than finding the sum by hand or with a calculator? Why or why not?

TRY THESE

Solve by using a simpler problem.

7. When Ben's bakery opened, a traffic light was installed at the corner. The traffic light changes every 30 s. The bakery has been opened for 1 y. How many times has the traffic light changed since the bakery opened?

a. Break the problem into simpler problems. How many times did the light change in 1 min? in 1 h?

b. Solve the problem and explain your solution.

8. Find the sum of all whole numbers from 1 to 100.
   a. What smaller set of numbers could you start with?
   b. How will you make pairs?
   c. Solve the problem and explain your solution.

ON YOUR OWN

Use any strategy to solve. Show your work.

9. A line of 1,500 people is waiting to see a museum exhibit. Every 20 min a guard allows 55 people to enter. The exhibit is open for 8 h. Will all 1,500 people get in?

10. The International Club serves Chinese, Mexican, German, and Lebanese food. Chris serves German or Lebanese food. Vincent does not serve Chinese food. Louis serves German food. Carla does not serve Mexican or Lebanese food. Each person serves only one kind of food. Who serves each food?

11. **Biology** For every quart of blood in your body, you have about 19 oz of plasma. An average adult has about 5 qt of blood. About how many quarts are plasma?

12. **Biology** A baby's heart beats about 120 times per minute. How many times does a baby's heart beat in a year?

13. **Consumer Issues** A 3-pack of flowering plants costs $1.59. A flat of the plants costs $11.59. There are 24 plants in a flat. Suppose you want to buy 30 plants. What is the least amount of money you could spend?

14. Ted's car averages 420 mi on 14 gal of gas. How many gallons will the car use if Ted drives 1,080 mi?

15. **Consumer Issues** Tickets to the circus are $6.50 per person. The cost of a ticket decreases to $5.00 per person for groups of ten or more people.
   a. How much do you save over the regular ticket price if you buy 18 tickets?
   b. How much would your class save on a trip to the circus?

Find the measure of the third angle of a triangle.

1. 42°, 60° 2. 90°, 65°

Compare. Use >, <, or =.

3. 0.39 ■ 0.399

4. 1.2 ■ 1.02

5. A train makes 5 stops. At the first stop there are 3 passengers. At the second 9. At the third 27. Continue the pattern to find the number of passengers at the fifth stop.

In the 1940s Dr. Charles Drew supervised the "Blood for Britain" project. This project preserved and stored blood plasma for transfusions on the battlefield during World War II.

What's Ahead

- Modeling addition and subtraction of decimals

3-5 Exploring Addition and Subtraction

WHAT YOU'LL NEED

✓ Graph paper

WORK TOGETHER

Work in pairs.

- Draw a model for 0.63 while your partner writes 0.63 in expanded form.
- Agree on two ways of describing 0.63 in words.
- Draw models for the sum 0.6 + 0.03 = 0.63.

THINK AND DISCUSS

You can use models to find any sum. The models below show 0.4 + 0.3 = 0.7.

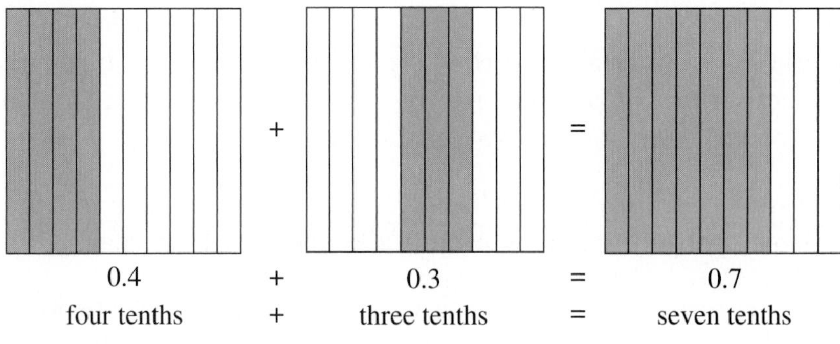

FLASHBACK

To find a sum you add. To find a difference you subtract.

1. Use models to find each sum.

a. 0.1 + 0.8 **b.** 0.3 + 0.09 **c.** 0.44 + 0.23

2. Use words to describe each sum in Question 1.

3. a. Use words to describe 0.8 + 0.5. What is the total number of tenths?

b. Thirteen tenths is equivalent to one and ■ tenths.

c. You can write the sum as:

$$\begin{array}{r} 0.8 \\ +\ 0.5 \\ \hline 1.3 \end{array}$$

Draw a model showing that 0.8 + 0.5 = 1.3.

4. a. Draw a model showing 1.6 + 0.8. Find the sum.

b. **Writing** Explain how you found the sum.

5. Find each sum. Use models if they help you.

   a. 0.6 + 0.9 b. 0.52 + 0.51 c. 0.4 + 0.92

6. a. Three hundredths + nine hundredths = ■ hundredths.
   b. Use decimals to write the sum described in part (**a**).
   c. Write this sum vertically as in Question **3c.**
   d. How could you find this sum without using models?
   e. Is it easier for you to think of the sum as "one tenth and two hundredths" or as "twelve hundredths"? Why?

7. Find each sum. Use models if they help you.

   a. $\begin{array}{r} 0.31 \\ +\ 0.49 \\ \hline \end{array}$ b. $\begin{array}{r} 0.06 \\ +\ 0.55 \\ \hline \end{array}$ c. $\begin{array}{r} 1.50 \\ +\ 0.92 \\ \hline \end{array}$ d. $\begin{array}{r} 0.87 \\ +\ 0.56 \\ \hline \end{array}$

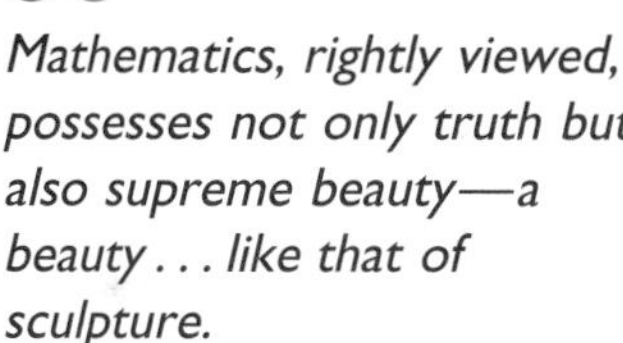

"Mathematics, rightly viewed, possesses not only truth but also supreme beauty—a beauty . . . like that of sculpture."

Bertrand Russell (1872–1970)

You can also use models to subtract decimal numbers. The models below show 1.4 − 0.6 = 0.8.

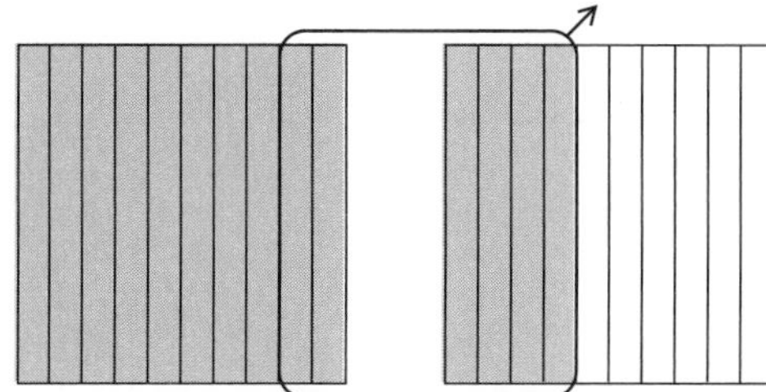

8. a. The number 1.4 is equivalent to ■ tenths.
   b. fourteen tenths − six tenths = ■ tenths
   c. **Writing** Explain how the model shows 1.4 − 0.6 = 0.8.

9. Use models to find each difference.

   a. 1.2 − 0.5 b. 0.92 − 0.75 c. 2.3 − 0.8

10. Think about the difference 0.52 − 0.07 in two ways.
    a. Draw a model for 0.52 and show the removal of 0.07. What is the answer?
    b. Write the difference as: $\begin{array}{r} {\scriptstyle 4\ 12} \\ 0.52 \\ -\ 0.07 \\ \hline 0.45 \end{array}$
    c. The number 0.52 is equivalent to four tenths and twelve hundredths. How does the model show this?

Mixed REVIEW

Is the figure a polygon?

1. [figure]   2. [figure]

Write *True* or *False*.

3. A ray has no endpoints.
4. Parallel lines do not intersect.
5. Mark does his laundry every six days. At the end of a year, how many times will he have done his laundry?

ON YOUR OWN

11. Find 1.03 − 0.08 in two ways, with and without a model.

Use models to help you complete each statement.

12. 1.6 = one and ■ tenths = ■ tenths
13. 0.47 = ■ hundredths = ■ tenths and ■ hundredths
14. 2.5 = 2 ones and ■ tenths = 1 one and ■ tenths
15. 3 tenths and 1 hundredth = 2 tenths and ■ hundredths

Write the sum or difference shown by the models.

16.

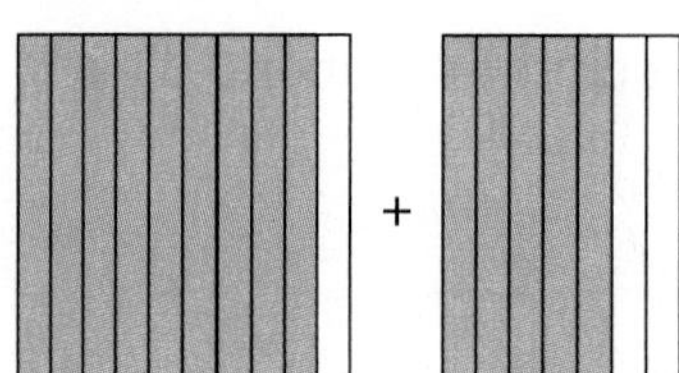

17.

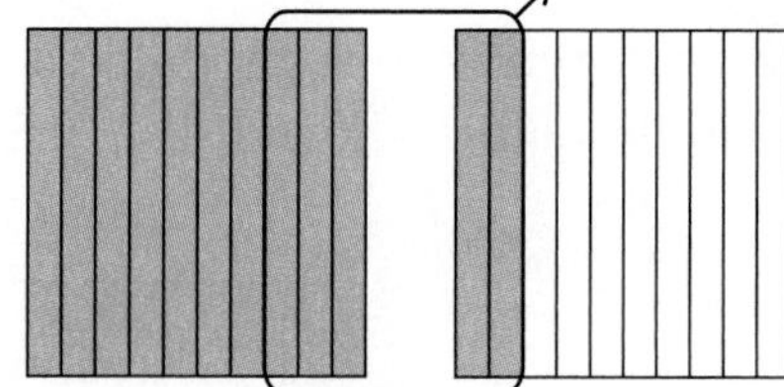

18.

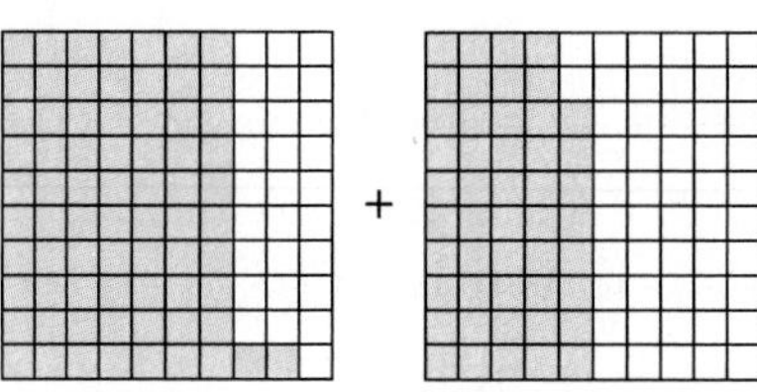

19.

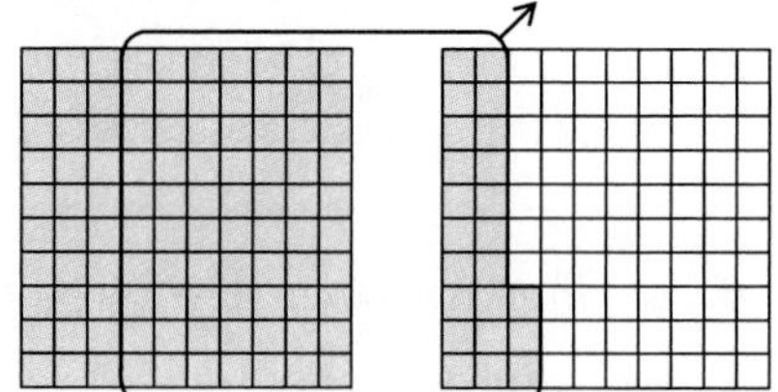

Add or subtract. Use models if they help you.

20. $\begin{array}{r} 1.8 \\ +\ 0.8 \\ \hline \end{array}$ 21. $\begin{array}{r} 0.73 \\ +\ 0.36 \\ \hline \end{array}$ 22. $\begin{array}{r} 2.5 \\ -\ 1.3 \\ \hline \end{array}$ 23. $\begin{array}{r} 1.18 \\ +\ 0.37 \\ \hline \end{array}$

24. $\begin{array}{r} 1.85 \\ -\ 0.86 \\ \hline \end{array}$ 25. $\begin{array}{r} 1.03 \\ +\ 0.97 \\ \hline \end{array}$ 26. $\begin{array}{r} 0.81 \\ -\ 0.34 \\ \hline \end{array}$ 27. $\begin{array}{r} 0.5 \\ +\ 1.26 \\ \hline \end{array}$

28. **Critical Thinking** When you subtract hundredths from hundredths, can the answer ever be thousandths?

29. **Writing** Explain why five tenths and eleven hundredths is equivalent to six tenths and one hundredth. Model each sum to support your explanation.

What's Ahead

- Rounding decimals
- Estimating sums and differences of decimals

WHAT YOU'LL NEED

✓ Newspapers or magazines 

3-6 Rounding and Estimating

THINK AND DISCUSS

Do you ever wonder what is in the food you eat? The circle graph shows the contents of whole-grain field corn. For example, 0.138 of a kernel of corn is water.

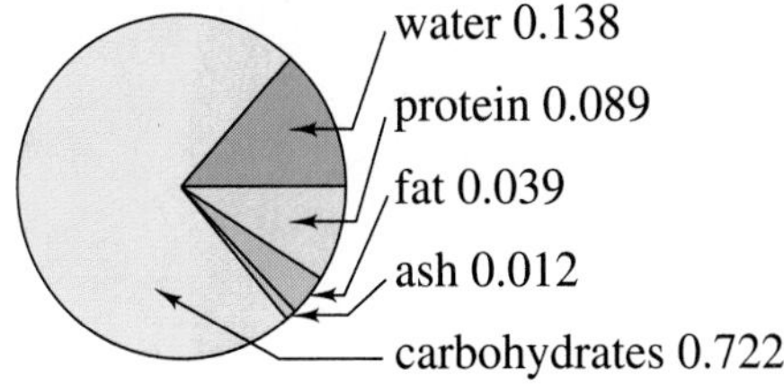

You can round decimals to any place.

1. To round 0.138 to the nearest hundredth do the following.
   a. What digit is in the hundredths' place? After rounding, this digit will stay the same or increase by one. So 0.138 will round to 0.1■ or 0.1■, whichever is closer.
   b. Is 0.138 closer to 0.13 or 0.14? Draw a number line to decide. Or, look at the digit 8. Is it 5 or more?
2. a. Round the five decimals in the circle graph to the nearest hundredth.
   b. **Discussion** To model the five rounded numbers, use graph paper and draw a hundredths' model. Use a different color shading for each rounded number. How is this model like the circle graph?

Make a tenths' model for the decimals in the circle graph.

Example 1 Round 0.138 to the nearest tenth.

- Find the digit in the tenths' place: 1. So 0.138 rounds to 0.1 or 0.2.
- Since $3 < 5$, 0.138 is closer to 0.1 than 0.2.

To the nearest tenth, 0.138 rounds to 0.1.

Corn has been an important part of Native American cultures. The kachina represents the spirit of corn to the Hopi tribes.

3. a. Round the decimals in the circle graph to the nearest tenth.
   b. **Discussion** Draw a tenths' model. Use a different color shading for each rounded number. What do you notice?

Popcorn Prices
1-gal tin $8.45
2-gal tin $10.95
3-gal tin $12.35
6-gal tin $17.95

You can use rounding to estimate a sum or a difference. To find the total cost of a 1-gallon and a 2-gallon tin of popcorn, round to the nearest dollar.

Round each number to the nearest dollar.

$$\begin{array}{rcr} \$\ 8.45 & \rightarrow & \$\ \ 8 \\ +\ 10.95 & \rightarrow & +\ 11 \\ \hline & & \$\ 19 \end{array}$$

The cost of the two tins is about \$19.

4. **Critical Thinking** Is the estimate higher or lower than the actual price? How can you tell?

5. Use rounding to estimate the total cost of two 2-gal tins.

6. About how much more does the largest tin of popcorn cost than the smallest tin? Use rounding to estimate.

To estimate sums, you can also use front-end estimation.

Example 2 Estimate the total cost of the four different size tins of popcorn.

$0 + 10 + 10 + 10 = 30$ **Add front-end digits.**

$8 + 2 + 7 = 17$
$0.45 + 0.35 \approx 1$
$0.95 + 0.95 \approx 2$ **Adjust by estimating the sums of the remaining digits.**

$30 + 17 + 1 + 2 = 50$ **Add the results.**

The total cost of the four tins is about \$50.

WORK TOGETHER

Work with a partner. Look through newspapers or magazines to find at least five decimal numbers. Complete a table like the one below. Decide whether or not each number is an estimate.

Decimal	Units	Context	Estimate?
47.05	feet	record depth of Mississippi River	no
24.1 million	dollars	profit	yes

Study the information in your table. Make several true statements about your decimals. For example, did you find many estimates? To what place were the decimals rounded?

TRY THESE

Round to the place of the underlined digit.

7. $2.643\underline{7}2$ 8. $0.58\underline{1}7$ 9. $0.7\underline{3}52$ 10. $3.4\underline{7}46$

Round to the nearest dollar to estimate.

11. $\$14.65 + 3.85$
12. $\$9.93 - 3.26$
13. $\$16.81 + 11.49$
14. $\$12.44 - 8.75$

15. Write five different decimal numbers that round to 6.7.

Use front-end estimation. Explain how you estimated.

16. \$1.29 + \$3.52 + \$8.89 17. \$3.89 + \$9.95 + \$6.59

18. **Consumer Issues** Unleaded gasoline costs \$1.259/gal. You pump \$5 worth into your automobile. About how many gallons of gasoline did you pump?

ON YOUR OWN

Round to the place of the underlined digit.

19. $0.\underline{0}87$ 20. $0.6\underline{8}73$ 21. $2.708\underline{4}2$ 22. $4.06\underline{2}5$

Round to the nearest dollar to estimate.

23. $\$\ 7.28 + 6.87$
24. $\$18.42 - 9.88$
25. $\$24.66 + 19.55$
26. $\$\ 7.42 - 2.58$

27. **Nutrition** Use the chart at the right. Estimate and round to the nearest tenth.
   a. About how much sugar will you have eaten if you have a soft drink and a granola bar? one of everything?
   b. About how much more sugar is in one-half cup of sherbet than in 8 oz of yogurt?
   c. About how much sugar is in the last three items combined?

28. **Critical Thinking** Rounding and front-end estimation are methods for estimating a sum. Think of three decimals that when added give the same estimated sum with both methods.

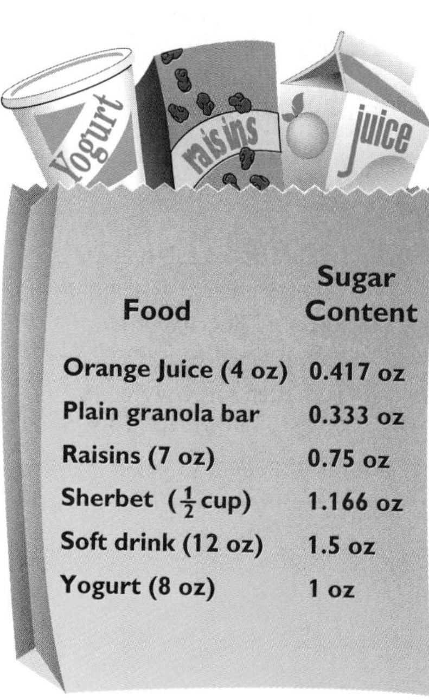

Food	Sugar Content
Orange Juice (4 oz)	0.417 oz
Plain granola bar	0.333 oz
Raisins (7 oz)	0.75 oz
Sherbet ($\frac{1}{2}$ cup)	1.166 oz
Soft drink (12 oz)	1.5 oz
Yogurt (8 oz)	1 oz

The largest and most expensive carousel is the Columbia at Paramount's Great America. It is 100 ft high and cost $1.5 million.

Mixed REVIEW

Use the figure below.

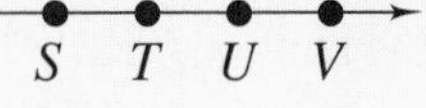

1. Name the line three different ways.
2. Name three rays.

Add or subtract.

3. 2.2 + 0.4
4. 1.05 − 0.95

5. A bookcase has three shelves. Each shelf holds 20 books. The maximum number of books is placed on each shelf. What is the total number of books in the case?

Data File 2 (pp. 38–39) **Use the data for Exercises 29–32.**

29. Use rounding to estimate the cost for a family of two adults and two children to enter Walt Disney World.

30. Use front-end estimation to find the cost for a family of one adult and three children to enter Kings Island.

31. Your family plans a trip to Ohio and you decide to save money for admission. Will it cost less to visit Kings Island or Cedar Point?

32. Choose an amusement park you would like to visit. Estimate the cost of admission for your family.

33. **Choose A, B, C, or D.** A low estimate of \$19 and a high estimate of \$22 is a good range for which sum?

    A. \$4.22 + \$10.85 + \$8.97 **B.** \$2.98 + \$13.75 + \$4.50

    C. \$6.05 + \$7.86 + \$9.22 **D.** \$15.32 + \$9.63 + \$0.45

34. Writing Describe a situation in which you might want your estimate to be high. Then describe one in which you might want your estimate to be low.

35. Use the numbers 13.228, 6.8, 8.87, 3.158, and 5.4.
    a. Which pair of numbers has an estimated sum of 10?
    b. Which pair has an estimated difference of 6?

36. Consumer Issues Is \$7 enough money to buy cereal for \$4.29, milk for \$2.47, and strawberries for \$.98? Explain.

37. Is an estimate of 22 higher or lower than the sum of 6.83, 9.57, and 4.712? How can you tell?

38. Is the statement true or false? Explain your answer.

    Tony has \$10 for school supplies. He will have about \$1 in change after buying pencils for \$2.79, a notebook for \$1.39, a ruler for \$0.85, and 3 pens for \$1.69 each.

39. Data File 3 (pp. 92–93) How much more valuable is the Honus Wagner card than the Mickey Mantle card?

40. Investigation (p. 94) Find an estimated range of costs for buying 8 cassettes from the Music Club.

Problem Solving Practice

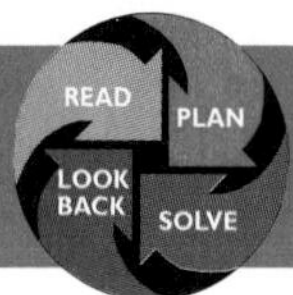

PROBLEM SOLVING STRATEGIES

Make a Table
Use Logical Reasoning
Solve a Simpler Problem
Too Much or Too Little Information
Look for a Pattern
Make a Model
Work Backward
Draw a Diagram
Guess and Test
Simulate a Problem
Use Multiple Strategies

WHEN? In 1894, the Holland Kinetoscope Parlor in New York City charged customers $.25 to view five short films on machines called *kinetoscopes.*

Solve. The list at the left shows some possible strategies you can use.

1. **Travel** On a business trip, Martha flew 331 mi from Montreal, Canada, to New York City. She flew 10 times that distance from New York to Paris, France. She returned from Paris through New York and then on to Montreal. About how many miles did she fly?

2. **Consumer Issues** Mr. Alvarez is purchasing juice in 12-oz cans for the school picnic. There are four 6-packs of juice in a case. For every 5 cases he buys, the store will donate 2 cases. How many cases should Mr. Alvarez buy to have 430 cans of juice?

3. Sara, Sue, Steve, and Sam are brothers and sisters. Sam is twice Sue's age, but he is younger than Steve. In four years Sara will be twice as old as Sue, and Sam will be the age Sara is now. Steve is the oldest. List them from oldest to youngest.

4. **Travel** A ship leaves Miami, Florida, on Friday at 4:40 P.M. The sailing time to Nassau is 16 h 30 min. On what day and at what time is the ship expected to arrive in Nassau?

5. **Travel** Keisha has 18,659 frequent flyer miles with an airline. She needs 35,000 mi to qualify for one free round-trip ticket. She flies about 1,500 mi a month. Estimate how long it will be before she can get a free ticket.

6. **Money** Terry is saving to buy a new bicycle that costs $120. For every $20 she saves, her parents will contribute $5. She plans to save $20 a month. How long will it take her to save the money for the new bicycle?

7. The McCormick family is going to the movies. There are 2 adults and 4 children. The adult tickets cost $7.00, and children go for half price. They brought a coupon for $.75 off each adult ticket and $.50 off each child's ticket. Is $25.00 enough for their admission? Why or why not?

What's Ahead

- Adding and subtracting decimals

3-7 Adding and Subtracting Decimals

WHAT YOU'LL NEED

✓ Calculator 

THINK AND DISCUSS

Manufacturers often package sports balls in boxes for display. A basketball weighing 21.8 oz is in a box that weighs 2.4 oz.

1. Add to find the total weight of the package.

2. How can you check to see if your answer is reasonable?

Before you add or subtract, it is a good idea to estimate the answer as a check. When you add, line up the decimal points and write zeros to make the columns even.

Example 1 Find the sum $3.026 + 4.7 + 1.38$.

Estimate: $3 + 5 + 1 = 9$

Add:

$$\begin{array}{r} 3.026 \\ 4.7 \\ +\ \underline{1.38} \end{array} \quad \rightarrow \quad \begin{array}{r} 3.026 \\ 4.700 \\ +\ \underline{1.380} \\ 9.106 \end{array}$$

Check 9.106 is reasonable since it is close to 9. ✓

3. Why can you write 4.7 as 4.700?

Most sports equipment sizes follow a standard. The table below lists minimum and maximum weights for sports balls.

A properly inflated basketball should bounce between 1.2 m and 1.4 m on a hard wooden floor if you drop it from a height of about 1.8 m. **Describe a way to test whether a basketball is inflated correctly.**

Source: *The Rules of the Game*

Official Standard Weights

Type	Minimum Weight	Maximum Weight
Basketball	21.16 oz	22.93 oz
Baseball	5 oz	5.5 oz
Football	14 oz	15 oz
Softball	6.25 oz	7 oz
Tennis ball	2 oz	2.06 oz
Volleyball	9.17 oz	9.88 oz

To find the range of standard weights for a type of sports ball, subtract its minimum weight from its maximum weight.

4. The difference 9.88 − 9.17 is the range of standard weights for which type of ball? Find this range.

5. Is a volleyball weighing 9.02 oz within the range of standard weights? What does this mean?

You can use a calculator to add or subtract decimals.

Example 2 Find the difference 10.028 − 3.7.

Estimate: 10 − 4 = 6

10 [.] 028 [−] 3 [.] 7 [=] *6.328*

Check 6.328 is close to the estimate 6. ✓

6. When you use a calculator to find 7.87 − 1.47, why will the display show 6.4 instead of 6.40?

Sometimes you need to write a whole number as a decimal.

Example 3 You use a $20 bill to pay for a CD costing $11.78. How much change will you get?

Estimate: $20 − $12 = $8

Write $20 as $20.00 and subtract:

$$\begin{array}{r} \$20.00 \\ -\ 11.78 \\ \hline \$8.22 \end{array}$$

Check $8.22 is close to the estimate $8. ✓

You will get $8.22 in change.

No major league pitcher has had 110 no-hitters, 35 perfect games, a lifetime batting average of 0.300, and a fast ball clocked at 118 mi/h. Between 1958 and 1976, a softball pitcher named Joan Joyce accomplished all of this.

Source: *The Superman Book of Super-human Achievements.*

WORK TOGETHER

Work with a partner. Use the chart of standard weights.

- List the names of the sports balls from heaviest to lightest.
- Find the range of standard weights for each sports ball.
- Use your data to decide if the following statement is true or false: The heavier the ball is, the smaller is its range of standard weights.

Things to Buy

Poster	$4.99
Birthday Card	$1.25
Film (12 exposures)	$3.89
or (24 exposures)	$4.59
Wrapping paper	$2.49
Bow	$.79

TRY THESE

7. The length of the Eurotunnel between England and France is 49.94 km. The Seikan Tunnel in Japan is 53.9 km long. How much longer is the Seikan Tunnel?

First estimate. Then find the sum or difference.

8. 0.6 + 3.4 **9.** 6.2 − 0.444 **10.** 8.001 − 0.77

11. 4.035 + 8.99 **12.** 22.2 − 4.3 **13.** 9.76 + 3.45

14. Consumer Issues You have a $10 bill and a $5 bill, and you wish to buy all the items on the list shown at the left. Can you buy the 24-exposure film?

ON YOUR OWN

First estimate. Then find the sum or difference.

15. 0.5 + 4.6 **16.** 8.7 − 0.368 **17.** 9.011 − 0.45

18. 2.091 + 5.75 **19.** 8.5 − 5.8 **20.** 12.34 + 1.68

21. 4.1 + 3.72 + 6.05 **22.** 7 + 11.436 + 3.08

Part of Energy Supply Produced by Natural Resources

Oil	0.39
Coal	0.27
Gas	0.17
Nuclear power	0.02
Hydro (water) power	0.02
Firewood/charcoal	0.12
Other	0.01

Use the data at the left for Exercises 23–27.

23. What part of the total energy is produced by coal?

24. Find the sum of the numbers given in the chart. What is the meaning of this sum?

25. Make a hundredths' model showing the parts of energy produced by each natural resource.

26. What part of all the energy is produced from oil and coal? Is it more than half? Explain.

27. Estimation Which two natural resources produce an amount of energy approximately equal to that of coal?

Mental Math **Find the missing number.**

28. 6.4 + 3.1 = ■ + 6.4 **29.** 0.43 + ■ = 0.43

30. (2.1 + 0.3) + 4 = 2.1 + (■ + 4)

Consumer Issues How much change will you get?

31. At the movie theater, you order popcorn for $2.75 and two drinks for $1.50 each. You pay with a $10 bill.

32. Pam used a calculator to find the following sums and differences. First estimate to see if the answer is reasonable. If it is not, what did Pam enter incorrectly?

 a. $5.85 + 6.24 = 629.85$ b. $36.8 - 7.2 = 29.6$

33. **Choose A, B, C, or D.** If you place the digits 1–6 in the boxes ■■.■ + ■.■■ to give the greatest possible sum, the digit in the third box from the left must be:

 A. 2 **B.** 3 **C.** 2 or 3 **D.** 4

Use a calculator and the given information.

When you order by mail, you pay for shipping and handling. The company may base the fee on the amount of the order or on the number of items.

34. a. Suppose you order one adult sweatshirt, size XXL, and three child T-shirts. How much do they cost without shipping and handling?

 b. Find the charge for shipping and handling your order in each of the charts. Explain the difference in price.

35. Suppose you order one of each item in size medium. Which shipping and handling method will cost less?

36. **Writing** If you were ordering more expensive items, which chart would you prefer? If you were ordering less expensive items, which chart would you prefer? Use examples to explain your answer.

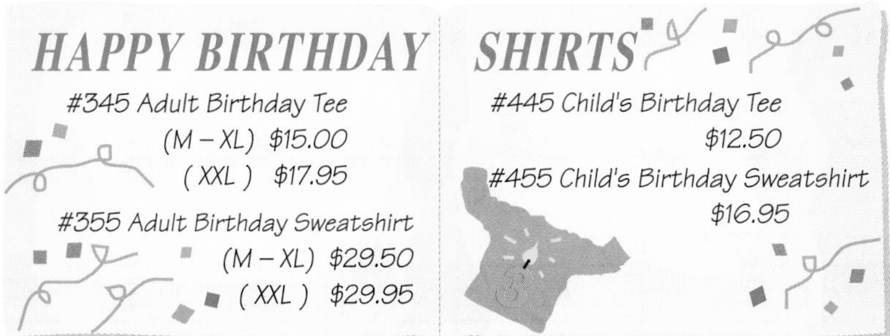

HAPPY BIRTHDAY SHIRTS
#345 Adult Birthday Tee
(M – XL) $15.00
(XXL) $17.95
#355 Adult Birthday Sweatshirt
(M – XL) $29.50
(XXL) $29.95
#445 Child's Birthday Tee
$12.50
#455 Child's Birthday Sweatshirt
$16.95

Mixed REVIEW

True or False?

1. The letter M has symmetry.

2. All triangles have symmetry.

Round to the place of the underlined digit.

3. 1.94872

4. 23.0384

5. Jonah had $340 in his bank account. He withdrew $52 and wrote a check for $18.50. Find the balance.

Shipping and Handling Charge by Dollar Amount of Order	
Under $15.00	$2.95
$15.00–$24.99	$3.95
$25.00–$39.99	$4.95
$40.00–$49.99	$5.95
$50.00–$74.99	$6.95
$75.00–$99.99	$7.95
$100.00 and over	$8.95

Shipping and Handling Charge by Number of Items Ordered	
1 Item	$3.15
2 Items	$4.95
3 Items	$6.95
4+ Items	$8.95

TECHNOLOGY

3-8 Keeping Track of Your Savings

What's Ahead

• Adding and subtracting decimals in bank accounts

• Using a computer spreadsheet to add and subtract decimals

WHAT YOU'LL NEED

✓ Computer 

✓ Spreadsheet software 

THINK AND DISCUSS

Suppose you need to save some money to buy a gift.

1. Where would you keep the money you save? How would you keep track of the amount of money you have saved?

You could open a savings account at a bank. It is a safe place to keep your money. Also, the bank pays you money, called **interest,** for having a savings account there.

2. Why do you think a bank would pay you interest, rather than charging you a fee, for a savings account?

Banks usually send you a report, or a **statement,** for your account. The statement shows the interest you earned on the account. It also shows **deposits,** money you put into the account, and **withdrawals,** money you take out of the account. A **balance** is the amount of money in the account at a given time.

3. Is interest like a deposit or a withdrawal?

4. You open an account with a $50 deposit. What is the balance?

5. **Discussion** Banks send statements monthly, quarterly, or annually. Why would you want to keep your own account record and check it against the bank statement?

At the age of 11, Andrew J. Burns became president of Children's Bank in Omaha, Nebraska. The bank is part of Enterprise Bank, where Andrew's father is president. Andrew helps young people open bank accounts. In 1993 Children's Bank had 500 accounts!

Source: *National Geographic World*

You can use a spreadsheet to keep track of your savings.

	A	B	C	D	E	F
1	Date	Balance	Withdrawal	Deposit	Interest	End Balance
2	11/3	73.47		100.00		173.47
3	11/14	173.47	98.00			75.47
4	11/31	75.47			1.99	77.46

6. What does the number in cell B2 mean? in cell D2?

7. How was the amount in cell F2 calculated? in F3? in F4?

8. Which cells show the same amounts? Why?

9. **Discussion** How can you use mental math to check the balance at the end of each day?

10. A withdrawal slip and a deposit slip are shown at the right. Show what the next two rows of the spreadsheet will look like after these transactions.

WITHDRAWAL
DATE 12/4
ACCOUNT NUMBER 12487592
AMOUNT $ 30.00

DEPOSIT
DATE 12/10
ACCOUNT NUMBER 12487592
AMOUNT $ 19.95

11. Suppose your savings account has a balance of $67.41. You deposit $37.75 and then withdraw $37.75. What is the new balance? Would you get the same result if you made the withdrawal first and then the deposit? Explain.

12. **Critical Thinking** Suppose you deposit $7.50. In your records, you accidentally subtract $7.50. By how much will your balance be off? Why?

DATE 1/23
ACCOUNT NUMBER 753164
AMOUNT $ 21.95
DEPOSIT
DATE 1/3
ACCOUNT NUMBER 753164
AMOUNT $ 40.00
DEPOSIT
DATE 1/9
ACCOUNT NUMBER 753164
AMOUNT $ 13.75
DRAWAL
DATE 1/27
ACCOUNT NUMBER 753164
AMOUNT $ 17.00
WITHDRAWAL
DATE 1/8
ACCOUNT NUMBER 753164
AMOUNT $ 25.00
WITHDRAWAL

WORK TOGETHER

13. **Computer** Use the five savings account slips and a spreadsheet to make a record for this account. The beginning balance is $68.74.
    a. How will you order the transactions?
    b. What is the final balance?
    c. What is the sum of all the deposits? the sum of all the withdrawals?
    d. Compute: (Beginning Balance) + (Sum of Deposits) − (Sum of Withdrawals). Compare with the final balance.
    e. **Writing** Describe the relationship you found in part (**d**). How can you use this to check your calculations?

Mixed REVIEW

Find the mean.

1. 44, 45, 43, 49
2. 2, 9, 7, 3, 2

Add or subtract.

3. $5.31 + 17.04$
4. $10.25 - 6.09$

5. Rod earns $10 for mowing one lawn. After mowing seven lawns, how much money has he earned?

WHO? Ruthie Barrientos is a champion baton twirler. Besides winning many titles, Ruthie finds time to perform while staying active in school affairs and making the honor roll. In 1988 Ruthie was named Athlete of the Year by the Houston Hispanic Chamber of Commerce.

ON YOUR OWN

14. Suppose this bank statement is for your savings account.

Date	Balance	Withdrawal	Deposit	Interest	Balance
1/5	38.64		22.50		61.14
1/11	61.14	21.00			40.14
1/17	40.14	14.00			40.00
1/23	40.00		37.50		2.50

a. Are there any errors? If so, how were mistakes made?

b. Which amounts can you keep track of yourself? Which amounts do you need to get from the statement?

15. Rita keeps the money she is saving in a small box in her room. She uses a notebook to keep track of the amount. One day, her dog Rex chewed the notebook.

Date	Start of Day	Took Out	Put In	Comment	End of Day
6/3			4.50	Allowance	24.50
6/8		7.00		Went to a movie	
6/9	17.50		1.99	Change from movie	
6/10			4.50	Allowance	
6/14			9.25	Mowed Miller's lawn	
6/15		25.00		Bought gift	

a. **Discussion** How is Rita's record like a spreadsheet?

b. What does Rita call deposits? withdrawals? balances?

c. How much money was in the box at the end of June 3?

d. Was there more or less than that in the box at the start of June 3? How do you know?

e. How much was in the box at the start of June 8?

f. Copy Rita's table and fill in the missing amounts.

16. **Writing** How could you check your answers to Exercise 15 by calculating the final balance in a different way?

Practice

Draw a model for each decimal.

1. 0.6 **2.** 0.27 **3.** 1.7 **4.** four tenths **5.** ten hundredths

Write each decimal in words.

6. 0.09 **7.** 0.5 **8.** 0.65 **9.** 0.70 **10.** 22.75 **11.** 75.03

Write a decimal for the given words.

12. three tenths **13.** forty-five hundredths **14.** seven and nine hundredths

What is the value of the digit 7 in each number?

15. 0.7 **16.** 5.007 **17.** 73.59 **18.** 0.532497 **19.** 431.07

Write each number in standard form.

20. one hundred fifty-one thousandths **21.** one hundred and fifty-one thousandths

Write each number in expanded form.

22. 438.9 **23.** 38.8015 **24.** two and one hundred forty-nine thousandths

Compare. Use >, < or =.

25. 7.7 ■ 7.3 **26.** 0.3978 ■ 0.39 **27.** 81.773 ■ 81.78 **28.** 12.70 ■ 12.7

29. Graph 0.59, 0.37, 0.5, 0.3, and 0.33 on a number line.

Round to the place of the underlined digit.

30. $0.\underline{0}54$ **31.** $6.18\underline{7}9$ **32.** $7.1\underline{3}48$ **33.** $95.3\underline{5}8$ **34.** $4\underline{5}.89$ **35.** $\underline{3}.09$

Round to the nearest dollar to estimate.

36. $\begin{array}{r} \$6.27 \\ +\ \ 5.73 \\ \hline \end{array}$ **37.** $\begin{array}{r} \$18.79 \\ -\ \ 9.78 \\ \hline \end{array}$ **38.** $\begin{array}{r} \$75.12 \\ +\ \ 73.81 \\ \hline \end{array}$ **39.** $\begin{array}{r} \$49.02 \\ 48.13 \\ \hline \end{array}$ **40.** $\begin{array}{r} \$107.55 \\ +\ \ \ .39 \\ \hline \end{array}$

First estimate. Then find the sum or difference.

41. 0.7 + 2.3 **42.** 7.8 − 0.375 **43.** 9.001 − 0.54 **44.** 12.43 + 2.86

45. 5.13 + 6.4 **46.** 8 − 2.3 **47.** 12.431 − 6.522 **48.** 4.181 + 1.299

What's Ahead

• Measuring using metric units

• Choosing appropriate units of measure.

WHAT YOU'LL NEED

✓ Metric Ruler

3-9 Metric Length

THINK AND DISCUSS

The metric system of measurement, like the decimal system, is based on tens. A *meter* is the basic unit of length. Other units you will use are *centimeter, millimeter,* and *kilometer.*

One centimeter (cm) is one hundredth of a meter (m).

1. a. **Discussion** Suppose you had a strip of paper to represent a meter. What could you do to the paper to model a centimeter?

   b. **Discussion** How is this model similar to the square hundredths' models you have been using?

   c. How many centimeters are there in one meter?

One millimeter (mm) is one thousandth of a meter.

2. a. Suppose you want to model millimeters. Into how many equal parts would you divide a segment that represents 1 m?

   b. How many millimeters are there in one meter?

   c. How many millimeters are there in one centimeter?

3. Use your models to complete the following.

   a. 1 cm = ■ m b. ■ cm = 1 m

   c. 1 mm = ■ m d. ■ mm = 1 m

   e. ■ mm = 1 cm f. 1 mm = ■ cm

WHAT? The meter was the first unit of measure based on something other than the body. Today the meter is based on the distance light travels in a certain amount of time.

When you need to measure short distances, you can use a centimeter ruler. To measure a segment, align the 0 mark on the ruler with one end of the segment. Then read the length.

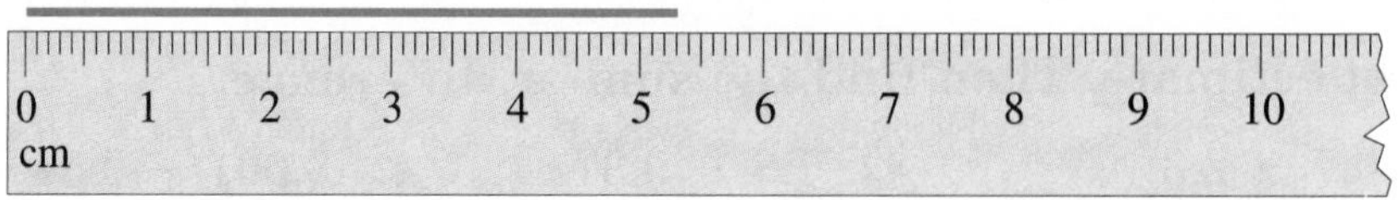

The segment is 53 mm, or 5.3 cm long.

4. a. What do the smaller marks on the ruler represent?
   b. What do the numbers 0, 1, 2, 3, and so on, represent?

5. Measure each segment in millimeters.
   a. ________ b. ______________________
   c. ________________________________
   d. **Estimation** What is the length of each segment to the nearest centimeter?
   e. Measure each segment in centimeters.

6. a. Draw a segment that is 16 cm long.
   b. Draw a segment that is 128 mm long.
   c. Which of the segments you drew is longer?

The **perimeter** of a figure is the distance around it. You find perimeter by adding the lengths of the sides of the figure.

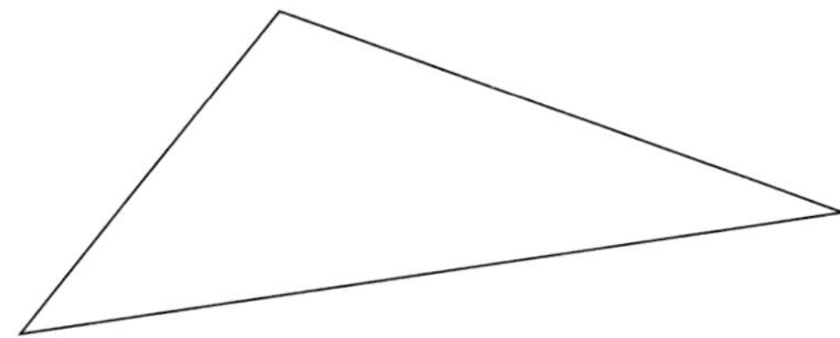

7. a. Measure each side of the triangle in millimeters.
   b. What is the perimeter of the triangle?

8. Describe some situations where you might need to know the perimeter of a figure.

When you measure an object you should first choose an appropriate unit of measure. To measure longer distances you would use kilometers (km). There are 1,000 m in 1 km.

Some groups raise funds by sponsoring 10 km (10K) races or walks. A participant asks people to pledge a set amount of money for each kilometer the participant walks.

9. Name two objects or distances you would measure using each unit.
   a. meter b. centimeter c. millimeter d. kilometer

10. What unit would you use to measure each item?
   a. perimeter of a backyard
   b. length of a shirt sleeve
   c. width of a nailhead
   d. distance between towns

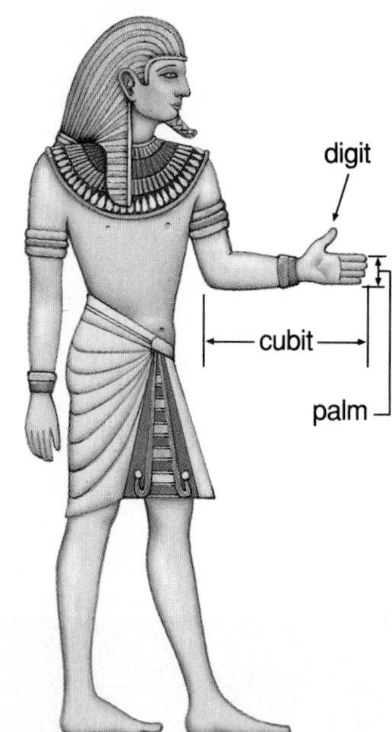

Ancient Egyptians based measures of length on the royal cubit, the palm, and the digit. The cubit (forearm) was the length from the elbow to the fingers. The palm was the width of the palm excluding the thumb. The digit was the width of the finger. **What standard measure is based on the human body?**

You can estimate the length or height of an object by using the length or height of an object you know.

11. a. The width of a door is about one meter. How can you estimate the length of a wall that contains the door?
    b. Estimate the length of your classroom wall using the method you just described.

12. The height of a desk or table is about one meter. Explain how to estimate the height of your classroom from the floor to the ceiling using the height of the desk or table.

WORK TOGETHER

Work with a partner to create your own set of units. First have your partner measure your handspan, the distance on your hand from the tip of your small finger to the tip of your thumb. Then have your partner measure the width of your finger, and the length of your foot. Use your units to estimate the length of two objects in your classroom. Are your units convenient?

ON YOUR OWN

Measure each segment in millimeters.

13. ____________

14. ____________

15. ____________

Find the perimeter of each figure.

16.

17.

18. Draw a figure that has a perimeter of 20 cm.

Problem Solving Hint

Try drawing a diagram.

19. **Pets** A rectangular dog kennel measures 4 m by 5 m. How much fence do you need to enclose the kennel?

20. **Writing** Explain how you can find the perimeter of the rectangle without measuring. Find the perimeter.

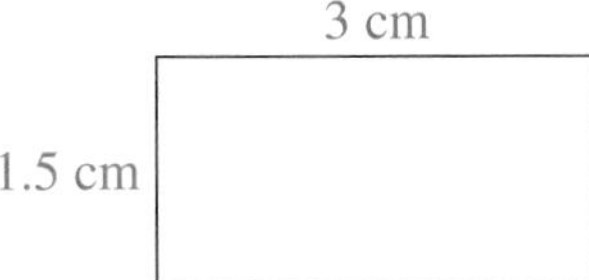

Is each measurement reasonable? If not, give a reasonable measurement.

21. The sidewalk in front of a house is 30 km long.
22. Your friend is about 160 cm tall.
23. Your pencil is 18 mm long.
24. Our kitchen table is about 123 cm long.
25. **Writing** Read the newspaper article at the right. List some possible reasons why the metric system is not more widely used in this country. Then tell whether or not you think it should be more widely used.
26. **Critical Thinking** The perimeter of a rectangular table is 8 m. The table is 1 m longer than it is wide. Find the length of each side. Explain how you got your answer.

U.S. Still Catching Up

The United States officially began to "go metric" in 1973. Since most of the rest of the world's countries were using the metric system, it seemed to be a good idea.

The transition has been very slow. Still, there are signs of metrification on highway signs and on some items on the shelves of supermarkets and hardware stores.

Choose an appropriate unit of measure for each.

27. your height
28. Width of a ring
29. perimeter of your state
30. height of the ceiling

CHECKPOINT

First estimate. Then find the sum or difference.

1. $1.25 + 6.07$
2. $9.06 - 0.8$
3. $5.59 + 12.6$
4. $37 - 7.8$

Round to the place of the underlined digit.

5. $12.0\underline{4}1$
6. $\underline{2}.40$
7. $9.06\underline{5}5$
8. $53.\underline{8}5$
9. **Choose A, B, or C.** Suppose you wish to buy three items priced $2.09, $.59, and $1.46. Which is the best estimate?
   A. $4.00 **B.** $3.50 **C.** $5.00

Mixed REVIEW

Find the measure of a supplementary angle.

1. 98°
2. 44°

True or False?

3. Some trapezoids are squares.
4. All squares are rectangles.
5. Randa has $25 in her bank account. She deposits $33, $18, and $19.80. She earns interest of $3.83. How much money does she have in her account now?

What's Ahead

- Determining and using elapsed time
- Reading, using, and making schedules

3-10 Times and Schedules

THINK AND DISCUSS

The amount of time between two events is **elapsed time.**

1. What time do you get up in the morning on a school day? What time does school begin? Find the elapsed time.
2. How long is your lunch period? Is this elapsed time?

Party for Joey	
11:00 A.M.	Friends arrive, play outside.
11:30 A.M.	Clown show
12:15 P.M.	Lunch
1:00 P.M.	Open presents
2:00 P.M.	Friends leave

You can use elapsed time when planning a party.

3. You plan a birthday party for your younger brother and make the schedule shown at the left.
   a. For how long do you plan the party to last?
   b. How much time did you allow for the clown show? for lunch? for presents?
   c. The clown calls at 10:30 A.M. to say that he will not be at the party until noon. Make a new party schedule.
4. Susan is having a party at 4:00 P.M. On the day of the party she needs to do the following activities:

decorate room (1 h)	mix cake (40 min)
bake cake (35 min)	cool cake (45 min)
frost cake (20 min)	shower (25 min)

   a. If Susan does the activities in the order given, at what time should she begin?
   b. Look more carefully at the activities. Which activities must be done in order? Could any be done at the same time? Figure out the latest time Susan could begin.
   c. Susan does not want to shower until she has frosted the cake. Does this change your answer?
   d. Susan decides she needs 25 min before the party to take care of last minute details. When should she begin her activities to allow for the extra 25 min?

Whiteface, Auguste,** and Character are the three types of clowns. **Find out what is different about each type of clown.

5. You decide to have a Halloween party. You want the invitations to arrive at least one week before the party. Mail usually takes two days in your city.

a. By what date should you mail the invitations?

b. **Discussion** What will you need to do before you can mail the invitations? How much time should you allow for these activities?

c. Your invitations ask people to let you know at least two days before the party if they are coming. If the people invited respond by mail or by telephone, between what dates should you hear from them?

When you attend a party, you also need to think about time.

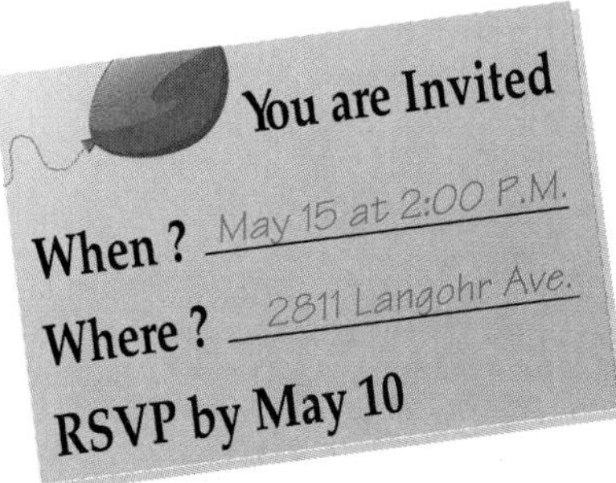

You are Invited
When ? May 15 at 2:00 P.M.
Where ? 2811 Langohr Ave.
RSVP by May 10

6. Suppose you received the invitation shown at the right. It is now 1:30 P.M. on May 15. You make a list and estimate the times for things you must do before the party.

Change clothes	5 min
Wrap present	10 min
Ride bike to store	5 min
Buy film at the store	5 min
Ride bike to the party	10 min

a. Suppose you start to get ready at 1:30 P.M. Will you get to the party on time?

b. **Writing** Explain how you solved this problem.

7. Lee is going to a party on Friday at 6:00 P.M. She will take the bus. The schedule is shown at the right. The bus stop at Willson Street is in front of Lee's house. The party is a 5-min walk from the bus stop at Kagy Boulevard.

a. By what time should Lee catch a bus to arrive at the party in time?

b. How many minutes will Lee be on the bus in each direction? how many minutes total?

c. By what time should Lee leave the party to catch a bus and be home by 9:00 P.M.?

d. Write down a schedule for Lee's travel plans.

Leave	Arrive
Willson St.	Kagy Blvd.
7:20 A.M.	7:45 A.M.
7:50 A.M.	8:15 A.M.
...	...
11:20 P.M.	11:45 P.M.
Kagy Blvd.	Willson St.
7:50 A.M.	8:15 A.M.
8:20 A.M.	8:45 A.M.
...	...
11:50 P.M.	12:15 A.M.

WORK TOGETHER

Work with a partner. Plan a party. Decide on an occasion and activities for the party. List all the things you will need to do to plan and have the party. Make a schedule for the party.

ON YOUR OWN

8. Use the bus schedule on the previous page.
   a. What time does the last bus of the day leave? Where does it end?
   b. **Critical Thinking** Could only one bus be used for all the scheduled trips? Explain your answer.

Ride bike home	*20 min*
Feed the dog	*10 min*
Do homework	*1 h*
Play outside	■
Help prepare dinner	*35 min*

9. Bonnie does the activities shown at the left after school but before dinner at 6:00 P.M. School is out at 3:30 P.M.
   a. How much time does she have to play outside?
   b. Make a schedule for Bonnie's afternoon.

GREAT EXPECTATIONS

Astronaut

I, Evin Demirel, would gladly like to be an astronaut. I have always found that space exploration into the unexplored fascinates me. To be on another planet in space would be a wonderous and great feeling. I would like to try to go to space camp in Huntsville to learn about how to be an astronaut. I also would like to learn about the planets. I have always had an interest in space. I took a program about it 2 years ago and decided to have a career in space science. I like to look at the perilous blackness up in the sky at night, and I also like looking at books with pictures of planets and other space objects. Right now, I wish I could be one of the first lucky persons to set foot on Mars and with a lot of determination and hard work, don't doubt me.

Evin Demirel

10. Investigation (p. 94) Identify any time or schedule obligations you make when you join the music club. Does this influence your decision to join or not?

11. Activity Name at least five activities you do between the time you get up in the morning and the time you arrive at school. Estimate the elapsed time for each activity. Time yourself tomorrow morning to see how close your estimates were.

Data File 2 (pp. 38–39) **Use the data for Exercises 12–14.**

12. Find the total time you would expect to spend for the Montezuma's Revenge ride at Knott's Berry Farm.

13. Which ride has a wait time slightly less than ride time?

14. Estimation At about 4:50 P.M. you get in line for Captain EO while your sister gets something to eat. At about what time should she meet you after the ride?

Mixed REVIEW

Classify the triangle with the following angles.

1. 45°, 45°, 90°
2. 38°, 65°, 77°
3. The lengths of the sides of a square are 1.5 mm. Find the perimeter.
4. What metric unit would you use to measure the height of your school?
5. Joelna has 3 h of homework tonight. She likes to take a $\frac{1}{2}$ h break. What is the latest she can begin studying to finish by 9:30 P.M.?

Dear Evin,

I was completely fascinated by your description of space and your wish to become a future space explorer. The experiences that I have had as a NASA astronaut have allowed me to see things from a slightly different view.

While on orbit inside a Space Shuttle vehicle, I circle the entire earth every 90 minutes, at a speed of about 7 miles every second! My concept of *neighbor* begins to include those living on different continents and in remote and isolated areas. As I view our Earth from space, the land masses are easily recognizable because they look just like the maps I studied in school. There are no boundaries or borders or fences visible from our lofty perch. It is awesome to see it and get the "big picture."

Frederick D. Gregory
NASA Astronaut

CHAPTER 3

Wrap Up

Place Value of Decimals — 3-1, 3-2, 3-3

You can write decimals in ***standard form, expanded form,*** or in words. Order decimals by comparing digits that have the same place value. Start with the digit on the left and move one place to the right as needed.

Write each number in standard form.

1. five tenths **2.** forty-eight hundredths **3.** nine and eight ten-thousandths

Compare. Use >, <, or =.

4. 1.8392 ■ 1.8382 **5.** 11.721 ■ 6.731 **6.** 0.81 ■ 0.81 **7.** 500.2 ■ 50.02

Estimation, Adding and Subtracting Decimals — 3-5, 3-6, 3-7, 3-8

You can use ***rounding*** or ***front-end*** estimation to estimate a sum. To estimate a difference, use rounding. Before adding or subtracting decimals, line up decimal points and annex zeros if necessary. Use estimation to check if answers are reasonable.

Money added to a bank account is a ***deposit.*** Money taken out is a ***withdrawal.*** The amount in the account is the ***balance.***

Round to the place value of the underlined digit.

8. $5.69\underline{8}3$ **9.** $0.8\underline{7}624$ **10.** $9.23\underline{5}7$ **11.** $3.\underline{9}876$ **12.** $4\underline{4}.095$

Add or subtract.

13. $\begin{array}{r} 0.9 \\ -\ 0.2 \\ \hline \end{array}$ **14.** $\begin{array}{r} 0.72 \\ +\ 0.96 \\ \hline \end{array}$ **15.** $\begin{array}{r} 1.741 \\ -\ \ 0.81 \\ \hline \end{array}$ **16.** 62.24 − 8.598 **17.** 337.4 + 20.08

Complete the spreadsheet.

	A	B	C	D	E	F
1	Date	Start Balance	Withdrawal	Deposit	Interest	End Balance
2	2/5/95	**18.** ■	20.00	0.00	0.00	65.62
3	2/15/95	**19.** ■	0.00	40.00	**20.** ■	106.02

Metric Length 3-9

Metric measurement is based on tens. The ***meter*** (m) is the basic unit of length. Other measures include ***millimeter*** (0.001 m), ***centimeter*** (0.01 m), and ***kilometer*** (1,000 m).

Choose the appropriate unit of measure for each.

21. altitude of an airplane **22.** your height **23.** perimeter of a classroom

Times and Schedules 3-10

Elapsed time is the amount of time between two events. You can use elapsed time to help plan your day.

24. It's 6:00 P.M. Can Lori do everything on her schedule and still have time to read for 25 min before her 9:30 P.M. bedtime? At what time will she complete her to-do list if she works continuously?

Eat dinner	40 min
Homework	55 min
TV program	30 min
Feed dog	10 min

Strategies and Applications 3-4

Solving a similar, simpler problem can help you see new ways to solve a given problem.

25. A clock chimes every 30 min. How many times will it chime in the month of June?

26. How many days have passed since you were born?

GETTING READY FOR CHAPTER 4

Sometimes you can estimate the product or quotient of two decimals by first rounding each decimal to the nearest whole number, and then multiplying or dividing.

Round each decimal to the nearest whole number. Then multiply or divide.

1. 3.5×2.1 **2.** 6.3×9.256 **3.** 10.1×119.2 **4.** $80.63 \div 8.9$

5. $72.4 \div 8.5$ **6.** $99.8 \div 9.8$ **7.** 32.5×0.55 **8.** $230.55 \div 0.5$

9. 47.8×39.9 **10.** $11.99 \div 4.33$ **11.** 70.008×3.15 **12.** $2.5 \div 0.99$

PUTTING IT ALL TOGETHER

Follow Up

The Music Club

The Music Club has been advertising for students in your school to join the club. The editor of the school newspaper has asked you to write a short article advising students on whether or not they should join. Look back at the decision you made when you considered the question at the beginning of the chapter. Revise your decision, if necessary, based on your study of the chapter. Then write an article outlining your decision and explaining why you made it. You may wish to document hidden costs or to recommend another club. The problems preceded by the magnifying glass (p. 100, # 43; p. 104, # 28; p. 114, # 40; and p. 131, # 10) will help you write your article.

Not long ago, CD and cassette clubs were called record clubs. But between 1988 and 1991, record sales plunged from $532 million to just $29 million annually. Cassette sales stayed about the same, but CD sales rocketed to more than $4 billion annually. Clearly, music lovers have switched to CDs.

Excursion: Find the average prices of cassettes and CDs over the past ten years. What trends do you see? What do you think will happen to the prices for cassettes and CDs over the next five years? Explain your reasoning.

IN ROUND NUMBERS

Any number of students may play.

- Each player cuts six 3 x 5 pieces of paper to make playing cards. On each card the player makes, he or she writes a decimal amount like $25.71.
- Mix all the cards together and place them face down in a pile.
- The first player turns over the top two cards and states the rounded sum of the two decimal amounts to the nearest dollar. If the player is correct, the player keeps the cards. If the player is incorrect, the cards are reshuffled into the deck. The player to the left now takes a turn.

The game ends when the pile of cards is gone. The player holding the most cards wins.

Variation: The rounded *difference* between the two decimal numbers is found.

Decimal Derby

The object of this game is to create the largest decimal number.

Rules:

- Play with three or more people.
- Use a place value chart with columns for Tens, Ones, Tenths, and Hundredths.
- Each player rolls a number cube four times. After each roll, the player writes the number in one of the columns on the place value chart.

Play continues in this manner until each player has had a turn. The player who makes the largest decimal number is the winner.

Variation: Each time you begin a new round, add another column to your place value chart.

A Time & A Place

Assume that you have three hours to spend at a science museum. There are 12 exhibits that you want to see during your visit. Make a schedule that includes at least 20 minutes for lunch. Remember to include a time allowance for you to reach each exhibit hall as well as the cafeteria.

Newspaper Numbers

Look through newspapers for 10 numbers, each with three to five digits. List each number and what it describes. It may be the number of people attending an event, a person's age, or the cost of an item. Next to each description, show the newspaper number rounded to the nearest one, ten, hundred, thousand, or ten thousand. Now look again at your newspaper numbers and their descriptions. How do the rounded numbers affect what is being described? Is your description still accurate? Do the rounded numbers change how well someone would understand what is being described?

Excursion: Think of five examples of when an exact number is necessary. Can you think of another five examples of when a rounded number is satisfactory? What makes the difference?

Assessment

1. **Writing** Is the number two hundred thirteen thousandths equal to two hundred and thirteen thousandths? Explain.

2. **Choose A, B, C, or D.** The value of the digit 3 in the number 24.1538 is ■.
   - **A.** three hundreds
   - **B.** three hundredths
   - **C.** three tenths
   - **D.** three thousandths

3. **Choose A, B, C, or D.** Which of the following is *not* true for the number 5.836?
   - **A.** 5.836 rounds to 5.84.
   - **B.** 5.836 > 5.85
   - **C.** The expanded form is 5 + 0.8 + 0.03 + 0.006.
   - **D.** It is read as "five and eight hundred thirty-six thousandths."

4. Compare. Use >, <, or =.
   - **a.** 2.34 ■ 2.4
   - **b.** 8.97 ■ 8.970
   - **c.** 32.12 ■ 32.42
   - **d.** 12.82 ■ 12.81

5. Find each sum.
   - **a.** 3.89 + 15.638
   - **b.** 8.99 + 6.35
   - **c.** 0.9356 + 0.208
   - **d.** \$4.38 + \$2.74 + \$1.17

6. **Estimation** Suppose your savings account has a balance of \$129.55. You deposit \$17.89 and withdraw \$83.25. What is the approximate balance?

7. Find each difference.
   - **a.** \$20 − \$15.99
   - **b.** 8.956 − 6.973
   - **c.** 536.79 − 95.8
   - **d.** 5.867 − 0.345

8. Find the perimeter in millimeters.

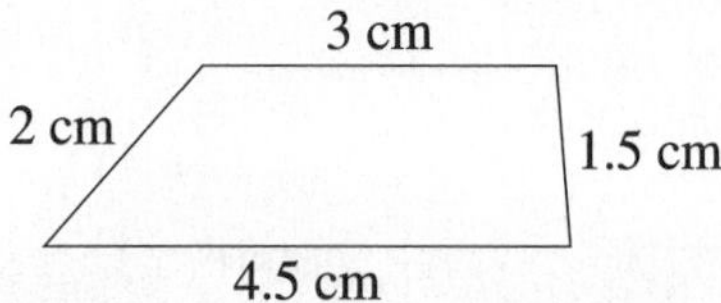

9. What unit of metric measure is appropriate for each item?
   - **a.** length of a pen
   - **b.** perimeter of a state
   - **c.** distance around a track
   - **d.** width of an automobile

10. Jackson plans to attend a beach party at 1:00 P.M. He needs to shower and dress (35 min), eat breakfast (25 min), do his chores (1 h 40 min), get his beach supplies (25 min), and bike to the party (20 min). Plan his schedule before he leaves for the beach party.

11. Graph 8.1, 8.2, 8.08, 8.15, and 8.03 on a number line.

12. What is the sum of all the whole numbers from 1 to 300?

CHAPTER 3

Cumulative Review

Choose A, B, C, or D.

1. Which is the decimal for thirty-four hundredths?

   A. 0.034 B. 0.34

   C. 3.40 D. 34.00

2. Which angle would have $\overrightarrow{XY}$ as one of its sides?

   A. $\angle XYZ$ B. $\angle XZY$

   C. $\angle ZXY$ D. $\angle YZX$

3. How would you find the range of five salaries?

   A. Add the salaries and divide by 5.

   B. Subtract the lowest salary from the highest.

   C. Arrange the salaries in order and choose the middle one.

   D. Choose the salary that occurs more than once.

4. If a quadrilateral has point symmetry, then it *cannot* be which of the following?

   A. rhombus B. square

   C. rectangle D. trapezoid

5. All five items in a data set are multiplied by 10. How is the mode changed?

   A. It is multiplied by 10.

   B. It is multiplied by 50.

   C. It is multiplied by 2.

   D. The mode does not change.

6. In $\angle ABC$, the measures of angles A and B are each 61°. What is the measure of $\angle C$?

   A. 58° B. 61° C. 78° D. 59°

7. Unleaded gasoline costs $1.29 per gallon. If you buy 12 gallons, estimate the amount of money you spend.

   A. $10 B. $29

   C. $14 D. $20

8. If 0.305 is represented by point B, what numbers could be represented by points A and C?

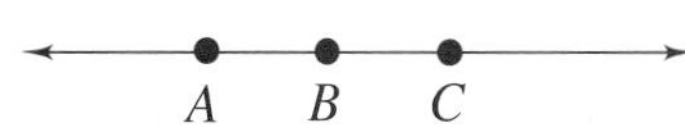

   A. A: 0.051, C: 0.7

   B. A: 0.03, C: 0.06

   C. A: 0.350, C: 0.4

   D. A: 0.29, C: 0.32

9. What is the *best* name for the triangle shown?

   A. acute B. obtuse

   C. scalene D. right

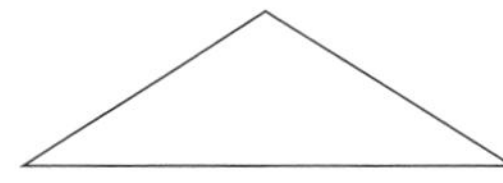

10. Without measuring, what is the best estimate for the perimeter of the triangle shown in Question 9?

    A. 7 mm B. 7 cm C. 7 m D. 7 km

CHAPTER 4

Multiplying and Dividing Decimals

In the 16th century, the Germans were using leg splints and arm stretchers to set broken limbs. The Greeks used splints, starched bandages, and clay casts to set broken bones.

It's All in the Bones

When scientists know the gender of a skeleton and the length of the tibia, femur, humerus, or radius, they can estimate the person's height when they were alive. The chart shows the formula used for each gender and bone.

Adult Height (in cm) Based on the Length of Major Bones

Male

(2.9 x length of humerus) + 70.6

(3.3 x length of radius) + 86.0

(1.9 x length of femur) + 81.3

(2.4 x length of tibia) + 78.7

Female

(2.8 x length of humerus) + 71.5

(3.3 x length of radius) + 81.2

(1.9 x length of femur) + 72.8

(2.4 x length of tibia) + 74.8

Source: *Arithmetic Teacher*

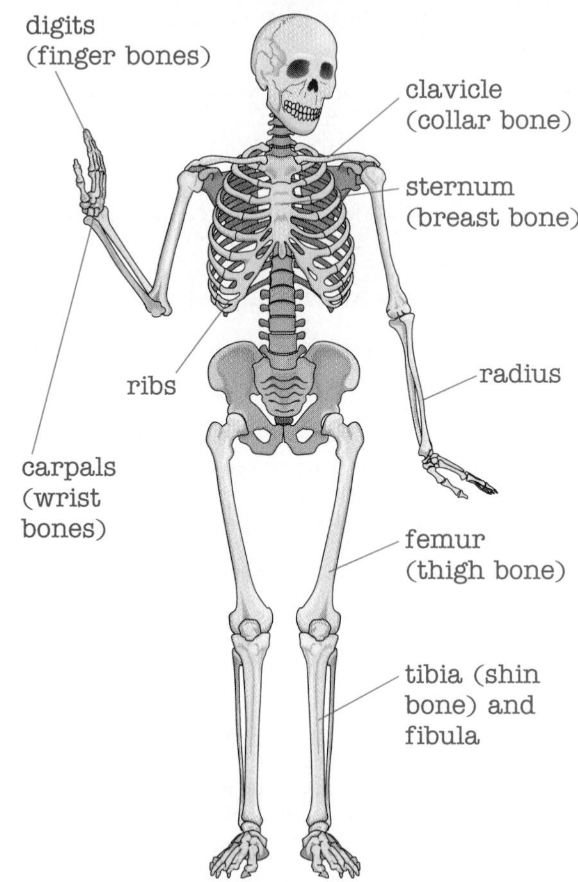

How Many Bones Do You Have?

A baby is born with more than 300 bones—that's more than an adult's 206 bones. As you grow, some of your bones grow together. This is called bone fusion. The last bones to grow together become the collarbone. Different people's bones grow and fuse in different ways. About one person in 20 ends up with an extra rib bone.

Source: *Macmillan Book of Fascinating Facts*

WHAT YOU WILL LEARN

- how to model decimal products and quotients
- how to estimate decimal products and quotients
- how to use technology to create databases
- how to solve problems with too much or too little information

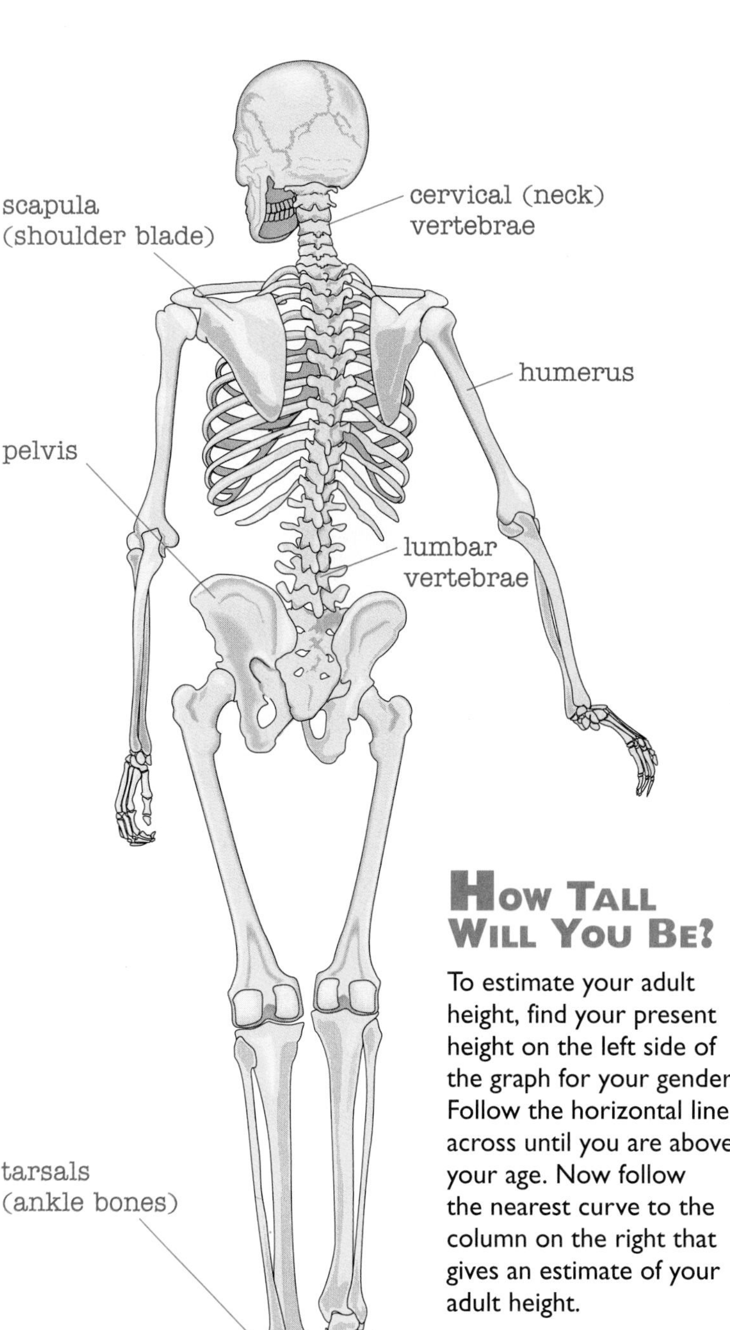

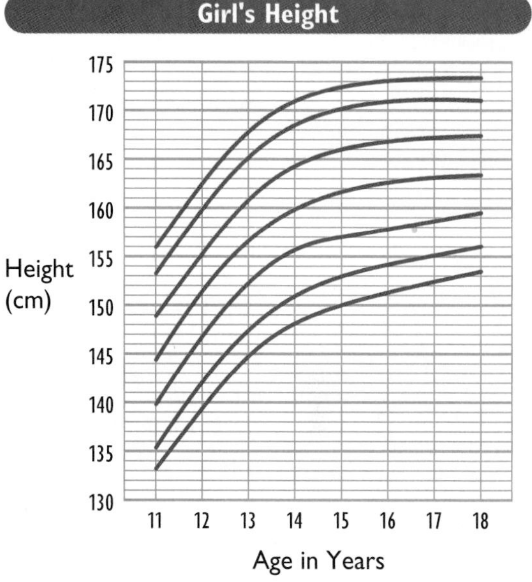

How Tall Will You Be?

To estimate your adult height, find your present height on the left side of the graph for your gender. Follow the horizontal line across until you are above your age. Now follow the nearest curve to the column on the right that gives an estimate of your adult height.

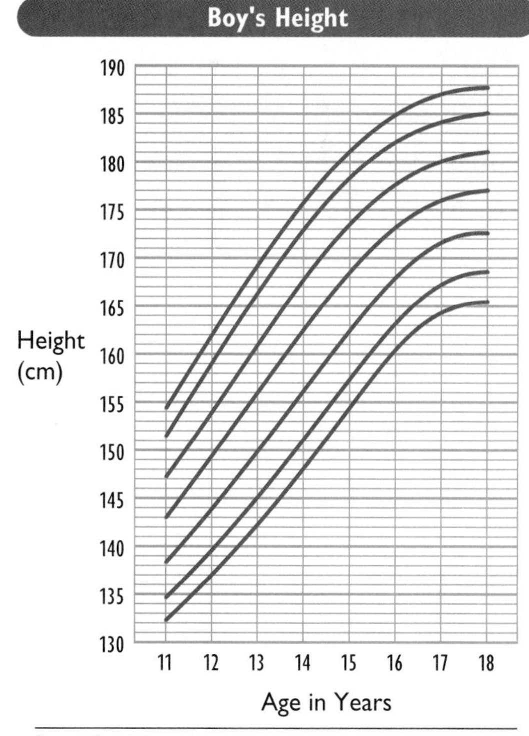

Source: *Ross Laboratories*

investigation

Project File

Memo

You are enrolled in a twelve week study course. Rumor has it that the teacher, Mr. Skim, gives a lot of notes! In fact, students who have taken the class say that Mr. Skim gives an average of four pages of notes each time the class meets and each daily assignment requires about two pages. Thinking this might be a good opportunity to begin practicing organizational skills, you decide to purchase a binder in which to keep your notes and daily assignments for the class. You find that there are 0.5 in., 0.625 in., and 1 in. binders available in the school store.

Mission: Find out what size binder will best hold your notes and daily assignments for the study skills course. Explain in detail how you reached your conclusion.

Leads to Follow

- ✓ How many sheets of paper will you need altogether for your notes and daily assignments?
- ✓ How thick is one sheet of notebook paper?
- ✓ How would a decision to write on both sides of each sheet of notebook paper affect the size binder you purchase?

What's Ahead

• Estimating decimal products and quotients

4-1 Estimating Products and Quotients

THINK AND DISCUSS

DH DH DH DH DH

Downtown Hardware

Employee
Lisa M. Smith

DAY	DATE	HOURS
MON	5/3	2.1
TUE		
WED	5/5	1.7
THU	5/6	3.5
FRI	5/7	4.0
SAT		
SUN		
TOTAL HOURS		11.3

DH DH DH DH DH

Lisa works at Downtown Hardware. Her hours vary weekly depending on the amount of work available. Her time card shows her daily and weekly hours worked. Lisa's hourly wage is \$4.25. Estimate how much she will earn this week.

1. a. What two numbers would you multiply to find how much Lisa will earn this week?
   b. Round each factor to the nearest whole number.
   c. Estimate Lisa's earnings for the week.

2. Estimate Lisa's weekly earnings two ways.
   a. Round both factors up. Is this estimate higher or lower than Lisa's actual weekly earnings? Explain.
   b. Round both factors down. Is this estimate higher or lower than Lisa's actual weekly earnings? Explain.

3. Is your estimate higher or lower than Lisa's actual weekly earnings? Explain.

4. Estimate the product 12.6×1.9. Round each factor to the nearest whole number.

Numbers that are easy to multiply or divide mentally are **compatible numbers.** You can use them to estimate products.

Example 1 Estimate the product 26.03×3.31.

$$\begin{array}{rcr} 26.03 & \rightarrow & 25 \\ \underline{\times\ 3.31} & \rightarrow & \underline{\times\ 3} \\ & & 75 \end{array}$$

Change to compatible numbers.

The product 26.03×3.31 is about 75.

5. What compatible numbers would you choose to estimate the product 3.89×16.03? Explain your choice.

6. Is it easier to estimate the product 29.26×11.62 by using compatible numbers or by rounding each factor to the nearest whole number? Explain.

When you estimate quotients you can use compatible numbers.

Example 2 The largest paper money ever issued was the Chinese one-kwan note. It was issued in the 14th century and was 92.8 cm long. The United States one-dollar bill is 15.6 cm long. About how many times as long as a one-dollar bill was the one-kwan note?

$92.8 \div 15.6$ **Write the quotient.**

$90 \div 15 = 6$ **Use compatible numbers.**

The one-kwan note is about six times as long as the one-dollar bill.

Party Supplies	Cost
Streamers (81 ft)	$.79
Paper tablecloths	$1.99
Plain napkins (50)	$2.49
Holiday napkins (8)	$.69
Colored balloons (20)	$2.29
Foil balloons (each)	$1.99
Cardboard cut-outs	$.29
Colored paper (24)	$1.16
Markers (10 colors)	$1.65
Games (4-6 players)	$9.95
Music	$8.78

WORK TOGETHER

Plan a party for your class. Work with a partner. Choose the supplies you need to make the party a success. Keep in mind that your class has to stay within a $26 budget.

- Choose a theme for your class party.
- Decide what you want for the party. Choose from the list at the left.
- How much of each item do you need? Make sure there is enough for everyone in the class.
- Estimate the total cost of the party.

TRY THESE

Round each factor to the nearest whole number. Estimate the product.

7. 15.3×2.6 **8.** 2.25×16.91 **9.** 3.5×2.72

Write a pair of compatible numbers. Then use the numbers to estimate.

10. $46.4 \div 4.75$ **11.** $39.3 \div 8.7$ **12.** 39.26×1.98

13. 18.8×4.3 **14.** $17.33 \div 5.49$ **15.** 2.18×24.19

16. Luisa earns \$4.75/h mowing lawns. Estimate how much money she will earn in 3.5 h.

17. Yuri earned \$33.25 in one week baby-sitting. He earns \$3.50/h. Estimate the number of hours he worked.

ON YOUR OWN

Round each factor to the nearest whole number. Estimate the product.

18. 0.95×22.8 **19.** 11.6×3.23 **20.** 15.25×3.9

21. 1.79×0.12 **22.** 4.01×0.62 **23.** 31.4×3.20

Use compatible numbers to estimate.

24. 41.5×18.75 **25.** $15.76 \div 2.51$ **26.** 3.5×8.9

27. $65 \div 8.4$ **28.** 12.2×2.96 **29.** $37.2 \div 6.12$

Mixed REVIEW

1. A bus trip from Austin to San Antonio takes 2 h 57 min. What time will the bus arrive, if it leaves Austin at 10:35 A.M.?

Complete.

2. ■ m = 54 cm
3. 18 km = ■ m
4. 400 mm = ■ cm

5. A year has two months in a row with a Friday the 13th. What months must they be?

The Soap Box Derby

The Derby held in Akron, Ohio, is a downhill race for cars without motors. The cars are built and driven by young people between the ages of 9 and 16. The cars race on a 953.75 ft downhill track.

Drivers can enter one of three racing divisions. To enter the masters division, the combined weight of the car and its driver must be exactly 236 lb. To compete in the Stock car or Kit Car divisions, the combined weight must be 206 lb. Sometimes the drivers need to add lead weights to the cars to reach the required weight for their division.

In 1992, 70 girls and 133 boys from 35 states and 6 countries entered the race. Carolyn Fox, an 11-year-old from Salem, Oregon, was the winner of the Kit Car division. Her winning time was 28.27 s.

30. To find speed divide the distance by the time. Estimate Carolyn Fox's average speed.

31. Suppose the track is 2.5 times its original length. Carolyn finishes the race in 52.56 s. Find her average speed.

Use the chart below to answer questions 32–34.

Food	Serving Size	Protein (grams)
American Cheese	1 slice	6.6
Canned Tuna	3 oz (drained)	24.4
Rye Bread	1 slice	2.3
Cheese Pizza	1 slice (14-in. pie.)	7.8

Protein makes new cells to help your body grow. Most food contains some protein. Meat, fish, nuts, milk, and cheese provide your body with large amounts of protein. A 12-year-old needs about 55 g of protein every day.

Source: *The Usborne Book of Food Fitness & Health*

32. About how many grams of protein are in 2 slices of pizza?

33. About how many grams of protein are in 8 slices of pizza?

34. **Nutrition** Estimate how many grams of protein are in a sandwich consisting of 2 slices of rye bread, 2 oz of tuna, and one slice of American Cheese.

35. **a.** **Mental Math** If you save \$6.25 each week, estimate how much you will save in one year.

b. **Mental Math** If you saved \$443.75 in one year, estimate how much you saved each week.

36. A librarian orders 3 copies of a book. The bill is \$38.85. Estimate the cost of 1 book. Is your estimate higher or lower than the actual cost of the book? Explain.

37. **Choose A, B, or C.** Between what two numbers is the quotient $18.7 \div 5.4$?

A. 2 and 3 **B.** 3 and 4 **C.** 4 and 5

38. **Sports** A volleyball weighs 283.5 g and a shipping crate weighs 595.34 g. Estimate the weight of a shipping crate containing 9 volleyballs.

39. **Social Studies** The Apennine Railroad Tunnel in Italy is 18.5 km long. The Seikan Tunnel in Japan is about 2.9 times as long. Estimate the length of the Seikan tunnel.

40. **Writing** If two different people estimate a product or quotient using compatible numbers, will they always get the same result? Use examples to support your answer.

41. **Data File 6 (pp. 226–227)** Estimate the appropriate seat height for you when riding a bicycle.

TECHNOLOGY

4-2 Decimals in Databases

What's Ahead

- Using a database to explore applications of decimals

WHAT YOU'LL NEED

✓ Computer 

✓ Database or spreadsheet software 

✓ Calculator 

THINK AND DISCUSS

A **database** is a collection of information organized by category. You could use a database to organize recipes or a comic book collection. A **field** is a category in a database. A group of fields relating to one entry is a **record.**

1. Suppose you have a stamp collection. What are some ways you might organize your collection? Name at least three fields you might use to organize your data.

The database shows one way to organize information about a comic book collection.

2. a. What fields are in the database? What other fields could you add to the database?

   b. What information does each record contain?

	A	B	C	D
1	Issue Number	Title	Value	
2	270	Batman	35.00	
3	1	Indiana Jones	2.50	
4	314	Justice League	11.00	
5	28	Spiderman	170.00	
6	1	The Atom	300.00	

Source: Wizzard

3. a. Which fields contain numbers? Which fields contain letters or text?

   b. **Discussion** How are the records alike? How are they different?

Some computers "talk" and "listen" to users. When "talking," a computer makes words from digital sounds and outputs them to a speaker. When "listening," a receiver recognizes the sounds and translates them so the computer understands.

One advantage of a database is the ability to **sort,** or order, data by field. Computers sort letters or text alphabetically and numbers from greatest to least or least to greatest.

4. How are the comic books sorted? What other ways could you sort the comic book database?

WORK TOGETHER

Your group has been asked to recommend a brand of sneakers for the track team. The database shows data for five different sneakers. Testers rated the sneakers on a scale of 1 (very good) to 5 (very poor) for their ability to dry out (evaporation rate) after wearing and for flexibility.

5. What factors are most important in making your recommendation?

6. What other information might you want before making your decision?

7. **Computer** Enter the information using database software. Sort the information in various ways to get the information you need.

8. Prepare a report.
   a. Tell which sneaker you recommend.
   b. Tell which sneaker to avoid.
   c. Give a second choice.

	A	B	C	D	E
1	Brand	Price	Weight	Evaporation Rate	Flexibility
2	Air Jumpers	33.50	13 oz	5.0	1.8
3	Cool Runners	60.00	12 oz	2.5	3.3
4	Floaters	75.95	16 oz	2.6	2.9
5	Foot Lights	125.35	17 oz	3.9	2.7
6	Hi Flyers	135.00	11 oz	1.5	4.1

ON YOUR OWN

	A	B	C	D
1	Coin	Composition	Condition	Cost
2	1993 United States Silver Eagle	0.999 oz pure silver	brilliant, uncirculated	$8.95
3	1992 Panda	0.999 oz pure silver	gem, brilliant, uncirculated	$18.95
4	Morgan silver dollar, uncirculated	0.90 pure silver	brilliant, uncirculated	$19.95
5	1986 Statue of Liberty silver dollar (2-coin set)	0.90 pure silver	gem, proof set	$29.95
6	1992 Mexico Libertad	0.999 oz pure silver	brilliant, uncirculated	$8.95

Source: *Quality Collectibles, LTD*

9. Use the database above.

a. Name the fields in the database.

b. How many records are in the database?

c. Suppose you sort the coins by condition. What would be the order?

d. Suppose you sort the coins by cost. What would be the order?

e. What is the value of all the coins in the collection?

f. What other fields could you add to the database?

10. Computer Use database software. Choose a topic from the list at the right or one of your own and create a database. Use at least three fields.

11. Writing Where might a database be useful? How might a teacher use a database?

12. Data File 8 (pp. 316–317)

a. Which data set would be appropriate for a database?

b. What are three fields the database would have?

c. What are two ways you might sort the data base?

Mixed REVIEW

Estimate the product.

1. 19.2 × 9.7

2. 4.3 × 6.73

3. Draw an acute ∠A. Construct an angle congruent to ∠A.

Find the difference.

4. 8 − 7.35

5. 25 − 21.984

6. Is $5 enough money to buy yogurt for $2.09, blueberries for $1.49, and bread for $.85?

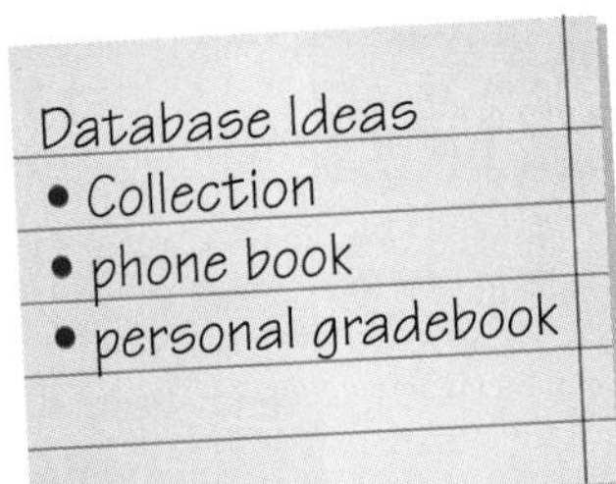

What's Ahead

- Evaluating expressions using order of operations

WHAT YOU'LL NEED

✓ Calculator 

4-3 The Order of Operations

WORK TOGETHER

Work with a partner. One partner uses a calculator and the other uses paper and pencil to find the value of the expressions shown below. Work from left to right. The partner who uses the calculator presses [=] only after entering the last number.

1. Record the value of each expression.
   a. $18 + 12 \times 5$
   b. $15 - 12 \div 3$
   c. $(6 + 18) \div 3 \times 6$
2. a. Compare your results with your partner's results. Did you both get the same values for the expressions?
   b. Is it possible to get two different values? Explain.
   c. How might getting two values for one expression cause problems?
3. Look at each calculator result and decide which operation the calculator performed first.

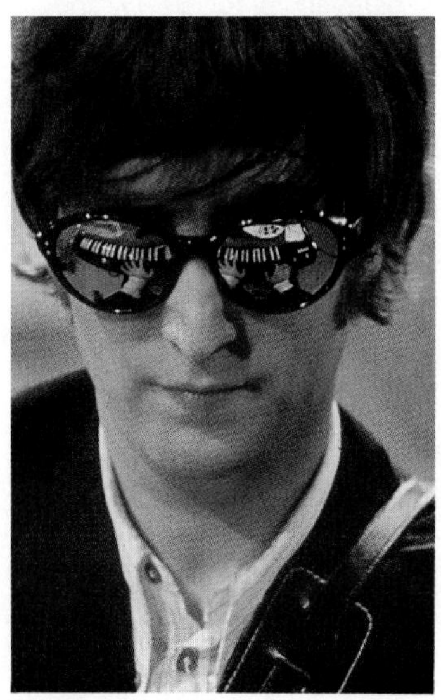

You say you've got a real solution.
Well, you know,
We'd all love to see the plan.
John Lennon

THINK AND DISCUSS

Sometimes getting different solutions to an expression can be confusing. There is a set of rules for evaluating expressions that guarantees everyone gets the same answer. We call this set of rules the **order of operations.**

Order of Operations

1. Do all operations within parentheses first.
2. Multiply and divide in order from left to right.
3. Add and subtract in order from left to right.

4. Now look at the expression $3 + 4 \times 5$. What are two possible values you might find for the expression? Which value is correct? Explain.

5. a. What is the value of the expression $(4 + 5) \times 5$?
   b. What is the value of the expression $4 + (5 \times 5)$?
   c. What is the value of the expression $4 + 5 \times 5$?
   d. What do you notice about the values of each expression in parts (a), (b), and (c)?

6. Consider the expression $2 + 6 \times 7$.
   a. Which operation would you perform first?
   b. What would you do next?
   c. What is the value of the expression?

7. Consider the expression $3 + 2 \times 5 \times 4$.
   a. Which operation would you perform first? Why?
   b. Write the expression after the first step.
   c. What would you do next?
   d. What is the last step and the final value?

ON YOUR OWN

Which operation would you perform first?

8. $8 - 2 \times 3$
9. $(4.6 - 0.6) \div 4$
10. $15 \times 8 \div 3$
11. $12 - 2 \times 3 \div 5$
12. $16 \div 4 \times (3.3 + 0.7) \times 4$

Evaluate.

13. $6 - 2 + 4 \times 2$
14. $3 + 3 \times 2$
15. $(3.3 - 1.4) + 6$
16. $4 \div (4.4 - 2.4)$
17. $6 \times (2 \times 5)$
18. $13 - (2.7 + 0.4)$

Mental Math **Evaluate.**

19. $5 + 2 \times 0$
20. $(12 - 7) \times 5 + 1$
21. $(6.3 - 4.8) \times 1$
22. $18 \div 6 - (5.6 - 4.6)$

23. Writing Explain the steps you would use to evaluate the expression $8 \div 4 \times 6 + (7.5 - 5.5)$.

Mixed REVIEW

1. Will has 2 copies of a *Batman* comic valued at $35 each and one *Spiderman* comic valued at $170. What is the value of his comic collection?

2. How many *Justice League* comics valued at $11 each would you need to trade to obtain the first issue of *The Atom* worth $300?

Estimate using compatible numbers.

3. 19.43×6.2
4. 493.8×1.869
5. $203.179 \div 22.039$

6. The lockers in the sixth grade corridor are numbered 100 to 275. How many lockers are there?

Replace ■ with <, >, or =.

24. $(3 + 6) \times 4$ ■ $3 + 6 \times 4$

25. $(8 - 2) \times (6 + 1)$ ■ $(8 - 2) \times 6 + 1$

26. $2 + (12 \div 3)$ ■ $2 + 12 \div 3$

27. $7 - 2 \times 3$ ■ $(7 - 2) \times 3$

28. $2 \times (15 - 3)$ ■ $2 \times 15 - 3$

29. **Critical Thinking** If you follow the order of operations to evaluate expressions when would you subtract before you multiply?

Place parentheses in each expression to make it true.

30. $12 + 6 \div 2 - 1 = 8$

31. $14 \div 2 + 5 - 1 = 1$

32. $1 + 2 \times 15 - 4 = 33$

33. $11 - 7 \div 2 = 2$

34. $14 - 3 - 2 \times 3 = 5$

35. $5 \times 6 \div 2 + 1 = 16$

In 1991, United States farmers received an average price of $.25/lb for apples.

Use a calculator to evaluate.

Sample: $3 \times (5 + 2)$

3 [×] [(] 5 [+] 2 [)] [=] 21

36. $(6.3 + 3.7) \div 5$

37. $4 \times (13 - 6)$

38. $13 \times (4.6 - 1.6)$

39. $(16 \times 4) \div (4.2 + 3.8)$

Insert operation symbols to make the equation true.

40. 21 ■ 3 ■ 4 = 11

41. 14 ■ 7 ■ 2 ■ 3 = 7

42. (6 ■ 9) ■ 4 ■ 6 = 10

43. (12 ■ 8) ■ (5 ■ 1) = 20

44. At a local grocery store the price of apples, 49 cents a pound, has been reduced by 20 cents. Next week the manager will double this reduced price.
    a. Should you use $49 - 20 \times 2$ or $(49 - 20) \times 2$ to find next week's price? Explain.
    b. What will the price of apples be next week?

What's Ahead

- Using the distributive property
- Finding areas of rectangles

WHAT YOU'LL NEED

✓ Graph paper 

✓ Scissors 

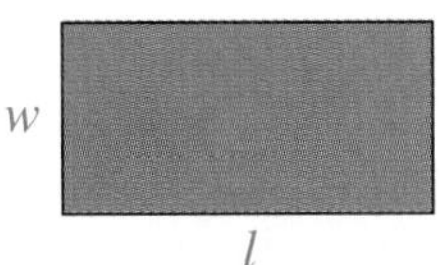

Area = length × width
$A = l \times w$

4-4 The Distributive Property

THINK AND DISCUSS

We call the number of square units that cover a rectangle its *area*. The **area** of a rectangle is equal to the product of its length times its width. We express area in square units.

1. Use graph paper to draw a rectangle that is 5 units wide and 6 units long.
   a. Count the number of square units in the rectangle to find its area.
   b. Multiply the length times the width to find the area of the rectangle. Do you get the same result?
   c. Compare parts (a) and (b). Which method appears easier? Explain.
2. Find the area of a rectangle 3 ft wide and 6 ft long.
3. Measure the length and the width of a binder or notebook. Find the area of the cover.

WORK TOGETHER

Work with a partner. Draw a rectangle with the given dimensions on graph paper. Cut out each rectangle.

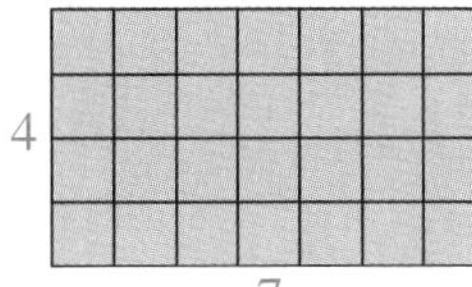

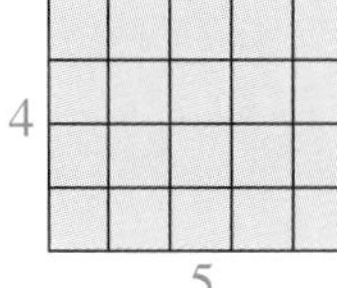

4. Find the area of each rectangle. Record each number.
5. Put the two rectangles end to end so the sides of equal length touch. What is the length and width of the new rectangle?
6. Find the area of the new rectangle. How does this area relate to the areas of the two smaller rectangles?

Around 300 B.C. Euclid wrote a book called *Elements.* In the book, Euclid shows how the distributive property works for area. "If one large rectangle is divided into 3 smaller ones, the area of the one is equal to the areas of the 3 smaller ones added together!"

There are at least two methods for finding the area of two rectangles with the same length or the same width.

Example 1 The Elliots have to cover two tables for the Memorial Day cookout. One table is 5 ft long and 3 ft wide. The other table is 5 ft long and 4 ft wide. How much contact paper will they need to cover both tables for the cookout?

Method 1

Find the area of each table top. Then add the areas.

Method 2

Place the tables end to end. Find the area of the combined table top.

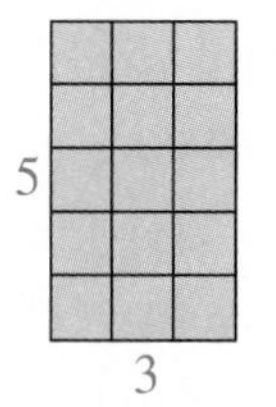

+

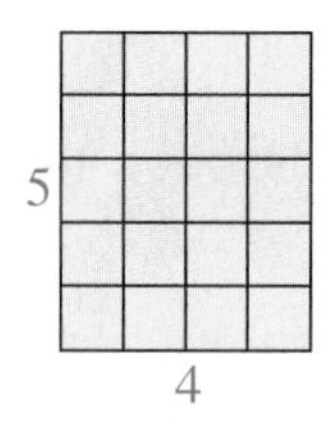

=

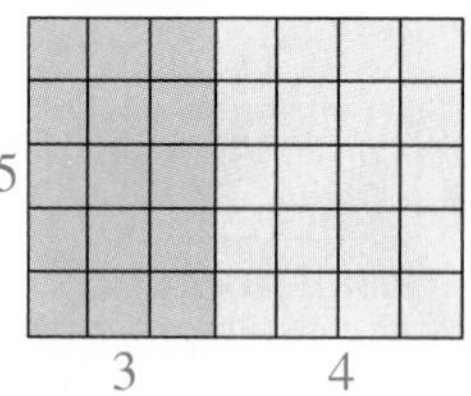

$$(5 \times 3) + (5 \times 4) = 5 \times (3 + 4)$$
$$15 + 20 = 5 \times 7$$
$$35 = 35$$

Both methods give the same total area. Therefore $5 \times (3 + 4) = (5 \times 3) + (5 \times 4)$. This is an example of the **distributive property.** You can use the distributive property to evaluate an expression that involves multiplication and addition.

Example 2 Use the distributive property to evaluate $(3 \times 4) + (3 \times 7)$.

$$(3 \times 4) + (3 \times 7) = 3 \times (4 + 7)$$
$$= 3 \times 11$$
$$= 33$$

7. Discussion Do you think the distributive property works for multiplication and subtraction? Make a conjecture. Try several examples to test your conjecture.

8. a. Evaluate $8 \times (100 - 3)$ using the distributive property.

b. Find $100 - 3$, then multiply by 8. Is your answer the same as part (a)? Explain.

c. In this problem, which method was easier, the method in part (a) or in part (b)? Explain your reasoning.

You can also use the distributive property to help you multiply mentally.

Example 3 Use the distributive property to find 8 × 56.

$8 \times 56 = 8 \times (50 + 6)$ Think of 56 as 50 + 6.

$= (8 \times 50) + (8 \times 6)$ Multiply mentally.

$= 400 + 48$ Add mentally.

$= 448$

Each side of an official singles tennis court is 27 ft wide by 39 ft long. ***Can you use the distributive property to find the area of the entire tennis court?***

TRY THESE

Write two expressions to describe the total area. Then find the total area.

9.

7

5 14

10.

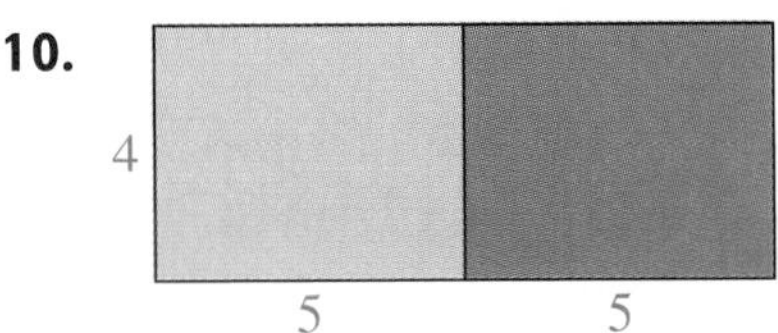

Write the missing numbers.

11. 6 × (12 + 2) = (■ × 12) + (6 × ■)

12. (10 × ■) − (■ × ■) = 10 × (6 − 3)

Use the distributive property to rewrite and evaluate each expression.

13. (4 × 6) + (4 × 3)

14. 6 × (20 − 4)

15. 12 × (4 + 10)

16. (5 × 3) − (5 × 2)

Mental Math **Use the distributive property to evaluate.**

17. 6 × 210

18. 8 × 109

19. 4 × 75

ON YOUR OWN

Draw a rectangular model for each expression.

20. 8 × (3 + 4)

21. (5 × 8) + (5 × 2)

22. Critical Thinking What would happen if you multiplied the width times the length to find the area of a rectangle? Use an example to support your answer.

Mixed REVIEW

Evaluate. Use the order of operations.

1. $16 - 3 \times 2 + 5$
2. $(6.3 + 8.7) - 6 \times 2$
3. $24 \div 3 - 2 \times 4$

Organize the data in a frequency table and in a line plot.

4. ages: 16 15 9 10 9 13 9 12 15 11 8 18
5. points: 8.5 9.8 7.4 7.4 8.5 10 6.8 9.1 8.5 10

6. Find the mean, median, and mode of each set of data in exercises 4 and 5.

Write two expressions to describe the total area. Then find the total area.

23.

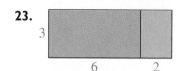

3

6 2

24.

Complete.

25. $(8 \times 3) + (■ \times 4) = 8 \times (■ + 4)$

26. $3 \times (8 - 1) = (■ \times 8) - (3 \times ■)$

Mental Math **Use the distributive property to evaluate.**

27. 8×42 **28.** 6×98 **29.** 5×112

Use the order of operations and the distributive property to evaluate.

30. $8 \times (2 + 3) \times 6 - 1$ **31.** $(7 + 3) \times 2 \times 4$

32. $4 + 2 \times 9 \times 3 + 1$ **33.** $7 \times (5 - 2) + 7 \times 8$

34. **Writing** Describe how using the *distributive property* can help you find 9×92.

CHECKPOINT

Estimate using rounding.

1. 2.2×9.4 **2.** 26.28×1.71 **3.** 4.9×12.2

Estimate using compatible numbers.

4. 39.4×2.34 **5.** 12.78×3.39 **6.** 28.75×51.23

Evaluate.

7. $5 - 4 \times 6$ **8.** $9 + 2 - 1 \times 5$ **9.** $4 + 36 \div 4 - 5$

10. **Choose A, B, C, or D.** Find the total area of a rectangle that is 3 units long and 4 units wide and a rectangle that is 3 units long and 6 units wide.

A. 25 sq units **B.** 18 sq units **C.** 30 sq units

Problem Solving Practice

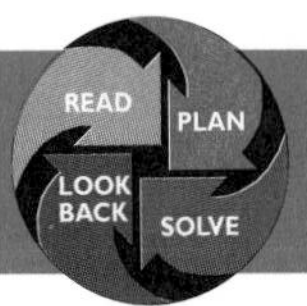

PROBLEM SOLVING STRATEGIES

Make a Table
Use Logical Reasoning
Solve a Simpler Problem
Too Much or Too Little Information
Look for a Pattern
Make a Model
Work Backward
Draw a Diagram
Guess and Test
Simulate a Problem
Use Multiple Strategies

Solve. The list at the left shows some possible strategies you can use.

1. Five friends decide that they will call each other tonight. They want to talk to each other only once. How many calls will be made in all?

2. **Music** Paul McCartney is a singer, songwriter, and former member of the 1960's rock group, The Beatles. He earns an estimated $72/min from his recordings and composing. To the nearest million dollars about how many dollars does Paul McCartney earn in one year?

3. A passenger train has rows of 5 seats across. There are 2 seats on one side and 3 seats on the other side of the center aisle. The conductor came through and collected 76 tickets. He noted that 4 seats in every row were occupied. How many rows of seats are in the car?

4. **Jobs** Magena has a job in a shoe store. During the last 5 weeks she sold 160 pairs of shoes. Each week she sold 7 more pairs than the previous week. How many pairs of shoes did Magena sell during each of the five weeks?

5. **Gardening** Rusty has a small greenhouse and waters his plants according to a schedule. He waters the zebra plants every 4 days, the coleus plants every 6 days, and the spider plants every 9 days. Rusty watered all the plants on April 1. On what date will he water all the plants again?

6. A section of a large city looks like a grid. There are 12 parallel avenues running north-south. There are 22 parallel cross-streets that intersect the avenues. How many intersections are there in this section of the city?

7. What is the perimeter of the 100th figure in the pattern?

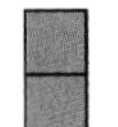 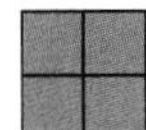  

***A Chinese wisteria** planted in Sierra Madre, CA in 1892 boasts branches that are 500 ft long.*

Source: *Guinness Book of Records*

What's Ahead

• Modeling decimal products

4-5 Exploring Decimal Products

✓ Decimal squares 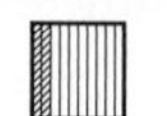

✓ Colored pencils

✓ Graph paper 

THINK AND DISCUSS

Jared went to the amusement park with some friends. He needs two tickets to ride the loop roller coaster. Each ticket costs $.70. How much does it cost to ride the roller coaster? You can use a sum or product to express the value of two tickets.

$$0.7 + 0.7 \text{ or } 2 \times 0.7$$

When you multiply a decimal and a whole number, you can use models to show multiplication as repeated addition.

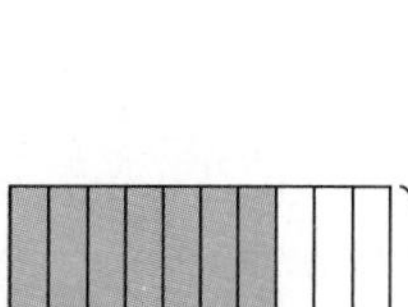

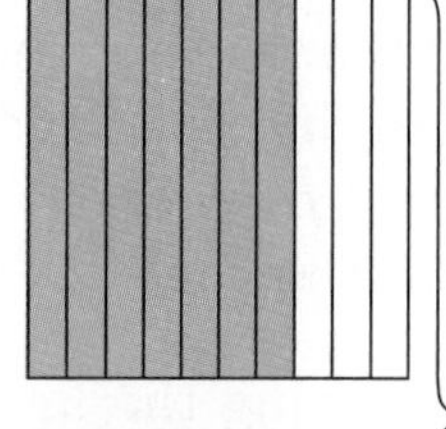

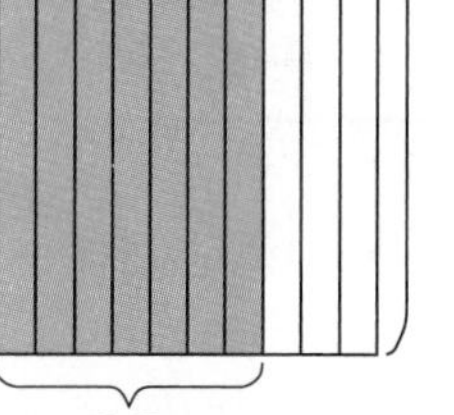

1. Use two decimal squares to model the product 2×0.7. Shade 7 columns to represent 0.7.
   a. How many tenths did you shade altogether?
   b. What decimal number represents the total shaded area?
2. Use 10 by 10 grids to model the product 4×0.5.
   a. How many grids do you need?
   b. How much of each grid do you need to shade?
   c. How many tenths did you shade altogether?
   d. Write an addition sentence that describes your model.

Use only one grid to model the multiplication of two decimals that are less than 1.

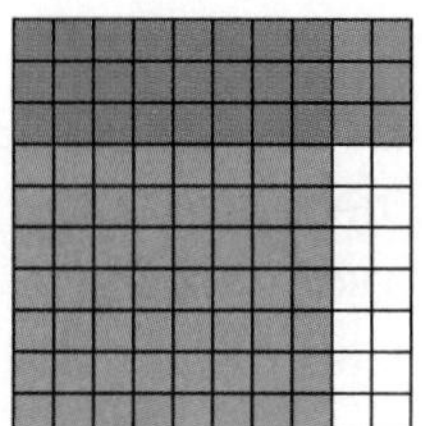

3. a. Shade 3 rows blue. What number does this represent?
   b. Shade 8 columns red. What number does this represent?
   c. The purple area where the shading overlaps represents the product. How many purple squares are shaded?
   d. What decimal number does this represent?
   e. Write a multiplication sentence that describes the model.
4. **Critical Thinking** When you multiply two decimals that are less than one, is your answer greater than or less than 1? Make a conjecture. Try several examples to test your conjecture.

WORK TOGETHER

5. Work with a partner. Make a model to show the product 1.5 × 0.5. Answer the following as you work.
   a. How many grids will you use?
   b. How many rows and columns will you shade and what numbers will they represent?
   c. What is the product?

ON YOUR OWN

Write a multiplication sentence to describe the model.

6. 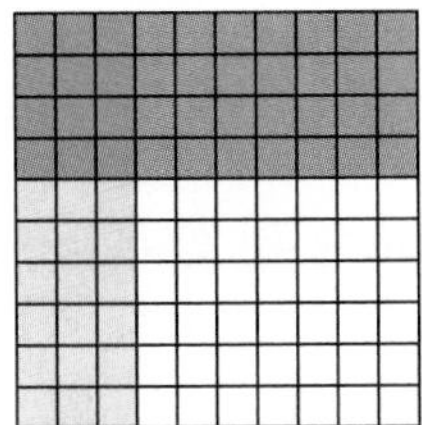

7. 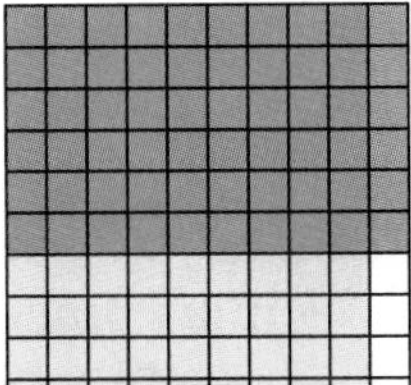

8. 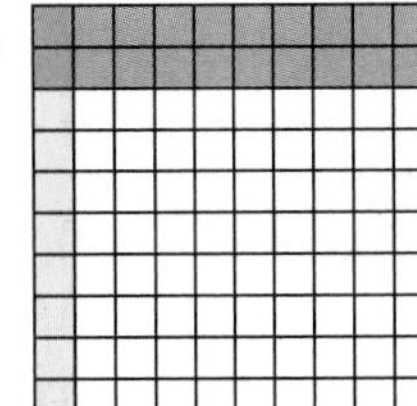

9. 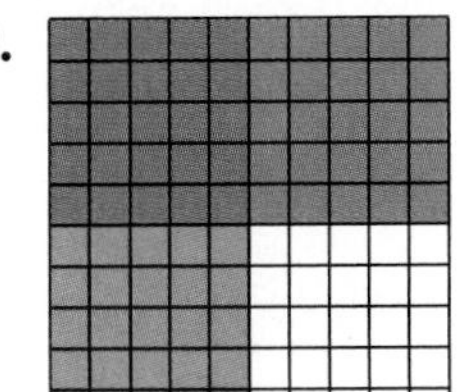

10. 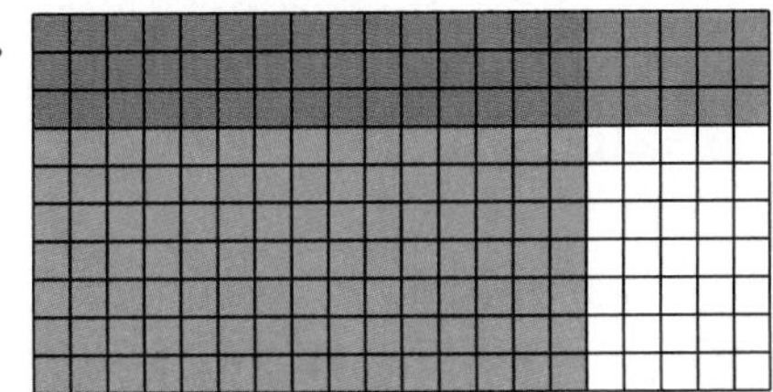

Draw a model to find each product.

11. 0.2 × 3
12. 2.2 × 0.4
13. 3 × 0.6
14. 0.4 × 0.1
15. 0.7 × 0.2
16. 1.3 × 0.2
17. 2 × 0.3
18. 1.7 × 0.5
19. 0.9 × 0.8

20. **Writing** Explain how to draw a model to find the product 1.2 × 0.4.

21. Draw a model to find the product 1.5 × 0.1. Write a multiplication sentence in words that describes the model.

22. You may or may not use a model to find a product. What are the advantages of using a model? Are there any disadvantages? Explain your reasoning.

Mixed REVIEW

Compare. Use >, <, or =.

1. 17.34 ■ 17.051
2. 0.105 ■ 0.15
3. Draw a pair of rectangles that are not similar.

Use the distributive property to find each product.

4. 24 × 5
5. 99 × 26
6. Find the average of the following quiz grades: 83, 98, 64, 90, and 78.

What's Ahead

• Multiplying decimals

4-6 Multiplying Decimals

WHAT YOU'LL NEED

✓ Graph paper 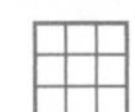

✓ Calculator 

WORK TOGETHER

Work with a partner. Use a calculator to find each product. Then answer the questions below.

31×65 $\quad$ 31×6.5 $\quad$ 3.1×6.5 $\quad$ 3.1×0.65

1. Compare the factors in each expression. How are they alike? How are they different?
2. Compare each of the products. How are they alike? How are they different?
3. Now compare the number of decimal places in the factors and the number of decimal places in each product. What do you notice?
4. Write a rule for multiplying decimals. Base your rule on the results of this Work Together activity. Use examples to test your rule.

THINK AND DISCUSS

Multiplying decimals is a lot like multiplying whole numbers.

***Earth's crust** continually moves, causing earthquakes, forming mountains, and separating continents.*

Example 1 Today North America is moving away from Europe at the rate of 0.8 in./year. About how far will North America move in 5 years?

$$\begin{array}{r} 0.8 \\ \underline{\times\ 5} \\ 4.0 \end{array} \begin{array}{l} \leftarrow \text{1 decimal place} \\ \leftarrow \text{no decimal places} \\ \leftarrow \text{1 decimal place} \end{array}$$

In 5 years, North America will move about 4.0 in. away from Europe.

5. About how far will North America move in 9 years?
6. Does the example above satisfy the rule you described in the Work Together? Explain.

When both factors are decimal numbers, you count the decimal places in both factors to find how many places are needed in the product.

***The eucalyptus** is the fastest growing tree in the world.*

Example 2 A eucalyptus tree in New Guinea grew 10.5 m in one year. How much will this tree grow in 2.5 years if it grows at the same rate?

Estimate: 11 × 3 = 33

```
  10.5    1 decimal place
×  2.5    1 decimal place
   525
+ 210
 26.25    2 decimal places
```

The eucalyptus tree will grow about 26.25 m.

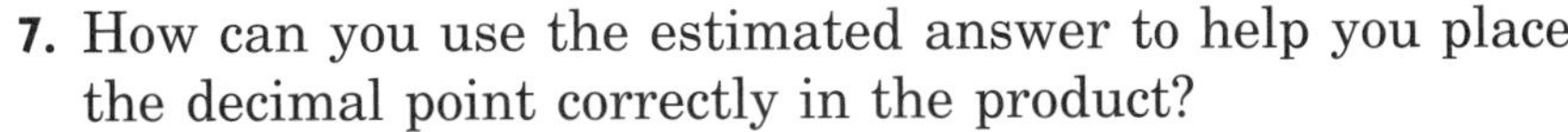

7. How can you use the estimated answer to help you place the decimal point correctly in the product?

When the factors are both less than 1, you may need to write zeros in the product.

Example 3 Find 0.13 × 0.02.

Press: 0.13 [×] 0.02 [=] 0.0026

The product of 0.13 and 0.02 is 0.0026.

8. Rewrite your rule for multiplying decimals to reflect any changes you notice in Example 3.

9. **Critical Thinking** When you use a calculator to find 0.05 × 0.36 you get 0.018 in the display. Why do you see 3 decimal places instead of 4 places?

10. **Calculator** Multiply 2.5 × 10, 2.5 × 100, and 2.5 × 1,000. Compare the products. Write a rule for multiplying a decimal by 10, 100, or 1,000.

11. **Calculator** Multiply 3 × 0.1, 3 × 0.01, and 3 × 0.001. Write a rule for multiplying by 0.1, 0.01, or 0.001.

These rules can help you multiply mentally.

Example 4 Find 1,000 × 0.26 mentally.

0.260 ← 260   **Use your rule for multiplying a decimal by 1,000.**

1,000 × 0.26 = 260

TRY THESE

Place the decimal point in each product.

12. $\begin{array}{r} 0.403 \\ \times\ 5 \\ \hline 2015 \end{array}$
13. $\begin{array}{r} 0.15 \\ \times\ 0.31 \\ \hline 00465 \end{array}$
14. $\begin{array}{r} 523 \\ \times\ 0.5 \\ \hline 2615 \end{array}$
15. $\begin{array}{r} 8.42 \\ \times\ 6.7 \\ \hline 56414 \end{array}$

Mental Math **Find each product.**

16. 0.1×257 17. 100×1.6 18. 0.47×10 19. 4.82×0.01

20. **Oceanography** A dolphin swims at a rate of about 27.5 mi/h. A person can swim about 0.1 as fast. How fast can a person swim?

ON YOUR OWN

Place the decimal point in each product.

21. $3.2 \times 4.6 = 1472$ 22. $0.145 \times 26 = 3770$

23. $5.05 \times 3.14 = 158570$ 24. $4.50 \times 3.8 = 17100$

Mental Math **Find each product.**

25. 6.2×10 26. 7.08×0.1 27. 3.5×1000 28. 26×0.01

Find each product.

29. $\begin{array}{r} 2.065 \\ \times\ 12 \\ \hline \end{array}$
30. $\begin{array}{r} 0.18 \\ \times\ 0.06 \\ \hline \end{array}$
31. $\begin{array}{r} 3.1 \\ \times\ 0.04 \\ \hline \end{array}$
32. $\begin{array}{r} 15.35 \\ \times\ 3.2 \\ \hline \end{array}$

33. $\begin{array}{r} 450 \\ \times\ 0.01 \\ \hline \end{array}$
34. $\begin{array}{r} 35.15 \\ \times\ 25 \\ \hline \end{array}$
35. $\begin{array}{r} 0.96 \\ \times\ 0.12 \\ \hline \end{array}$
36. $\begin{array}{r} 7.6 \\ \times\ 0.06 \\ \hline \end{array}$

37. Is $(2.3 \times 3) \times 6$ equal to $2.3 \times (3 \times 6)$? Does this seem unusual? Why or why not?

True or False? Give an example to support your answer.

38. The product of any number and zero is always zero.

39. If you change the order of the factors, the product will also change.

40. Any number multiplied by 1 is itself.

Mixed REVIEW

Use the distributive property to find each product.

1. 68×8 2. 95×4

3. Draw a figure that has no symmetry.

4. Draw a figure that has vertical and horizontal symmetry.

Solve.

5. Efra drinks two juice packs a day. Each pack contains 355 mL. 1L = 1,000 mL. How many liters of juice does she drink in one week?

6. Mr. Garcia punched in at 7:37 A.M. and out at 4:19 P.M. He took a 15-min. lunch. How long did he work?

41. **Data File 4 (pp. 138–139)** How closely does the length of your femur predict your height in centimeters?

42. **Astronomy** The circumference of Earth is about 40,200 km at the equator. The circumference of Jupiter is 11.2 times as great. What is the circumference of Jupiter?

43. **Investigation (p. 140)** A ream consists of 500 sheets of paper. The thickness of one sheet of paper is 0.01 cm. Calculate the thickness of a ream of paper.

44. **Writing** Explain how multiplying 0.3×0.4 is like multiplying 3×4. How is it different?

Use the article and the chart to answer each problem.

Calorie Counter

Your body uses food to make energy, which is used for all the things you do each day. The food you eat and the energy you use are measured in calories.

Not all foods have the same number of calories and not all activities use the same number of calories. A 120 lb person would use about 80 calories by sitting for 1 h. The same person would use 336 calories playing tennis for 1 h. Your body weight is also a factor in the number of calories you use. For example, a 120 lb person would use about 216 calories in 1 h of bicycle riding, but a 60 lb person would use only about 108 calories.

Activity	Calories/ min/lb
Bicycling	0.03
Playing Catch	0.03
Dancing	0.05
Jumping Rope	0.07
Roller Skating	0.05
Running	0.10
Skateboarding	0.05
Playing Soccer	0.05
Playing Softball	0.04
Standing	0.02
Walking	0.03

The expression tells about how many calories you use for different activities.

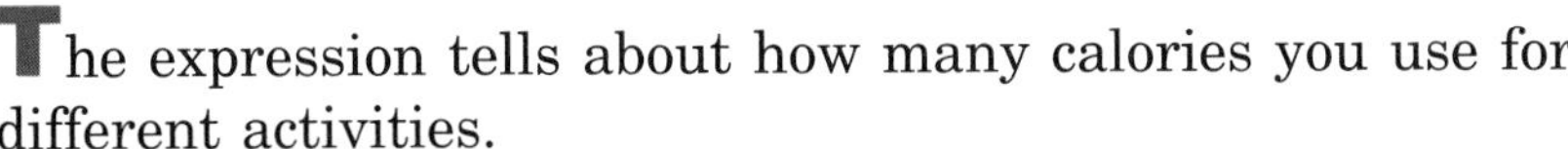

Weight × Number of minutes of activity × Calories used per minute per pound

45. A 100-lb male jumps rope for 15 min. How many calories will he use?

46. An 80-lb female dances for 2 h. How many calories will she use?

47. You weigh 70-lb. How many calories will you use playing softball for 1 h 10 min? Would you use more or fewer calories if you play soccer instead?

PROBLEM SOLVING

4-7 Too Much, Too Little Information

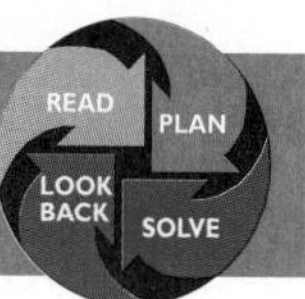

What's Ahead

- Solving problems with too much or too little information.

Sometimes you do not have enough information to solve a problem. Other times problems have more information than you need. You have to decide.

The first annual *One Sky, One World* global kite-fly was held in 1986. The focus was on global peace and the protection of the environment.

Source: *UNESCO Courier*

Pablo is making a box kite for a festival out of wood dowels and paper strips. The top and bottom of the kite are square. The sides of each square are 26.5 cm long. Pablo has $10.00 to spend on supplies. The eight dowels cost $4.50. Other supplies such as glue, string, and nails cost $4.27 altogether. Paper strips wrap around the kite. Find the total length of the paper strips he will need.

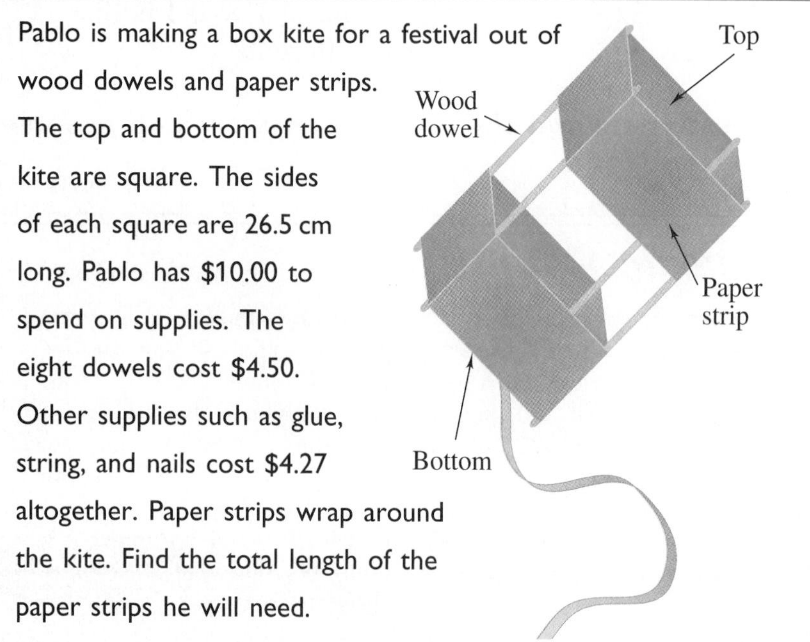

READ

Read and understand the given information. Summarize the problem.

1. Think about the information that is given.
   a. What do you need to find out?
   b. What information do you need to solve the problem?

PLAN

Decide whether there is enough information. Plan a method to solve the problem.

2. **a.** What is the shape of the top and bottom of the kite?
   b. What is the length of each side?
   c. How can you use this information to solve the problem?
   d. How will you find the total length of paper needed?
3. Now that you have decided what information you need, what information is given that is not needed?

4. One way to solve the problem is to find the perimeter of the square. Then double the perimeter to find the total length of paper needed for the two paper strips.
   a. What is the length of paper Pablo needs for the two strips?
   b. What is another way to solve the problem?

SOLVE

Use your method to find the solution.

5. Pablo wants to know how much it will cost to make the kite.
   a. What information is given to help you find the cost of making the kite?
   b. What information is missing?

LOOK BACK

If there is too little information to solve the problem, determine what facts are needed.

TRY THESE

Solve if possible. If not, tell what information is needed.

6. Nathan bought two new bicycle tires for $21.90. The diameter of each tire is 20 in. by 1.75 in. The combined weight of the two tires is 2.9 lb.
   a. How much does each tire cost?
   b. What information did you use to solve part (a)?
   c. How much does one tire weigh?
   d. What information did you use to solve part (c)?
   e. What information is given that is not needed for either part (a) or part (c)?
7. **Money** Manos buys some comic books at a local store. He hands the clerk $10.00 and receives $1.45 in change. Each comic book has the same price. How much does each comic book cost?
   a. What information is given to help you find the cost of each comic book?
   b. What information is missing?
8. Coretta bought a pair of curtains for $69.99. Each curtain measures 45 in. long by 98 in. wide, and the pair weighs 1.50 lbs.
   a. How much does each curtain weigh?
   b. What information is given that is not needed?

Mixed REVIEW

Find each product.

1. 1.9×0.8
2. 0.95×6
3. How many lines of symmetry does a regular octagon have?
4. Find two numbers whose sum is 28 and whose product is 96.

Arrange the numbers in increasing order.

5. 0.05   5.55   0.505   0.55
6. 9.04   90.4   900.4   9.004
7. You have two 25¢ stamps and three 30¢ stamps. How many different amounts of postage can you have?

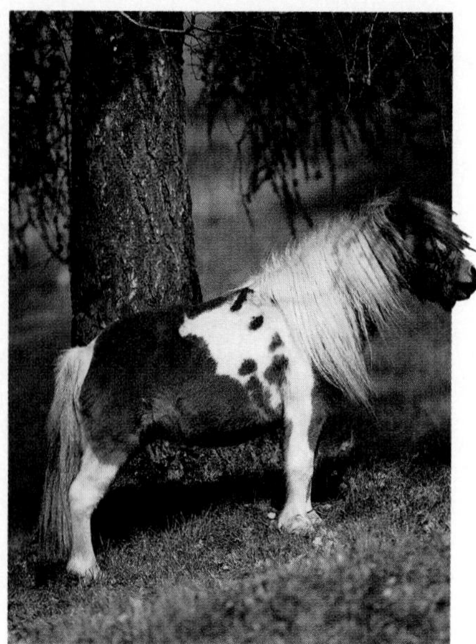

A pony is a small horse that is under 14.2 hands tall. ***How many inches would that be?***

ON YOUR OWN

Solve if possible. If not, tell what information is needed.

9. The telephone company charged Rebecca for a phone call. The rates were $2.40 for the first minute and $.60 for each additional minute. How many additional minutes was Rebecca charged for?

10. A quilt pattern has a 5-by-5 grid of squares. The design of the grid calls for alternating blue and red squares. How many squares of each color does the grid contain?

11. The record shoulder height for a horse is 78 in. A horse's height is measured in hands. One hand is about 4 in. What is the record shoulder height of a horse in hands?

12. **Jobs** Percy works at a pet store after school. At present he works Monday, Wednesday, and Friday for 2 h each day. He is saving to buy a bike that costs $245. If he earns $6 per hour, how many weeks must he work to be sure he has enough money?

13. A dressmaker sent 250 dresses to several local department stores. If this dressmaker sent every store the same number of dresses, how many dresses did each store receive?

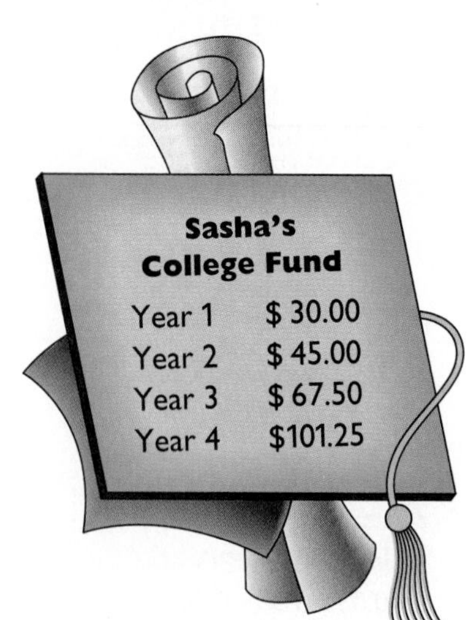

Sasha's College Fund

Year 1	$ 30.00
Year 2	$ 45.00
Year 3	$ 67.50
Year 4	$101.25

14. **Banking** When Sasha was 7 years old her mother started a college fund. She began with $30. Every year she put a little more money into the fund as shown in the table. If she continues this pattern, how much will she put into the fund when Sasha is 16?

15. **a.** **Writing** Write a word problem with too much information.

b. Write a word problem with too little information.

16. **Hobbies** Alexis likes to collect picture postcards when she travels. On her last vacation she collected 15 postcards. Some of the cards cost $.79 and some cost $1.19. She spent a total of $14.25 for the cards. How many postcards did she buy from each price group?

17. **Data File 7 (pp. 272–273)** Find the average water level at high tide in Bay of Fundy, Canada.

Practice

Round each factor to the nearest whole number. Estimate.

1. 8.2×3.7
2. $34.5 \div 4.96$
3. $17.8 \div 6.2$
4. 12.79×9.68

Use compatible numbers to estimate.

5. $14.3 \div 2.9$
6. 19.3×5.1
7. 2.18×51.3
8. $36.1 \div 4.84$
9. $101.5 \div 24.3$
10. $24.1 \div 8.39$

Use the order of operations to evaluate each expression.

11. $8 - 3 + 5 \times 3$
12. $(6.4 - 1.2) \times 3$
13. $5 \div (1.6 + 3.4)$
14. $15 \div 5 + 10$
15. $(15 + 12) \div 9 \times 3$
16. $25 \div 5 \times (8.4 + 0.6) - 5$

Insert operation symbols to make the equation true.

17. 24 ■ 3 ■ 3 = 5
18. (12 ■ 8) ■ (5 ■ 1) = 100
19. 49 ■ 20 ■ 2 = 9
20. 14 ■ 2 ■ 5 ■ 1 = 11

Complete.

21. 6 × (15 + 4) = (■ × 15) + (6 × ■)
22. 22 × (10 − 3) = (22 × ■) − (■ × 3)

Use the distributive property to evaluate each expression.

23. $(3 \times 7) + (3 \times 4)$
24. $8 \times (70 + 3)$
25. $(7 \times 4) - (7 \times 2)$
26. $6 \times (4 + 10)$
27. $5 \times (20 - 8)$
28. $(12 \times 7) - (12 \times 3)$

Mental Math **Use the distributive property to evaluate.**

29. 4×57
30. 7×203
31. 9×89
32. 3×312

Find each product.

33. 2.12×0.3
34. $1{,}000 \times 0.43$
35. 5.2×1.33
36. 2.3×0.01
37. 8.2×0.06
38. 3.045×25
39. 0.28×0.09
40. 60.4×0.09

What's Ahead

- Modeling decimal quotients

4-8 Exploring Quotients of Decimals

THINK AND DISCUSS

WHAT YOU'LL NEED

✓ Calculator 

✓ Graph paper 

Bik is making yogurt shakes for customers at her health food restaurant. She has 0.8 lb of sliced strawberries. She uses 0.2 lb in each shake. The expression below represents the number of yogurt shakes Bik can make using the strawberries.

$$0.8 \div 0.2$$

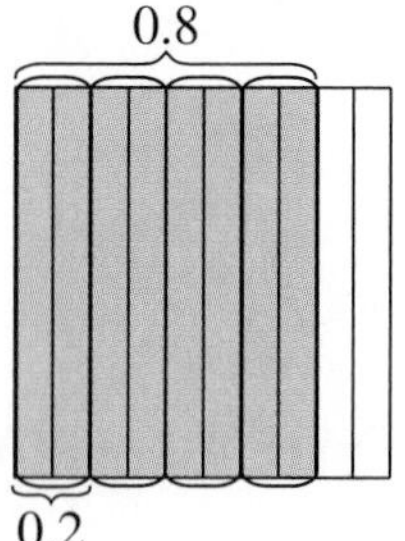

You can use a model to divide a decimal number by tenths.

1. Use the model at the left to answer each question.
   a. How is 8 tenths, 0.8, shown in the model?
   b. How is 2 tenths, 0.2, shown in the model?
   c. How many groups of 0.2 are there in 0.8?
   d. **Calculator** Find the quotient $0.8 \div 0.2$. How does your answer relate to the model?

2. Draw a model to find each quotient.
   a. $0.8 \div 0.4$ b. $0.9 \div 0.3$ c. $1 \div 0.4$

You can also use a model to divide a decimal number by hundredths.

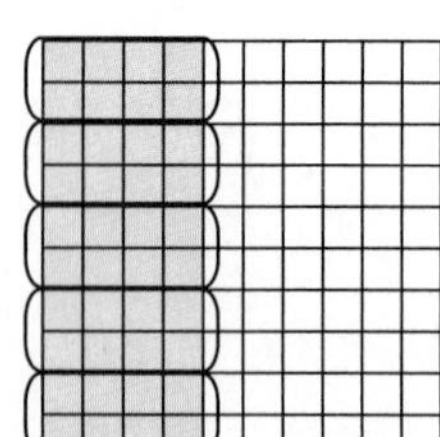

3. Use the model at the left to answer each question.
   a. What number does the shaded region show?
   b. The shaded region is divided into groups. What decimal does each group represent?
   c. How many groups are in the shaded area?
   d. Complete the sentence: $0.4 \div 0.08 = \blacksquare$.

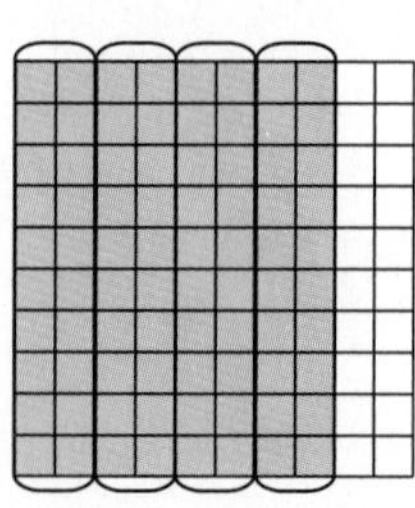

4. Draw a model to find each quotient.
   a. $0.3 \div 0.06$ b. $0.9 \div 0.15$ c. $0.6 \div 0.12$

5. **Critical Thinking** In the sentence $0.8 \div 0.2 = 4$ the divisor, 0.2, represents the size of each group. What does the quotient, 4, represent?

WORK TOGETHER

Work with a partner. Draw a model to find each quotient. First decide how many decimal squares you need. Next shade your model to show the dividend. Then circle groups of equal size. Remember, the divisor tells you the size of each group.

6. $1.8 \div 0.3$ **7.** $1 \div 0.2$ **8.** $2 \div 0.4$

FLASHBACK

Each number in a division sentence has a special name.

$24 \div 8 = 3$

24 Dividend
8 Divisor
3 Quotient

ON YOUR OWN

Complete each sentence.

9. 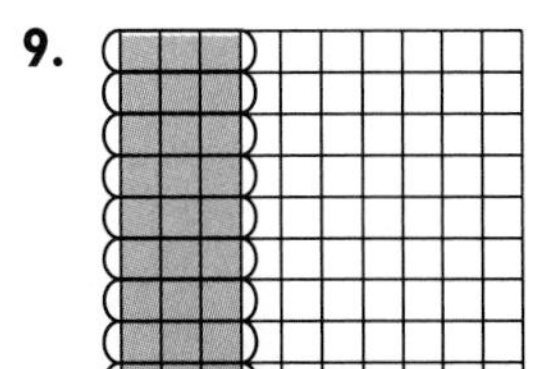

$0.3 \div 0.03 = ■$

10. 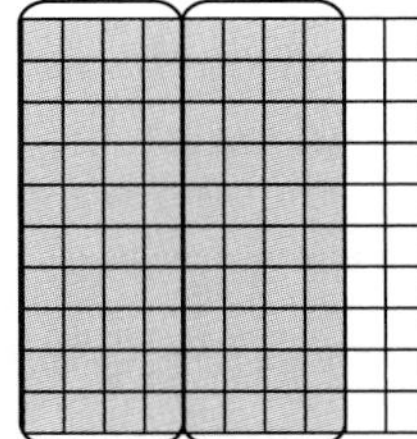

$■ \div 0.4 = 2$

11. 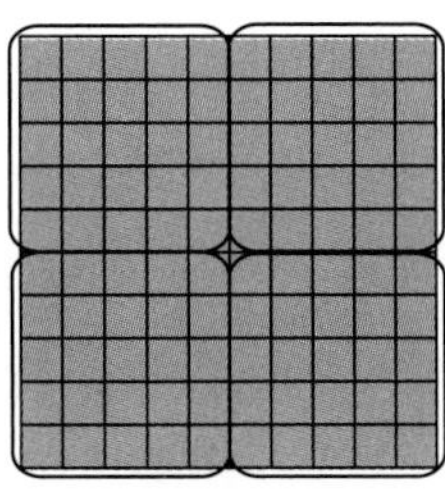

$1 \div ■ = 4$

12. 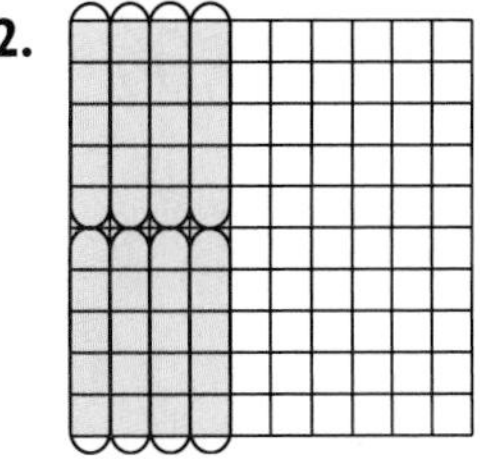

$0.4 \div ■ = 8$

13. 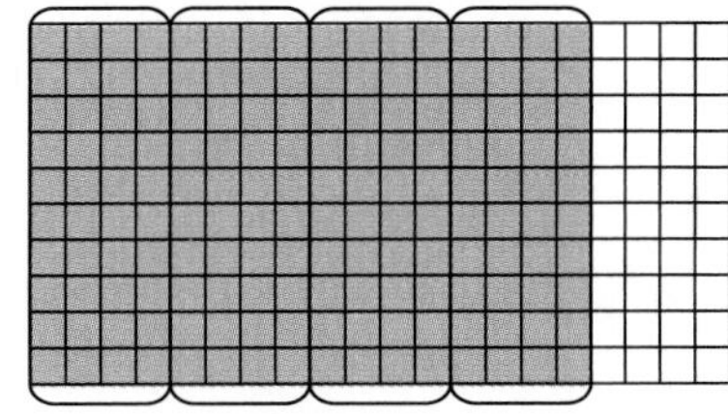

$■ \div 0.4 = 4$

Draw a model to find each quotient.

14. $0.6 \div 0.2$ **15.** $0.8 \div 0.05$ **16.** $1.6 \div 0.8$

17. $2 \div 0.5$ **18.** $1.5 \div 0.06$ **19.** $0.3 \div 0.15$

20. $1.2 \div 3$ **21.** $2.4 \div 0.8$ **22.** $0.36 \div 4$

23. Writing Explain how to draw a model to find the quotient of $2.4 \div 0.6$.

24. a. Draw a model to find the quotient $2.1 \div 7$.

b. In this problem, what does the divisor, 7, represent?

Mixed REVIEW

Place a decimal point in each product.

1. $5.9 \times 0.46 = 2714$

2. $0.08 \times 0.09 = 00072$

3. $0.3 \times 0.2 = 0006$

Solve if possible. If not, tell what information is needed.

4. Twelve-year-old Yuri swam the 100-m freestyle in 29.56 s. His best time in 1993 was 29.6 s. What time does he need to break the pool record?

5. Make four equilateral triangles using only six toothpicks.

What's Ahead

• Dividing decimals

4-9 Dividing Decimals

WORK TOGETHER

WHAT YOU'LL NEED

✓ Calculator 

Work with a partner. Answer the questions below.

$0.24 \div 0.06 \qquad 2.4 \div 0.6 \qquad 24 \div 6$

1. Compare the numbers in each expression. How are they alike? How are they different?

2. Use a calculator to find each quotient. Compare the quotients. Describe the pattern.

3. a. **Calculator** Find the quotient $2.4 \div 6$.
   b. Does this expression fit the pattern you described above? Why or why not?

4. Does the expression $0.024 \div 0.006$ fit the pattern above? What would you expect the quotient to be? Check your answer using a calculator.

THINK AND DISCUSS

Dividing decimals is a lot like dividing whole numbers.

Example 1 The Seto Bridge is 7.64 mi long. How long would it take to cross the bridge if you walk at 4 mi/h?

Estimate: $7.64 \div 4 \approx 8 \div 4 = 2$

```
   1.91    Divide. Place the decimal point
 4)7.64    in the quotient
  -4
   36
  -36
    04
   - 4
     0
```

It would take 1.91 h to walk across the bridge.

WHAT? **The Great Seto Bridge,** opened on April 10, 1988, crosses Japan's Inland Sea and is the longest road/railway suspension bridge in the world.

Source: *Guinness Book of World Records*

5. **Discussion** How is dividing decimals different than dividing whole numbers? How is it the same?

When you divide a decimal by a decimal it helps to write the divisor as a whole number.

Example 2 Find the quotient $0.312 \div 0.06$.

$$0.06\overline{)0.312} \rightarrow 06.\overline{)031.2}$$

$$\begin{array}{r} 5.2 \\ 06.\overline{)031.2} \\ -\ 30 \\ \hline 1\ 2 \\ -\ 1\ 2 \\ \hline \end{array}$$

Check Multiply the quotient by the divisor.

$5.2 \times 0.06 = 0.312$ ✓

So, $0.312 \div 0.06 = 5.2$.

LOOK BACK By what number did you multiply to write the divisor as a whole number?

6. a. Find the quotient $1.22 \div 0.4$. Describe your method.
   b. You move the decimal point in 0.4 one place to the right. This is the same as multiplying by what?

7. a. By what do you multiply to write 0.015 as 15?
   b. Find the quotient $0.54 \div 0.015$.
   c. **Critical Thinking** How does your answer in part (a) help you find the quotient in part (b)?

The record distance for walking on your hands is 870 m. The record speed is 54.68 yd in 17.44 s.

You can use patterns to divide mentally. Complete the equations at the right to answer each question.

8. a. Make a conjecture. What happens to the quotient as the divisor increases?
   b. How is the number of zeros in each divisor related to the number of places the decimal point "moves" left?
   c. Find $0.8 \div 100$ mentally. Explain what you did.
   d. Write a rule for dividing a decimal by 10, by 100, or by 1,000.

	Divisor		Quotient
2.9 ÷	10	=	■
2.9 ÷	100	=	■
2.9 ÷	1,000	=	■

9. a. What happens to the quotient as the divisor decreases?
   b. How can you tell how many places to "move" the decimal point to the right?
   c. Find $3.6 \div 0.01$ mentally. Explain what you did.
   d. Write a rule for dividing a decimal by 0.1, 0.01, or 0.001.

	Divisor		Quotient
0.52 ÷	0.1	=	■
0.52 ÷	0.01	=	■
0.52 ÷	0.001	=	■

10. The tallest cake ever made was 1214.5 in. high. Beth Cornell and her helpers completed the cake at the Shiwassee County Fairgrounds, MI, on Aug. 5, 1990. The cake consisted of 100 tiers of equal height. Find the height of each tier.

11. Melba is given a stack of paper to pass out to her class of 25 students. The stack measures 0.9 cm thick. Each piece of paper is 0.01 cm thick.

    a. How many pieces of paper does Melba have in the stack?

    b. Does Melba have enough paper so each student in her class can have three pieces? If so, how much does she have left over? If not, how many pieces of paper does she need?

TRY THESE

Find each quotient.

12. $82\overline{)155.8}$	13. $29 \div 0.4$	14. $0.34\overline{)0.204}$
15. $33\overline{)237.6}$	16. $51 \div 0.06$	17. $81 \div 5.4$

Mental Math **Find each quotient.**

18. $14.2 \div 1000$	19. $6.4 \div 0.1$	20. $0.7 \div 10$

21. On Thursday 1.4 in. of rain fell. On Friday 2.2 in. of rain fell. What was the average rainfall for the two days?

22. Discussion Would you use a model, calculator, pencil and paper, or mental math to find $0.035 \div 0.7$? Explain.

Mixed REVIEW

Draw a model to find each quotient.

1. $0.9 \div 0.06$
2. $1.8 \div 0.2$
3. Mrs. Dunn earned $443.75 in one week. She worked 35.5 h. What was her hourly rate?

Find each product or quotient.

4. 0.07×4.8
5. $9.8 \div 2.8$

ON YOUR OWN

Find each quotient.

23. $7.5 \div 3$	24. $36\overline{)\$19.80}$	25. $4\overline{)0.012}$
26. $0.5\overline{)66}$	27. $0.3 \div 15$	28. $5.6\overline{)16.24}$
29. $0.04 \div 0.8$	30. $75.03 \div 6.1$	31. $8.9\overline{)0.6497}$

Mental Math **Find each quotient.**

32. 0.48 ÷ 1000 **33.** 3.8 ÷ 0.1 **34.** 7.3 ÷ 10

35. 64.5 ÷ 0.01 **36.** 11.2 ÷ 100 **37.** 0.32 ÷ 0.01

38. A pack of 15 baseball cards costs $.75. How much does one of these baseball cards cost?

39. **Money** A stack of 300 Susan B. Anthony dollar coins is 23.7 in. thick. Find the thickness of one of these coins.

40. **Investigation (p. 140)** Describe any methods you can think of for finding the thickness of a page in a book.

41. **Writing** Describe how to find the quotient 12.5 ÷ 0.04.

42. **Choose A, B, or C.** Which expression is equivalent to three and eight-tenths divided by thirty-two thousandths.

A. 0.032 ÷ 3.8 **B.** 3.8 ÷ 0.032 **C.** 3.8 ÷ 0.32

43. a. **Critical Thinking** Find the quotient 3.5 ÷ 0.7.

b. Is the quotient greater or less than 3.5? 0.7? Does this seem reasonable? Explain.

WHAT ? The Susan B. Anthony dollar was issued on July 2, 1979. A coin was made rather than a paper dollar to increase the circulation life of the currency, thus reducing long-term production costs.

Source: *A History of U.S. Coinage*

Problem Solving Hint

Use a decimal model to help you.

CHECKPOINT

Write the missing numbers.

1. (9 × 8) + (9 × 4) = ■ × (■ + 4)

2. 6 × (5 − 2) = (6 × ■) − (■ × ■)

Place a decimal point in each product.

3. 5.2 × 6.3 = 3276 **4.** 0.239 × 8.2 = 19598

5. Dalia earns $6.50 an hour as a cashier. For any time over 40 h, she earns $9.75 an hour. Dalia worked 45 h in a recent week. How much overtime did she earn that week?

Find each quotient.

6. 8.5 ÷ 2 **7.** $3.4\overline{)\$48.28}$ **8.** $0.13\overline{)2.132}$

MATH AND CONSUMER ECONOMICS

What's Ahead

- Using decimals in real-world situations.

4-10 Working with Data

WHAT YOU'LL NEED

✓ Calculator

✓ Ruler

✓ Graph paper

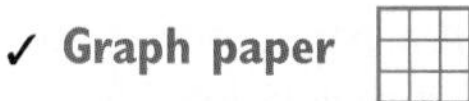

THINK AND DISCUSS

Prices change from year to year. Some prices go up and some prices go down.

1. **a.** For which items in the graph did prices go up?
   b. For which items in the graph did prices go down?
   c. **Discussion** Pick an item whose price went up and one whose price went down. Give at least two reasons for each change.
   d. Do you see any pattern in the way the prices changed?

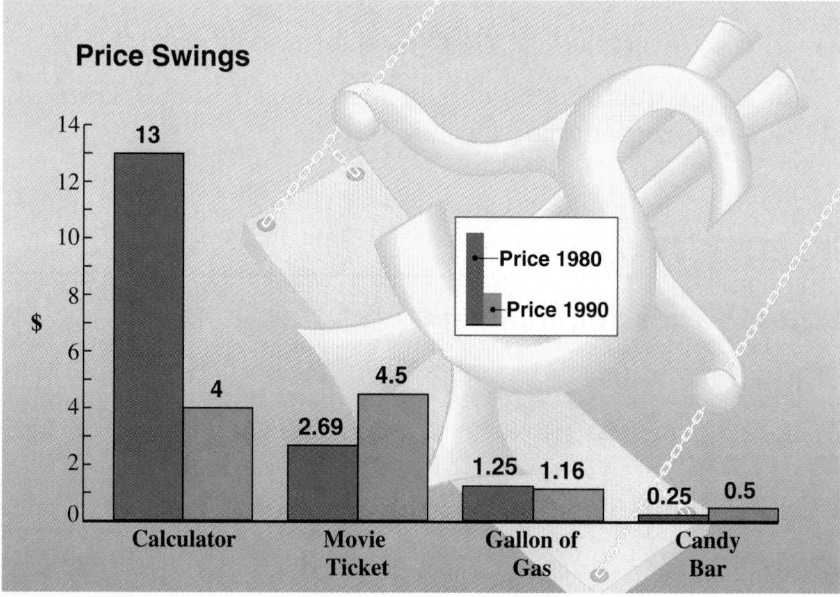

You can estimate how much prices changed over the ten year period.

2. **a.** Which item doubled in price from 1980 to 1990?
   b. About how many times less was the price of a calculator in 1990 than in 1980? Would you expect this kind of price reduction in calculators to continue? Why or why not?

c. Suppose movie tickets continued to increase by the amount in the graph. How much would you expect a movie ticket to cost in 2000? in 2005?

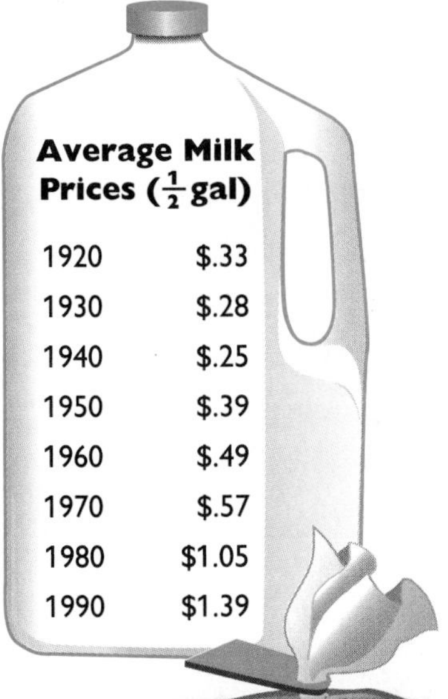

Average Milk Prices ($\frac{1}{2}$ gal)

Year	Price
1920	$.33
1930	$.28
1940	$.25
1950	$.39
1960	$.49
1970	$.57
1980	$1.05
1990	$1.39

3. a. Look at the changes in milk prices from 1920 to 1940. Describe any patterns you see.

b. Look at the changes in milk prices from 1940 to 1990. Describe any patterns you see.

c. **Discussion** Did the change in the price of milk remain about the same from year to year? Can you use the data in the table to predict the price of milk in five years? Why or why not?

WORK TOGETHER

- Work with a partner. Use the data in the table at the right to write three statements that compare bread prices.
- Make a graph showing the change in the bread prices. Explain why you chose the type of graph you used.
- One student observed that the price of bread doubled every ten years. Do you agree? Explain your reasoning.

60 Years of Bread Prices (1 lb loaf)

Year	Price
1930	$.04
1940	$.08
1950	$.14
1960	$.20
1970	$.24
1980	$.51

TRY THESE

4. a. How much more was bread in 1980 than in 1950?

b. How many times greater was the price of a loaf of bread in 1970 than in 1940?

c. **Discussion** What factors might cause the price of bread to change?

5. In 1991 the average cost of a 16-oz jar of peanut butter was $2.04. The recommended serving size is 1 oz. What is the cost of 1 serving? Round to the nearest cent.

6. When you buy items priced 2 for $1.69 or 3 for $1, the price of a single item is usually rounded up to the nearest cent.

a. Erasers are 3 for $1.00. Find the price of one eraser.

b. **Discussion** Why do you think the price is rounded up?

ON YOUR OWN

Choose Use a calculator, pencil and paper, estimation, or mental math.

7. In 1992 the average cost of a movie ticket was $5.05. In 1980 the average price was $2.69.
   a. About how much did it cost to purchase 4 tickets in 1992?
   b. How much less did 4 tickets cost in 1980 than in 1992?

Average Hourly Wage Retail Sales	
1970	$2.44
1980	$4.88
1990	$6.76

8. Use the hourly wage chart at the left.
   a. The 1980 hourly wage is how many times greater than the 1970 hourly wage?
   b. Suppose Anita worked 10 h/wk in 1980. How much more would she make than working the same number of hours in 1970?
   c. Estimation About how many times greater is the 1990 hourly wage than the 1970 hourly wage?

9. Investigation (p. 140) Find the thickness of each page in your math book. Describe the process you used.

GREAT EXPECTATIONS

Pediatrician

I would like to be a pediatrician when I grow up. I want to be one because I like to help people with their medical problems. I know that they help children when they are sick. I have had experiences with pediatricians with my own health problems. Being a pediatrician ties in with math because I will have to know ratios for comparing size with how much medicine a patient should take. I will also have to know the metric system of weight measurement.

Justin Rankin

10. **Activity** Use newspaper ads or ask an adult to help you find today's prices for each item on the list at the right.

   a. Make a double bar graph comparing the 1985 prices for the items on the list at the right and the current prices.

   b. Did all the prices increase? Which items increased the most? Give at least two reasons why one item might increase in price more than another.

   c. What would be the total cost to buy the items on the list in the given amount today? in 1985?

11. **Writing** There are at least two ways to solve the problem below. Explain two ways and solve the problem.

   In 1991 new cars averaged about 27.3 mi/gal of gas. In 1974, new cars averaged 13.2 mi/gal. How much farther could a 1991 car travel than a 1974 car on 12 gal of gas?

12. In 1962 the average comic book sold for a price of $.12. A comic book in 1988 cost $.75.

   a. How much more did a comic book cost in 1988?

   b. **Estimation** About how many comic books could you get at the 1962 price for the cost of a comic book in 1988?

1985 Prices	
Ground beef (lb)	$1.68
Lettuce (1 head)	$.45
Orange Juice (qt)	$1.09
Bananas (lb)	$.32
Large eggs (doz)	$.91

Mixed REVIEW

Use mental math.

1. $3.9 \div 10$
2. $191 \div 100$
3. $0.82 \div 1000$

Complete if $\triangle RWF \cong \triangle MLK$.

4. $MK = \blacksquare$
5. $\angle R \cong \blacksquare$

6. Name the ways you could make change for $.45 with no pennies.

Dear Justin,

I am a pediatrician in the inner city area of Milwaukee, Wisconsin. Since I was a young boy your age, I wanted to be a doctor. Like you, I always wanted to do something that would help people. I like working with children and their families. I like helping sick kids get better. At my clinic, we take care of people from many different backgrounds. I have come to know many interesting and wonderful families.

I use math all day, every day. I use ratio just like you said. I also make graphs to show a baby's weight and height. The graph helps me decide whether a baby is growing properly. I always liked math a lot when I was in school. I am lucky I get to use math so much in my work.

David A. Waters, M.D.

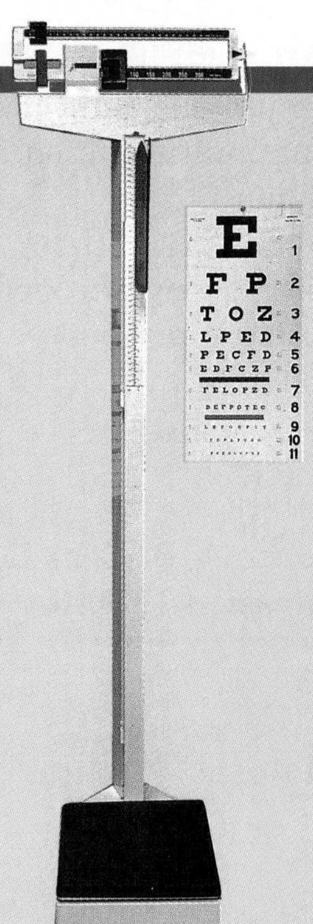

CHAPTER 4

Wrap-up

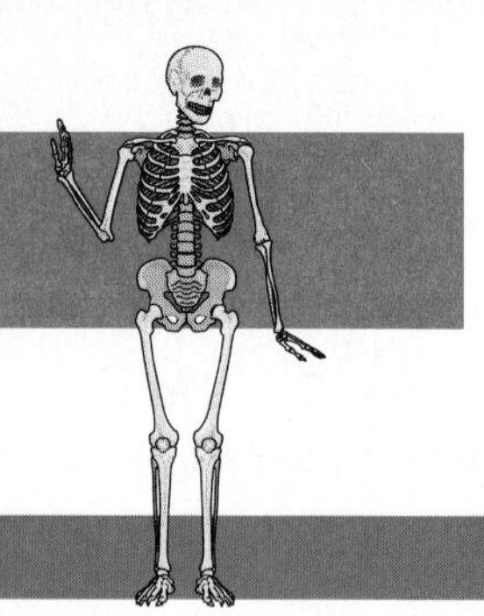

Estimating Products and Quotients 4-1

You can round to estimate decimal products. You can use compatible numbers to estimate products and quotients.

Estimate using rounding or compatible numbers.

1. 23.78×5.3
2. 3.25×9.12
3. $34.1 \div 6.67$
4. 19.03×4.79

Using Databases 4-2

A ***database*** is a collection of information organized into ***records.*** A ***field*** is a category in a record.

5. **Writing** How would you set up a database for a class directory with information about name, address, phone number, subject, and teacher? How many records and how many fields do you need?

Order of Operations and the Distributive Property 4-3, 4-4

The ***order of operations*** shows how to evaluate an expression.

You can use the ***distributive property*** to evaluate expressions involving multiplication and addition or multiplication and subtraction.

Evaluate using the order of operations and the distributive property.

6. $5 \times (4 + 12) - 8$
7. $9 + 21 \div 3 - (6.3 - 2.6)$
8. $11 \times 6 + 7 \times 6 - 3$
9. $9 \times (50 - 9) - 27 \div (4.1 - 1.1)$
10. **Choose A, B, C, or D.** When you insert parentheses in the expression $18 \div 6 - 3 + 2$, the greatest possible value is:

A. 8 **B.** 3.6 **C.** 18 **D.** 36

Complete:

11. $5 \times 97 = (5 \times ■) + (5 \times 7) = ■$
12. $8 \times 27 = 8 \times (■ - 3) = ■$

Multiplying Decimals and Dividing Decimals 4-5, 4-6, 4-8, 4-9

You can use decimal squares or 10 by 10 grids to model multiplication and division of decimals.

13. Write a multiplication sentence to describe the model.

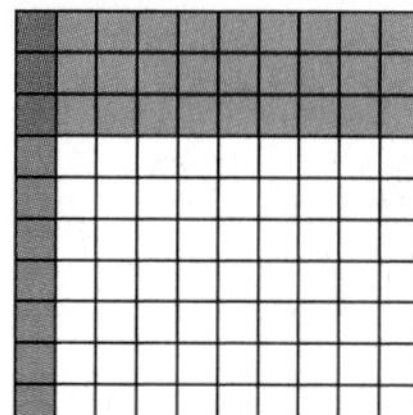

14. Write a division sentence to describe the model.

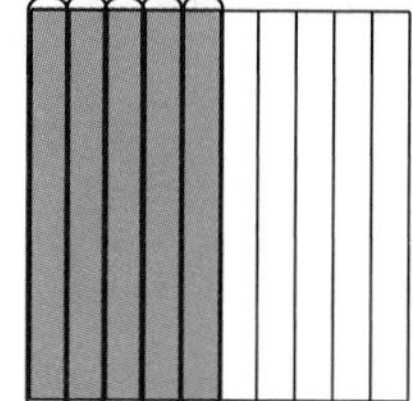

To multiply decimal numbers, count the decimal places in both factors to find how many places are needed in the product.

To divide by a decimal, move the decimal point in the divisor to make it a whole number. Then move the decimal point in the dividend the same number of places.

Find each product or quotient.

15. $\begin{array}{r} 3.215 \\ \times\ 0.04 \\ \hline \end{array}$ **16.** $\begin{array}{r} 30.72 \\ \times\ 1.5 \\ \hline \end{array}$ **17.** $4.5 \div 6$ **18.** $3.2\overline{)96}$

Draw a model for each product or quotient.

19. $1.2 \div 0.4$ **20.** $0.6 \div 0.03$ **21.** 0.7×3 **22.** 0.8×0.2

Strategies and Applications 4-7, 4-10

Some problems have too little information to solve them. Some problems have more information than you need.

Solve if possible. If not, tell what information you need.

23. Les will take a bus to a game. Tickets are $5. He plans to take about $7 for food. Students will share evenly the $125 rental fee for the bus. How much money will Les need?

24. Sharon is 152.4 cm tall and weighs 44.5 kg. Her twin sister Karen is 1.1 cm taller and weighs 0.9 kg more. How tall is Karen?

GETTING READY FOR CHAPTER 5

1. Writing Explain the difference between the area of a rectangle and its perimeter.

2. Critical Thinking Use the distributive property to complete the sentence: $(x \times y) + (x \times z) = ■ \times (■ + ■)$.

PUTTING IT ALL TOGETHER

Follow Up

In a Bind

Take another look at the explanation you prepared at the beginning of this chapter. Revise the explanation based on your study of this chapter. The following are suggestions to help you be sure that you have chosen the most appropriate binder for your notes and daily assignments.

- ✓ Make a chart showing how you found the number of sheets of paper you would need for the course.
- ✓ Make a graph showing the number of sheets of notebook paper that will fit in each size binder.

The problems preceded by the magnifying glass (p. 161, # 43; p. 171, # 40; and p. 174, # 6) will help you complete the investigation.

Excursion: Corinne bought a ream of paper. The clerk told her that the paper was "20-pound" paper. Corinne weighed the ream at home but found that it weighed far less than 20 pounds. Find the meaning of the word **pound** as it is applied to commercially sold paper.

Who to Talk To:

- the manager of a stationery store

FIVE-MINUTE Shopping Spree

Materials:
Advertising flyers from several different stores

Rules:

- Three or more players
- Players have 5 minutes to "purchase" items that total less than \$500. There must be at least 6 items on each player's list. The player who comes closest to spending \$500 without going over that amount, is the winner.

Play Your Cards Right

4561234567890123
4567890
1234567890123456
7890123

Any number may play.

- Each player has five 3" x 5" cards. Players write a math problem on each of their five cards. Sample problems are shown below.

  two decimal numbers with a difference of 0.052

  two numbers with a quotient less than 0.75

  two decimal numbers with a sum of 10.09

  two numbers with a quotient of 3.5

  two numbers with a difference of 2.93

- Shuffle the cards together and give each group member five cards. The first player to solve five problems correctly is the winner.

Fall Into Place

Find the mystery number: I am a 6-digit number. All 6 digits are different. My tenths digit is two more than my thousands digit. I have no 0, 1, 4, or 8. My greatest digit is my ones digit. My least digit is my hundredths digit. My thousands digit is 5. My tens digit is equal to one half of my hundreds digit. What number am I?

Excursion: Create your own riddle to challenge a classmate. Be sure there is only one possible number.

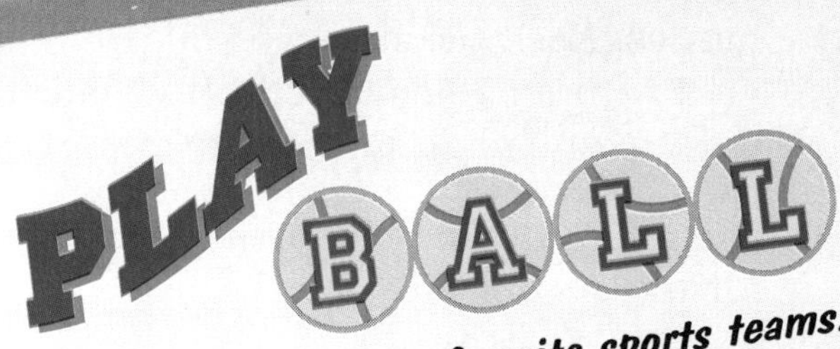

Research three of your favorite sports teams. Find out the final score for several of their last games. Calculate the average number of points scored by each team. Display your data on a poster, using a graph or chart to organize your information.

Excursion: Research the scores for twice the number of games. Perform the same calculations again. Is the data for twice as many games similar or different? Why do you think this is so?

Assessment

1. Estimate using rounding.

   a. 7.3 × 29.7 b. 4.63 × 50.4

2. Estimate using compatible numbers.

   a. 21.14 × 4.89 b. 17.9 ÷ 3.6

   c. 98.13 ÷ 24.27 d. 38.95 × 2.78

3. Write a multiplication expression for the model.

4. **Choose A, B, C, or D.** Which expression gives you a value of 18?

   A. 26 − 5 × (2 + 2)

   B. (26 − 5) × (2 + 2)

   C. 26 − (5 × 2) + 2

   D. (26 − 5) × 2 + 2

5. Insert operation symbols to make each equation true.

   a. 9 ■ 6 ■ 3 = 27

   b. 8 ■ 2 ■ 4 ■ 6 = 10

   c. (5 ■ 2) ■ (5 ■ 2) = 17

   d. 35 ■ 2 ■ 10 ■ 2 = 50

6. **Mental Math** Use the distributive property to evaluate.

   a. 5 × 112 b. 4 × 58

7. Use the distributive property to evaluate.

   a. 5 × (6 + 10)

   b. (7 × 6) + (7 × 5)

   c. 9 × (3 + 10)

8. Use the order of operations and the distributive property to evaluate.

   a. 3 × (6 + 5) × 4 − 3

   b. 8 + 7 × 3 × 4 − 6

   c. 2 + 3 × 9 − 1

   d. (4 + 3) × 2 × 5

9. **Writing** Explain how to make a model for the expression 0.8 × 0.7.

10. Find each product.

    a. 9.063 × 24 b. 0.85 × 0.06 c. 5.2 × 0.17

11. Jamal bought three tickets to the movies. Each ticket cost $4.50. He paid with a $20-dollar bill. How much did it cost Jamal for the three tickets?

12. **Writing** Explain how to use a model for the quotient 0.6 ÷ 0.12.

13. Find each quotient.

    a. $3.2\overline{)8.832}$ b. $45\overline{)\$32.85}$

    c. 0.4 ÷ 0.25 d. 63.72 ÷ 0.03

14. Seedless grapes cost $1.79 per pound. Find the cost a bunch of grapes that weigh 2.2 lb. Round your answer up to the nearest cent.

CHAPTER 4

Cumulative Review

Choose A, B, C, or D.

1. Which is the best estimate of the product 34.3×5.98?

   A. 34×6 B. 35×6
   C. 35×5 D. 34×5

2. What is the best unit of measurement to use to measure the length of your driveway?

   A. millimeters B. centimeters
   C. meters D. kilometers

3. Name two triangles in the diagram that appear to be similar but not congruent.

   A. $\angle ABC$, $\angle MNC$
   B. $\angle MNB$, $\angle MNC$
   C. $\angle BMC$, $\angle AMB$
   D. $\angle ABC$, $\angle ADC$

4. Kevin bought six muffins for $2.39. He paid the cashier with three one-dollar bills and some pennies. If he received no pennies in change, how many pennies did he give the cashier?

   A. 1 B. 2 C. 3 D. 4

5. Where would you insert parentheses so that $6 - 2 \times 9 \div 3 + 15$ has the value 5?

   A. $(6 - 2) \times 9 \div 3 + 15$
   B. $6 - (2 \times 9) \div 3 + 15$
   C. $6 - 2 \times (9 \div 3) + 15$
   D. $6 - 2 \times 9 \div (3 + 15)$

6. Which quotient is equal to $0.317 \div 0.08$?

   A. $317 \div 8$ B. $31.7 \div 8$
   C. $317 \div 0.8$ D. $3.17 \div 8$

7. Kim has sixty-five cents in quarters, dimes, and nickels. (She has at least one of each of these coins.) What number of nickels can she *not* have?

   A. 1 B. 2 C. 3 D. 4

8. Which number is *not* equal to 4.3?

   A. four and thirty hundredths
   B. three and thirteen tenths
   C. two and twenty-three tenths
   D. four and three thousandths

9. Which polygon shown below cannot be used to tessellate a plane?

   A. 
   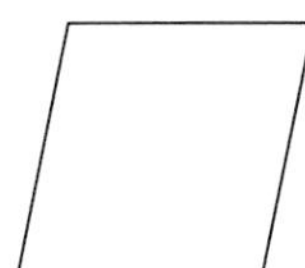
   B. 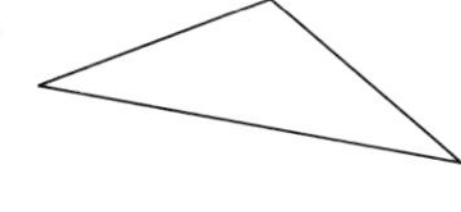
   C. 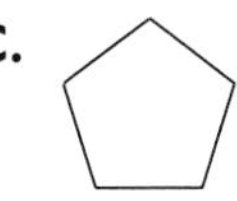
   D. 

10. Which set of numbers are all between 0.5 and 1.95?

   A. 0.504, 1.9, 1.951
   B. 0.194, 1, 1.94
   C. 0.618, 1, 1.009
   D. 0.6, 1.04, 2

CHAPTER 5 Patterns, Functions, and Equations

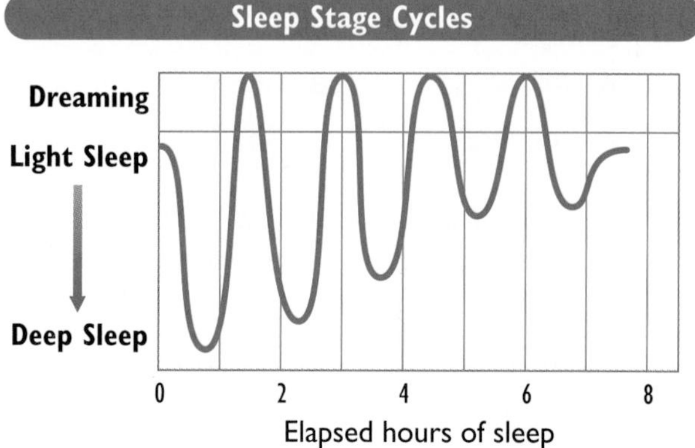

Source: *Prentice Hall Health*

Mechanical Clocks

Unwinding-springs or falling-weights power gears to keep mechanical clocks operating. The gears make sure that the minute hand and the hour hand move in the correct pattern.

Pinion

Driving wheel

Mainspring

Sleep Time

Creature	Average hours/day
two-toed sloth	20
armadillo	19
mountain beaver	14
pig	13
jaguar	11
rabbit	10
human child	10–12
human adult	8
mole	8
cow	7
sheep	6
horse	5
giraffe	4
elephant	3
shrew	less than 1

Source: *3•2•1 Contact*

Data File 5

WHAT YOU WILL LEARN

- how to model patterns and exponents
- how to model and write expressions and equations
- how to use technology to graph functions
- how to solve problems by looking for a pattern

SLEEP

The amount of sleep you need changes throughout your life. The chart shows some variations for people in different age groups.

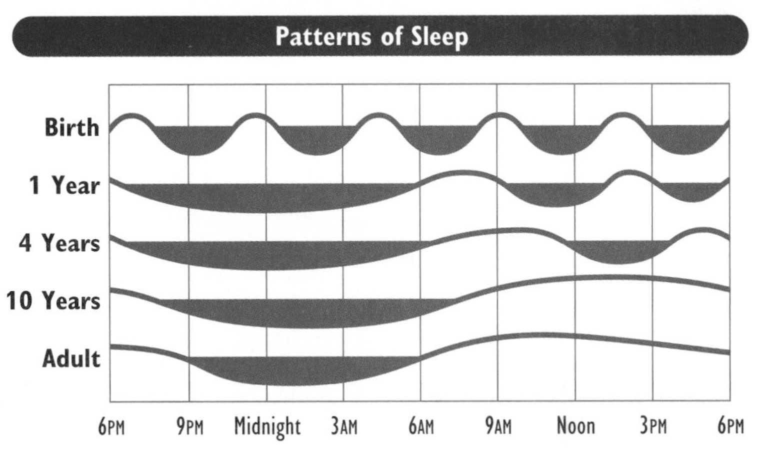

Source: *Encyclopedia Britannica*

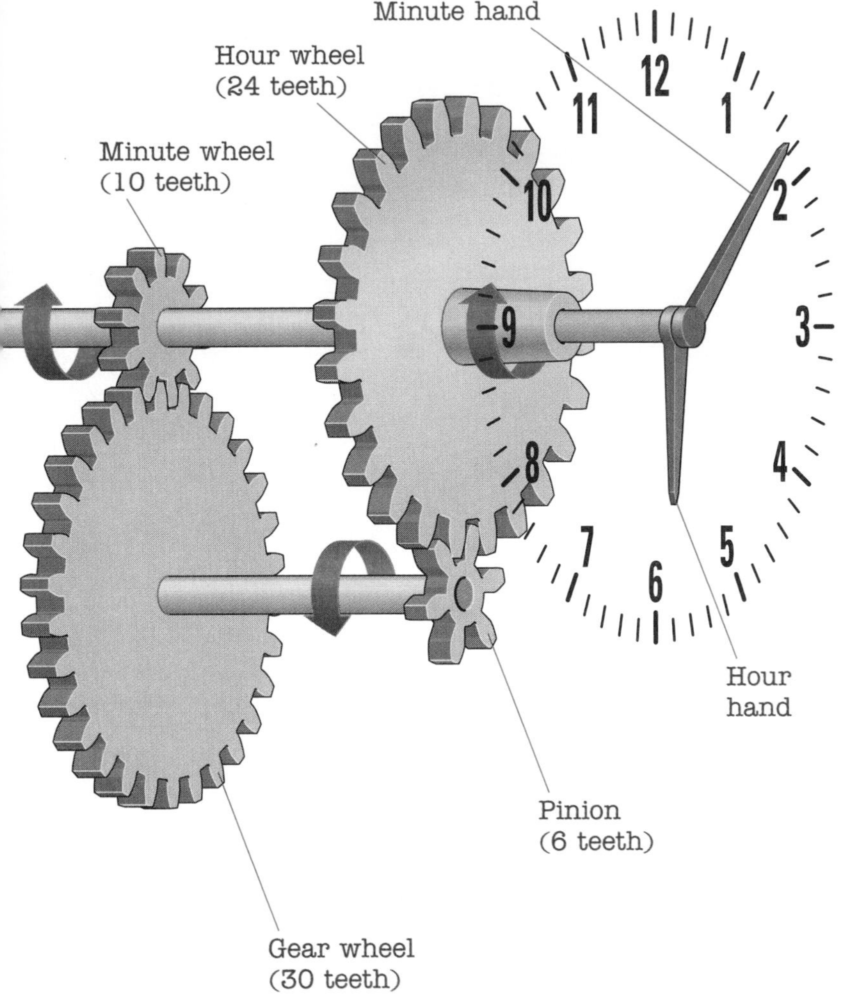

In 1955 L. Essen and J. Parry of Great Britain made the first cesium atomic clock. The 1955 clock was accurate to within one second every 300 years.

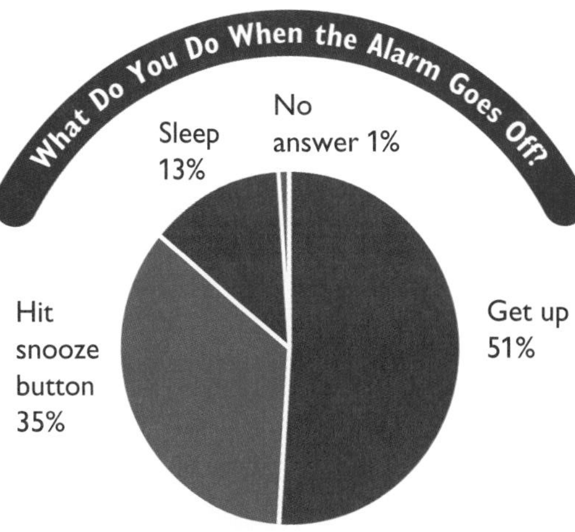

inVestigation

Project File

Memo

We live in a throwaway society. Each hour, Americans throw away 2.5 million plastic bottles. Each day, we toss out half a million tons of trash. Each week, we throw away enough glass bottles and jars to fill one of the 1,350-ft towers of the World Trade Center in New York City. As much as 90% of our household trash could be recycled. But Americans recycle only about 10% of glass and 30% of paper.

Mission: Write a letter to your principal proposing a plan for reducing the amount of garbage produced in your school. Your plan should include a statement of where the garbage comes from, an estimate of the amount that is produced, and a list of steps that students, teachers, administrators, and custodial staff can follow to cut down on garbage.

Leads to Follow

- ✓ What types of garbage are produced in your classroom? What could be done to reduce this trash?
- ✓ What other types of waste are produced in your school?
- ✓ What kinds of changes in behavior can you realistically expect people to be willing to make?

What's Ahead

- Finding the next term in a number pattern
- Writing a number pattern in words

WHAT YOU'LL NEED

✓ Graph paper

5-1 Number Patterns

THINK AND DISCUSS

The first three designs in a pattern made up of squares are shown below.

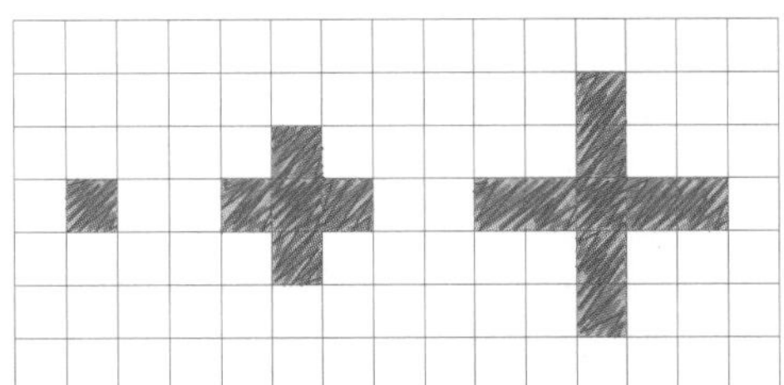

1. a. Sketch the fourth and fifth designs so that they continue the pattern.
   b. How many shaded squares are in the fourth design? the fifth design?
   c. **Discussion** Imagine the sixth design. Describe the design in words.

You can use the pattern of designs above to form the number pattern 1, 5, 9, ... Each number in the pattern is called a **term.**

2. How are the first, second, and third terms in the number pattern related to the first, second, and third designs?

3. What are the fourth and fifth terms in the number pattern?

FLASHBACK

The three dots, . . . , indicate that the pattern continues without end.

You can also describe the number pattern 1, 5, 9, . . . with a rule. *Start with the number 1 and add 4 repeatedly.*

4. a. Write the first five terms in the following number pattern: *Start with the number 3 and add 4 repeatedly.*
   b. **Discussion** Why is it important to tell what number to start with when describing a number pattern with a rule?

The Difference Engine is a computer designed by Charles Babbage (1791–1871), an English scientist. If you feed it a list of numbers, it will look for a pattern and continue the list. **Why do you think the computer was given this name?**

Source: *Dynamath*

5. a. Sketch the fifth and sixth designs in the pattern below.

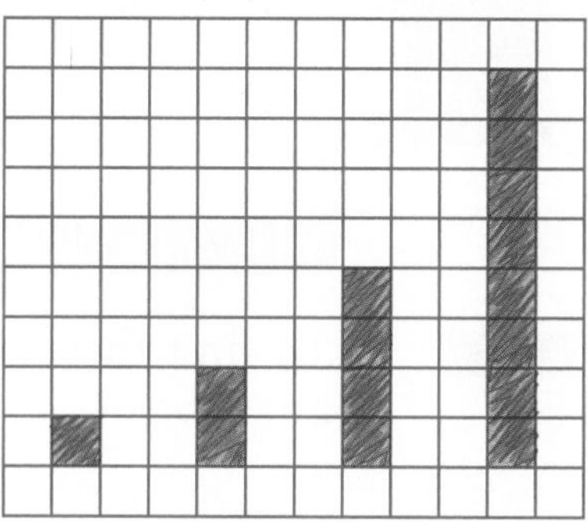

b. Use the pattern of designs to form a number pattern.

c. Write a rule to describe the number pattern.

d. **Discussion** Tell how this rule is different from the one that describes the number pattern 1, 5, 9, ...

WORK TOGETHER

Work with a partner.

Biology Kangaroos are the only large mammals that hop. When kangaroos reach speeds between 10 km/h and 35 km/h, the distance they hop is fairly predictable.

Speed (km/h)	Length of Hop (m)
10	1.2
15	1.8
20	2.4
■	■
■	■

6. a. Copy and complete the table above.

b. Write a rule to describe each number pattern that you used to complete each column in the table.

c. About how far does a kangaroo hop when it reaches a speed of 35 km/h?

d. Construct a line graph to display your data. Use the line graph to estimate how far a kangaroo hops when it reaches a speed of 27 km/h.

ON YOUR OWN

Use graph paper to sketch the next three designs in each pattern.

7. 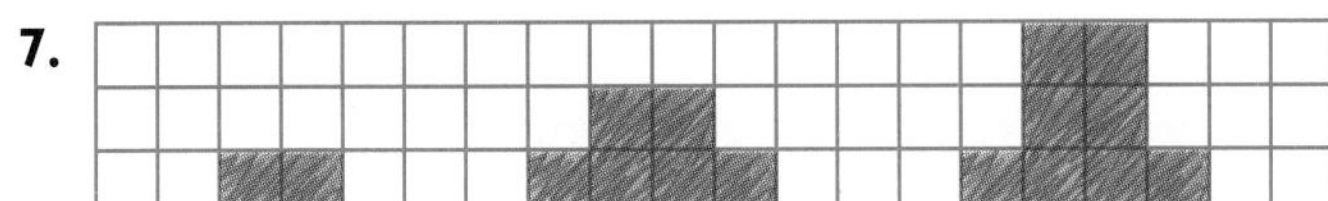

8. 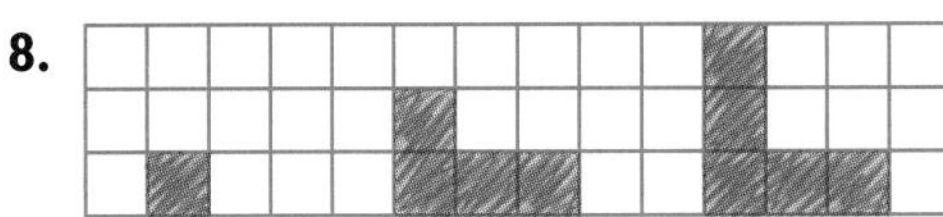

Find the next three terms in each number pattern. Write a rule to describe each number pattern.

9. 7, 14, 21, 28, ■, ■, ■

10. 1, 3, 9, 27, ■, ■, ■

11. 0.25, 0.5, 0.75, ■, ■, ■

12. 1, 3, 5, 7, ■, ■, ■

13. $1, \frac{1}{2}, \frac{1}{4}, \frac{1}{8}$, ■, ■, ■

14. 1, 0.1, 0.01, 0.001, ■, ■, ■

15. **Calculator** Write the first five terms in the following number pattern: *Start with the number 1 and multiply by 1.5 repeatedly.*

16. **Astronomy** Halley's comet is named for scientist Edmund Halley (1656–1742). Halley first saw the comet in 1682 and correctly predicted that it would return about every 76 years.
    a. **Calculator** Based on Halley's theory, when was the last time the comet appeared? When is the next year that the comet is expected to return?
    b. About how old will you be when Halley's comet appears again?
    c. **Writing** Did Edmund Halley get to see the comet appear a second time? Explain.

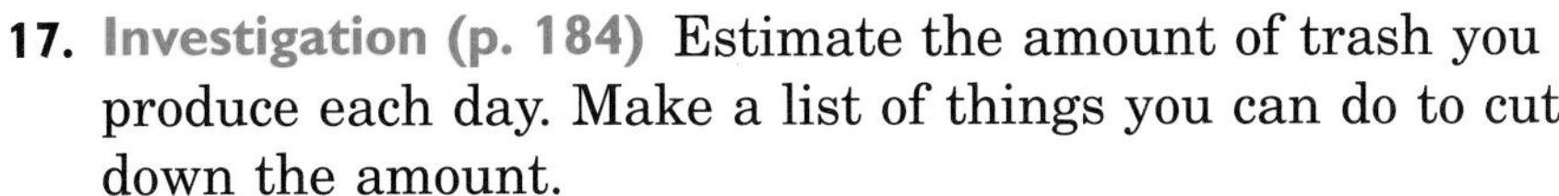

17. **Investigation (p. 184)** Estimate the amount of trash you produce each day. Make a list of things you can do to cut down the amount.

18. **Data File 5 (pp. 182–183)** Describe the sleep pattern of a newborn baby.

Round to the nearest tenth.

1. 44.68
2. 8.146

Find each answer.

3. \$59.36 ÷ \$7.42
4. \$189.32 + \$33.79

Write each decimal in words.

5. 0.73
6. 386.908

7. Maria spent \$35 on a pair of jeans and \$18 on a shirt. She has \$24 left. How much money did she start with?

Giotto, a European spacecraft, passed within 375 mi of Halley's comet the last time that it appeared. Pictures taken from the spacecraft revealed that the nucleus, or center, of the comet measured about 5 mi by 10 mi.

Source: *Reader's Digest Book of Facts*

MATH AND HISTORY

What's Ahead

- Understanding how to use patterns to multiply greater numbers

WHAT YOU'LL NEED

✓ Ruled paper

✓ Scissors

5-2 Napier's Rods

THINK AND DISCUSS

John Napier (1550–1617) invented a series of ten rods that allows you to multiply two numbers by using only addition.

Napier's rods each have nine boxes. The top box contains a digit from 0 to 9. The other boxes each contain two digits separated by a diagonal line. Two of Napier's rods are shown.

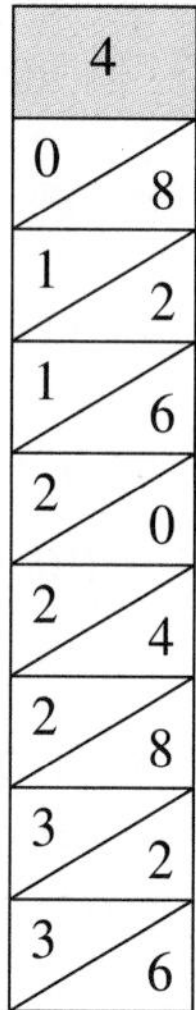

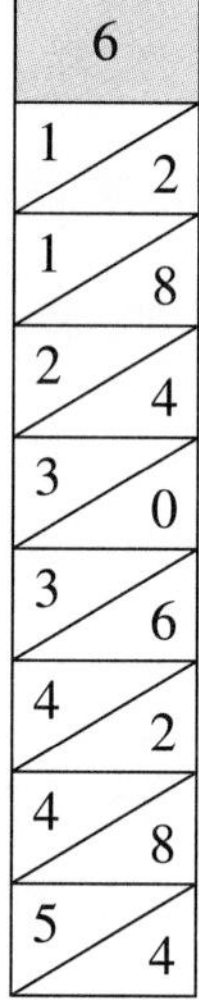

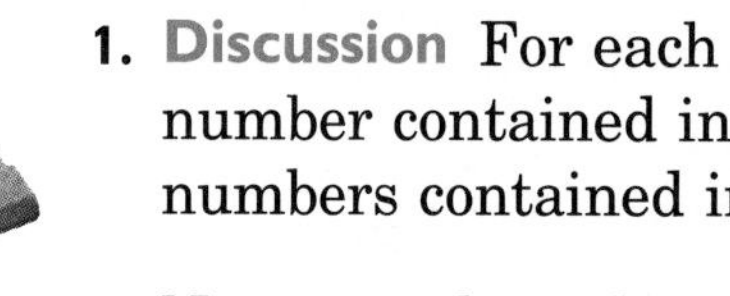

Napier's rods were often used by merchants to keep track of their accounts. They would carry a set of rods, made of ivory or wood, with them to make calculations.

Source: *The Joy of Mathematics*

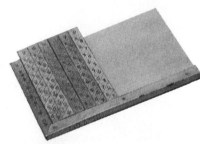

1. **Discussion** For each of Napier's rods, how does the number contained in the top box of each rod relate to the numbers contained in the second through ninth boxes?

2. Name a rule to describe the number pattern that you would use to complete each rod.

a.

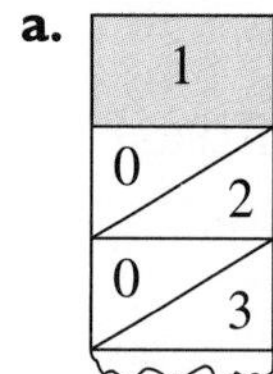

b.

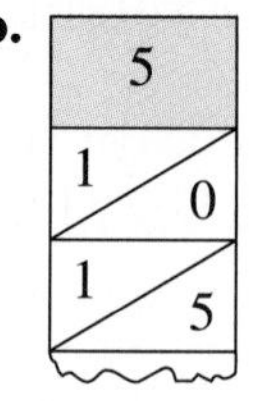

c.

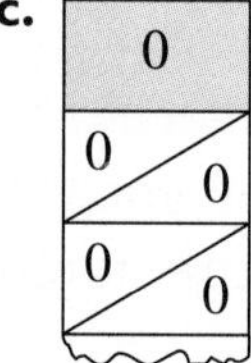

3. Draw all ten of Napier's rods on a sheet of ruled paper. Cut them out.

You can use your set of Napier's rods to find a product.

Example 1 Find the product of 864 × 6.

- Pick out the 8, 6, and 4 rods. Line up the top digits in order from left to right.

8	6	4

- Count down to the sixth row, because you are multiplying by 6. Copy the digits in the upper half of each box in the sixth row, in order. Then attach a zero.

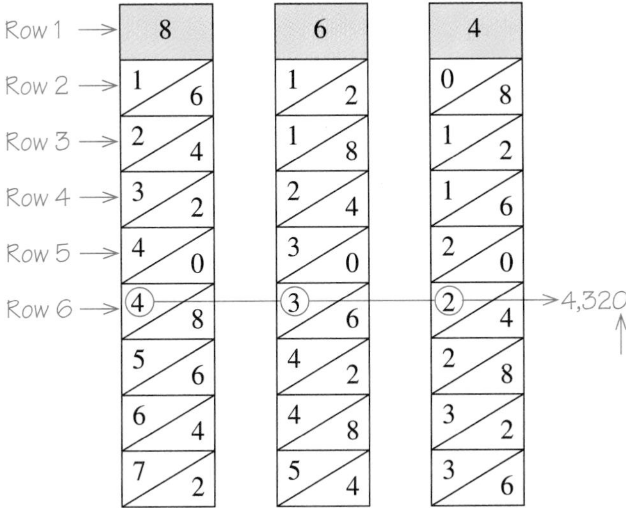

- Copy the digits in the lower half of each box in the sixth row. Do not add any extra digits.

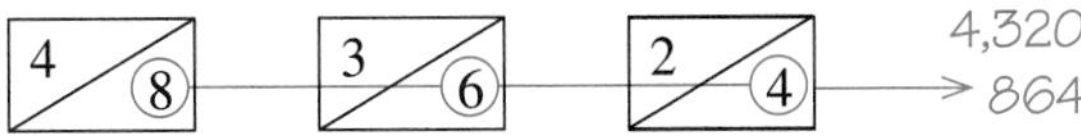

- Add these numbers   4,320 + 864 = 5,184

4. a. In terms of place value, describe the numbers found in the lower right corner of each box containing a diagonal.

b. In terms of place value, describe the numbers found in the upper left corner of each box containing a diagonal.

c. **Discussion** Why is a zero attached when working with the numbers found in the upper left corner of the boxes containing a diagonal?

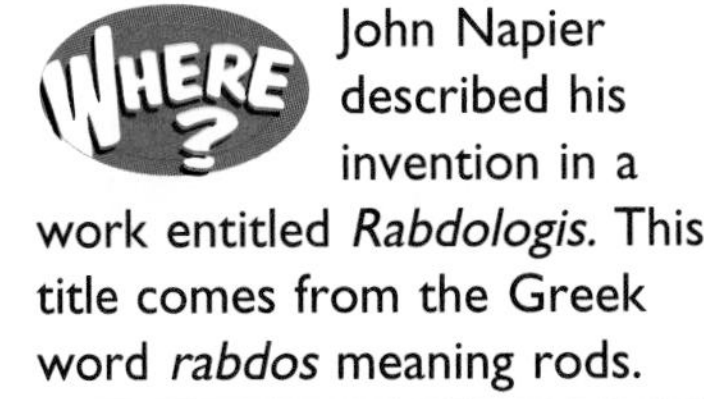

John Napier described his invention in a work entitled *Rabdologis.* This title comes from the Greek word *rabdos* meaning rods.

Source: *Historical Topics for the Mathematics Classroom*

Mixed REVIEW

Find each answer.

1. 19.2 ÷ 6
2. 122 ÷ 6.25

Find the next three terms in each number pattern.

3. 1, 4, 16, 64, ■, ■, ■
4. 0.2, 0.5, 0.8, ■, ■, ■

Evaluate.

5. 8 − 2 × 3 + 5
6. 6 + 2(12 ÷ 4)

7. The sum of two numbers is 17. Their product is 60. Find the two numbers.

TRY THESE

Use Napier's rods to find each product.

5. 39 × 8
6. 836 × 9
7. 602 × 7
8. 4,186 × 7
9. 16,573 × 8
10. 836,724 × 5

11. a. Work with a partner to find the product of 7,872 × 2.
    b. **Writing** Explain why it was helpful to work with a partner to find this product.

12. **Data File 2 (pp. 38–39)** Suppose you and all of your classmates are planning to take a field trip to Kings Island. Your teacher is collecting money for admission to the amusement park. Anyone 4 ft or taller is required to pay adult admission. How much money will your teacher need to collect?

GREAT EXPECTATIONS

Archaeologist

I am interested in becoming an archaeologist because of the history involved in the job. I love learning about how people in ancient times lived and worked. I want to know what they believed, how they raised their children, and why they fought.

If I am an archaeologist I can tell people about their past and their ancestors. I want to tell people about their ancestors' mistakes so they will never repeat them.

Katherine Shell

ON YOUR OWN

Use Napier's rods to find each product.

13. 43×7 **14.** 671×9 **15.** 908×4

16. $7{,}482 \times 5$ **17.** $42{,}793 \times 6$ **18.** $207{,}416 \times 8$

19. $32{,}749 \times 8$ **20.** $206{,}831{,}954 \times 7$

21. There are 28 students in Mrs. Chin's history class. Each student must give a 5 minute speech about a favorite president. How many minutes of class time must Mrs. Chin set aside for these speeches?

22. Mr. Leonard can type 43 words each minute. About how many words can he type in one hour? (*Hint:* 1 h = 60 min)

Ancient Egyptians multiplied by using repeated duplications. To multiply 2,801 × 7 they did the following:

1	2,801
2	5,602
+4	+11,204
7	19,607

How would they have found the product 3,468 × 3?

Source: *Historical Topics for the Mathematics Classroom*

Dear Katherine,

I've been fascinated with archaeology since I was in the fourth grade when we studied California Indians in school. The more I learned about Native Americans, the more I thought about how badly they had been treated in this country. If we could just learn more about Native Americans, I reasoned, we could do something to help them.

And, I figured, what better way to learn than through archaeology? I'd see articles in the newspaper about archaeological digs, and the neat new finds they made. Although archaeologists were digging up stuff that was old, this kind of history was really new.

People are always surprised to hear this. Many think that archaeology is mostly ancient art, remote places, and dangerous expeditions. That part is all true, but in the everyday life of an archaeologist, we deal with science and math all the time.

David Hurst Thomas
Curator of Anthropology
American Museum of Natural History

In the 15th century, Native Americans were using baskets for grinding corn and for storage.

What's Ahead

- Understanding and using exponents

5-3 Exponents

WHAT YOU'LL NEED

✓ Calculator

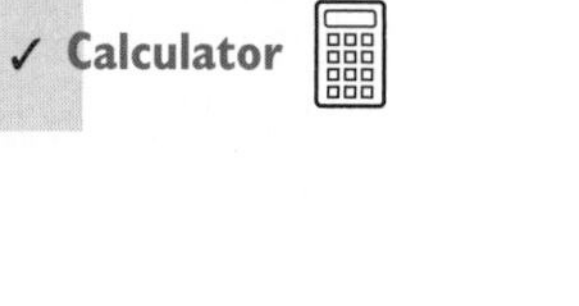

THINK AND DISCUSS

Elis F. Stenman built a house along with the furniture in it from approximately 100,000 newspapers. You can express 100,000 as the product $10 \times 10 \times 10 \times 10 \times 10$. You can express this product using an *exponent.*

$$\underbrace{10 \times 10 \times 10 \times 10 \times 10}_{\text{5 factors}} = 10^5 \leftarrow \text{exponent}$$

↑ **base**

The **exponent** tells you how many times a number, or **base,** is used as a factor.

1. Name the base and the exponent in 3^6.

2. Express the product $5 \times 5 \times 5 \times 5$ using an exponent.

You call a number that is expressed using an exponent a **power.** You read 10^5 as "ten to the fifth power."

3. Read each of the following powers out loud: 8^4, 3^6, 10^8.

The exponents 2 and 3 have special names.

4. a. Complete: The area of the *square* is 3×3 or $3^{■}$.

   b. Why do you think the exponent 2 is read as "squared"?

3

3

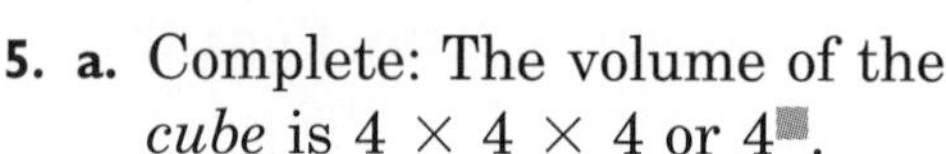

5. a. Complete: The volume of the *cube* is $4 \times 4 \times 4$ or $4^{■}$.

   b. Why do you think the exponent 3 is read as "cubed"?

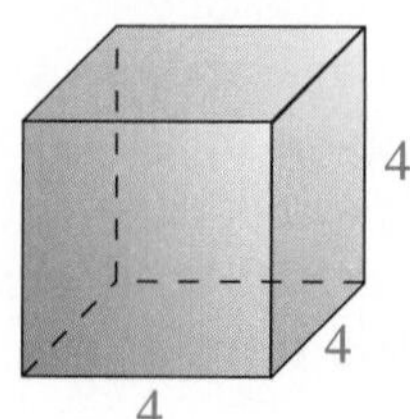

6. Read each of the following powers out loud: 6^3, 7^2, 12^3.

Elis F. Stenman made the walls of his house by pasting and folding layers of newspaper. He used papers rolled into different sizes to make the furniture, which includes tables, chairs, lamps, and a grandfather clock.

Source: *The Kids' World Almanac of Records and Facts*

You can **evaluate,** or find the value of, a power by first writing it as a product.

Example 1

a. Evaluate 4^3.

$4^3 = 4 \times 4 \times 4 = 64$

b. Evaluate 1^2.

$1^2 = 1 \times 1 = 1$

A calculator is helpful when you are working with exponents. You can use the [y^x] key to evaluate *any* power.

Example 2

a. Evaluate 6^8.

6 [y^x] 8 [=]  1679616

b. Evaluate 25^2.

25 [y^x] 2 [=] 625

You can use the [x^2] key to square a number.

Example 3 Evaluate 26^2.

26 [x^2] 676

7. Discussion How can you use the [x^2] key to evaluate 12^4?

The French mathematician René Descartes (1596–1650) introduced the use of Hindu-Arabic numerals as exponents on a given base.

Source: *Historical Topics for the Mathematics Classroom*

You can extend the order of operations to include powers.

The Order of Operations

1. Do all operations within parentheses first.
2. Do all work with exponents.
3. Multiply and divide from left to right.
4. Add and subtract from left to right.

The phrase *Please Excuse My Dear Aunt Sally* can help you to remember the order of operations. **What does the first letter of each word in the phrase stand for?**

Example 4

a. Evaluate $2 \times (4^2 - 5)$.

$2 \times (4^2 - 5) = 2 \times (16 - 5)$ — $4^2 = 4 \times 4 = 16$; Subtract 5 from 16.

$= 2 \times 11$ — Multiply 2 and 11.

$= 22$

b. Evaluate $2^3 - 9 \div 3$.

$2^3 - 9 \div 3 = 8 - 9 \div 3$ — $2^3 = 2 \times 2 \times 2 = 8$; Divide 9 by 3.

$= 8 - 3$ — Subtract 3 from 8.

$= 5$

8. Discussion How can you use a calculator to evaluate each expression in Example 4?

TRY THESE

Name the base and the exponent.

9. 4^5
10. 3^2
11. 6^3

Write using an exponent.

12. $6 \times 6 \times 6$
13. $3 \times 3 \times 3 \times 3 \times 3$

Mental Math Evaluate.

14. 5^2
15. 2^3
16. $2 \times 4^2 - 32$
17. $21 + (7^2 - 40)$
18. $(3^2 - 1) \div 2^2$

Mixed REVIEW

Estimate each product.

1. 48×195
2. 79×28

Find the next three terms in each number pattern.

3. 2, 4, 6, ■, ■, ■
4. 6, 12, 18, ■, ■, ■
5. The distance to your grandmother's apartment is 24 blocks. Suppose you walk 3 blocks and then take the bus 16 blocks. How much farther is it to your grandmother's?

ON YOUR OWN

Name the base and the exponent.

19. 7^9
20. 8^1
21. 10^3

Write using an exponent.

22. $8 \times 8 \times 8 \times 8$
23. $4 \times 4 \times 4 \times 4 \times 4 \times 4$

Choose Use a calculator, mental math, or paper and pencil to evaluate.

24. 11^7
25. $5 \times 3^2 - 10$
26. $7^1 \times 2^4$
27. $175 + (128 \div 4^2)$
28. $16 + 32 \div 2^3$
29. $6^3 \div (2 \times 6) + 64$
30. $674 - (14 - 6)^3$
31. $498 + (2^{12} \div 2^4) \div (2^5 \times 2) - 2^1$

Express each area or volume using an exponent.

32.
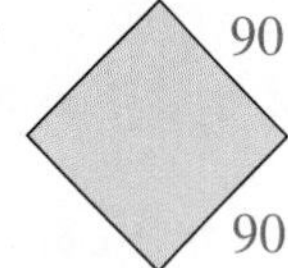

33.
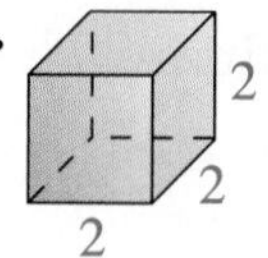

34. **Critical Thinking** What is the value of any number raised to the first power? What is the value of 1 raised to any power? Give an example to justify each answer.

35. a. Copy and complete the table below.

Power	Standard Form
10^1	10
10^2	100
10^3	1,000
10^4	■
■	■

FLASHBACK

A number in standard form is separated into groups of three digits by commas.

b. Writing How is the exponent related to the number of zeros that follow the numeral 1 when the power is expressed in standard form?

c. Express each power in standard form: 10^8, 10^{10}, 10^{12}.

36. Entertainment The size of the image of a motion picture is related to the distance of the projector from the screen. Use the table at the right to answer each question.

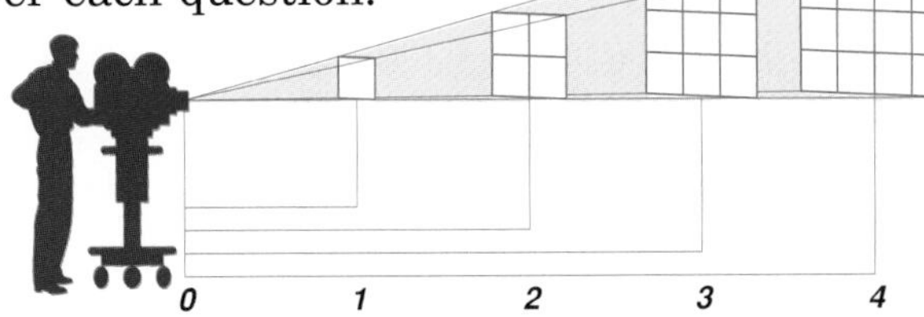

Distance from Screen (units)	Picture Size (square units)
1	1
2	4
3	9
4	16

a. Writing Describe how the size of a motion picture is related to the distance from the projector to the screen.

b. A projector is 25 ft from the screen. How big will the image of the motion picture be?

CHECKPOINT

1. Write the first five terms in the following number pattern: *Start with the number 4 and multiply by 2 repeatedly.*

2. Music Use an exponent to express the number of singles a recording artist must sell in the U.S.A. to get a gold record.

Gold Records	
Country	**Singles Sold**
Austria	100,000
Spain	100,000
Finland	10,000
U.S.A.	1,000,000
Ireland	100,000
Italy	1,000,000

Source: *The Kids' World Almanac of Records and Facts*

Evaluate.

3. 9^7

4. $7 \times 3^4 - 99$

5. 3×2^1

6. $(2 \times 4^2) \div 8$

7. $50 \div (5^2 \div 5) + 4$

What's Ahead

- Understanding variables
- Evaluating variable expressions

WHAT YOU'LL NEED

✓ Algebra tiles 

5-4 Variables and Expressions

THINK AND DISCUSS

A **magic square** is an arrangement of numbers in a square in which the rows, columns, and diagonals each have the same sum. A magic square is shown at the right.

■	7	2
1	5	■
8	■	4

To find the missing values in a magic square first identify a row, column, or diagonal in which all the values appear. The sum of the completed diagonal in the magic square shown above can be represented by the *numerical expression* $8 + 5 + 2$. A **numerical expression** contains only numbers and mathematical symbols.

1. What is the sum of each row, column, and diagonal of the magic square shown above?

You can represent the missing value in each square by a *variable,* as shown at the right. A **variable** is a symbol, usually a letter, that stands for a number.

a	7	2
1	5	b
8	c	4

2. Name the variables in the magic square.

The *variable expression* $a + 7 + 2$ represents the sum of the entries in the first row. A **variable expression** is an expression that contains at least one variable.

3. a. **Mental Math** What is the value of a?
   b. Name another variable expression that you could use to determine the value of a.

4. a. What variable expressions could you use to determine the value of b? of c?
   b. **Mental Math** What is the value of b? of c?

The *lo-shu* is the oldest known magic square. It was found on the back of a tortoise shell by Emperor Yu of China about 4000 years ago. The drawing above gives you an idea of what the lo-shu may have looked like. **How would you represent this magic square?**

Source: *Math Activities for Child Involvement*

You can use tiles to model expressions. The yellow tiles represent ones, and the green tiles represent variables.

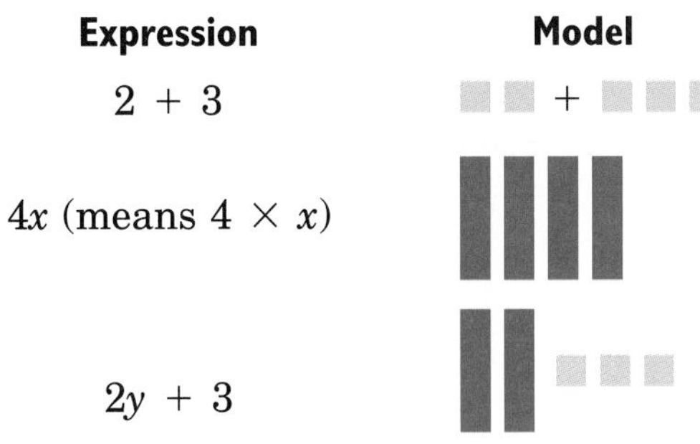

5. **Discussion** Why is the symbol × used to show multiplication in numerical expressions but not in variable expressions?

You can evaluate a variable expression using tiles.

Example 1 Evaluate $2x + 1$ for $x = 3$.

Model the expression $2x + 1$.

Replace each green tile with 3 yellow tiles.

The value of $2x + 1$ for $x = 3$ is 7.

6. Use tiles to evaluate $6 + 3t$ for $t = 2$.

You can also evaluate a variable expression by replacing the variable with a number. Then follow the order of operations.

Example 2 Evaluate $a + 8$ for $a = 7$.

$a + 8 = 7 + 8$ **Replace *a* with 7.**

$= 15$ **Use mental math.**

b. Evaluate $b^2 - 12$ for $b = 6$.

$b^2 - 12 = 6^2 - 12$ **Replace *b* with 6. Evaluate the power.**

$= 36 - 12$ **Subtract 12 from 36.**

$= 24$

FLASHBACK

To follow the order of operations you first multiply and divide from left to right. Then add and subtract from left to right.

7. **Discussion** Will the expressions $2c^2$ and $(2c)^2$ result in the same value for $c = 4$? Explain.

WHO? A counting horse named Muhamed lived in Germany in the late 1800s. His owner trained him to add, subtract, multiply, and divide. Muhamed would give an answer of 25 by tapping his left hoof twice, and his right hoof five times. **How would he give the answer to the numerical expression 97 − 12?**

Source: *The Kids' World Almanac of Animals and Pets*

A variable expression can have more than one variable.

Example 3 Evaluate $r(36 - s)$ for $r = 0.5$ and $s = 8$.

$r(36 - s) = 0.5(36 - 8)$ — Replace *r* with 0.5 and *s* with 8.

$= 0.5(28)$ — Subtract 8 from 36.

$= 14$ — Multiply 0.5 and 28.

TRY THESE

Choose a variable and write a variable expression for each model.

8. 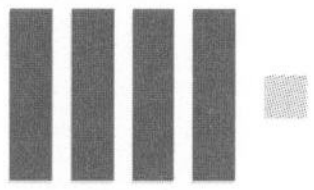

9. 

Mental Math Evaluate each expression for $x = 8$.

10. $x + 12$ **11.** $80 \div x$ **12.** x^2

13. $0.25 + 2x$ **14.** $3x \div 2$ **15.** $2(x - 3)$

ON YOUR OWN

Model each variable expression.

16. $3y + 5$ **17.** $c + 3$ **18.** $5b + 2$

Choose Use a calculator, mental math, or paper and pencil to evaluate.

19. $24 \div d$ for $d = 3$

20. $p + 8$ for $p = 6$

21. $3r - 2$ for $r = 65$

22. $x^2 - 12$ for $x = 8$

23. $n \div 10$ for $n = 30$

24. $0.75s$ for $s = 29.98$

25. $(2c)^3$ for $c = 3$

26. $2ab$ for $a = 3.5$ and $b = 0.3$

27. $8 - y^2$ for $y = 2$

28. $2r + s$ for $r = 7$ and $s = 30$

4	9	*r*
s	7	3
6	5	*t*

29. Copy and complete the magic square shown at the left. Find the values of *r*, *s*, and *t*.

Copy and complete each table by evaluating the expression for the given values of *x*.

30.

x	$x + 6$
1	7
4	10
7	■
10	■
■	20

31.

x	$7x$
2	■
4	■
6	■
8	■
■	70

32.

x	$100 - x$
20	■
35	■
50	■
72	■
■	88

33. Choose A, B, or C. Which numerical expression has a value closest to 176?

A. $11.5 \times 14 + 25.5$ **B.** $7.5 + 3 \times 50$

C. $(35 \times 2.5 + 300) \div 2$

34. Writing What is the difference between a numerical expression and a variable expression?

Use the article below to answer each question.

Smooth as Silk

Silk is the most precious fabric by weight. The silkworm spins silk to create a cocoon. Each cocoon consists of a single thread up to 1.6 km long. It takes 110 cocoons to make a man's silk tie, 630 cocoons for a blouse, and 3,000 cocoons for a kimono. It takes a silkworm about 3 days to spin the entire cocoon. During that time the worm will have shaken its head about 300,000 times.

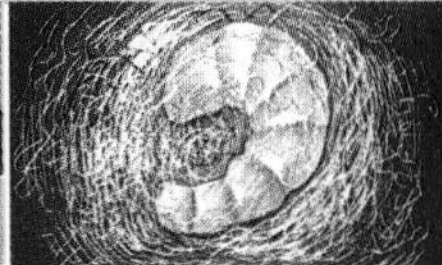

35. Write a numerical expression to represent the number of cocoons it takes to make both a tie and a blouse.

36. How many days would it take one silkworm to spin the silk needed to make a kimono? About how many kilometers of thread are needed to make a kimono?

Mixed REVIEW

Use the data: 9, 16, 21, 10, 12, 17, 20.

1. Find the mean.

2. Find the median.

Write using an exponent.

3. $5 \times 5 \times 5 \times 5$

4. $9 \times 9 \times 9$

5. Write the first five terms of the following number pattern: start with 2 and add 7 repeatedly.

6. Margarite is standing in the middle of a line to buy concert tickets. There are 47 people in front of her. How many people are in the line?

PROBLEM SOLVING

5-5 Look for a Pattern

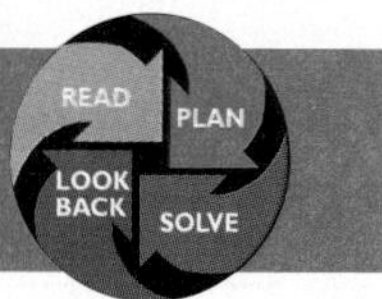

What's Ahead

- Solving problems by looking for patterns

> Imagine that the Bits and Bytes Computer Club, which now has 15 members, is planning to install its own communications system. The system will connect each club member's home computer with each of the other 14. How many cables will the communications system require?

READ

Read and understand the given information. Summarize the problem.

Think about the information you are given and what you are asked to find.

1. How many members belong to the computer club?
2. What does the problem ask you to find?

PLAN

Decide on a strategy to solve the problem.

Draw diagrams for simpler cases. Record the number of cables needed for each case.

3. How many cables do you need to connect 2 computers?

4. How many cables do you need to connect 3 computers?

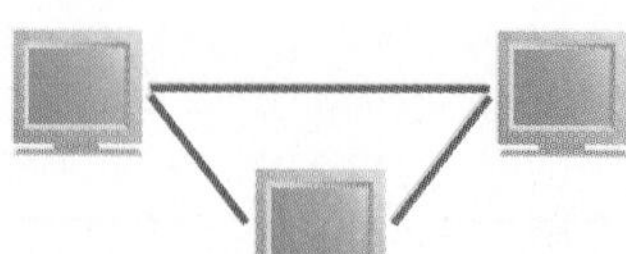

5. How many cables do you need to connect 4 computers?

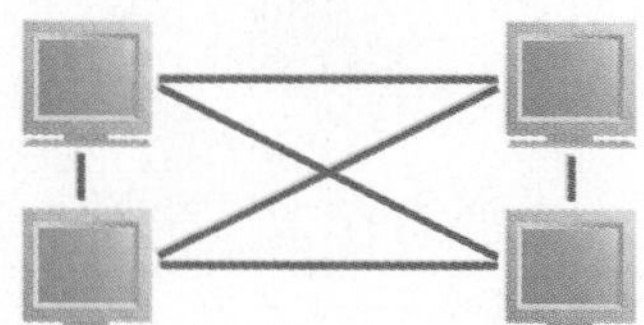

6. How many cables do you need to connect 5 computers?

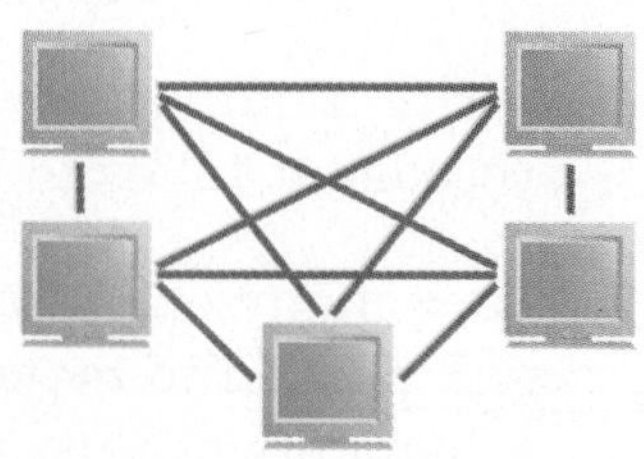

How Do Kids Use Computers?

games	84%
homework	40%
word processing	25%
graphics	12%

Record the information in a table like the one shown below and look for a pattern in the data.

Number of Home Computers	Number of Cables
2	1
3	3
4	6
5	10
6	■
7	■

+2
+3
+4
■
■

SOLVE

Try out the strategy.

7. a. How many cables would you need to connect 6 computers? 7 computers?

b. Describe the pattern.

8. Continue the pattern. Find the number of cables you need to connect all 15 members of the computer club.

You may have wanted to draw a diagram to show the number of cables you need to connect all 15 members of the computer club.

LOOK BACK

Think about how you solved this problem.

9. Do you think this is a good strategy to use to answer the problem? Why or why not?

TRY THESE

Use Look for a Pattern to solve each problem.

10. Germaine plans to save \$1 the first week, \$2 the second week, \$4 the third week, \$8 the fourth week, and \$16 the fifth week. If Germaine can continue this pattern, how much money will he save the twelfth week?

11. What is the sum of the first 20 even numbers?

12. There are 12 people at a party. If each person shakes hands with each of the others exactly once, how many handshakes will there be altogether?

President Theodore Roosevelt holds the record for the most hands shaken by a public figure at an official function. He shook 8,513 hands at a New Year's Day White House presentation in Washington, D.C., in 1907.

Source: *The Guinness Book of Records*

ON YOUR OWN

Use any strategy to solve each problem. Show all your work.

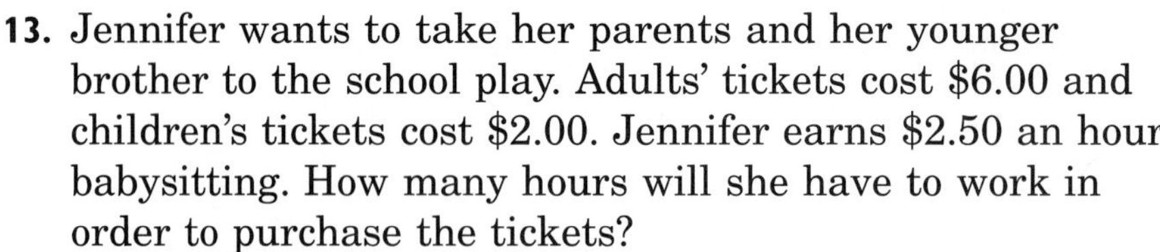

13. Jennifer wants to take her parents and her younger brother to the school play. Adults' tickets cost \$6.00 and children's tickets cost \$2.00. Jennifer earns \$2.50 an hour babysitting. How many hours will she have to work in order to purchase the tickets?

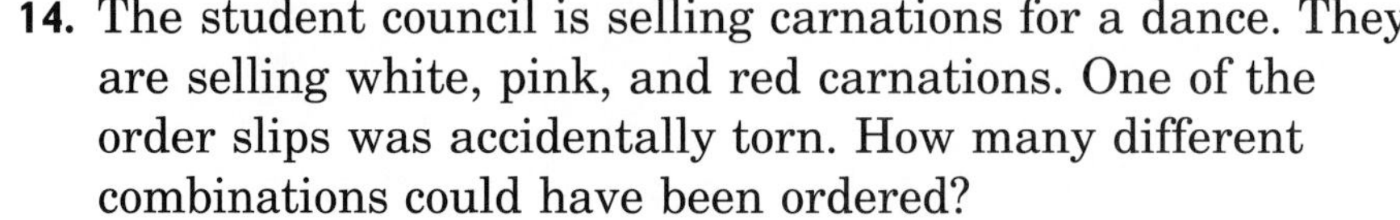

14. The student council is selling carnations for a dance. They are selling white, pink, and red carnations. One of the order slips was accidentally torn. How many different combinations could have been ordered?

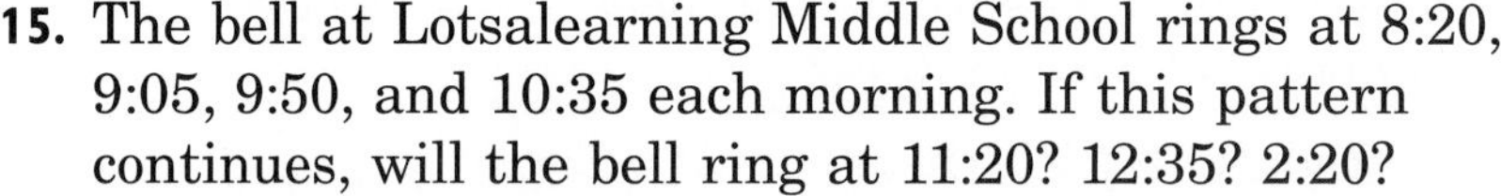

15. The bell at Lotsalearning Middle School rings at 8:20, 9:05, 9:50, and 10:35 each morning. If this pattern continues, will the bell ring at 11:20? 12:35? 2:20?

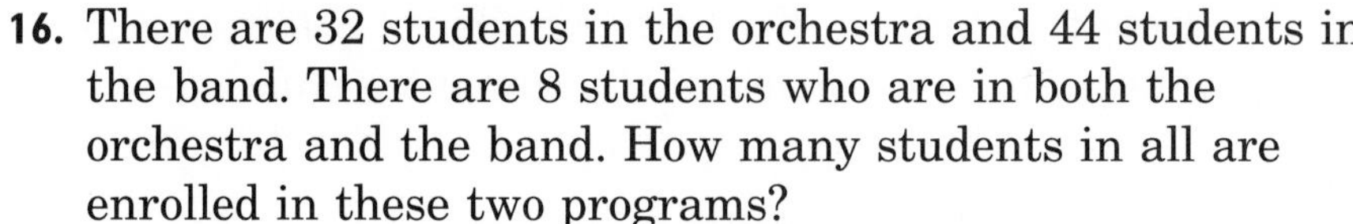

16. There are 32 students in the orchestra and 44 students in the band. There are 8 students who are in both the orchestra and the band. How many students in all are enrolled in these two programs?

17. Find two numbers with a product of 63 and a sum of 16.

18. The lead contained in a brand new pencil could draw a line 35 mi long. About how many pencils would it take to draw a line around the circumference of Earth? (*Note:* The circumference of Earth is 24,902 mi.)

19. You open a book, and the product of the two facing page numbers is 600. To what pages have you opened?

20. Mrs. Snyder rented a car for two days. The rate was \$26.50 per day and \$.35 per mile. Mrs. Snyder traveled 225 mi. How much was she charged?

21. Anita, Cheryl, Beth, and Althea went to the library to work on a project. When they left the library, each of them accidentally picked up a coat belonging to someone else in the group and a hat of yet someone else. Cheryl took Anita's hat, and the girl who took Althea's hat took Beth's coat. What hat and coat did each of the girls take?

Mixed REVIEW

Find each answer.

1. $48.8 + 3.47$
2. $2.863 - 0.174$

Name the variable in each expression.

3. $4(n - 6)$
4. $6f \div 3$

Evaluate.

5. $r^2 + 9$ for $r = 6$
6. $8p - 2q$ for $p = 7$ and $q = 9$

7. Karenna has a white blouse, a green blouse, a blue blouse, a plaid skirt, and a striped skirt. How many different outfits can she make?

Practice

Find the next three terms in each number pattern. Write a rule to describe each number pattern.

1. 2, 4, 6, 8, ■, ■, ■

2. 1, 2, 4, 8, ■, ■, ■

3. 0.2, 1.2, 2.2, ■, ■, ■

Name the base and the exponent.

4. 3^2 **5.** 7^4 **6.** 6^3 **7.** 2^8

Express each area or volume using an exponent.

8. 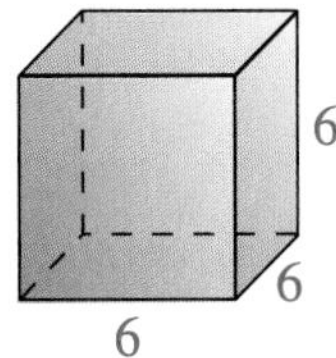

9. 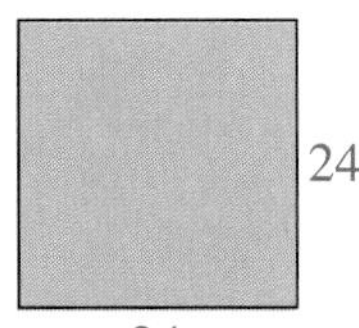

10. 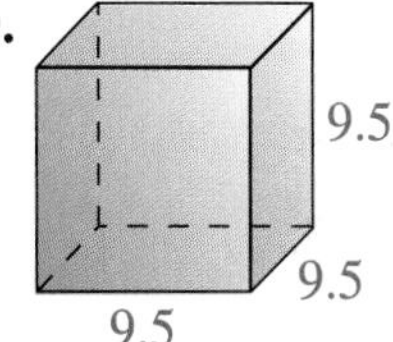

Choose Use a calculator, mental math, or paper and pencil to evaluate.

11. $(5^2 - 7) \div 3$

12. $7 \times (4 + 7)$

13. $9^8 \div 3^1$

14. $6(34 + 3^4) \div 30$

15. $(2 \times 4^2) \div 8$

16. $135 + 64 \div 4^2$

17. $7 \times 3^4 - 99$

18. $50 \div (5^2 \div 5) + 4$

Choose a variable and write a variable expression for each model.

19. 

20. 

21. 

Mental Math Evaluate each expression for the given values of the variables.

22. $6x$ for $x = 8$

23. $a + 0.75$ for $a = 4.25$

24. $b^2 - 21$ for $b = 9$

25. rs for $s = 7$ and $r = 3$

26. $88 - 2c$ for $c = 40$

27. $72 \div h$ for $h = 6$

28. $5ab$ for $a = 1.5$ and $b = 6$

29. $8b + 3c$ for $b = 3$ and $c = 2$

What's Ahead

• Writing variable expressions and word phrases

5-6 Writing Variable Expressions

WORK TOGETHER

1. Work with a partner to make a list of all the words or phrases you can think of that indicate each of the following operations: addition, subtraction, multiplication, and division.

2. Use your lists to describe each numerical expression in words. Try to find as many different ways as you can.

   a. $5 + 8$ **b.** $10 - 4$ **c.** 10×3 **d.** $18 \div 6$

THINK AND DISCUSS

Word phrases are also used to describe variable expressions as shown in the table below.

Word Phrase	Variable Expression
the sum of *m* and 45	$m + 45$
22 more than a number	$n + 22$
w less than 55	$55 - w$
the product of *w* and 10	$10w$
the quotient of *r* and *s*	$r \div s$

3. Name two word phrases to describe each of the following variable expressions: $b + 15$, $m - n$, $10x$, and $18 \div p$.

4. Write a variable expression for the word phrases *five plus a number y* and *6 times the quantity q*.

5. The length of the largest lasagna was 56 ft more than its width. Let w represent the width of the lasagna.

   a. Write a variable expression for the length of the lasagna.

   b. **Discussion** Why is w a good variable to choose to represent the width of the lasagna?

The largest lasagna in the U.S. weighed 3,477 lb and measured 63 ft × 7 ft.

Source: *The Guinness Book of Records*

TRY THESE

Write two word phrases for each variable expression.

6. $z + 24$ **7.** $y - x$ **8.** $7s$ **9.** $g \div h$

Write a variable expression for each word phrase. Choose an appropriate variable to represent an unknown quantity.

10. eight less than s

11. six more than a number

12. 7 times the number of hats

13. b divided by 3

14. three inches shorter than Caleb

15. Write a variable expression for the perimeter of the triangle.

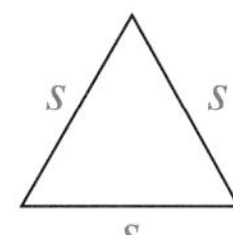

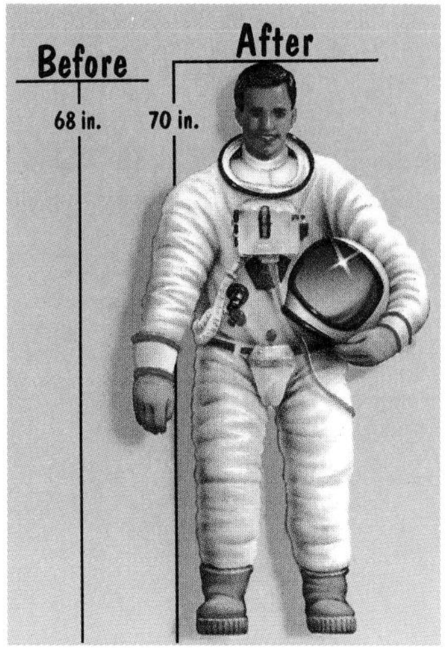

At the end of a space flight, an astronaut's height can temporarily be 2 in. greater than normal. This happens in the absence of gravity as the cartilage disks in the spine expand. Let the variable expression $h + 2$ describe this situation. **What must h represent?**

Source: *Reader's Digest Book of Facts*

ON YOUR OWN

Write two word phrases for each variable expression.

16. $t + 6$ **17.** $18 - h$ **18.** ab **19.** $21 \div m$

Write a variable expression for each word phrase. Choose an appropriate variable to represent an unknown quantity.

20. three more than h

21. twenty-two less than k

22. the sum of r and s

23. the product of three and m

24. twenty students separated into some number of groups

25. three times the number of books

Write a variable expression to describe each table.

26.

x	■
1	3
2	6
3	9
4	12

27.

a	■
2	5
5	8
6	9
7	10

28.

m	■
5	2
10	7
15	12
20	17

41	43	45	47	49
31	33	35	37	39
21	23	25	27	29
11	13	15	17	19
1	3	5	7	9

29. Use the sample below and the pattern at the left to find each value.

Sample Find the value of 15 $\uparrow$.

Locate the number 15 in the pattern. Then, move one unit in the direction of the arrow. The value is 25.

a. Find the values 27 $\uparrow$ and 33 $\uparrow$.

b. If the pattern continues, what is the value of 47 $\uparrow$?

c. Let n represent any number in the shaded region. Write a variable expression for the values of $n\uparrow$, $n\downarrow$, $n\leftarrow$, and $n\rightarrow$.

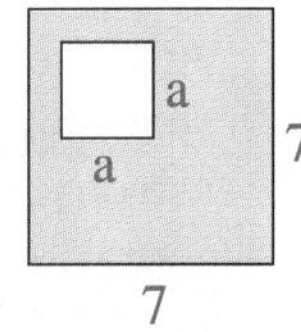

30. Choose A, B, C, or D. Which variable expression describes the area of the shaded region in the diagram at the left?

A. $a^2 + 14$ **B.** $49 - 2a$

C. $a^2 - 49$ **D.** $49 - a^2$

31. Aaron is x years old. Write an expression for Aaron's age:

a. 3 years ago **b.** 10 years from now

c. z years ago **d.** t years from now

Find each answer.

1. 36.18 × 4

2. 517.6 × 0.01

Compare using >, <, or =.

3. 0.630 ■ 0.63

4. 3.6 ■ 3.06

5. Suppose you cut a piece of string in half and then cut those pieces in half. If you continue this process, how many pieces of string will you have after the 5th round of cuts?

32. Paloma has \$3.25 in her purse. She has m dollars in her pocket. Write a variable expression for the amount of money Paloma has altogether.

33. Data File 2 (pp. 38–39) Suppose you spend the day riding the Waimea while visiting Raging Waters Park.

a. Let t represent the number of times you go on the water ride. Write a variable expression for the number of seconds you spend riding the Waimea.

b. Critical Thinking Write a variable expression for the number of minutes you spend riding the Waimea.

34. Writing Do the word phrases *twenty-two less than x* and *x less than twenty-two* result in the same variable expression? Explain.

35. Investigation (p. 184) Collect data on the amount of glass and paper produced in your school each day. Estimate how much glass and paper is being recycled and how much is simply being thrown away.

Problem Solving Practice

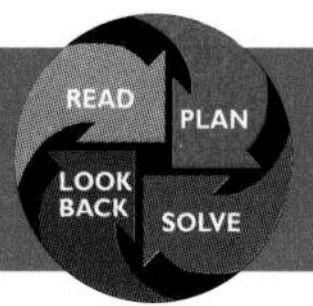

PROBLEM SOLVING STRATEGIES

Make a Table
Use Logical Reasoning
Solve a Simpler Problem
Too Much or Too Little Information
Look for a Pattern
Make a Model
Work Backward
Draw a Diagram
Guess and Test
Simulate a Problem
Use Multiple Strategies

Solve. Use an appropriate strategy or a combination of strategies.

1. Aiesha earns $15/day babysitting, and Yvonne earns $8/day looking after neighbors' pets. After how many days has Aiesha earned $42 more than Yvonne?

2. An apartment building has 8 stories. It takes 6 s for the elevator to go from the first floor to the third floor. How long does it take for the elevator to go from the first floor to the sixth floor?

3. Four friends are running in a race. Harry is 0.25 km ahead of Joe. Joe is twice as far as Frank. Steve is 0.25 km behind Joe. If Harry has run 2.75 km, how far have each of the others run?

4. Sasha sold wrapping paper and greeting cards to help raise money for her school. Each roll of paper costs $3.25 and each box of cards costs $3.75. Sasha collected a total of $44.75. How many of each item did Sasha sell?

5. The art teacher uses four push pins, one in each corner, to hang a drawing on a bulletin board. If she overlaps the corners, she can hang two drawings with only six push pins. What is the minimum number of push pins the art teacher needs to hang eight drawings?

6. How many squares are there on a 4×4 checkerboard like the one shown at the left?

7. A carpenter cuts a wooden plank into four pieces in 12 s. At the same rate, how many seconds would it take the carpenter to cut the plank into five pieces?

8. Hanukkah is a Jewish holiday that lasts eight days. Two candles are lit on the first night of Hanukkah. Every night after that the candles are replaced and one more is added. How many candles have been used by the time Hanukkah ends?

TECHNOLOGY

5-7 Graphing Functional Data

What's Ahead

- Making graphs from tables
- Using computers to explore graphs

WHAT YOU'LL NEED

✓ Graph paper 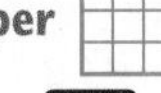

✓ Computer

✓ Software 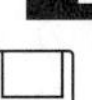

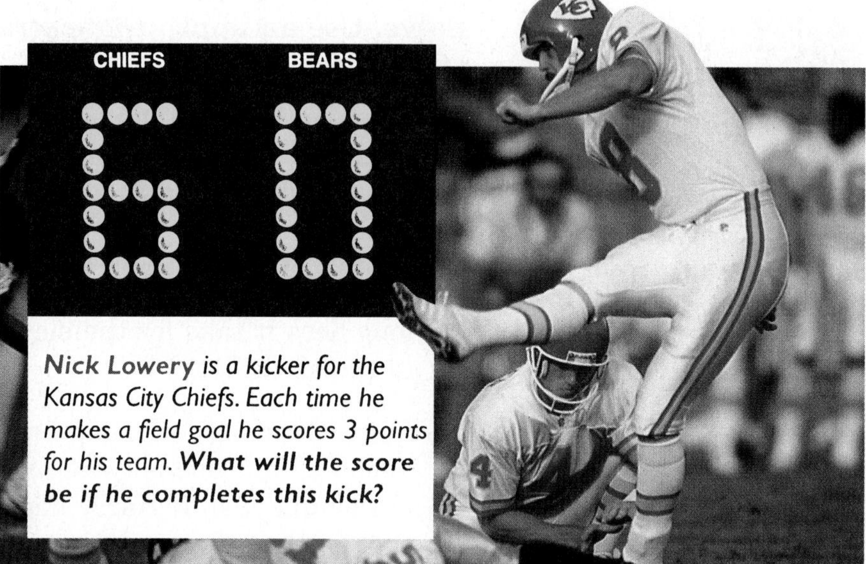
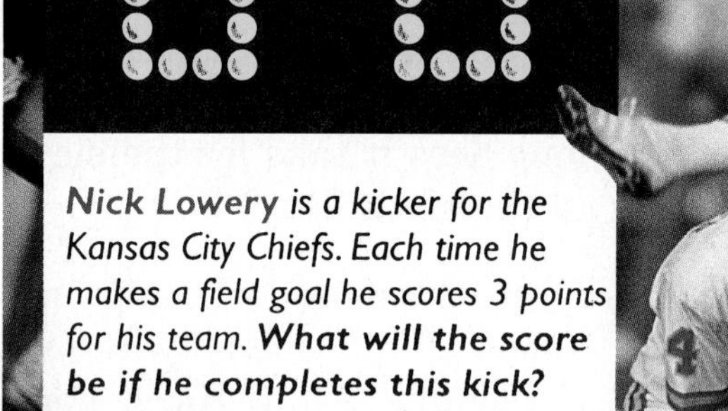

Nick Lowery is a kicker for the Kansas City Chiefs. Each time he makes a field goal he scores 3 points for his team. ***What will the score be if he completes this kick?***

THINK AND DISCUSS

In 1990 a kicker named Nick Lowery scored over 100 points in field goals. The computer spreadsheet below shows how many points you would receive for different numbers of field goals.

	A	B
1	Number of Field Goals	Points
2	1	3
3	2	6
4	3	9
5	4	12
6	5	

1. **a.** What number belongs in the blank cell, or box?
   b. How are the numbers in column B related to the numbers in column A?
   c. If f stands for the number of field goals, what variable expression represents the number of points?

You can create a graph to show how the two sets of numbers in the spreadsheet are related. This relationship is called a *function.* Point P represents the pair of numbers (1, 3) in the second row of the spreadsheet.

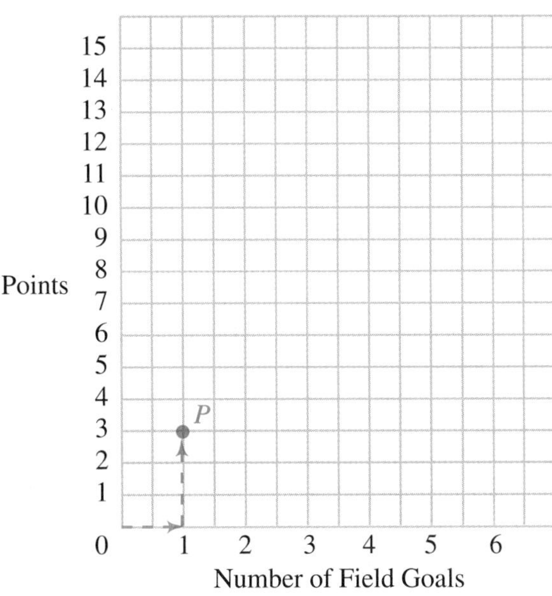

2. a. **Discussion** How is the location of point P determined?
   b. Copy the graph shown above. Plot a point for the pair of numbers (2, 6) in the third row of the spreadsheet.
   c. Plot points for the rest of the data in the spreadsheet. Are these points collinear or noncollinear?
   d. Draw a line through the points on your graph.

3. a. Mark the point on your line that represents 6 field goals. Draw a horizontal line through this point that intersects the vertical axis. What number do you hit?
   b. Does your result fit the pattern in the table? Explain.
   c. **Discussion** Do you think *every* point on the line fits the *pattern* in the table? Why or why not?
   d. **Discussion** Does *every* point on the line represent data that could appear in the table? Why or why not?

4. **Computer** Create a spreadsheet and a graph to show how many points you get for each type of score in football.
   a. touchdown (6 points) b. safety (2 points)
   c. **Discussion** How are the graphs alike? different?

At age 12, Kishae Swafford scored 20 touchdowns for the Marshall Minutemen, her Pop Warner football team. She was one of the league's fastest runners.

Source: *Sports Illustrated for Kids*

WORK TOGETHER

Work with a partner to answer the following questions.

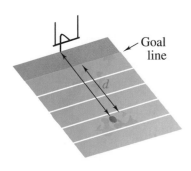

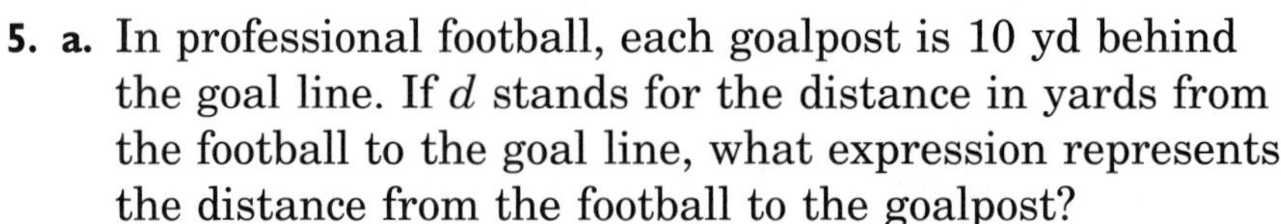

5. a. In professional football, each goalpost is 10 yd behind the goal line. If d stands for the distance in yards from the football to the goal line, what expression represents the distance from the football to the goalpost?

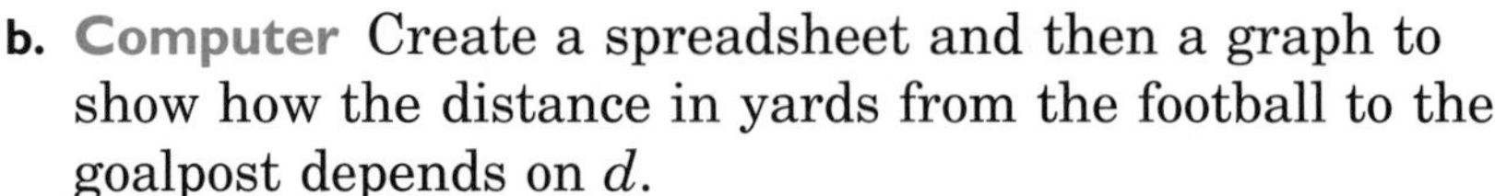

b. Computer Create a spreadsheet and then a graph to show how the distance in yards from the football to the goalpost depends on d.

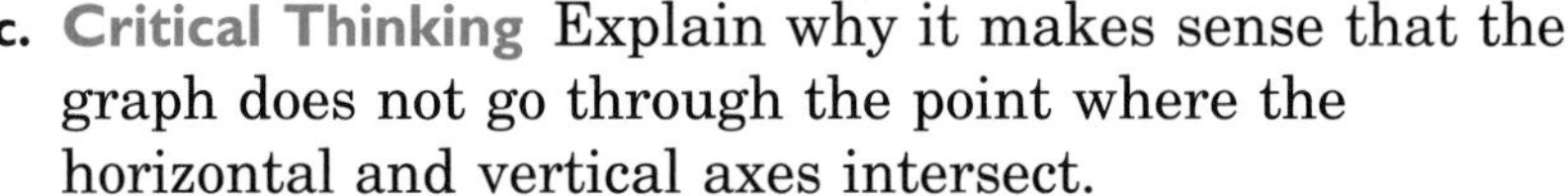

c. Critical Thinking Explain why it makes sense that the graph does not go through the point where the horizontal and vertical axes intersect.

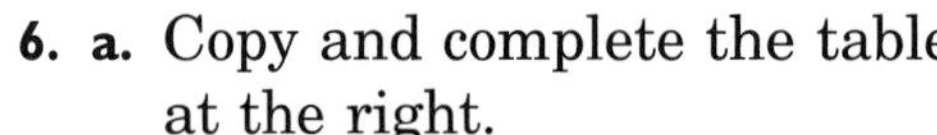

6. a. Copy and complete the table at the right.

b. Graph the data. Connect the points with a smooth curve. How is this graph different from the other graphs you have made in this lesson?

0	0
1	1
2	4
3	9
4	16
5	■

ON YOUR OWN

Goalposters, Inc.	
No. of Tees	Final Price
1	8
2	■
3	■
4	■

The Good Sports Shop	
No. of Tees	Final Price
1	2
2	■
3	■
4	■

7. Goalposters, Inc. sells kicking tees by mail for \$3 each, but adds on a shipping charge. The shipping charge is \$5 regardless of how many kicking tees you order.

The Good Sports Shop sells tees in its store for \$4 each. Of course, there is no shipping charge. Better still, if you use a coupon, you get \$2 off of your bill.

a. Copy and complete each table at the left. Remember to include the shipping charge and to use your coupon.

b. Let n stand for the number of tees you order. Write expressions to represent the final price of tees from Goalposters, Inc. and The Good Sports Shop.

c. Will the graphs be straight lines? Why or why not?

d. Will the graphs go through the point where the horizontal and vertical axes intersect? Why or why not?

e. Graph the data to check your predictions.

8. **Choose A, B, C, or D.** Your coach has received brochures from four companies who will sew your team name SAILORS on your uniforms. Professional Lettering charges \$2 per letter. Football Fans charges \$1 per letter plus a fee of \$5. The Sports Page charges \$1 per letter plus a fee of \$2. Speedy Lettering charges a flat fee of \$15. What graph represents the fees of the company that would be most economical for your coach to hire? (*Hint:* Only the cost for 1 to 6 letters is shown on each graph.)

A.

B.

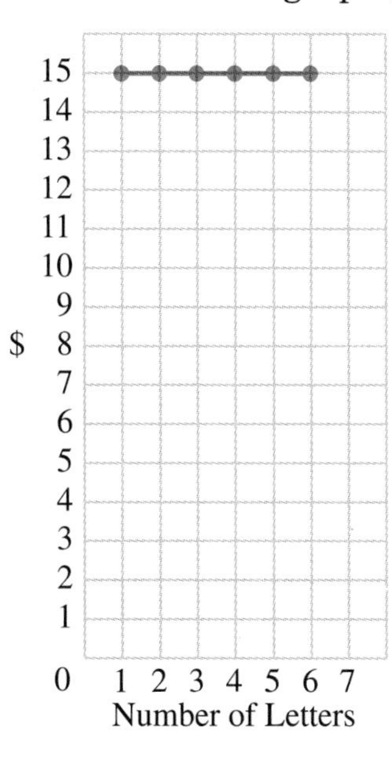

C.

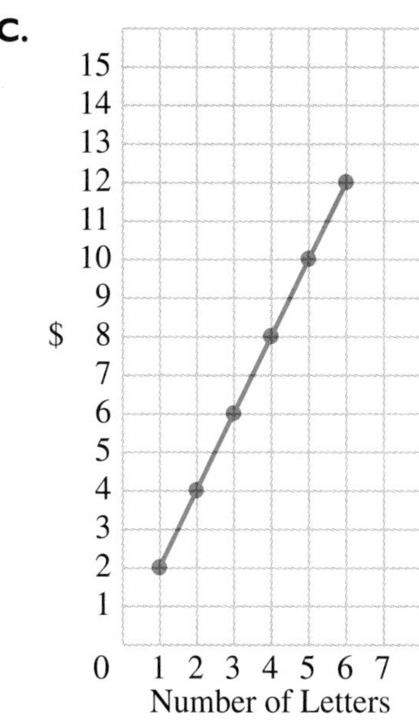

D.

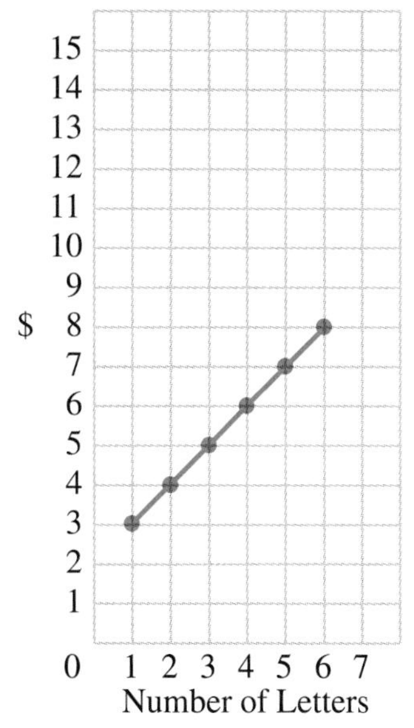

Mixed REVIEW

True or false?

1. All parallelograms are rhombuses.
2. A trapezoid is a parallelogram.

Write a word phrase for each variable expression.

3. $x \div 5$
4. $s + 14$

Write an expression for each word phrase.

5. 3 less than t
6. 8 more than a number n

7. Your town has 8 soccer teams. They are playing in a tournament. Each team will be out of the tournament after 1 loss. How many games will be played?

What's Ahead

- Solving addition and subtraction equations

WHAT YOU'LL NEED

✓ Algebra tiles 

✓ Calculator  

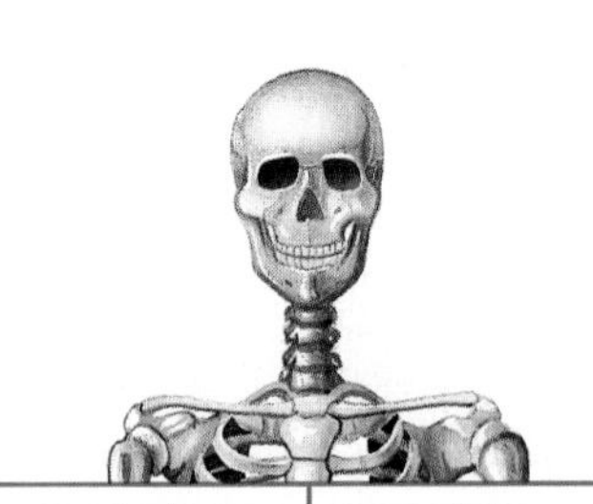

Body Part	No. of Bones
Arm	32
Leg	31
Skull	29
Spine	26
Chest	25

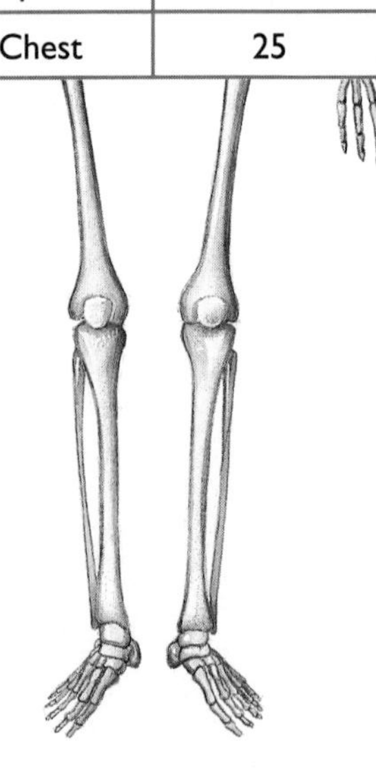

5-8 Addition and Subtraction Equations

WORK TOGETHER

Work with a partner to answer each question. Use the table at the left.

1. **a.** Write a numerical expression to represent the total number of bones in your arm and chest.
   b. Write a numerical expression to represent the total number of bones in your leg and spine.
   c. What do you notice about the value of each of these expressions?
2. Write five numerical expressions that have the same value as the sum of your age and your partner's age.

THINK AND DISCUSS

You can say that two numerical expressions are equal when they have the same value.

3. **Discussion** Explain why the numerical expression $4 + 6$ is equal to $12 - 2$, but the numerical expression $3 + 6$ is *not* equal to $4 + 8$.

You can write an equation to show that two expressions are equal. An **equation** is a mathematical sentence that contains an equal sign. The symbol = is read "is equal to."

4. Read each equation out loud.
   a. $5 + 9 = 14$ **b.** $9 + 6 = 15$ **c.** $21 = 25 - 4$
5. **Discussion** Explain why the equation $4 + 6 = 10$ is true and the equation $3 + 7 = 12$ is false.
6. State whether each equation is true or false.
   a. $16 = 9 + 7$ **b.** $3 + 11 = 15$ **c.** $8 + 12 = 20$

Equations can also contain variables. You **solve** an equation that contains a variable when you replace the variable with a number that makes the equation true. A number that makes the equation true is a **solution.**

7. a. Is the number 3 a solution to the equation $x + 4 = 7$? Why or not not?

b. Is the number 5 a solution to the equation $x + 4 = 12$? Why or why not?

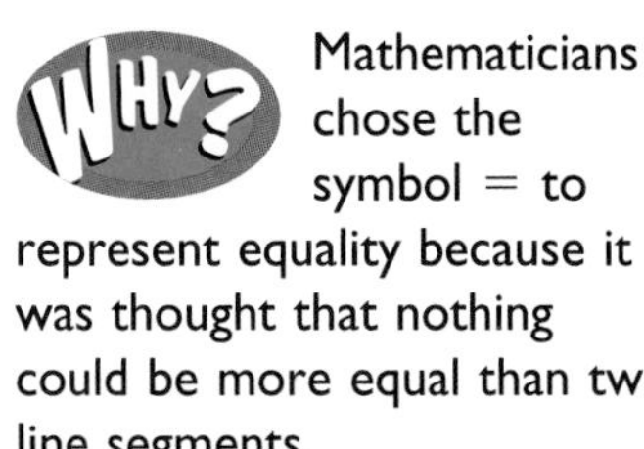
WHY?

Mathematicians chose the symbol = to represent equality because it was thought that nothing could be more equal than two line segments.

Source: *Historical Topics for the Mathematics Classroom*

8. State whether each number is a solution to the equation.

a. $y - 6 = 24; y = 18$ **b.** $20 = p + 4; p = 16$

c. $150 = k - 50; k = 200$ **d.** $j + 30 = 70; j = 100$

You can use tiles to model and solve addition equations.

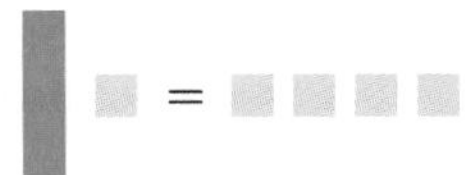

9. What equation is modeled above?

You can find the solution to an addition equation by isolating the variable, or getting the variable alone on one side of the equal sign.

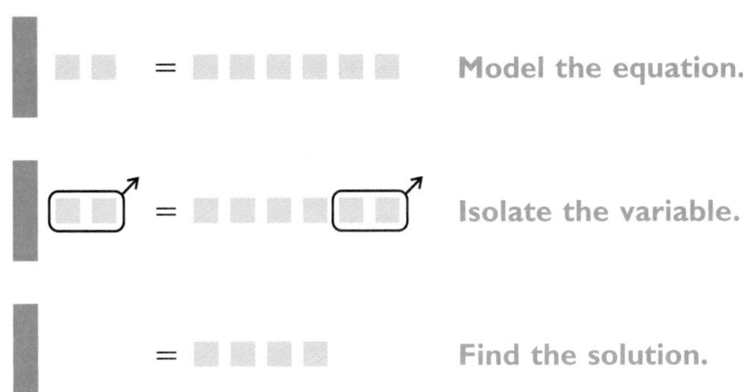
Model the equation.
Isolate the variable.
Find the solution.

10. a. What equation is modeled in the first step?

b. Discussion What was done to isolate the variable? What operation does this action represent?

c. What is the solution to the equation?

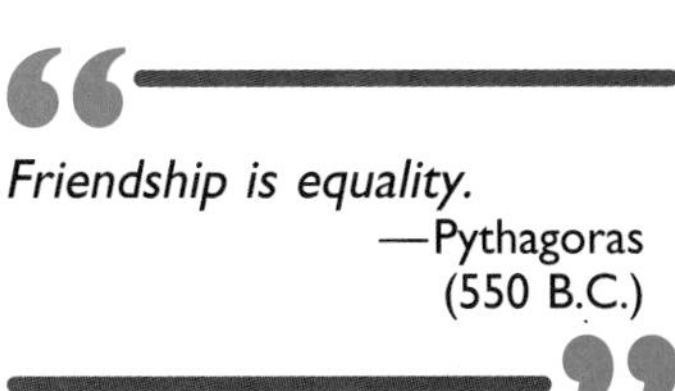

Friendship is equality.

—Pythagoras (550 B.C.)

11. Use tiles to solve each addition equation.

a. $m + 4 = 7$ **b.** $6 + k = 11$ **c.** $9 = h + 3$

You can use mental math to solve addition and subtraction equations.

12. a. In the addition equation $r + 8 = 15$, what does the value of r have to be to make the two sides of the equation equal?

b. In the subtraction equation $m - 4 = 10$, what does the value of m have to be to make the two sides of the equation equal?

13. Mental Math Solve each equation.

a. $8 = 3 + h$ **b.** $a + 5 = 8$

c. $m - 2.5 = 10$ **d.** $15 = g - 5$

e. $5 = n - 10$ **f.** $8 = k + 7.25$

If an equation cannot be solved using tiles or is too difficult to use mental math, you can use a calculator.

14. a. Discussion How could you use a calculator to solve the addition equation $x + 3{,}687 = 5{,}543$?

b. When you solve an addition equation, what operation key do you use?

15. Calculator Solve each addition equation.

a. $f + 1{,}478 = 3{,}652$ **b.** $12{,}597 = h + 6{,}954$

c. $183.35 = 119.75 + b$ **d.** $50{,}876 + s = 877{,}942$

16. a. Discussion How could you use a calculator to solve the subtraction equation $x - 4{,}621 = 1{,}347$?

b. When you solve a subtraction equation, what operation key do you use?

17. Calculator Solve each subtraction equation.

a. $y - 432 = 127$ **b.** $10{,}006 = k - 67{,}948$

c. $z - 11{,}897 = 34{,}954$ **d.** $189.622 = p - 24.752$

18. Discussion Explain what is meant by the statement *addition and subtraction undo each other.*

Operations that undo each other, such as addition and subtraction, are called **inverse operations.**

Julia B. Robinson (1920–1985), a mathematics researcher at the University of California–Berkeley, showed that there was no automatic method of determining whether an equation had a whole number solution.

Source: *The Book of Women's Firsts*

ON YOUR OWN

State whether each equation is true or false.

19. $5 + 10 = 15$ **20.** $9 - 3 = 2$ **21.** $24 = 6 + 18$

State whether the given number is a solution to the equation.

22. $h + 6 = 14; h = 7$ **23.** $k + 5 = 16; k = 11$

24. $p - 10 = 20; p = 20$ **25.** $18 = m - 4; m = 22$

26. $25 = 14 + y; y = 11$ **27.** $t - 5 = 25; t = 15$

Choose Use tiles, mental math, or a calculator to solve each equation.

28. $x + 2 = 7$ **29.** $152 = p + 64$ **30.** $16 = k + 7$

31. $h + 49 = 97$ **32.** $6 + w = 9$ **33.** $20 = m - 6.6$

34. $62 + r = 83$ **35.** $y - 265 = 124$ **36.** $w - 7 = 10$

37. $437.782 + y = 512.36$ **38.** $18{,}943 = x - 11{,}256$

39. **Writing** How are the words *equation* and *equilateral* related?

40. **Critical Thinking** Is the equality of an equation affected when you add or subtract the same value on both sides? Support your answer using examples.

41. **a.** Continue the next three rows of the pattern of equations shown below.

$1 + 3 = 4 \text{ or } 2^2$

$1 + 3 + 5 = 9 \text{ or } 3^2$

$1 + 3 + 5 + 7 = 16 \text{ or } 4^2$

b. What is the relationship between the number of addends and the base of the power?

c. How would you find the sum of the first ten odd numbers? What is their sum?

d. Find the sum of the first twenty odd numbers.

42. **Language** How is an equation like a sentence?

Name each polygon.

1. a polygon with 6 sides

2. a polygon with 10 sides

A record club sells CDs for $10.50 each plus $1.50 shipping charge per order.

3. Make a table showing the cost of ordering 1, 2, 3, 4, and 5 CDs.

4. Graph the data in your table.

5. A bus can hold 44 passengers. It starts out empty and picks up 1 passenger at the first stop, 2 at the second stop, 3 at the third stop, and so on. If no one gets off of the bus, at what stop will the bus become full?

The *addends* in the equation $6 + 8 = 14$ are 6 and 8.

Use the article below to answer each question.

A Dream Come True

Dwight Collins was ten years old when he first thought about crossing the Atlantic Ocean. Twenty-six years later, in June and July of 1992, he set out to live his dream. He set a record by pedaling his boat, *Tango,* from Newfoundland to London in just 40 days—14 days faster than the previous record. Can you imagine biking 2,250 miles across the ocean? Not even a storm with over 50 miles per hour winds could stop Dwight Collins from making his dream come true!

43. After the storm, Dwight still had about 1,200 mi of pedaling ahead of him. Let p represent the number of miles Dwight had already pedaled. Write and solve an equation to determine how many miles into the journey Dwight encountered the storm.

44. **a.** About how many miles did Dwight travel each day?

b. **Critical Thinking** Do you think he traveled this distance every day? Why or why not?

CHECKPOINT

1. **Choose A, B, C, or D.** Which expression has a value closest to the area of the parallelogram?

A. $x^2 + 3$ when $x = 8$

B. $2(b \div 2) + 1$ when $b = 70$

C. $10^2 - 3c$ when $c = 5$

D. $2a$ when $a = 32$

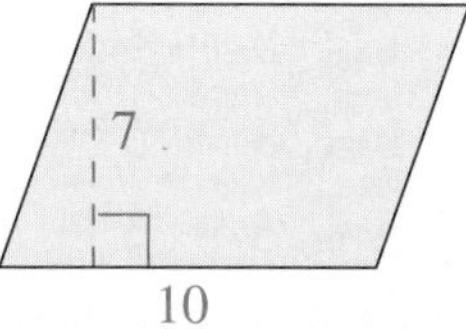

Write a variable expression for each word phrase.

2. twelve more than y

3. b increased by five

4. six decreased by w

5. r less than twenty-two

Solve each equation.

6. $b + 25 = 75$

7. $256 = m - 129$

8. $6 = 4 + y$

What's Ahead

- Solving multiplication and division equations

5-9 Multiplication and Division Equations

WHAT YOU'LL NEED

✓ Algebra tiles

✓ Calculator

Sport	Number of Players on Team
Baseball	9
Basketball	5
Soccer	11
Volleyball	6

WORK TOGETHER

The number of players on sports teams varies, as shown in the table at the left.

1. Suppose 30 students sign up for intramural sports.
   a. **Mental Math** How many volleyball teams can be formed?
   b. **Discussion** Let t represent the number of volleyball teams that can be formed. Does the multiplication equation $6t = 30$ or $30t = 6$ represent this situation? Explain.
   c. **Critical Thinking** How would the equation change if basketball teams are being formed?

THINK AND DISCUSS

You can use tiles to model and solve multiplication equations.

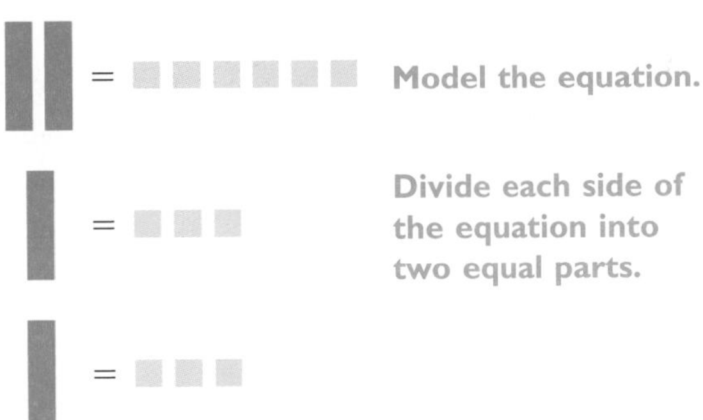

2. a. What equation is modeled in the first step?
   b. **Discussion** What was done to find the value of the variable? What operation does this action represent?
   c. What is the solution to the equation?

3. Use tiles to solve each multiplication equation.
   a. $2b = 8$ b. $2g = 10$ c. $3x = 12$

WHERE? Three sports were started in the United States: basketball, volleyball, and baseball.

Source: *The Information Please Kids' Almanac*

You can use mental math to solve multiplication and division equations.

4. a. In the multiplication equation $10r = 90$, what does the value of r have to be to make the two sides of the equation equal?

   b. In the division equation $h \div 4 = 6$, what does the value of h have to be to make the two sides of the equation equal?

5. **Mental Math** Solve each equation.

   a. $5c = 35$ b. $n \div 2 = 30$

   c. $100 = k \div 20$ d. $10 = 2.5h$

   e. $11m = 121$ f. $b \div 100 = 1{,}000$

Mrs. Shakuntala Devi of India used mental math to multiply the numbers 7,686,369,774,870 and 2,465,099,745,779. She got the correct answer in an amazing 28 seconds.

Source: *The Guinness Book of Records*

You can also solve multiplication and division equations using a calculator.

6. a. **Discussion** How could you use a calculator to solve the equation $125x = 1{,}875$?

   b. When you solve a multiplication equation, what operation key do you use?

7. **Calculator** Solve each multiplication equation.

   a. $125v = 2{,}750$ b. $4{,}731 = 57g$ c. $125.3p = 4{,}097.31$

   d. $83.5375 = 25.625s$ e. $123{,}456n = 97{,}406{,}784$

8. a. **Discussion** How could you use a calculator to solve the equation $x \div 429 = 6{,}864$?

   b. When you solve a division equation, what operation key do you use?

9. **Calculator** Solve each division equation.

   a. $s \div 62{,}409 = 289$ b. $t \div 5.88 = 75.38$

   c. $2{,}256 = g \div 1{,}111$ d. $p \div 287 = 64{,}685$

10. **Discussion** Explain what is meant by the statement multiplication and division are inverse operations.

11. **Critical Thinking** Compare multiplication and division equations with addition and subtraction equations. How are they alike? How are they different?

ON YOUR OWN

State whether the given number is a solution to the equation.

12. $6h = 60; h = 10$

13. $g \div 8 = 7; g = 64$

14. $15 = 5p; p = 3$

15. $36 = m \div 3; m = 12$

Choose Use tiles, mental math, or a calculator to solve each equation.

16. $3m = 15$

17. $g \div 5 = 25$

18. $805 = 7b$

19. $2.5h = 45$

20. $10 = k \div 20$

21. $y \div 43 = 1{,}204$

22. $16 = 4h$

23. $5.25c = 8.6625$

24. $h \div 20 = 9$

25. $204{,}425 = 1{,}258k$

26. $d \div 1{,}000 = 100$

27. **Writing** Without solving the equation $0.8t = 4$, state whether the value of t is greater than or less than 4. Explain.

28. **Choose A, B, C, or D.** Leon participated in a swimathon to raise money for the local food pantry. His neighbor, Mrs. Tram, sponsored him for $.20 per lap. Leon asked Mrs. Tram for $4.40. Choose the equation that Mrs. Tram could solve to determine how many laps Leon completed.

A. $0.20(4.40) = s$

B. $0.20s = 4.40$

C. $0.20 \div s = 4.40$

D. $0.20 = 4.40s$

29. Gasoline is $1.28 per gallon. Laila's bill is $16.

a. To determine how many gallons of gasoline Laila received would you use the equation $1.28g = 16$ or $16g = 1.28$?

b. How many gallons of gasoline did Laila receive?

Calculator Complete each equation. Predict the fifth and sixth equations for each pattern.

30.
$1 \times 8 + 1 = ■$
$12 \times 8 + 2 = ■$
$123 \times 8 + 3 = ■$
$1{,}234 \times 8 + 4 = ■$

31.
$99 \times 12 = ■$
$99 \times 13 = ■$
$99 \times 14 = ■$
$99 \times 15 = ■$

Mixed REVIEW

Find the perimeter of each rectangle.

1. length 8 cm, width 5 cm

2. length 2 m, width 56 m

Solve each equation.

3. $k + 8 = 14$

4. $m - 2 = 15$

5. The houses on Twelfth Avenue are numbered in order from 1 through 85. How many house numbers contain at least one digit 3?

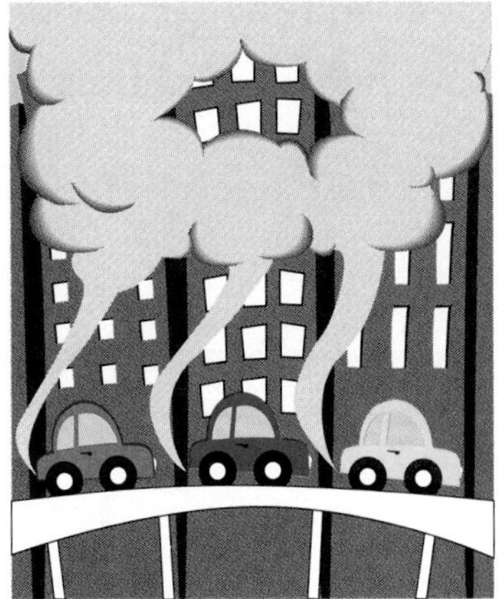

One gallon of gasoline produces about 20 pounds of carbon dioxide. The more carbon dioxide released into the air, the more polluted the air is.

Source: *50 Simple Things You Can Do To Save The Earth*

CHAPTER 5

Wrap Up

Patterns and Napier's Rods 5-1, 5-2

Each element of a pattern is a ***term.*** You can describe a number pattern with a rule that tells the first term and what to do to get each of the following terms.

1. Find the next three terms in the number pattern 2, 6, 18, 54, ... Write a rule to describe the pattern.

Exponents 5-3

Exponents show repeated multiplication. For 2^3, the base is 2, and the exponent is 3. Two is used as a factor 3 times: $2^3 = 2 \times 2 \times 2$.

Use the order of operations to evaluate numerical expressions.

- Do operations within parentheses first.
- Do all work with exponents.
- Multiply and divide from left to right.
- Add and subtract from left to right.

Evaluate each expression.

2. 3^2 **3.** $5^2 + 4^3$ **4.** $(6 + 2)^2 \div 4$ **5.** $(6 + 2^2) \div 8$

Variables and Variable Expressions 5-4, 5-6

A ***variable*** is a symbol that stands for a number. A ***variable expression,*** such as $2x - 3$, is an expression that contains at least one variable. To evaluate a variable expression, first replace each variable with a number. Then find the value of the numerical expression.

Write a variable expression for each phrase.

6. 5 less the number x **7.** the number y divided by p

8. Choose A, B, C, or D. Between which two numbers is the value of $(2 + x)^3$ for $x = 5$?

A. 1 − 99 **B.** 100 − 199 **C.** 200 − 299 **D.** 300 − 399

Patterns and Problem Solving 5-5, 5-7

One strategy for solving a problem is to look for a pattern. You can use a graph to show how numbers are related.

9. The cost of a 1-min call from Brookfield to the neighboring town Carnstown is \$.07. The cost of a 2-min call is \$.15 and a 3-min call is \$.23. If this pattern continues, what is the cost of a 5-min call?

10. a. Graph the data in Exercise 9. Draw a line through the points.

b. Writing Explain how you could use the graph to find the cost of an 8-min call.

Equations 5-8, 5-9

An equation is a mathematical sentence that contains an equal sign. You solve an equation that contains a variable by finding the ***solution*** that makes the equation true. You can solve an equation by using ***inverse operations,*** operations that undo each other.

For each equation, state the inverse operation that will help find the value of the variable. Then solve.

11. $x + 7 = 12$ **12.** $m - 8 = 15$ **13.** $4a = 32$ **14.** $t \div 4 = 32$

15. Choose A, B, C, or D. Ruth bought a calculator for x dollars. She gave the clerk \$20. She received \$7.54 in change. Which equation could you use to find the cost of the calculator?

A. $7.54x = 20$ **B.** $x - 20 = 7.54$ **C.** $x \div 7.54 = 20$ **D.** $x + 7.54 = 20$

GETTING READY FOR CHAPTER 6

1. Describe how to find the perimeter and area of a rectangle.

Evaluate each variable expression.

2.

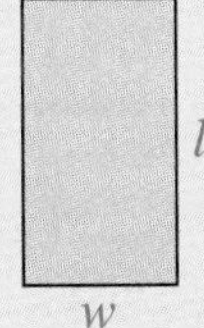

lw for $l = 5.2$ and $w = 3$

3.

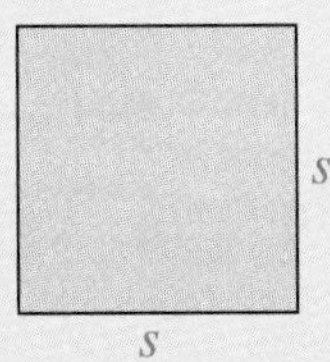

s^2 for $s = 17$

4.

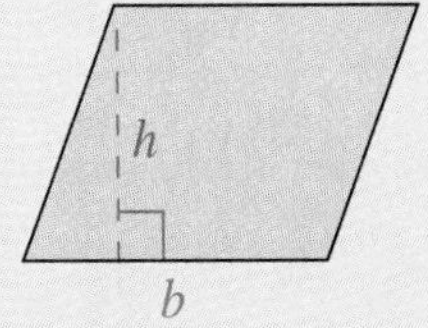

bh for $b = 12$ and $h = 10$

Putting It All Together

Follow Up

Mountains of Garbage

During the time you have been studying this chapter, Americans have thrown out several million tons of trash. Before it is too late, present your proposal for school garbage reduction to the principal. Revise your plan based on your study of the chapter. The following are suggestions to help you support your proposal.

- ✓ Make a graph showing trends in school trash production.
- ✓ Make a poster.
- ✓ Conduct a survey on student/faculty willingness to follow your trash-reduction plan.

If you worked the problems preceded by the magnifying glass (p. 187, # 17; and p. 206, # 35), the data you collected will also help you support your proposal.

Your efforts to cut down on your trash production can have major results. If each of us reduces the amount of garbage we produce by only one-fourth, we can each save more than 300 pounds of raw materials annually!

Excursion: Recycling not only saves the recycled materials themselves, it saves money. Estimate the amount of money your school could save by recycling. Explain how you made your estimate. Then suggest some ways the school could use the money it saves.

Who to Talk To:

- representatives of your local or state solid-waste agency

In the Blink of an Eye

Work with a partner. Count how many times each of you blink in one minute. Use a variable to represent this amount, such as: *b* (blinks per minute) = 20. Use this variable to write a multiplication expression that would show how many times your partner would blink in an hour, a day, a week, and a year. Solve each expression. Share your results with your classmates. Determine the average amount of blinks per minute for the entire class.

Express Yourself

You and two other friends have just started your own business doing odd jobs in your neighborhood. The number of hours you work each day varies. You charge each customer the same wage per hour for the work you do. At the end of each work day, you and your two friends split your earnings evenly. Using two variables, write an expression to describe the amount of money you would earn each day.

What's the Trick?

- Pick a number greater than 1.
- Add 3 to your number.
- Double your result.
- Subtract 6.
- Subtract your original number.
- Record your final result.
- What's the trick?

WHAT'S MY NUMBER?

Rules:

- Three or more players
- Each player has ten 3" x 5" index cards. Players write a division or multiplication fact with one missing number on each of their ten cards to make an equation.
- Shuffle all cards together.
- Players take turns drawing a card and solving the equation. When a player gives the correct answer, the product or quotient is that player's score. If the player does not give a correct answer, the player receives no score and play continues to the left.
- The player with the highest score wins.

CHAPTER 5

Assessment

1. a. Find the next three terms in this number pattern: 7, 16, 25, 34, ...
   b. Write a rule to describe the pattern.

2. **Choose A, B, or C.** Which number pattern can be described by the following rule: *Start with the number 3 and add 7 repeatedly?*
   A. 3, 10, 17, ...
   B. 7, 10, 13, ...
   C. 1, 3, 7, ...

3. **Writing** How would you use Napier's rods to multiply 724×9?

4. Evaluate each expression.
   a. $500 + (12 - 8)^3$
   b. $3^5 \times 2^4$
   c. $8^2 \div 4 - 2^4$
   d. $8 + 4^2 \div 2$

5. Compare using <, >, or =.
   $3 + (2)^3$ ■ $(3 + 2)^3$

6. Carol is training for a swim meet. The first week she swims 4 laps per day. The second week she swims 8 laps per day, the third week 12 laps per day, and the fourth week 16 laps per day. She continues this pattern. How many laps per day will Carol swim in the eighth week?

7. Choose a variable. Then write an expression for each model.
   a. 
   b. 

8. Evaluate $2a^2 + b$ for $a = 5$ and $b = 18$.

9. Write and solve the equation represented by each model.
   a. =
   b. 

10. Write a variable expression for each word phrase.
    a. eight less than *d*
    b. twice as many as *q*

11. **Mental Math** Solve each equation.
    a. $14 = y - 8$
    b. $2m = 26$

12. Solve each equation.
    a. $25 + b = 138$
    b. $n - 46 = 84$
    c. $135 = 10y$
    d. $k \div 12 = 3$

13. Al made a rocket for science class. The table shows the height of the rocket after a given number of seconds.

Time (s)	Height (ft)
1	2
2	3
3	6
4	10
5	■
6	■

    a. Copy and complete the table. Then graph the data.
    b. Are the points collinear? Explain.

CHAPTER 5

Cumulative Review

Choose A, B, C, or D.

1. Which number is the *best estimate* for 2.17 − 0.014?

   A. 2 **B.** 2.1 **C.** 2.15 **D.** 2.2

2. Which name is *not* a name for an acute angle shown in the diagram?

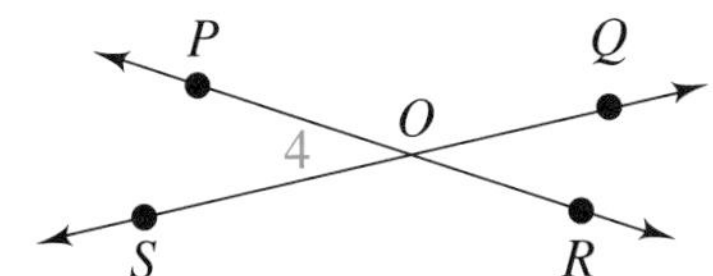

   A. $\angle 4$ **B.** $\angle POS$
   C. $\angle SOR$ **D.** $\angle ROQ$

3. In a set of data, what name is given to the number found by subtracting the smallest number from the largest?

   A. mean **B.** median
   C. mode **D.** range

4. What rule could you use to describe the number pattern 4, 8, 12, 16, 20?

   A. Start with 4 and add 4 repeatedly.
   B. Start with 4 and multiply by 2.
   C. Start with 4 and write the square.
   D. Write the first five powers of 4.

5. Which set of decimals below is in order from least to greatest?

   A. 0.2, 0.02, 0.22 **B.** 0.15, 0.51, 1.05
   C. 0.24, 0.3, 0.05 **D.** 0.49, 0.4, 0.05

6. If 31.2 × ■ = 0.00312, what is the value of ■?

   A. 10,000 **B.** 0.0001
   C. 1,000 **D.** 0.001

7. What is the value of $3 + 4 \cdot 2^3$?

   A. 56 **B.** 35 **C.** 515 **D.** 27

8. What information do you NOT need to know in order to solve the problem?

   "At McFast Food, a cheeseburger costs 99¢; fries cost 20¢ less than a cheeseburger, and milk costs 75¢. If Jan has three dollars, can she buy two cheeseburgers and milk for lunch?"

   A. the cost of a cheeseburger
   B. the cost of fries
   C. the cost of milk
   D. Jan has three dollars.

9. Give the name of the polygon that is *not* a quadrilateral.

   A. trapezoid **B.** parallelogram
   C. rhombus **D.** pentagon

10. The Amazon River in South America flows through one of Earth's largest tropical rainforests and carries one sixth of Earth's water that flows into oceans. About what percent of water flowing into oceans is this?

    A. 16% **B.** 10% **C.** 12.5% **D.** 6%

11. Name a pair of triangles that do *not* appear to be congruent.

    A. $\triangle KNO$, $\triangle KLO$
    B. $\triangle MON$, $\triangle MOL$
    C. $\triangle NKL$, $\triangle NML$
    D. $\triangle KMN$, $\triangle KML$

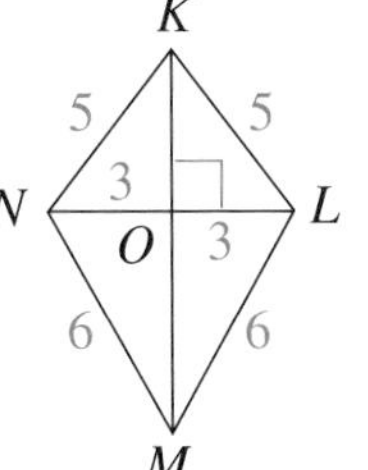

CHAPTER 6

Measurement

Use Your Head

Wearing a properly fitting helmet while biking can reduce the risk of serious head injury by 85%. In the past five years if all the bicyclists in the United States had worn a helmet:

- a life could have been saved every day
- a head injury could have been prevented every 4 min.

7 rear-wheel sprockets plus 3 chain wheels = 21 combinations → 21 speed bike
26" diameter rim → a 26" bicycle

rear-wheel sprocket

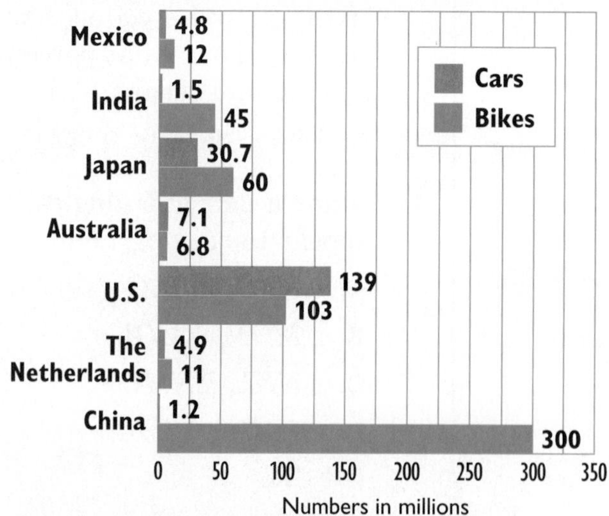

Source: *Information Please Environmental Almanac*

sprung-rollers

Data File 6

WHAT YOU WILL LEARN

- how to estimate and find area of geometric figures
- how to use and apply measurement concepts
- how to use technology to explore PI
- how to solve problems by making a model

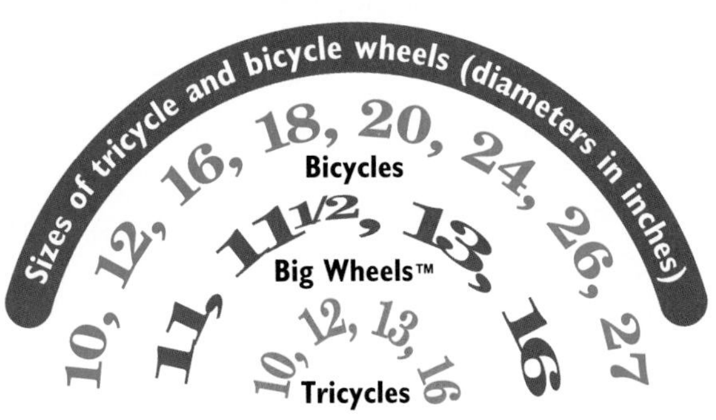

Source: *Arithmetic Teacher*

The Sumerians are credited with inventing the wheel in about 3,500 B.C.

U.S. Cycling Federation National Records for 20 km

Male

Age	min:s	km/h
12 and under	33:33	35.77
14 and under	28:06	42.86
16 and under	25:21	47.34
18 and under	25:04	47.87

Female

Age	min:s	km/h
12 and under	37:42	31.83
14 and under	32:22	37.08
16 and under	30:39	39.15
18 and under	29:42	40.40

Source: U.S. *Cycling Federation*

seat height = 1.09 x leg length (inseam measurement)

handlebar

brake levers

seat height

chain wheel

26 inches

pedal

chain

investigation

Project File

Memo

Orlando used tiles to build squares. He labeled the squares according to the number of tiles in each row and each column. Pictured are a 2-square and a 3-square.

He compiled three pieces of data about each square:

a. number of tiles used
b. number of tiles used in border
c. number of tiles needed to build the square from the previous square

For the 3-square, he used 9 tiles. He used 8 tiles for the border. He needed 5 additional tiles to build the 3-square from the 2-square. After studying his squares for a long time, he said: "It would take 300 tiles to make a 30-square. There would be 120 tiles in the border. I would need 61 tiles to build the 30-square from the 29-square." Was he right?

Mission: Decide whether Orlando was right or wrong about each of his claims. Then write an explanation telling how you reached your decision.

Leads to Follow

- ✓ Can you reach a decision by building a 30-square?
- ✓ How can you use patterns in your investigation?
- ✓ How did Orlando find the data for the 3-square?

What's Ahead

- Estimating area

6-1 Estimating Area

THINK AND DISCUSS

When you find the number of *square units* inside a figure, you are finding the area of the figure.

1. How many square units are in each figure? Describe your method for finding each area.

a. 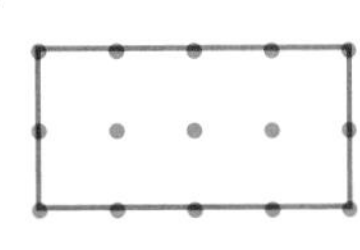

b. 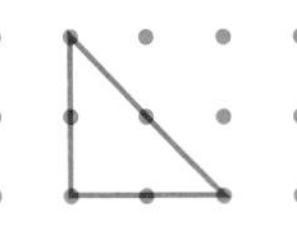

c. 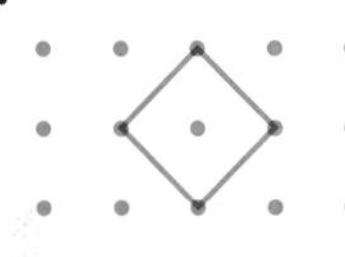

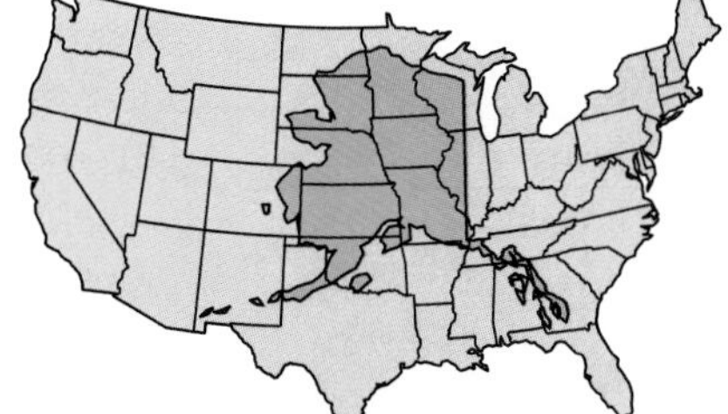

If the United States was made up of states the size of Alaska, there would only be enough area for six states. **How many states do you think would fit if they all were the size of your state?**

Source: *Comparisons*

Some of the standard units we use to measure area are square centimeters (cm^2), square meters (m^2), square inches ($in.^2$), square feet (ft^2), and square yards (yd^2).

2. Name some other units of area.

This figure is shown on centimeter graph paper.

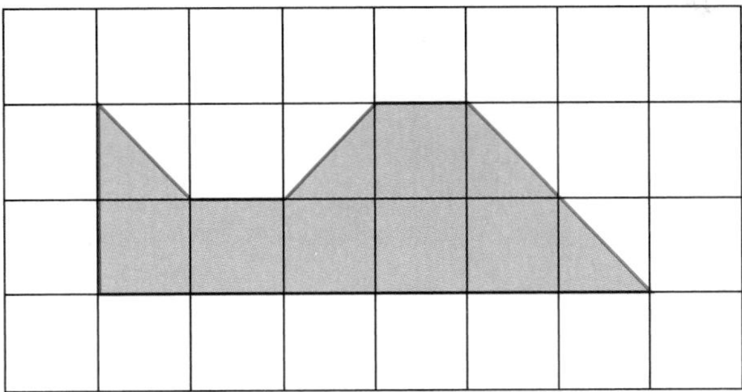

3. a. What is the area of each square of the graph paper?
   b. What is the area of the shaded figure?
   c. How did you find the area?
   d. Suppose each square represents 9 m^2. What is the area?

Sometimes an exact area is difficult to find but an estimate is enough. If you are using a graph, you can decide whether each square is full, almost full, about half full, or almost empty.

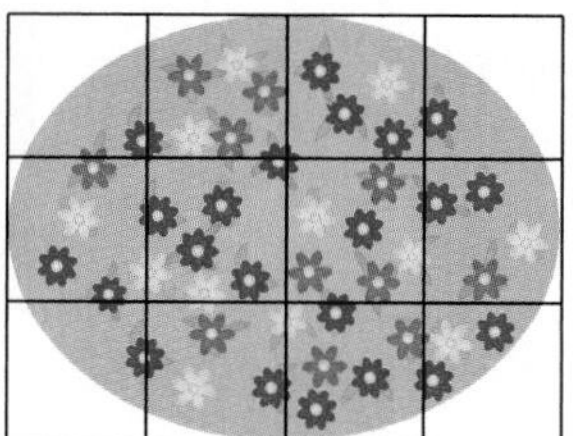

4. Estimate the area of the flower bed. Each square represents 1 m^2.

5. Each square below represents 4 mi^2.
   a. How many squares are filled or almost filled?
   b. How many squares are about half filled?
   c. Estimate the area of the lake.

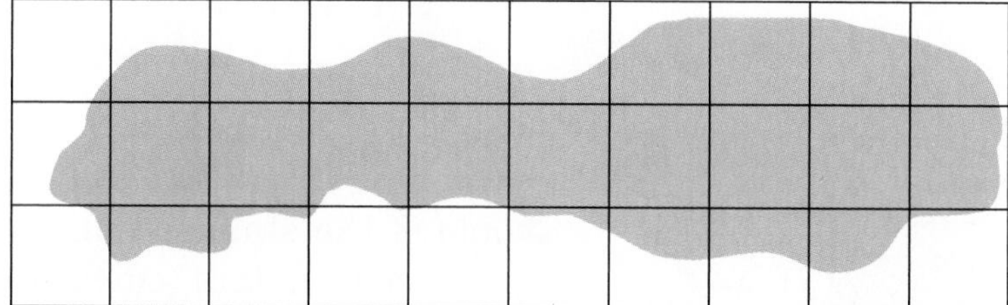

WORK TOGETHER

Work with a partner to estimate the area of Australia. Each square represents an area 240 miles by 240 miles.

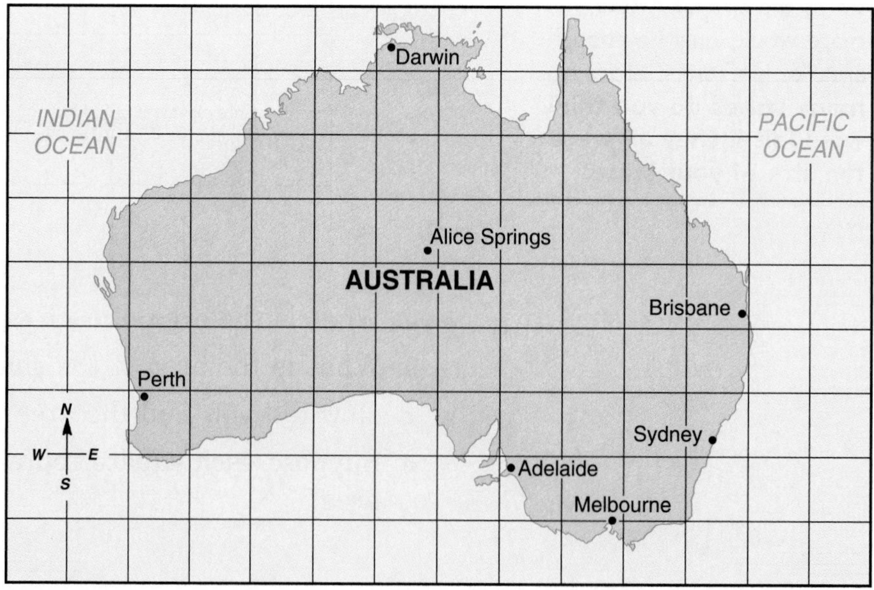

ON YOUR OWN

Find the area of each figure. The area of each square is 1 cm².

6. 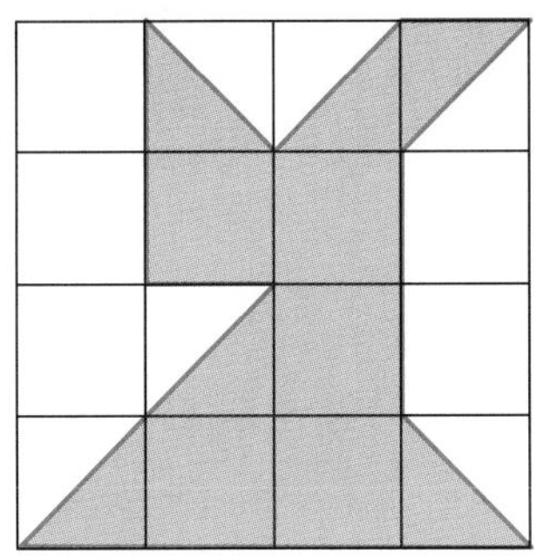

7. 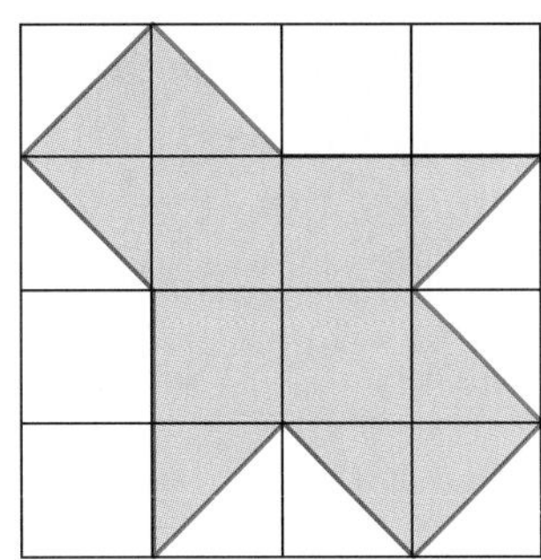

Estimate the area of each figure. Assume that each square represents 1 in.².

8. 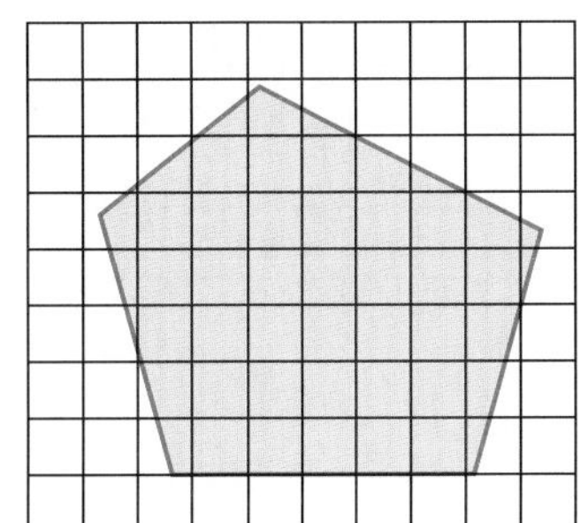

9. 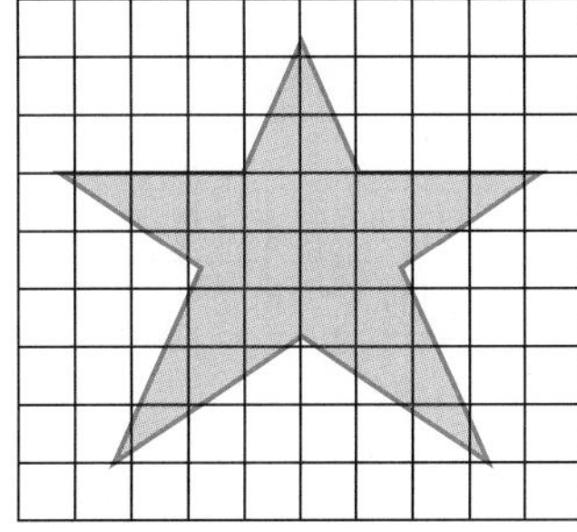

Estimate the area of each figure. Assume that each square represents 4 cm².

10. 

11. 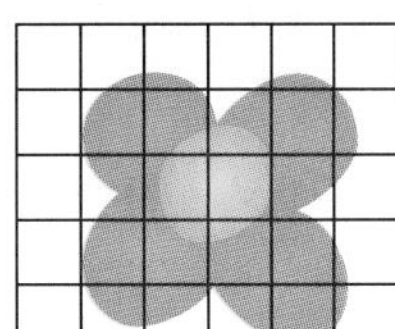

12. **Activity** Place your hand, with fingers touching, on centimeter graph paper. Trace around your hand. On a second sheet of centimeter graph paper, trace around your hand with the fingers spread apart. Try to draw a line at the same place on the wrist for both drawings.
    a. Estimate the area of each hand.
    b. **Critical Thinking** What might account for any differences in your two estimates for part (a)?

Mixed REVIEW

1. What is the sum of the first 20 odd numbers?

Solve each equation.

2. $3x = 27$
3. $17 = y \div 9$

Evaluate each expression.

4. 4^2
5. $(3 + 2)^2$

6. Use the digits 1, 3, 5, 7, and 9 in any order to write a multiplication problem with the greatest product.

13. **Writing** Describe two situations where finding an estimate of an area, rather than actually measuring the area, is sufficient.

14. **Choose A, B, C, or D.** Each square represents 100 m^2. Which is the best estimate for the area of the figure?

A. 3,000 m^2 **B.** 15.5 cm^2

C. 1,550 m^2 **D.** 15.5 m^2

15. Which region has the greatest area? Which has the least area?

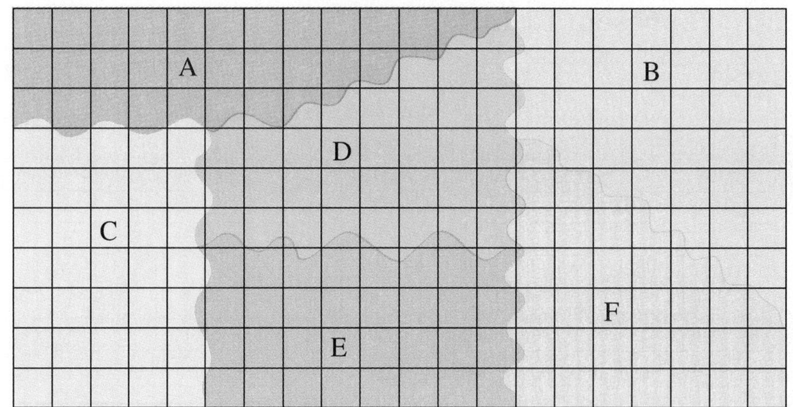

The Homestead Act provided opportunities for thousands of people. The act allowed settlers to get 160 acres of land for free. If settlers didn't want to improve the land, they could pay $1.25 per acre.

16. **Critical Thinking** How many square inches are in a square yard? Use a drawing to show how you found your answer.

Estimate Estimate the area of each name. Each square represents 1 in.^{2}.

17.

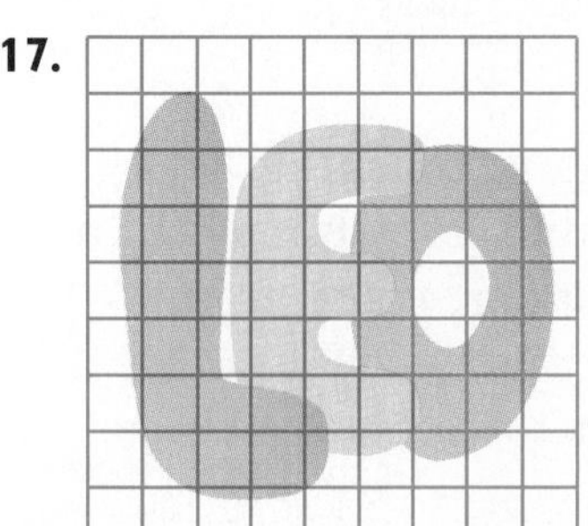

18.

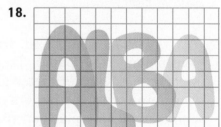

19. Draw your name on graph paper. Estimate the area of your name in square units.

What's Ahead

- Finding area and perimeter of rectangles and squares

6-2 Area of Rectangles and Squares

WHAT YOU'LL NEED

✓ Square tiles

✓ Graph paper

THINK AND DISCUSS

Moses is planning a garden. He decides to use 12 square garden plots that measure 1 m on each side. He wants to arrange them in a rectangle. After he lays out the plots, he will put a fence around the outside of the garden.

Problem Solving Hint

Drawing diagrams may help.

1. **a.** How could Moses arrange the plots so that he would have the least perimeter and use the least amount of fence?

   b. How could Moses arrange the plots so that he would have the greatest perimeter?
2. **a.** What is the area of the arrangement with the least perimeter?

   b. What is the area of the arrangement with the greatest perimeter?

   c. Will the area change if Moses arranges the plots in a nonrectangular shape? Why or why not?

WHEN? In 600 B.C. Nebuchadnezzar had the Hanging Gardens of Babylon built. They were so beautiful and complex that they became one of the seven wonders of the ancient world.

Source: *Encyclopedia Britannica*

In the garden-plot problem you can count the square plots to find the area of the rectangular arrangement. When you do not have squares to count, you can find the area A of a rectangle by multiplying the length l and the width w. You can find the perimeter P by adding $l + w + l + w$ to get $2l + 2w$, or $2(l + w)$.

l

w

Area and Perimeter of a Rectangle

$$A = l \times w$$

$$P = 2(l + w)$$

A square is a rectangle in which the length and the width are equal. You can find the area A of a square by squaring the length s of a side. The perimeter P is $4s$.

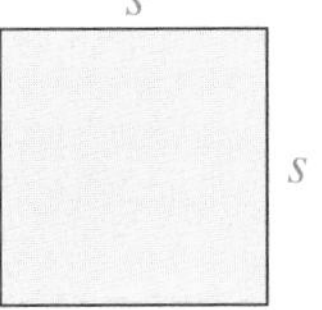

Area and Perimeter of a Square

$$A = s \times s = s^2$$

$$P = 4s$$

3. Find the perimeter and the area of a square with sides 8 cm long.

Example Find the area and perimeter of the backyard.

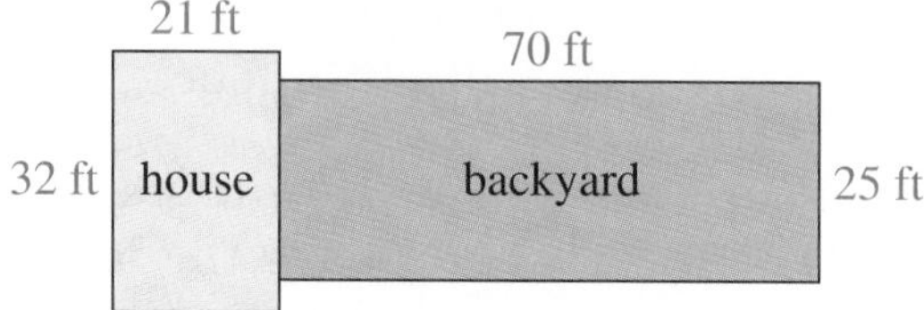

- The length of the backyard is 70 ft. The width is 25 ft. To find the area, use $A = l \times w$.

  $A = l \times w = 70 \times 25 = 1{,}750$

- To find the perimeter, use $P = 2(l + w)$.

  $P = 2(l + w) = 2(70 + 25) = 2 \times 95 = 190$

The area of the backyard is 1,750 ft^2. The perimeter is 190 ft.

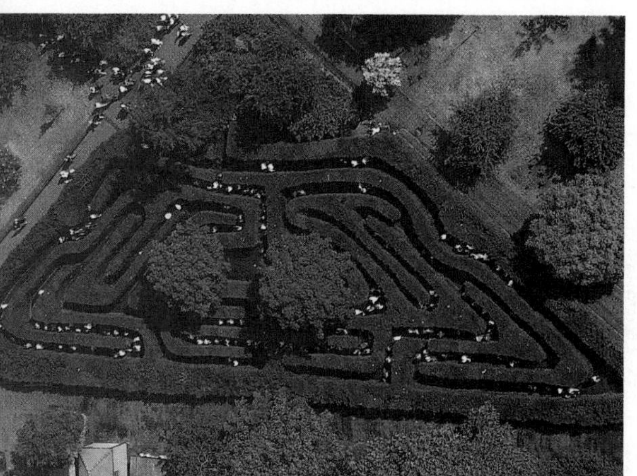

***The 1,250 m^2 garden** maze at Hampton Court in England had its 300th anniversary in 1991. Every year thousands of tourists pay $2.15 to try to find their way through the 2.5 m tall hedges.*

Source: *Encyclopedia Britannica*

4. In the Example, why was the area given in square feet and the perimeter in feet?

5. If you were to fence the backyard in the Example, would you need 190 ft of fence? Why or why not?

WORK TOGETHER

Use square tiles to form the following rectangles. Record the results on graph paper.

6. Form at least two rectangles where the area (in square units) is less than the perimeter (in units).

7. Form at least one rectangle where the area is equal to the perimeter.

8. Form at least two rectangles where the area is greater than the perimeter.

TRY THESE

Find the area and perimeter of each rectangle.

9.

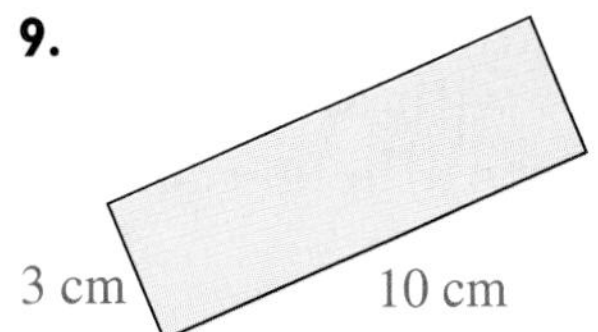

10.

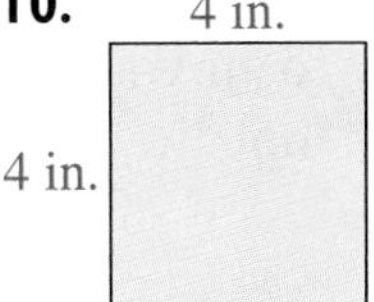

11.

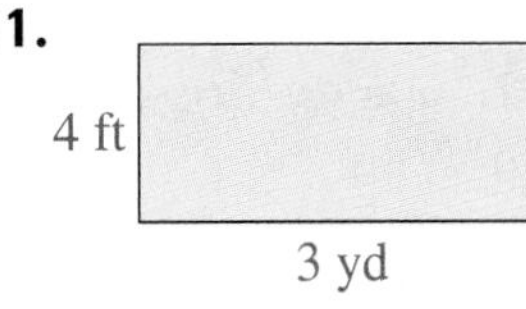

FLASHBACK

1 yd = 3 ft

ON YOUR OWN

Use a centimeter ruler to measure the length and width of each rectangle. Then find the perimeter and area.

12.

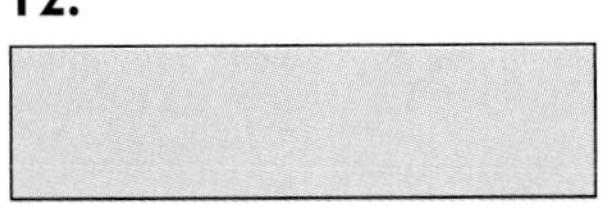

13.

14.

Choose **Use a calculator, paper and pencil, or mental math.**

15. The length of a rectangle is 20 in. The width is 10 in.

a. What is the area?

b. What is the perimeter?

16. The area of a rectangle is 24 in^2. One dimension is 6 in. What is the perimeter?

17. The perimeter of a square is 12 in. What is the area of the square?

18. The length of a rectangle is 16.5 cm. The width is 8.2 cm. What is the area of the rectangle?

19. The perimeter of a rectangle is 22 ft. The width is 4 ft. What is the length?

20. a. How much fencing do you need to enclose a rectangular garden that is 9 ft by 6 ft?

b. If you use fence sections that are 3 ft wide, how many sections will you need?

Mixed REVIEW

Use Napier's rods to find each product.

1. 46×8

2. 912×9

Estimate the area of the figure in square units.

3.

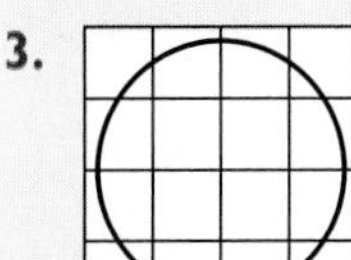

4. Yuma plans to drive 1,350 mi. His car averages 25 mi/gal. The gas tank holds 15 gal. Gas costs $1.299 per gallon.

a. How many tankfuls will he need?

b. How much will the gas cost?

21. Each side of a square is 0.5 m long.
   a. What is the perimeter?
   b. What is the area?

22. **Gardening** You'd like to have a garden with area 18 ft^2. You have a space 6 ft long in which to put the garden. How wide should it be?

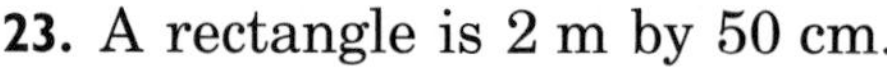

23. A rectangle is 2 m by 50 cm.
   a. What is the perimeter?
   b. What is the area?

24. **Data File 3 (pp. 92–93)** Find the area of the world's smallest stamp.

25. **Choose A, B, C, or D.** A rectangle is 15.95 m by 8.25 m. Which of the following is the best estimate for the area?
   A. about 48 m
   B. about 48 m^2
   C. about 128 m
   D. about 128 m^2

26. The area of a rectangular parking lot is 24 yd^2. Find all the possible whole-number dimensions in yards of the parking lot.

27. The perimeter of a rectangle is 10 m. Find all the possible whole-number dimensions in meters.

28. Estimate the area of this rectangle.

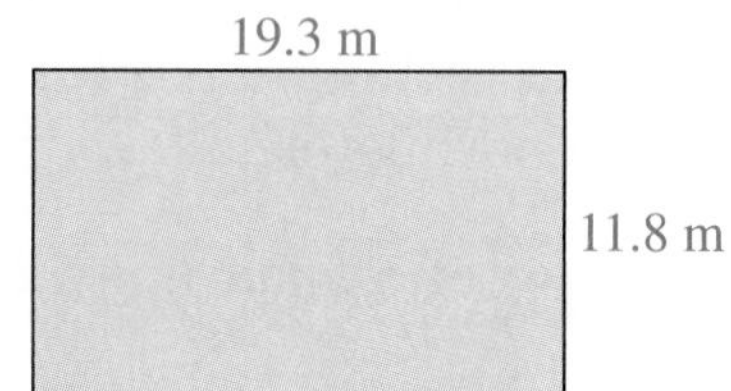

29. **Writing** Suppose you know the area of a rectangle. Can you then find its perimeter? Why or why not? Use examples to illustrate your answer.

30. a. **Investigation (p. 228)** Make a table that shows the number of tiles you would need to build each tile square from a 1-square through a 10-square.
   b. Describe the relationship between the number of tiles needed to build a tile square and the area of the square.

The Great Wall of China spans 2,971 km along a mountain range in Northern China. The wall is 14 m high and 7 m thick in some places. **If you traveled along the wall at 10 km/h, how long would it take you to travel its length?**

Source: *A Ride Along the Great Wall*

What's Ahead

- Developing and using area formulas for parallelograms and triangles

WHAT YOU'LL NEED

✓ Graph paper 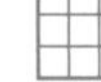

✓ Scissors 

6-3 Area of Parallelograms and Triangles

WORK TOGETHER

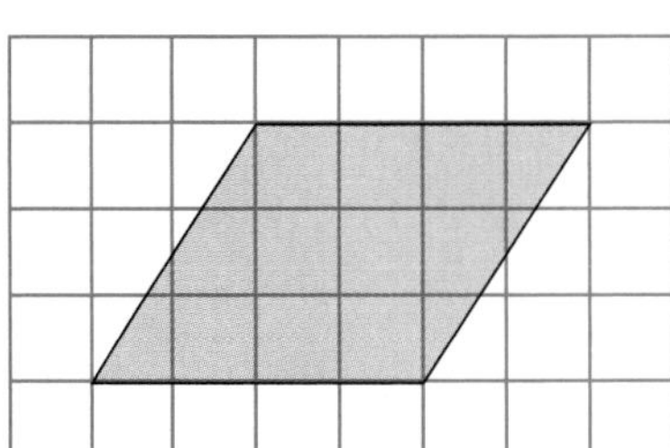

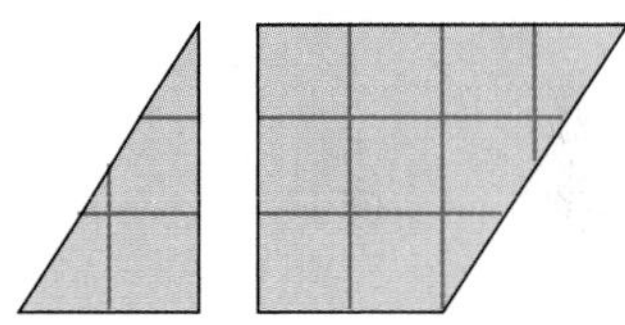

- Draw a nonrectangular parallelogram on graph paper.
- Draw the perpendicular segment from one vertex to the base.
- Cut the parallelogram out and cut along the perpendicular segment.
- Rearrange the two pieces to form a rectangle.

1. a. What is the area of the rectangle?
   b. What was the area of the original parallelogram? Why?
   c. Compare your models to those made by other groups. Are the results the same?

Use centimeter graph paper to draw two congruent triangles. Cut out the triangles. Arrange them to form a parallelogram.

2. How does the area of each triangle compare to the area of the parallelogram?

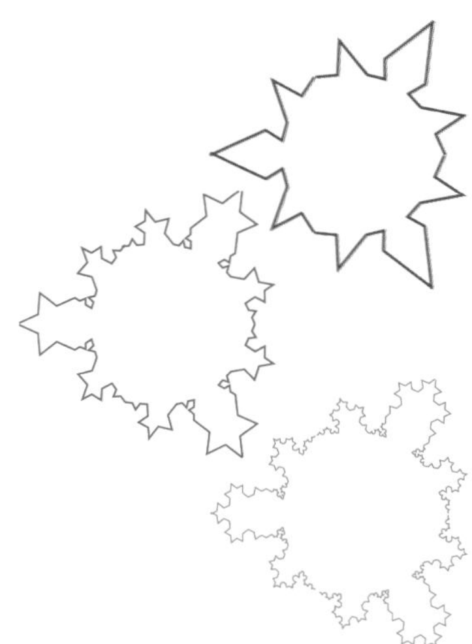

In this pattern, the perimeter doubles each time, while the area increases slightly. If you repeat the steps, the perimeter gets gigantic but the area stays less than four times the area of the original figure.

THINK AND DISCUSS

Any side of a parallelogram or triangle can be considered the base, with length b. The *height* h of the parallelogram or triangle is the length of a perpendicular segment from a vertex to the line containing the base.

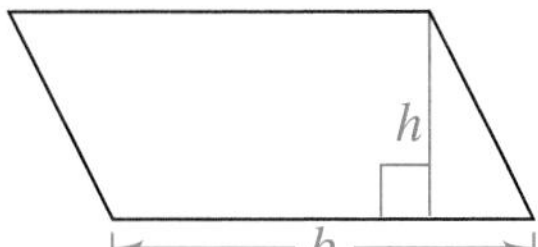

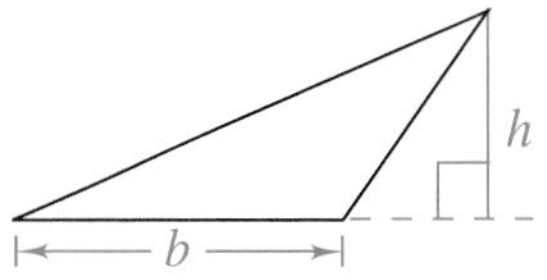

In the Work Together activity you found that the area of a parallelogram is the same as the area of a rectangle with the same dimensions. The area of a triangle is related to the area of a parallelogram with the same base length and height.

Area of Parallelograms and Triangles

Area of a parallelogram = base length × height = bh

Area of a triangle = $\frac{1}{2}$ × base length × height = $\frac{1}{2}bh$

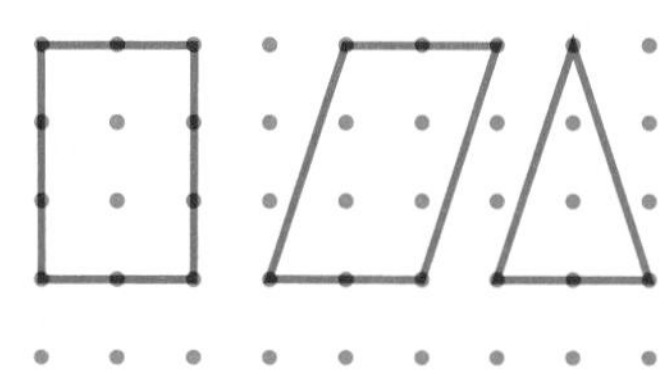

3. What is the area of the rectangle?
4. What is the area of the parallelogram that is not a rectangle?
5. What is the area of the triangle?

Sometimes it helps to divide a figure into smaller polygons. Then you can find the areas.

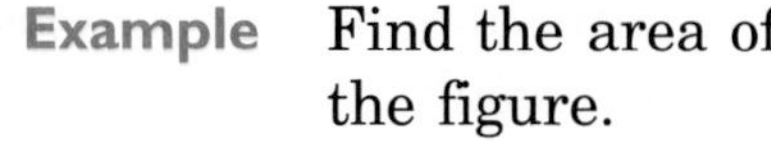

Example Find the area of the figure.

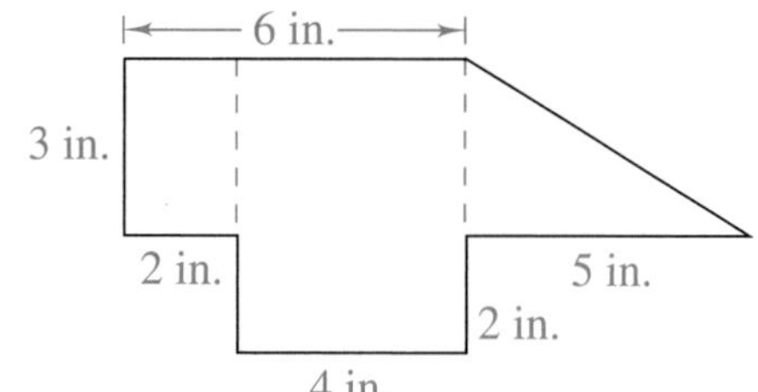

You could divide the polygon into two rectangles and a triangle, as shown by the dashed lines.

Then find the area of each of the polygons.

Area of smaller rectangle $= 3 \times 2 = 6 \text{ in.}^2$

Area of larger rectangle $= 5 \times 4 = 20 \text{ in.}^2$

Area of triangle $= \frac{1}{2}(5 \times 3) = \frac{1}{2} \times 15 = 7.5 \text{ in.}^2$

Add the three areas to find the area of the composite figure.

$6 \text{ in.}^2 + 20 \text{ in.}^2 + 7.5 \text{ in.}^2 = 33.5 \text{ in.}^2$

LOOK BACK What other ways could you divide the figure to find the area?

***The Edmonton Mall** in Alberta, Canada covers 5.2 million ft^2. The mall even has an indoor roller coaster.*

Source: *Guinness Book of Records*

TRY THESE

Find each area.

6.

7.

8.

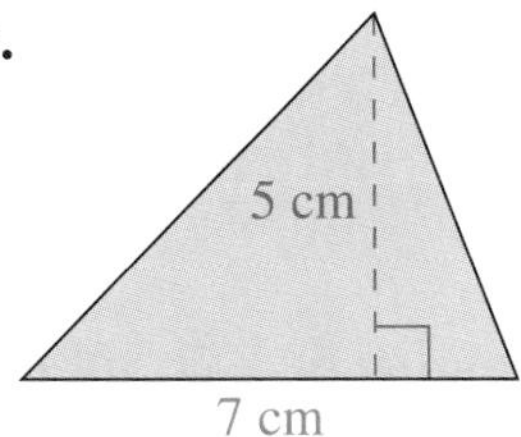

9.

> *Equations are just the boring part of mathematics. I attempt to see things in terms of geometry.*
>
> —Stephen Hawking (1942–)

ON YOUR OWN

Find each perimeter and area.

10.

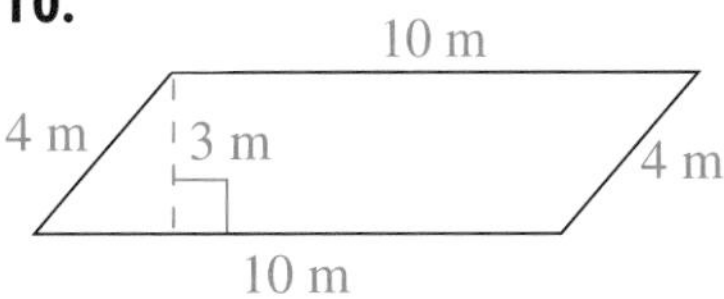

11.

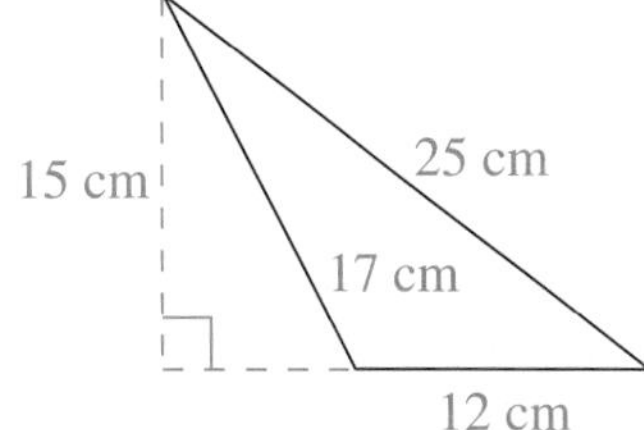

Copy each figure on dot paper. Then find its area by dividing it into polygons for which you can find the areas.

12.

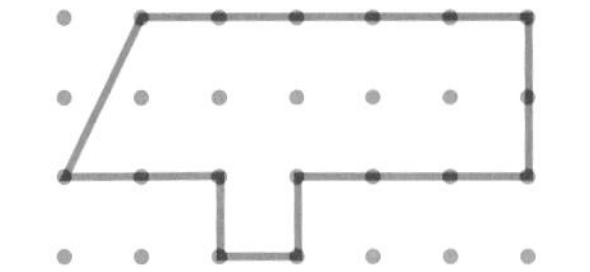

13.

14.

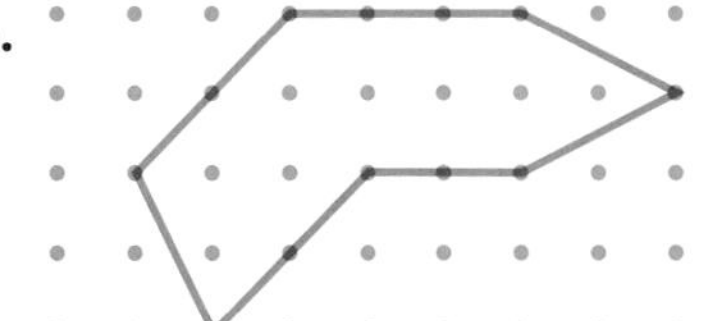

15.

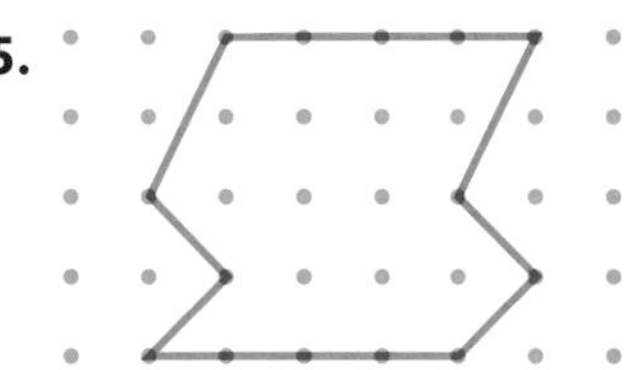

Write *true* or *false*.

1. A butterfly's wings are symmetric.
2. Your hand is symmetric.

Find each area.

3. a square with sides 4 in.
4. a rectangle with length 8 ft and width 3 ft
5. A flim is worth more than a flam. A flum is worth more than a flom. If a flam is worth less than a flom, which is greater, a flum or a flam?

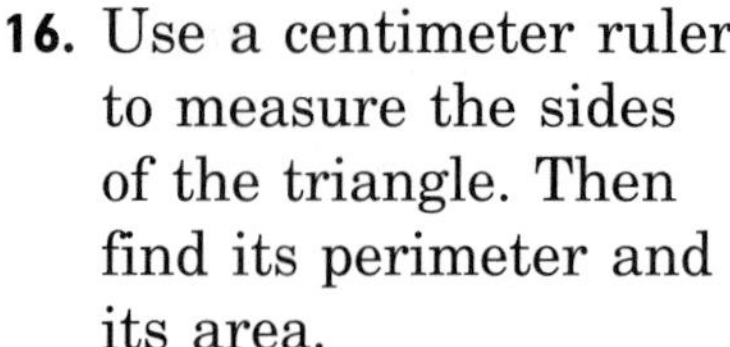

16. Use a centimeter ruler to measure the sides of the triangle. Then find its perimeter and its area.

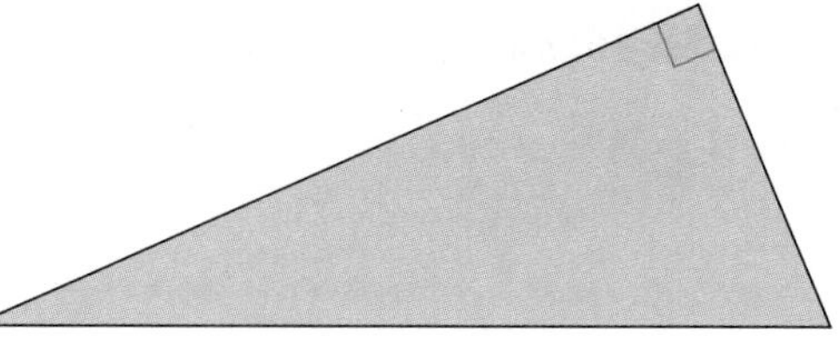

17. Find the area of each parallelogram.

a.

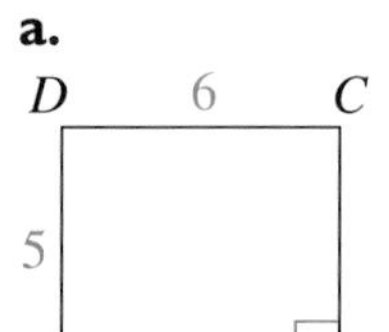

b.

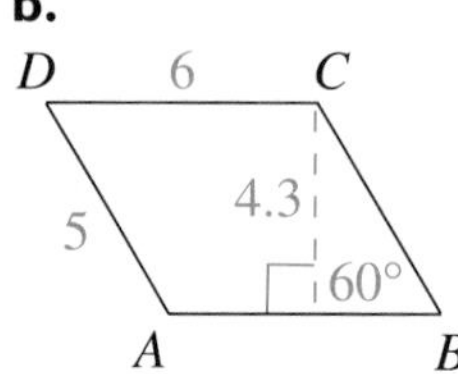

c.

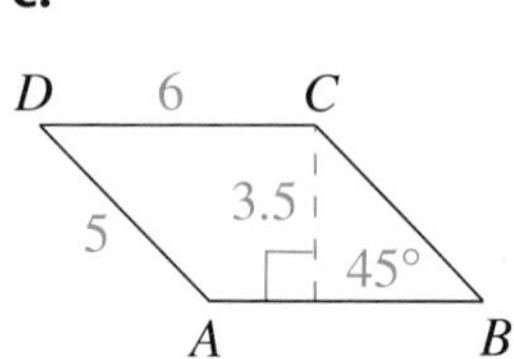

d. **Critical Thinking** How does the measure of $\angle B$ affect the area of the parallelogram?

18. **Choose A, B, C, or D.** Which statement is false?

A. A nonrectangular parallelogram and a rectangle can have the same area.

B. A square is always a parallelogram.

C. You can divide a parallelogram into two congruent triangles.

D. Two rectangles with the same area always have the same perimeter.

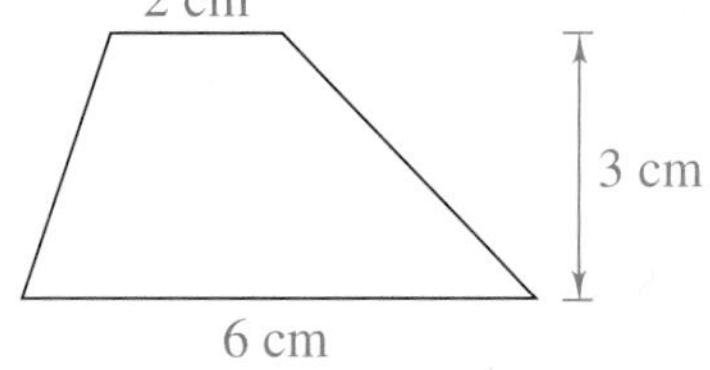

19. **a.** Copy the trapezoid on your paper. Divide it into two triangles. Then find its area.

b. **Writing** Explain, using this trapezoid, how you can find the area of a trapezoid by dividing it into two triangles.

CHECKPOINT

1. A rectangle is 35 in. long. Its width is 5 in. What are its area and perimeter?
2. How much lace do you need to trim a rectangular tablecloth that is 72 in. long and 48 in. wide?

Find the perimeter and area of each figure.

3. rectangle: $l = 7$ in., $w = 12$ in.
4. square: $s = 8.5$ cm

Problem Solving Practice

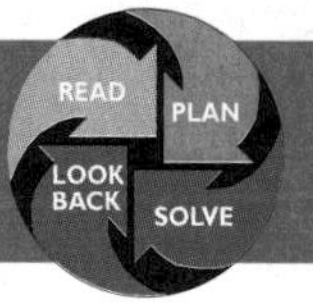

PROBLEM SOLVING STRATEGIES

Make a Table
Use Logical Reasoning
Solve a Simpler Problem
Too Much or Too Little Information
Look for a Pattern
Make a Model
Work Backward
Draw a Diagram
Guess and Test
Simulate a Problem
Use Multiple Strategies

Use any strategy to solve each problem. Show all your work.

1. Matsuda is saving his money to buy some basketball shoes that cost $78. He has $17 right now. Each week Matsuda earns $8 by mowing his neighbor's lawn. In how many weeks will he be able to buy the shoes?

2. Jamaica watched people walking dogs in the park. She counted a total of 17 people and dogs and a total of 54 legs. How many people did she count? How many dogs did she count?

3. Rachel wants to make a fenced rectangular area in her backyard for her dog Skipper. She has 36 m of fencing for the penned region. What are the whole-number dimensions in meters of the different rectangular regions she can fence?

4. Todd planted 60 seeds in his garden. Not all of the seeds grew into plants. Thirty more seeds grew into plants than did not grow. How many of the 60 seeds grew into plants?

5. At her school carnival, Nia played a game that involved tossing four bean bags at this number board. One bean bag did not hit the board. The other three landed on different numbers. Nia's score was 34. Find the possible combinations of numbers on which the bean bags could have landed.

6. Rashida and her mother like to play number games. Rashida tells her mother she is thinking of a number between 50 and 125. If her mother adds 23 to the number and divides by 2, the answer is 37. What number is Rashida thinking of?

7. A square gameboard is 16 in. long and 16 in. wide. A square that measures 2 in. $\times$ 2 in. is cut from each corner of the board. What is the perimeter of the original figure? of the new figure?

TECHNOLOGY

What's Ahead

- Using π to solve circumference problems

6-4 Exploring π

WHAT YOU'LL NEED

✓ Computer

✓ Geometry software

✓ Calculator

WORK TOGETHER

The Going in Circles band plans to live up to its name. The group will perform its next concert on a circular stage.

Imagine you are designing the circular stage. You are going to have red lights around the edge and a string of blue lights across the middle. How will the size of the stage affect the number of red lights and blue lights you will need?

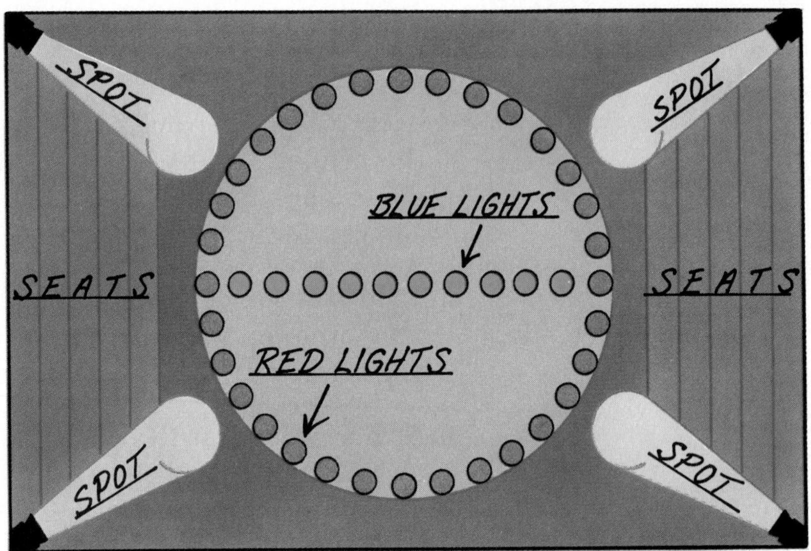

The distance around a circle is its **circumference.**

FLASHBACK

The distance across a circle (through its center) is *the diameter.*

1. a. **Computer** Use geometry software to explore the relationship between the circumference and the diameter. Make different circles and measure the circumference and diameter of each. Calculate the quotient of circumference and diameter for each circle.
   b. **Writing** Summarize your results.
   c. How does the number of red lights you need compare to the number of blue lights? Does that change if the circle changes?

2. a. Use your results to estimate the circumference of the circle at the right. Find the perimeter of the square.

   b. **Critical Thinking** Is the circumference of the circle less than the perimeter of the square? Does that make sense? Explain.

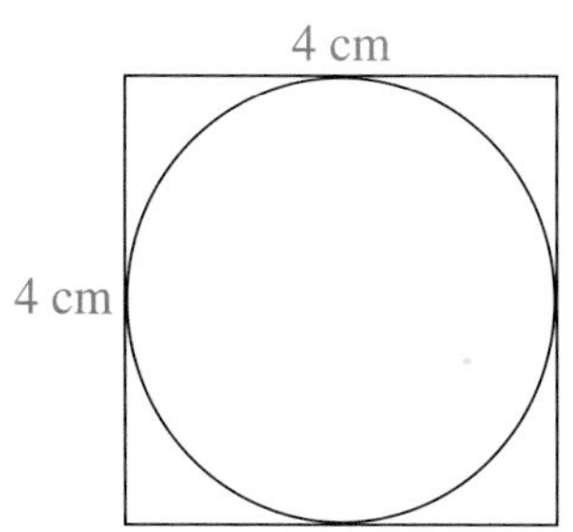

THINK AND DISCUSS

The relationship between the circumference and diameter of a circle is a powerful tool for solving problems.

3. The stage designer for the Going in Circles concert wants to know whether 200 red light bulbs will be enough. The diameter of the stage is 83 ft. The light bulbs must be 1 ft apart.

   a. Estimate the circumference of the stage.

   b. How did you make your estimate?

   c. Will 200 red light bulbs be enough to go completely around the stage? How do you know?

Problem Solving Hint

Drawing a diagram may help.

4. If the stage turns too quickly, the musicians may get dizzy. The guitar player plans to stand 25 ft from the center of the stage. The stage makes a complete revolution each minute.

   a. Make a diagram. Draw a circle that shows the guitar player's path as the stage turns.

   b. What is the diameter of the guitarist's path?

   c. About how far does the guitarist move in 1 min?

   d. About how far does the guitarist move in 1 s?

   e. Write the speed as feet per second (ft/s). Will the guitar player be moving faster than 10 mi/h?

FLASHBACK

5,280 ft = 1 mi

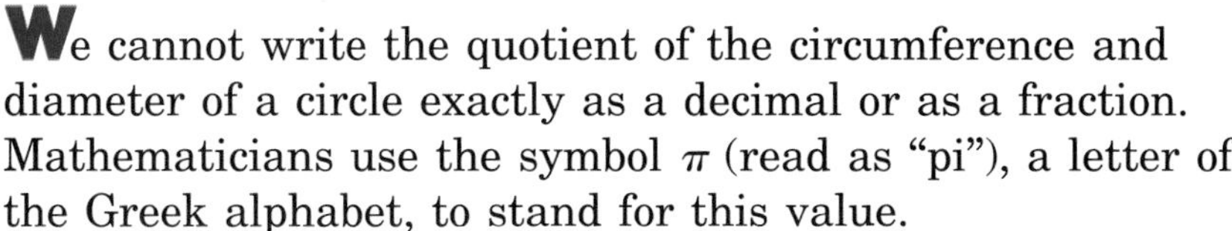

We cannot write the quotient of the circumference and diameter of a circle exactly as a decimal or as a fraction. Mathematicians use the symbol π (read as "pi"), a letter of the Greek alphabet, to stand for this value.

5. Which point on the number line represents π? Explain.

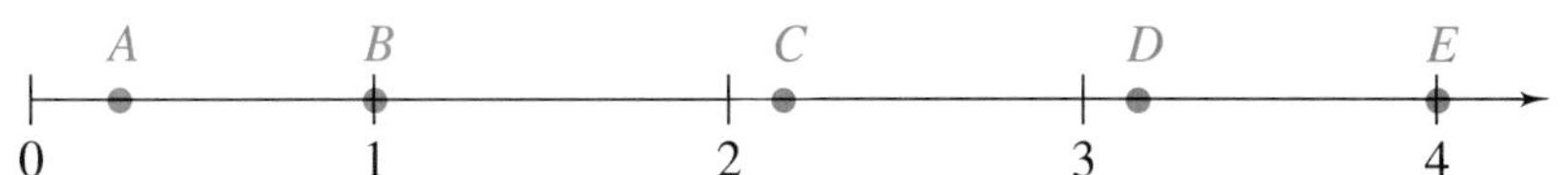

Mixed REVIEW

Find each sum.

1. 4.5 + 0.04
2. 0.7 + 0.12

Evaluate.

3. 17^2 4. 5.2^2
5. Find the area of a parallelogram with base 3 cm and height 7 cm.
6. Find the area of a triangle with base 2 m and height 11 m.
7. How many circles are in the figure?

Problem Solving Hint

Draw a diagram. Show the tire track and the spot where the pebble makes a mark.

Because $\frac{C}{d} = \pi$, $C = \pi d$.

Circumference of a Circle

$C = \pi d$ (Circumference = pi × the diameter)

$C = 2\pi r$ (Circumference = 2 × pi × the radius)

6. Why does $C = 2\pi r$ follow from $C = \pi d$?

Thanks to computers, we can write a long decimal, with thousands of digits, that is close to the actual number π. For most situations an approximation such as 3.14 is close enough. Many calculators have a π key.

7. **Calculator** Press the π key on your calculator. What is the result?

8. The diameter of a basketball hoop is 45 cm. A manufacturer wants to know how much metal it will take to make the rim.
   a. **Calculator** Find the circumference of the basketball hoop in the following two ways. Use 3.14 for π, and then use the π key. Compare the results.
   b. How far is it around a basketball hoop? Round to the nearest centimeter.

9. A pebble stuck in a bicycle tire left a tell tale mark in the tire track every 82 in. How good a detective are you?
   a. What is the circumference of the tire? How do you know?
   b. Estimate the diameter of the tire.
   c. **Calculator** Use the π key. Find the tire's diameter. Round to the nearest half inch.
   d. **Critical Thinking** Could a spoke that is 14 in. long belong to the bicycle that made the track? Explain.

ON YOUR OWN

Mental Math **Use 3 for π to estimate the circumference of a circle with the given radius or diameter.**

10. $d = 5$ cm   11. $d = 11$ m   12. $r = 1$ in.   13. $r = 3$ m

Calculator Find the circumference of a circle with the given radius or diameter. Round to the nearest unit.

14. $d = 15$ ft **15.** $d = 50$ m **16.** $r = 17$ in. **17.** $r = 64$ m

18. $d = 3.9$ m **19.** $d = 17.5$ ft **20.** $r = 9.5$ in. **21.** $r = 0.39$ m

Calculator Find the diameter of a circle with the given circumference. Round to the nearest unit.

22. 192 ft **23.** 85 cm **24.** 22 in. **25.** 56.5 m

26. 27.5 ft **27.** 68.7 cm **28.** 3.75 in. **29.** 19.67 m

Use 3.14 for π or use a calculator if appropriate.

30. Data File 6 (pp. 226–227) About how many times will each wheel on the bicycle shown revolve when the bicycle travels 1,000 ft?

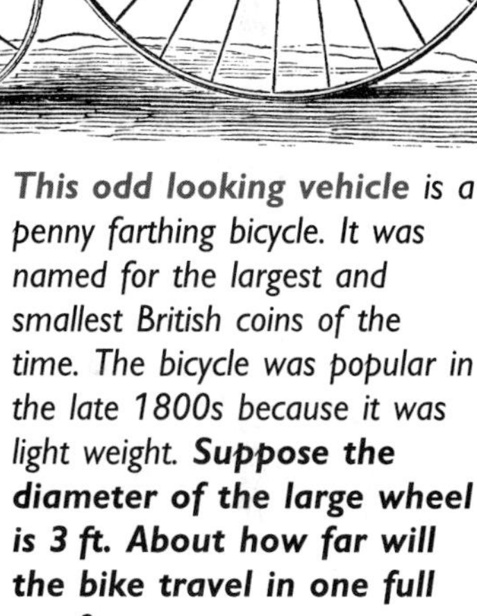

This odd looking vehicle** is a penny farthing bicycle. It was named for the largest and smallest British coins of the time. The bicycle was popular in the late 1800s because it was light weight. **Suppose the diameter of the large wheel is 3 ft. About how far will the bike travel in one full turn?

Source: *Guinness Book of Records*

31. A dog tied to a post gets exercise by running in a circle. One day the dog ran around the post 100 times with the 10-ft rope stretched tightly. Did the dog run at least 1 mi (5,280 ft)?

32. Suppose you want to draw a circle with a circumference of 10 cm. How wide should you set your compass (to the nearest 0.1 cm)?

33. On the rotating stage described in the Work Together activity, the drummer is 15 ft from the center of the stage. The keyboard player is 30 ft from the center. The stage makes a complete revolution once each minute.

a. At the end of 5 min, which musician makes more turns? Explain.

b. At the end of 5 min, which musician travels farther? Explain.

c. How far does the drummer travel in 1 min? Round to the nearest 0.1 ft.

d. The keyboard player is twice as far from the center as the drummer. Does she travel twice as far in 1 min? Explain.

34. Writing Make up a problem that you would use π to solve.

What's Ahead

- Finding the area of a circle

6-5 Area of a Circle

WHAT YOU'LL NEED

✓ Centimeter graph paper

✓ Compass

✓ Straightedge

✓ Scissors

✓ Calculator

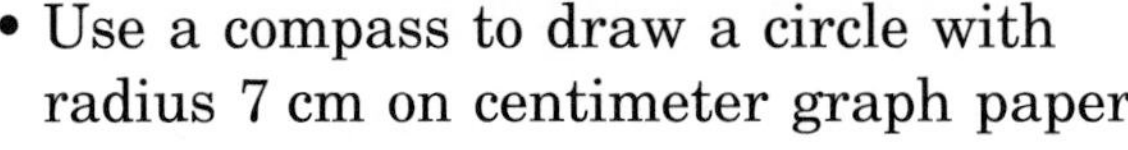

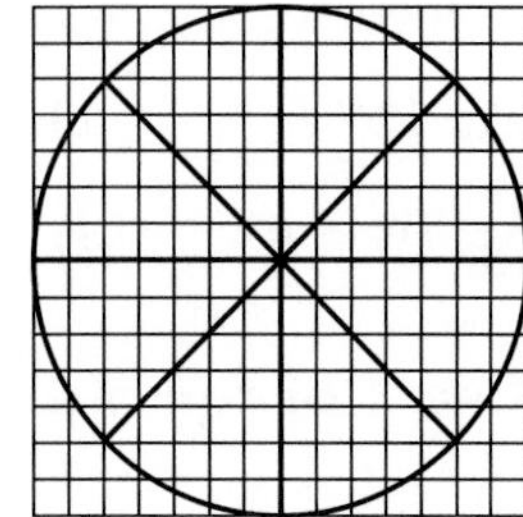

- Use a compass to draw a circle with radius 7 cm on centimeter graph paper.
- Divide the circle into eight congruent regions.
- Cut out the circle. Cut out the eight regions. Rearrange the regions as shown below.

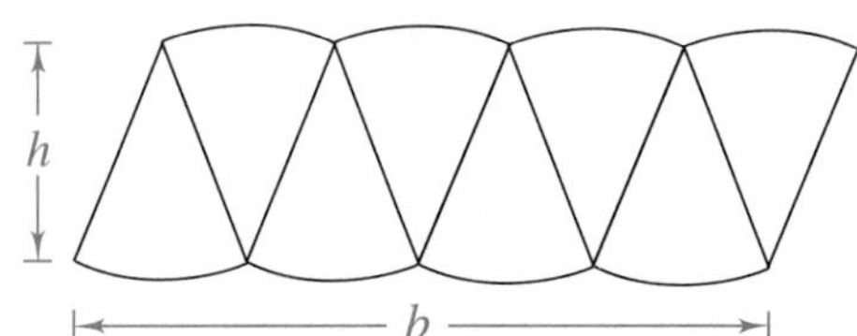

1. What was the circumference of the original circle?
2. After you rearrange the eight regions, what geometric figure does the new shape remind you of?
3. Estimate the base length b and the height h.
4. Use your answers to Questions 2 and 3 to estimate the area of the new figure.

THINK AND DISCUSS

You can generalize what you did in the Work Together activity.

5. a. Suppose the radius of the circle in the Work Together activity is r. What is the height of the parallelogram?
   b. What would be the circumference of the circle? What would be the base length of the parallelogram?
   c. What would be the area of the parallelogram?

You have just found the formula for the area A of a circle.

Area of a Circle

$$A = \pi \times r \times r = \pi r^2$$

6. a. Calculator What is the area of a circle with radius 7 cm?

b. How does the area you found in part (a) compare to the area you found in Question 4 of the Work Together?

Archery targets *are made up of different color rings that are all the same width. The properties of circle areas make each succeeding ring have the area of the last ring plus two bullseyes.* ***The area of the bullseye on this target is 10 cm². What is the area of the first ring?***

Example 1 Find the circumference and area of a circle with radius 5 cm.

Estimate: $C = 2\pi r \rightarrow C \approx 2 \times 3 \times 5 = 30$

$A = \pi r^2 \rightarrow A \approx 3 \times 5^2 = 3 \times 25 = 75$

Use a calculator.

2 [×] [π] [×] 5 [=] 31.415927 $C = 2\pi r$

[π] [×] 5 [x^2] [=] 78.539816 $A = \pi r^2$

Round to a convenient place. The circumference is about 31 cm and the area is about 79 cm².

You can find the area of a figure with both polygons and circles.

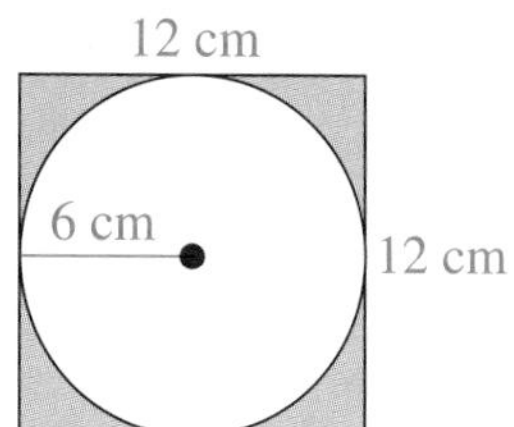

Example 2 Find the area of the shaded region in the figure at the right.

Estimate: Area of square $\rightarrow 12^2 = 144$

Area of circle $\rightarrow 3 \times 6^2 = 3 \times 36 = 108$

Square area $-$ Circle area $= 144 - 108 = 36$

Use a calculator.

$A = (12)^2 = 144$ $A = s^2$

[π] [×] 6 [x^2]  113.09734 $A = \pi r^2$

$144 - 113 = 31$

The area of the shaded region is about 31 cm².

7. Compare the estimates to the calculated answers in each example. Explain the variations.

TRY THESE

Calculator **Find the circumference and the area of each circle. Round each answer to the nearest tenth of a unit.**

8.

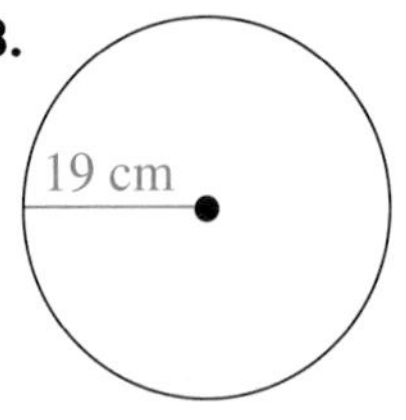

9.

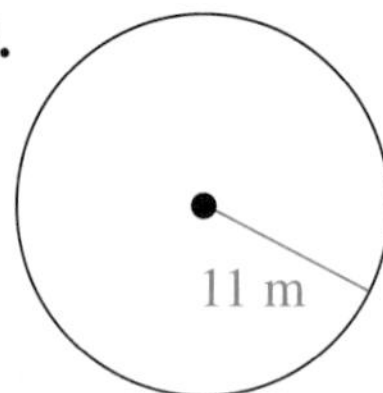

10.

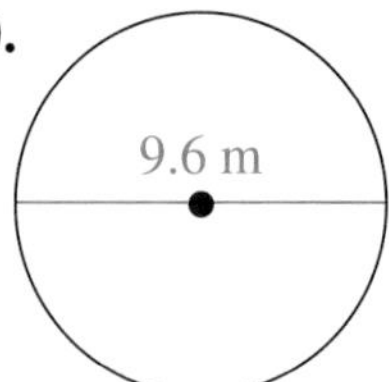

ON YOUR OWN

Calculator **Find the area of a circle with the given radius or diameter. Round each answer to the nearest tenth of a unit.**

11. $r = 9$ cm **12.** $d = 7$ cm **13.** $r = 25$ m

Calculator **Find the area and distance around each figure. Round each answer to the nearest tenth of a unit.**

14.

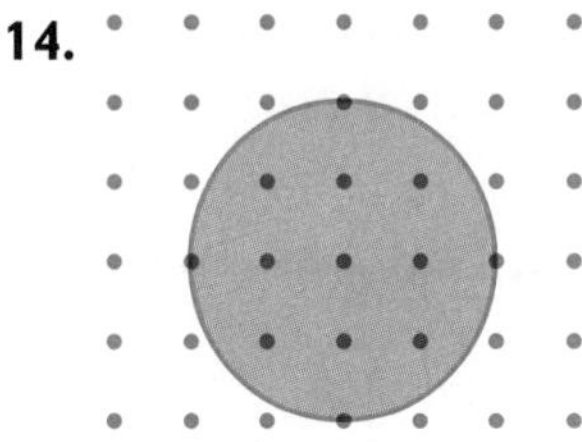

15.

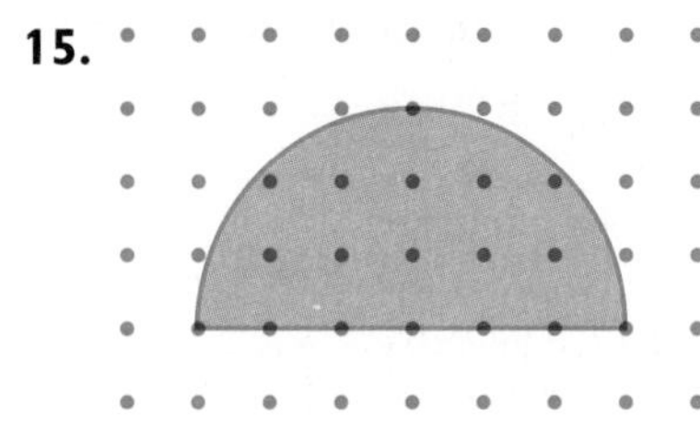

Mental Math **Use 3 for π to estimate the area of a circle with the given radius or diameter.**

16. $r = 2$ in. **17.** $d = 2$ m **18.** $d = 10$ cm

19. Writing Which is larger: a pan with a radius of 10 in. or a pan with a diameter of 18 in.? Explain.

20. You can pick up the radio signal for station WAER FM 88 in Syracuse, New York, within a 45 mi radius of the station, depending upon the hills in the surrounding region. What is the approximate area of the broadcast region? Use 3.14 for π.

Mixed REVIEW

Round to the place of the underlined digit.

1. 3.9<u>5</u>7
2. 34<u>5</u>.008

Find the circumference of a circle with the given radius or diameter.

3. $r = 5$ in.
4. $d = 32$ cm
5. How many triangles are in the figure shown below?

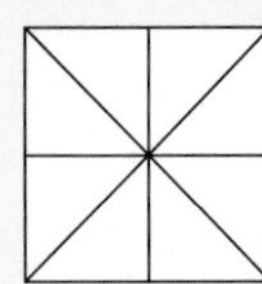

Calculator Find the area of the shaded region. Round to the nearest unit.

21. 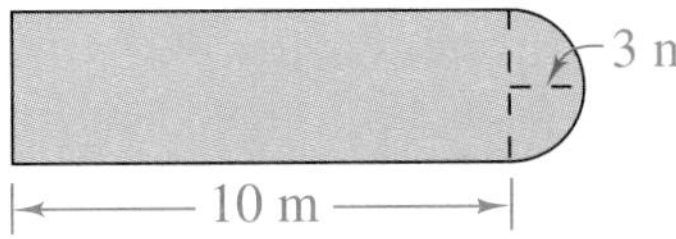

22. 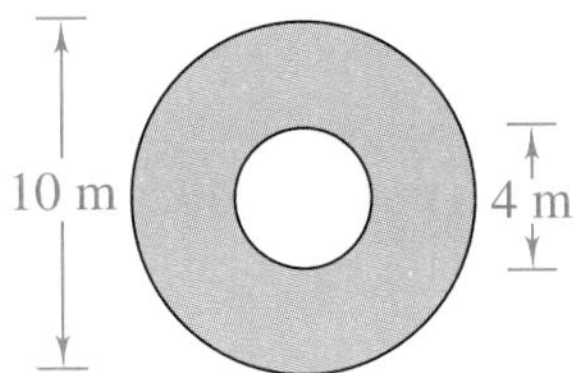

23. 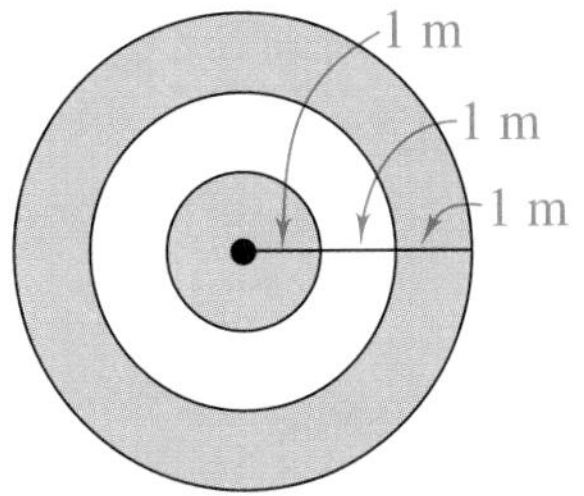

24. 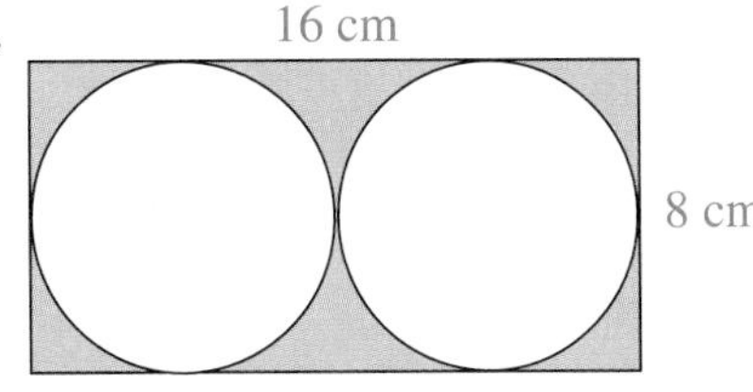

25. a. Investigation (p. 228) Make a table showing the number of tiles you would use in the borders of each tile square from a 2-square through a 10-square.

b. Describe any patterns you see in the data in part (a).

Follow the Sun

The Sun Stone or Aztec calendar is remarkable because it shows the Aztecs' accurate knowledge of astronomy and mathematics. The Aztecs carved the calendar on a circular stone 3.6 m in diameter with a mass of 24 T. They began working on the calendar in 1427 and completed the work in 1479. The center circle of the stone shows the face of Tontiuh, the Aztec sun god. There are four squares surrounding the center that are followed by 20 squares that name the days of the Aztec month. There were 18 Aztec months with 20 days each. The next circular section has eight squares with 5 dots each that seem to represent weeks that were 5 days long.

26. Find the area of the Sun Stone. Use 3.14 for π.

27. How long did it take the Aztecs to complete the calendar?

28. How many days were in the Aztec calendar?

Practice

Estimate the area of each figure. Assume each square represents 5 cm².

1. 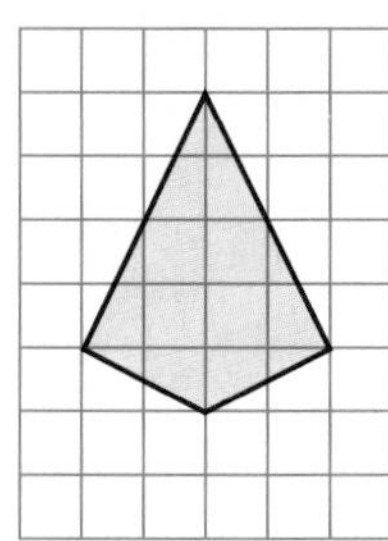

2. 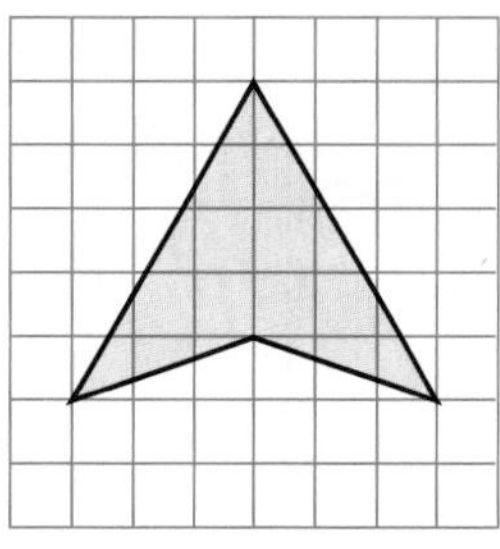

3. 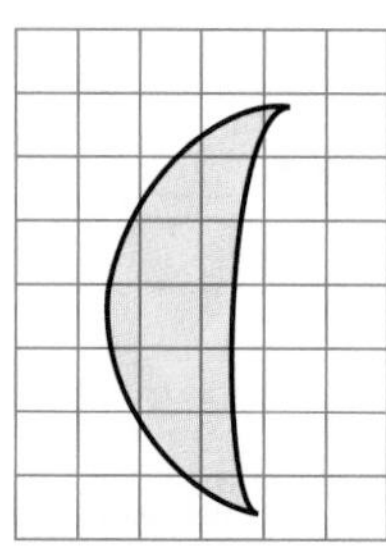

4. 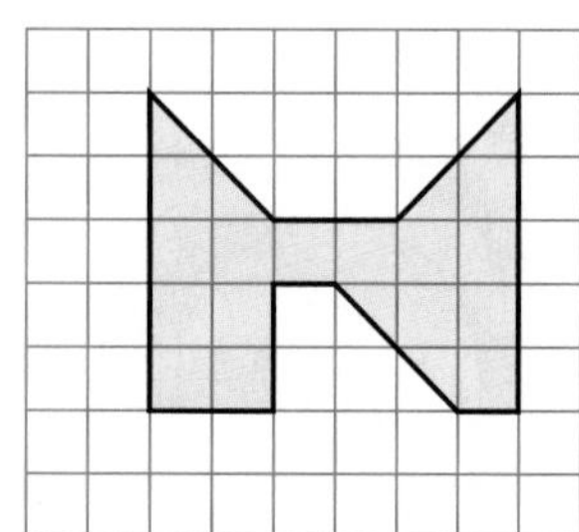

Find the area and perimeter of each figure.

5. 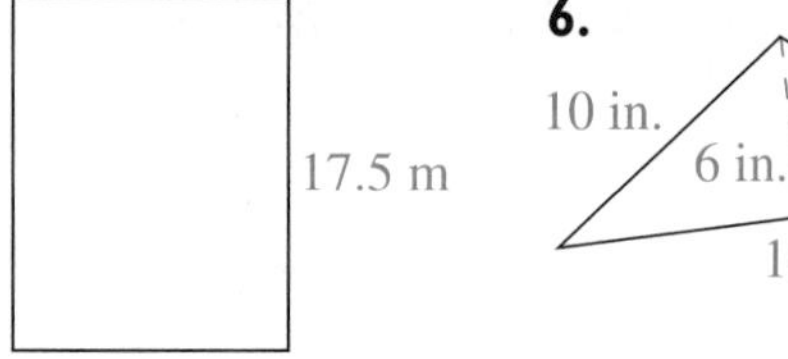

6. 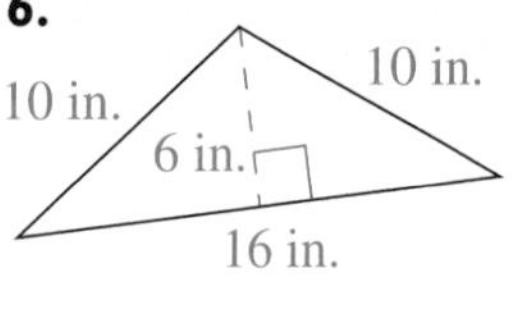

7. 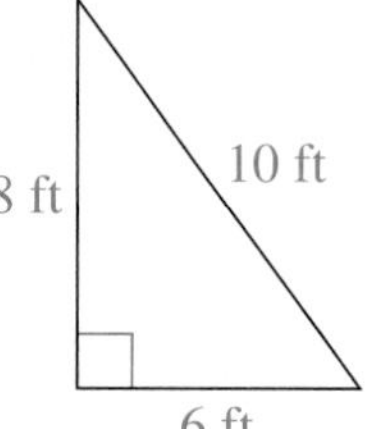

8. 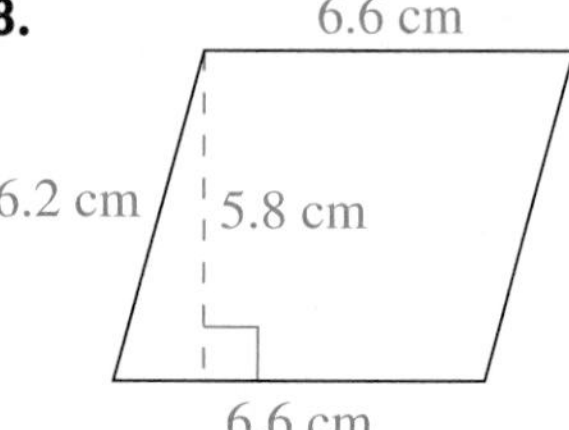

9. The area of a square is 144 in.². What is its perimeter?

10. The area of a rectangle is 45 cm². One dimension is 5 cm. What is the other dimension?

Use 3 for π. Estimate the circumference and area of a circle with the given radius or diameter.

11. $d = 10$ cm **12.** $d = 7$ m **13.** $r = 2$ cm $r = 8$ m

Calculator **Find the circumference and area of a circle with the given radius or diameter. Round to a convenient place.**

15. $d = 21$ in. **16.** $d = 17.5$ ft **17.** $r = 72$ m **18.** $r = 13$ in.

Find the area of each figure. Round to a convenient place.

19. 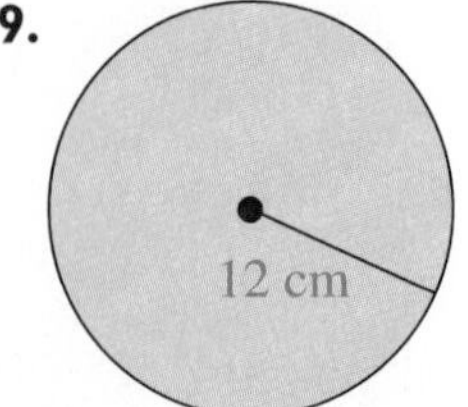

20. 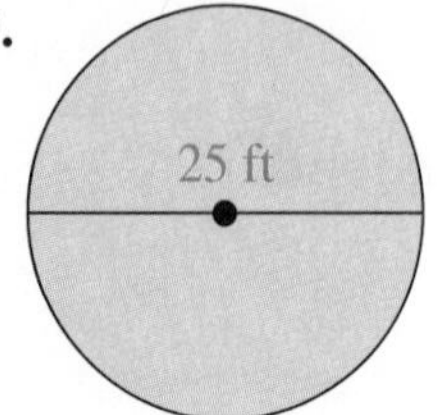

21. 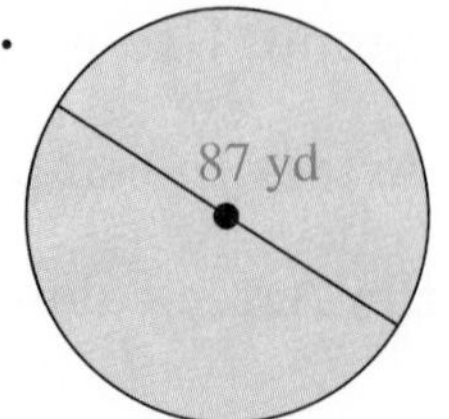

22. 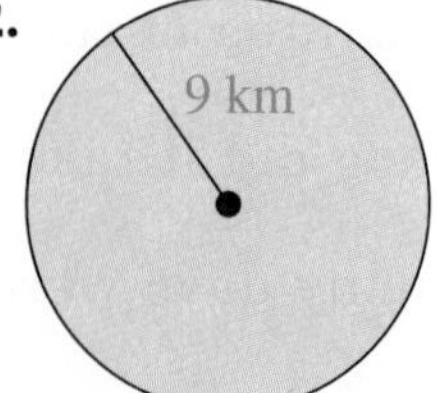

MATH AND ARCHITECTURE

What's Ahead

- Identifying three-dimensional figures

6-6 Three-Dimensional Figures

THINK AND DISCUSS

WHAT YOU'LL NEED

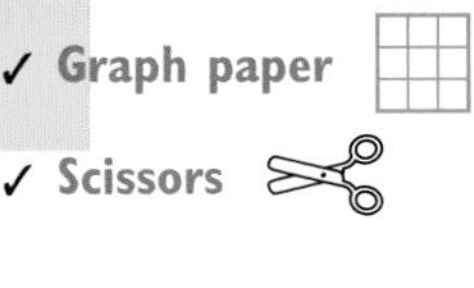

✓ Graph paper

✓ Scissors

1. What polygons do you see in the buildings shown above?

Figures, such as buildings, that do not lie in a plane are *three-dimensional figures.* Some three-dimensional figures have only flat surfaces shaped like polygons, called *faces.*

Most large buildings are in the shape of *rectangular prisms.* A **prism** is a three-dimensional figure with two parallel and congruent polygonal faces, called *bases.* You name a prism by the shape of its bases.

2. What shape are the bases of a rectangular prism?

When you draw a rectangular prism, you usually draw it as if you could see three faces. You can use dashed lines to show segments that you could not see unless the prism was transparent.

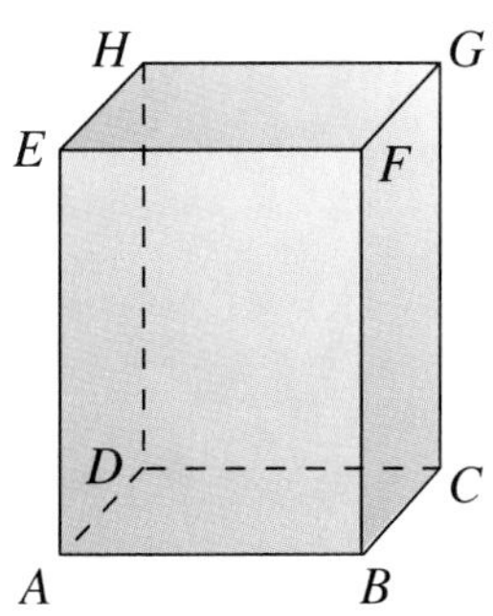

3. Why do you think that a drawing of a rectangular prism usually does not show a view directly from the front?

4. What shape are the bases of the prism in the drawing? What shape would they be in a real 3-d figure?

5. Which faces are "hidden from view" in this drawing?

6. Match each prism with its name: choose from triangular prism, rectangular prism, pentagonal prism, or hexagonal prism.

a. 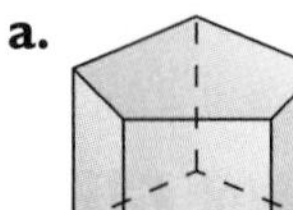

b. 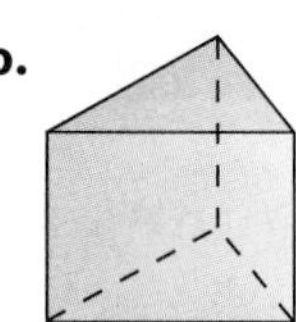

A pyramid has one polygonal base.

7. What name would you give each pyramid?

a. 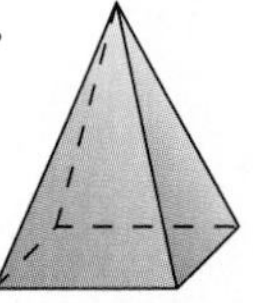

b. 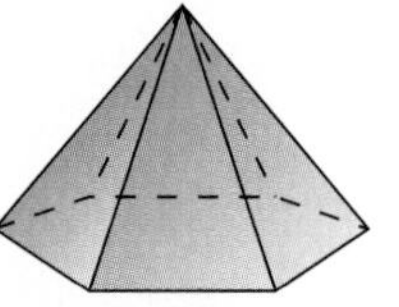

c. 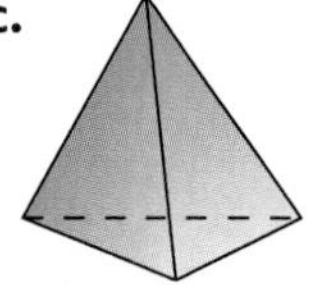

8. What shape is a face of a pyramid that is not a base?

Two faces of a prism or pyramid intersect in a segment called an *edge*. Each point where edges meet is a *vertex*.

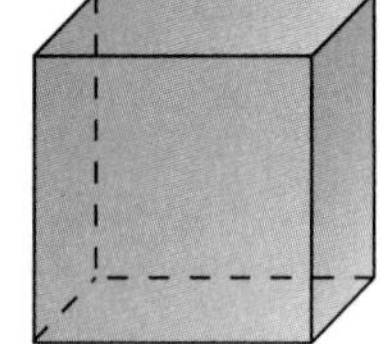

9. How many faces does this figure have?

10. How many edges does the figure have?

11. How many vertices does the figure have?

A cube is a rectangular prism with six congruent faces.

12. What shape is each face of a cube?

13. How do the lengths of the edges of a cube compare?

Some three-dimensional figures do not have polygonal faces.

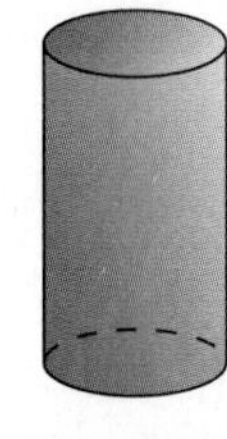

cylinder

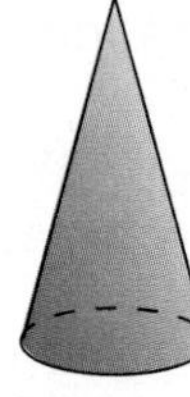

cone

sphere

The geosphere at Epcot Center is the first building of its kind. It is a sphere with a diameter of 164 ft made up of 954 triangles of varying sizes enclosing 2,200,000 ft^3.

Source: *Fodor's Walt Disney World Guide*

14. Which of the figures at the bottom of page 252 have bases? What shape are the bases?

15. How are a cylinder and a cone alike? How are they different?

16. What has the artist done to make the drawing of a sphere look different from a circle?

WORK TOGETHER

The pattern that you cut out and fold to form a three-dimensional figure is called a **net.**

- Suppose you cut out this net and fold it. What kind of three-dimensional figure do you think would be formed?
- Work with a partner to see if you are right. Draw the net on graph paper, cut it out, and fold it.

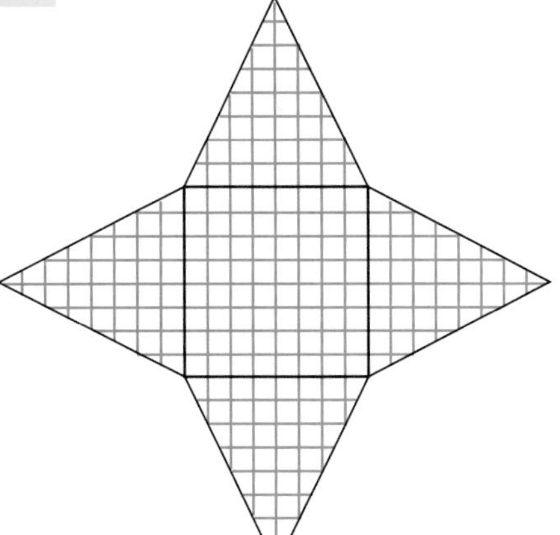

ON YOUR OWN

Identify each three-dimensional figure.

17. 

18. 

19. 

20. 

Mixed REVIEW

Find each product.

1. 0.24×7
2. 4.1×0.5

Find the area of a circle with the given radius or diameter.

3. $r = 9$ ft
4. $d = 14$ m

Evaluate.

5. $5^2 + 2(6 + 4)$
6. $3^2 + 6^2$

7. An issue of *Teen Monthly* is $2.25. A yearly subscription costs $25.08. How much can you save by subscribing for a year?

21. This photograph was taken at Expo 70 in Japan. What three-dimensional figures can you identify?

22. a. Identify the figure.

b. Find the number of faces, edges, and vertices the figure has.

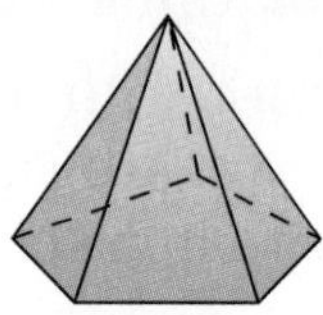

GREAT EXPECTATIONS

Marine Biologist

I would like to be a marine biologist because I think the ocean is an unknown place. I would like to learn more about animals and plants of the ocean. Then I could help them. I want to learn more because I have seen pictures and it is beautiful under water. I have always loved the beach and the ocean and have wondered about what lived there. I think the ocean is kind of like outer space in a way because it is an area unknown and an area being discovered. I would love to be part of that discovery.

Jane Broussard

23. **Writing** Describe, in your own words, a *square pyramid.*

24. **Choose A, B, C, or D.** Which of the following is not a possible view of a cylinder?

A. 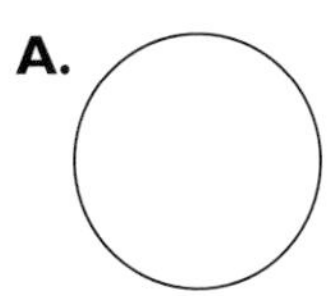

B.

C.

D.

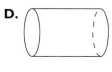

Name the figure you can form from each net.

25. 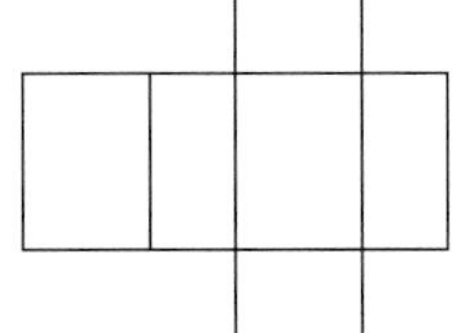

26. 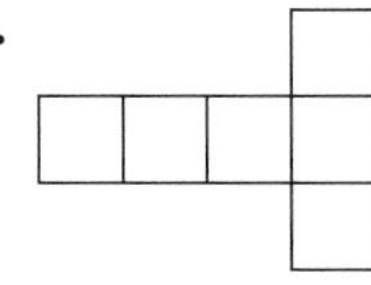

27. 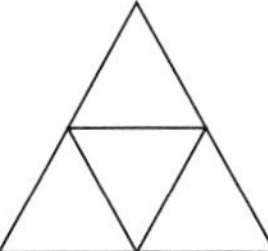

28. 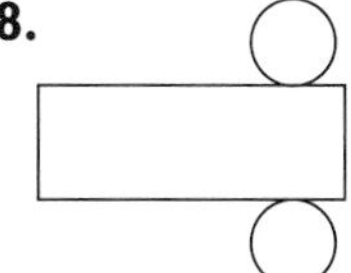

Dear Jane,

Your letter makes several important points. Because children are our best hope for the future of our oceans, I'd like to address each point.

The oceans are indeed like outer space. Under water, an aquanaut can become weightless, gliding over coral reefs like astronauts glide among the stars in their space shuttle. Having been an underwater explorer for 13 years, I can truly say that each dive is a unique educational experience.

Although many of the world's oceans have been explored, much more exploration is needed. Why? For one reason, many scientists feel that the cure for cancer and other diseases may be found in a marine plant or animal. Sharks are a prime area of study because they can't get cancer.

I hope you pursue your interest in marine biology. I have one suggestion: also become a writer. Then you can help the marine environment and share your knowledge and enthusiasm with many others.

Rick Sammon,
President CEDAM International

What's Ahead

- Finding the surface area of rectangular prisms

6-7 Exploring Surface Area

If you unfold a rectangular prism, one net you might get is shown at the right.

- Find the area of the net.

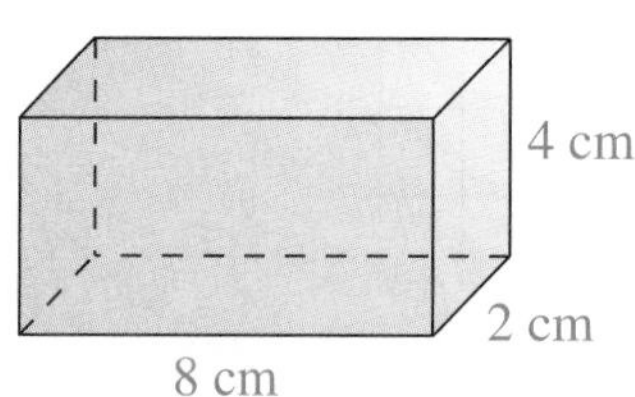

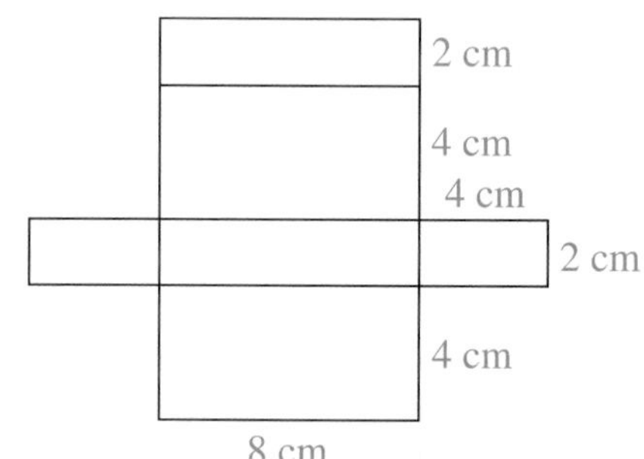

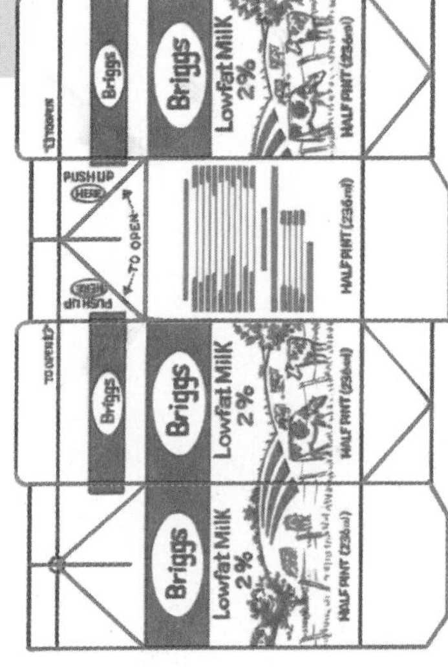

***Package designers** need to know the dimensions and shapes of package surfaces.*

THINK AND DISCUSS

The sum of the areas of the faces of a rectangular prism is the **surface area** of the prism.

1. a. Describe the faces of the prism in the Work Together activity. Include in your description the dimensions of the faces and whether any faces are congruent.
   b. **Critical Thinking** Is there more than one way to find the surface area of the rectangular prism? Explain.

2. a. What is the best name for the rectangular prism?
   b. Describe the faces.
   c. Find the surface area.

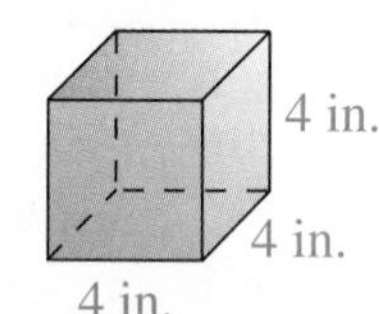

3. a. Describe the faces of the rectangular prism.
   b. Find the surface area.

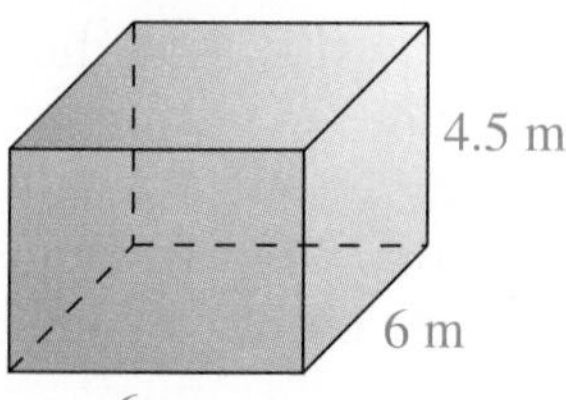

ON YOUR OWN

Choose **Use a calculator, paper and pencil, or mental math to find the surface area of the rectangular prism.**

4\. 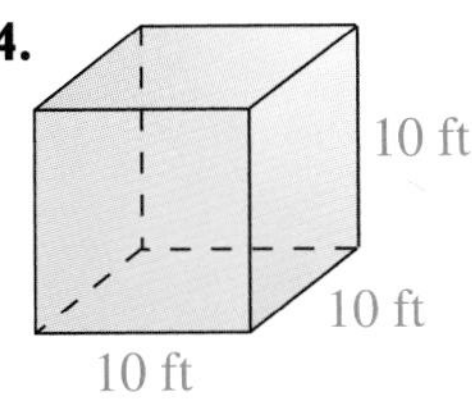

5\. 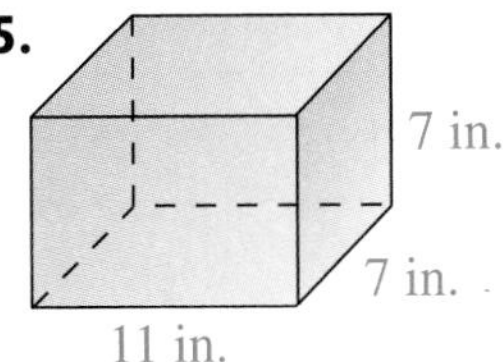

6\. 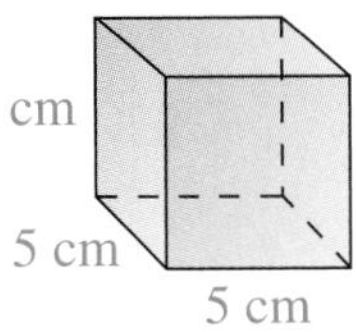

7\. 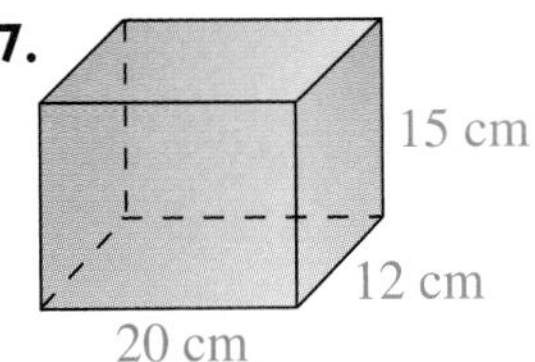

8\. 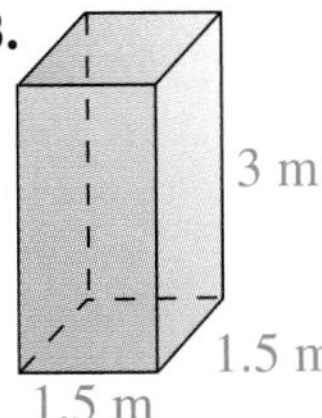

9\. 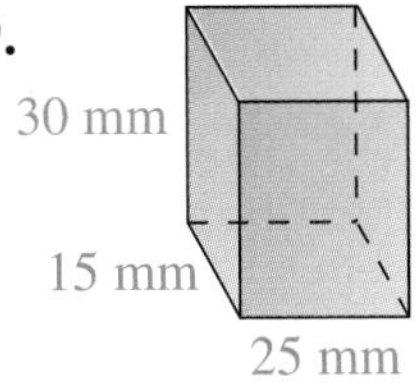

Find the surface area of the rectangular prism that has the given net.

10\. 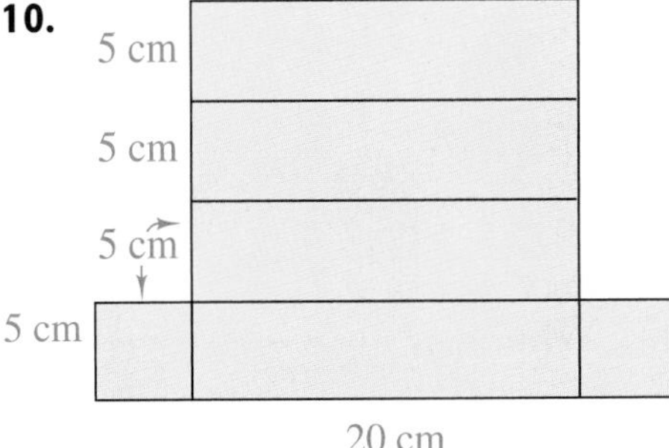

11\. 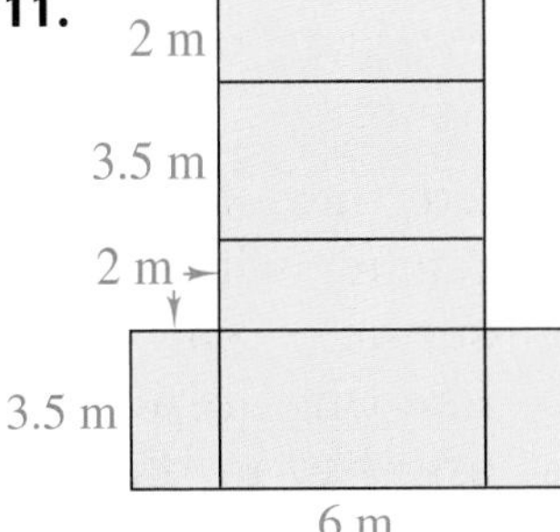

12\. a. Draw a net that you could fold to form the rectangular prism.

b. Find the surface area of the prism.

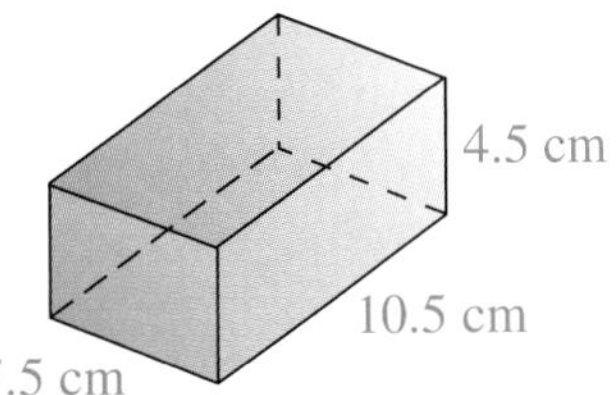

13\. **Writing** Explain how you would find the surface area of a cube.

14\. The surface area of the cube shown at the right is 24 cm^2. What is the length of each edge?

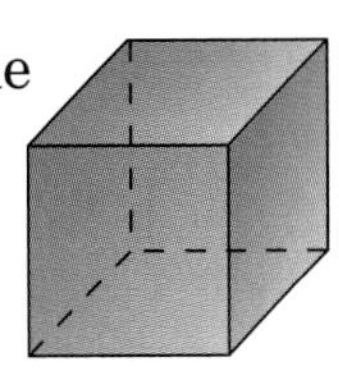

Mixed REVIEW

Find each quotient.

1\. $25 \div 0.5$

2\. $3.2 \div 0.8$

Give the mathematical name for each figure.

3\. a baseball

4\. a brick

Evaluate.

5\. $12 \times 7 \times 15$

6\. $3.3 \times 2.5 \times 10.1$

7\. Suppose two pizzas cost the same amount. Which is a better buy: a 10-in. round pizza or a 9-in. square pizza?

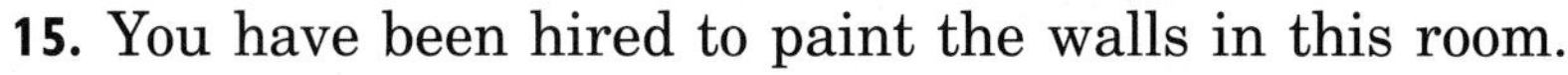

15. You have been hired to paint the walls in this room.

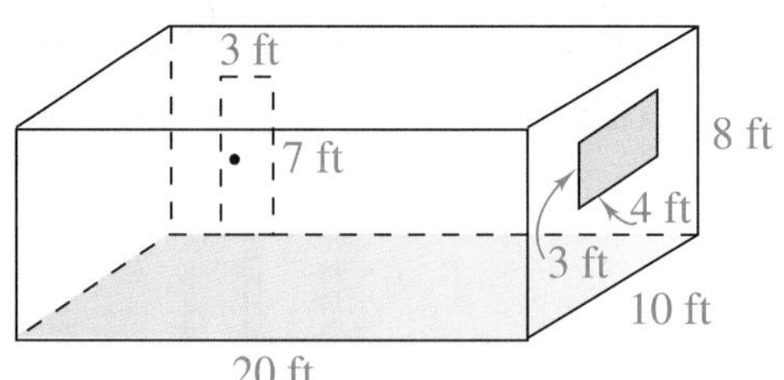

a. Find the area of the two walls that do not have doors or windows.

b. Find the area of the surface you will paint on the other two walls. (Assume that you will not paint the door or the window.)

c. What is the surface area of the region you will paint?

d. A gallon of the paint you will use covers about 400 ft^2. How many gallons will you need?

Americans use three million gallons of paint and stain every day. That would be enough to coat both sides of a 5-ft high fence 17,000 mi long.

Source: *In One Day*

16. **Critical Thinking** Each small cube in the figure below measures 1 cm on a side.

a. Find the surface area of the figure.

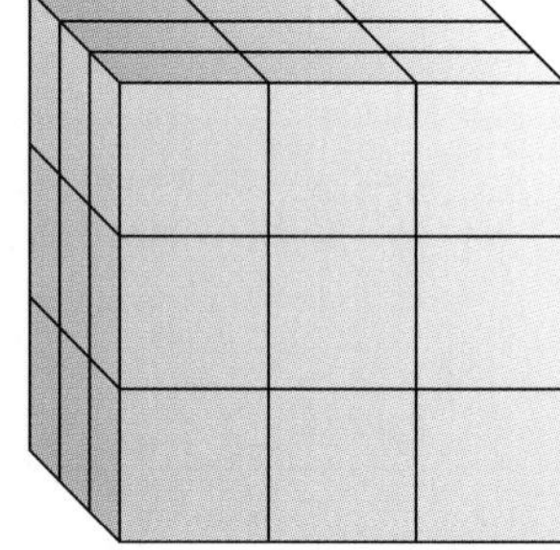

b. Are there any cubes you can remove without changing the surface area? How many cubes like this are in the figure? Where are they in the figure?

c. Are there any cubes you can remove that will increase the surface area by 2 cm^2? How many cubes like this are in the figure? Where are they in the figure?

d. Are there any cubes you can remove that will increase the surface area by 4 cm^2? How many cubes like this are in the figure? Where are they in the figure?

Problem Solving Hint

Building a model may help.

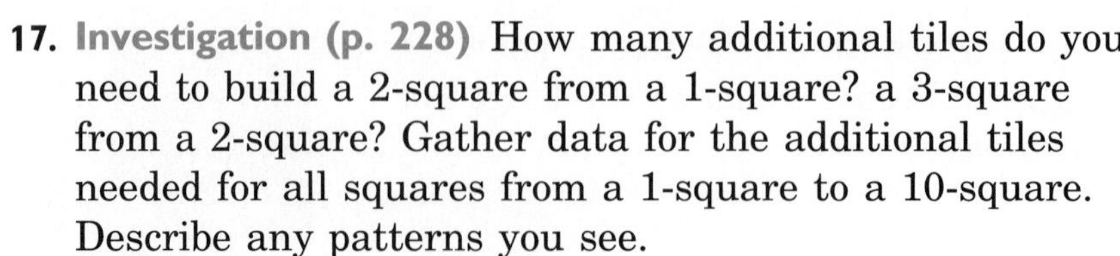

17. **Investigation (p. 228)** How many additional tiles do you need to build a 2-square from a 1-square? a 3-square from a 2-square? Gather data for the additional tiles needed for all squares from a 1-square to a 10-square. Describe any patterns you see.

What's Ahead

- Finding the volume of rectangular prisms

6-8 Volume of Rectangular Prisms

WHAT YOU'LL NEED

✓ Unit cubes

WORK TOGETHER

Use unit cubes to build a rectangular prism. Use 3 rows of 6 cubes to make the bottom layer of cubes. Then add a second layer of cubes.

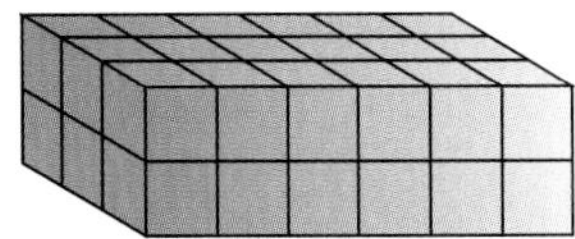

The **volume** of a three-dimensional figure is the number of cubic units needed to fill the space inside the figure.

1. a. Suppose the volume of each cube is 1 cubic unit. What is the volume of the rectangular prism?
   b. How did you determine the volume?
2. Build a different rectangular prism and find its volume.

The familiar cereal box *measures about 7.0 cm × 10.2 cm × 4.2 cm.* ***Estimate the volume in cubic centimeters.***

THINK AND DISCUSS

We measure area in square units because we multiply two factors *length* and *width* to find area. We measure volume V in cubic units because we multiply three factors the *length* l, the *width* w, and the *height* h to find volume.

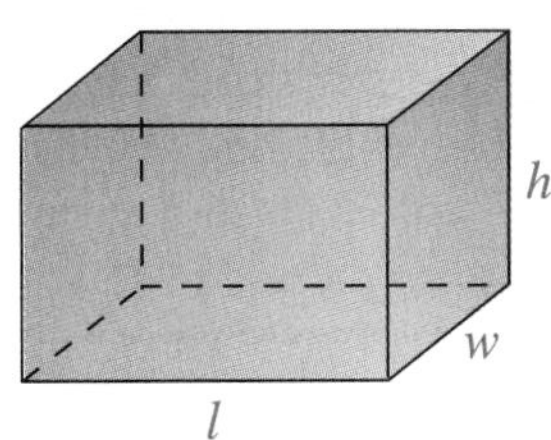

Volume of a Rectangular Prism

Volume = length × width × height

$V = lwh$

3. What are the length, width, and height of the rectangular prism you built in the Work Together activity?

The gram is the basic unit of mass in the metric system. One gram is officially equal to the weight of one cubic centimeter of distilled water at 4°C.

Source: *Webster's New World Dictionary*

We measure volume in units such as cubic centimeters (cm^3), cubic meters (m^3), and cubic inches ($in.^3$).

Example 1 Find the volume of the rectangular prism.

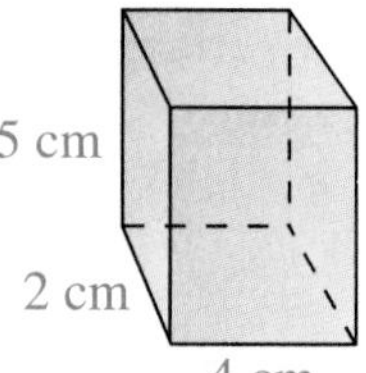

Use $V = lwh$.

$$V = 4 \times 2 \times 5 = 40$$

The volume is 40 cm^3.

4. **Critical Thinking** Suppose you turn the prism in Example 1 so that the base is 2 cm by 5 cm and the height is 4 cm. Is the volume the same? Why or why not?

In 1978, millions of cube puzzles were sold. Despite the trillions of possible combinations, some people practiced solving the cubes until they could restore the colors from any random position in under 45 s.

Source: *The Simple Solution to Rubik's Cube*

If you know the volume and two of the dimensions of a rectangular prism, you can find the third dimension.

Example 2 The volume of a rectangular prism is 105 $in.^3$. The height of the prism is 5 in. The length is 7 in. What is the width of the prism?

Use $V = lwh$.

$105 = 7 \times w \times 5$ **Substitute.**

$105 = 35w$

$\frac{105}{35} = \frac{35w}{35}$ **Divide each side by 35.**

$w = 3$

Check $7 \times 3 \times 5 = 105$ ✓

The width is 3 in.

5. The volume of a rectangular prism is 36 m^3. The area of the base is 9 m^2. What is the height of the prism?

TRY THESE

Find the volume of each rectangular prism.

6.

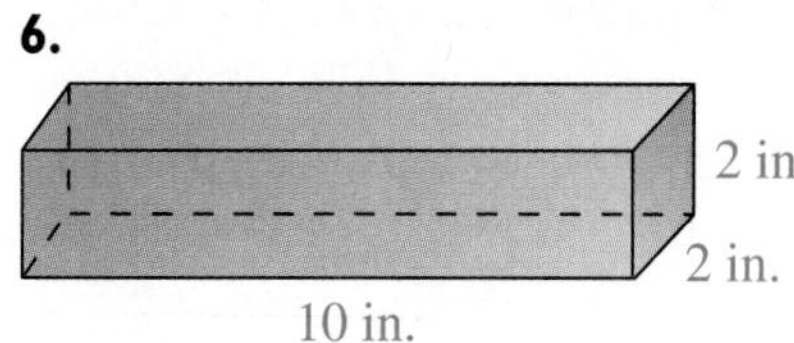

7.

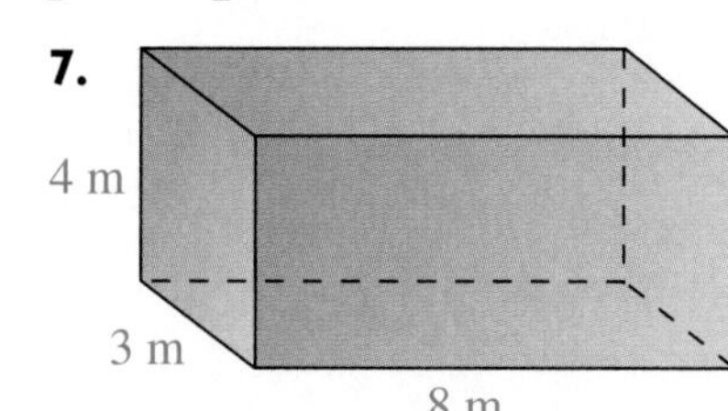

ON YOUR OWN

Find the volume of each rectangular prism.

8.

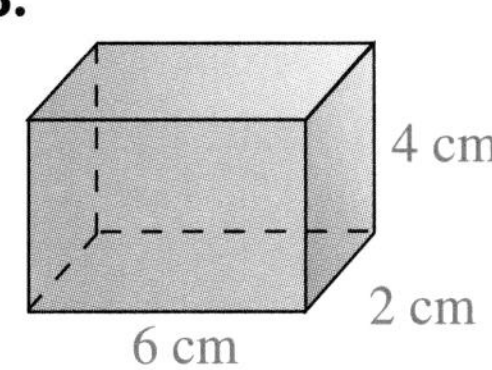

9.

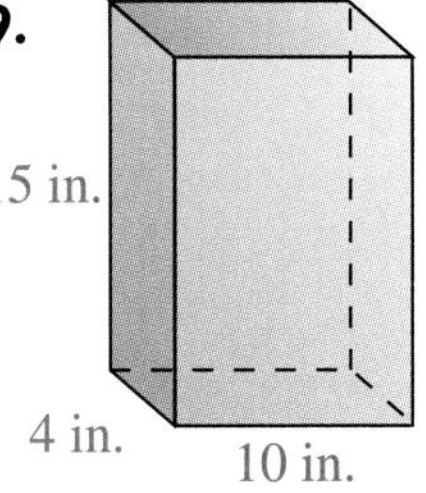

10.

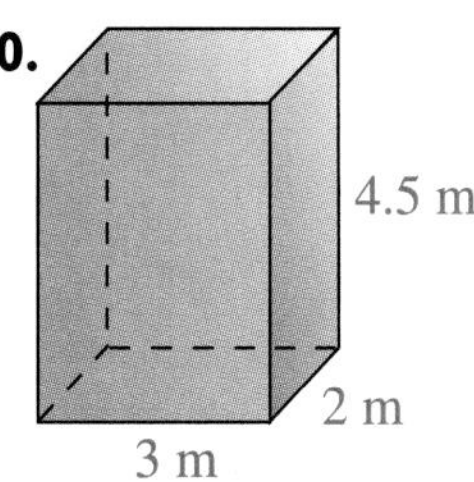

11. $l = 5$ mm, $w = 4$ mm, $h = 9$ mm

12. $l = 14$ cm, $w = 7$ cm, $h = 2.5$ cm

13. $l = 6$ ft, $w = 1$ ft, $h = 7$ ft

The volume and two dimensions of a rectangular prism are given. Find the third dimension.

14. $V = 154$ yd^3, $h = 11$ yd, $w = 2$ yd

15. $V = 120$ cm^3, $w = 4$ cm, $h = 6$ cm

16. $V = 108$ ft^3, $l = 6$ ft, $w = 2$ ft

17. a. Find the volume of the cube.

b. Writing How could you write the formula for the volume of a cube in a different way than $V = lwh$? Explain.

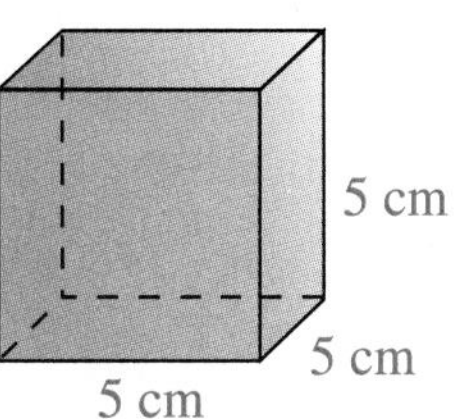

18. Choose A, B, C, or D. This rectangular prism is made of cubes measuring 1 cm on each side. If the top level of cubes is removed, what is the volume of the remaining prism?

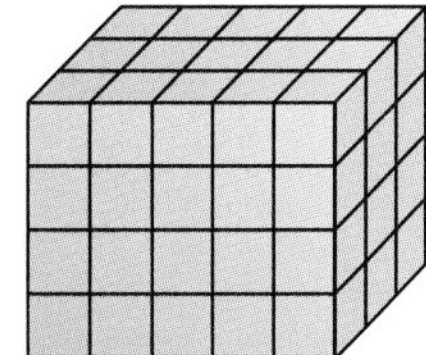

A. 45 cm^3 **B.** 60 cm^3

C. 48 cm^3 **D.** 40 cm^3

19. Choose A, B, C, or D. A rectangular prism is 2 m long, 50 cm wide, and 1 m high. What is its volume?

A. 100 m^3 **B.** 100 cm^3 **C.** 1 m^3 **D.** 10,000 cm^3

Mixed REVIEW

1. Draw a figure that will tessellate.

2. Draw a figure that will not tessellate.

3. a. Name the figure.

b. Find the surface area.

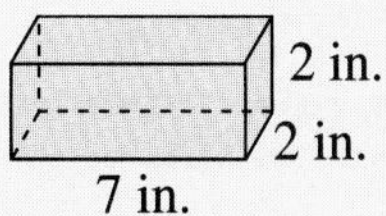

4. Melanie has 19 nickels. Jerry has 11 dimes. Who has more money? How much more?

20. How do the volumes of these rectangular prisms compare? How do the surface areas compare?

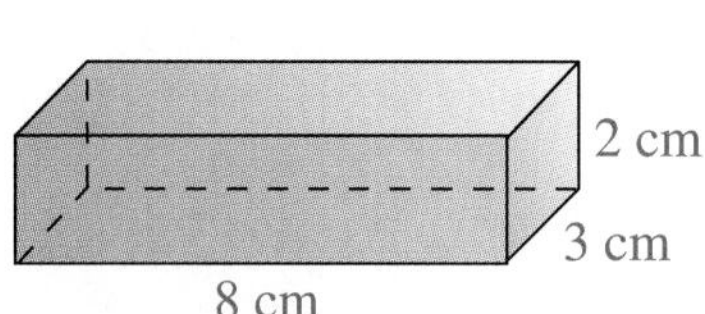

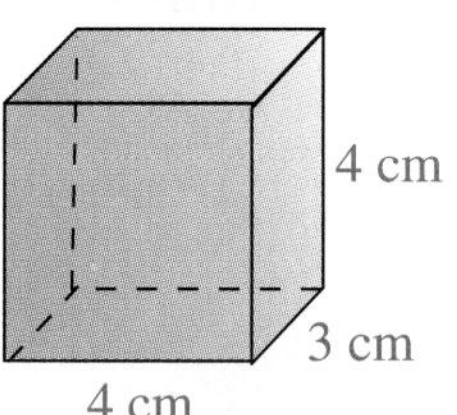

Problem Solving Hint

A 2 cm × 3 cm × 5 cm prism is the same as a 3 cm × 5 cm × 2 cm prism.

Find the whole-number dimensions of all possible rectangular prisms that have the given volume.

21. $V = 32\text{ cm}^3$

22. $V = 48\text{ cm}^3$

23. A rectangular municipal swimming pool is 24 m long and 16 m wide. The average depth of the water is 2.5 m.
   a. What is the volume of the water?
   b. We use units of *capacity,* like the *liter,* to measure liquids. A volume of 1 m^3 is equivalent to 1,000 L of capacity. What is the capacity, in liters, of the swimming pool?
   c. What would be the dimensions of a cover large enough to cover the surface of the water?

24. Data File 9 (pp. 368–369) What is the volume of a finishing post at a track meet?

CHECKPOINT

Name each space figure. Give the number of faces, edges, and vertices.

1.

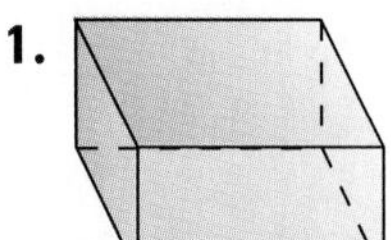

2.

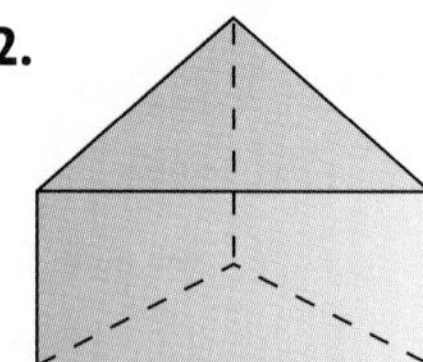

Find the surface area of each figure.

3.

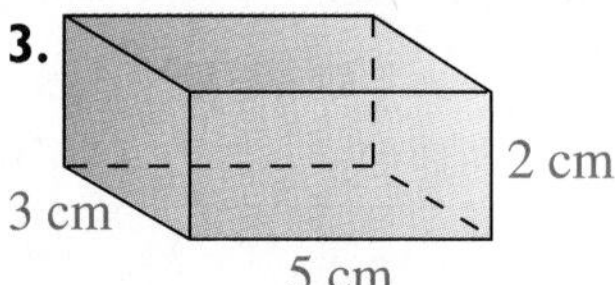

4.

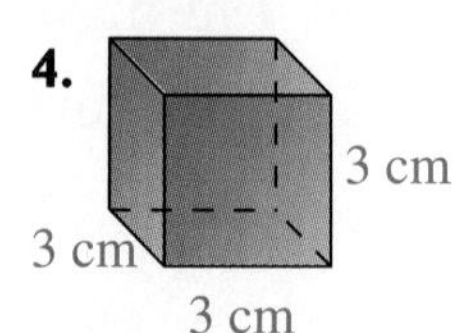

PROBLEM SOLVING

6-9 Make a Model

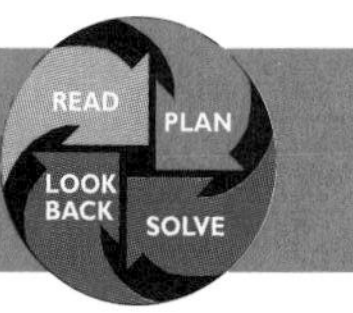

What's Ahead

- Solving problems by making a model

WHAT YOU'LL NEED

✓ Pennies 

✓ Centimeter ruler

Sometimes a physical model can help you solve a problem.

> Danny collects pennies. He keeps his pennies in a box with interior dimensions 21 cm by 21 cm by 21 cm. How many pennies will the box hold?

READ

Read and understand the given information. Summarize the problem.

1. Think about the information you are given and what you are asked to find.
   a. What does the problem ask you to find?
   b. Are you given all the information you need? What else do you need to know?

PLAN

Decide on a strategy to solve the problem.

Making a model will help you solve the problem. If you have enough pennies, you can find out how many are needed to form one layer that fits inside a square 21 cm by 21 cm. However, it will be enough to find out how many pennies you can fit in a row no longer than 21 cm.

2. Do you need to have a stack of pennies 21 cm high in order to find out how many layers will fit in the box? Why or why not?

SOLVE

Try out the strategy.

3. Work with your group to make models you can measure.
   a. How many pennies can you fit in a row 21 cm long?
   b. How many pennies will fit in a stack of pennies 21 cm high?
4. a. How many pennies will fit in one layer?
   b. How many pennies will fit in the box?

LOOK BACK

Think about how you solved this problem.

5. Suppose you measure the diameter and height of only one penny. How could you use the information to get the same result?

TRY THESE

Make a model to solve each problem.

6. Lincoln's head is right-side-up on the penny on the left. If you roll the penny halfway around the other penny, will Lincoln's head be right-side-up, upside-down, or neither?

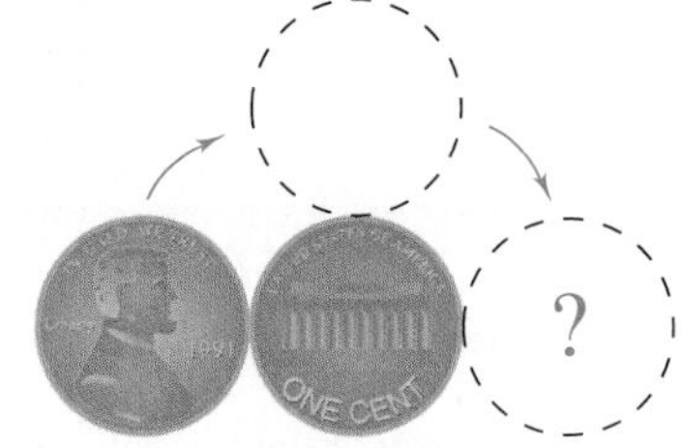

7. It takes Clarence 12 min to cut a log into 4 pieces. How long will it take him to cut a log that is the same size into 5 pieces?

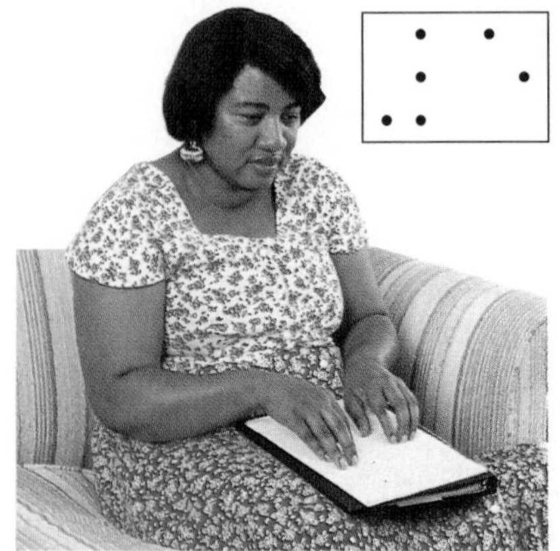

Blind people can use the Braille system to read books. Letters and numbers are indicated by combinations of six raised dots. The number 5 is shown above.

ON YOUR OWN

Use any strategy to solve each problem. Show all your work.

8. The numbered pages in the book *Why Do Clocks Run Clockwise?* go from 1 to 251. How many of these page numbers contain at least one 2?

9. **a.** Find three numbers that continue the pattern.

1, 2, 4, ■, ■, ■

b. Find another three numbers that continue the pattern in a different way.

10. Which of the following nets could you fold to form a box without a top?

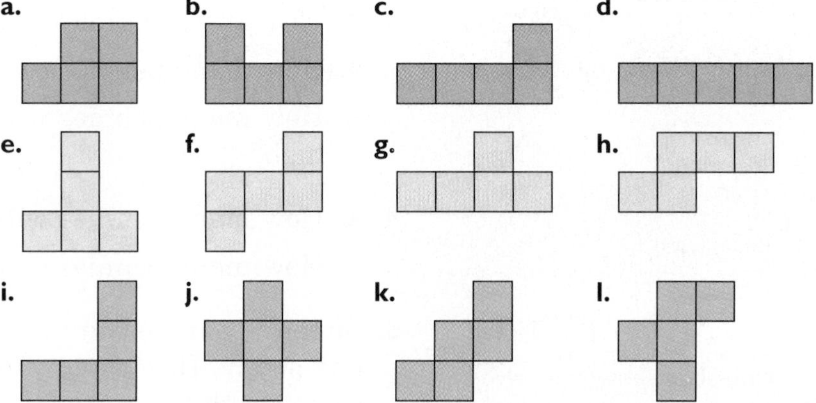

11. What is the area of the triangle?

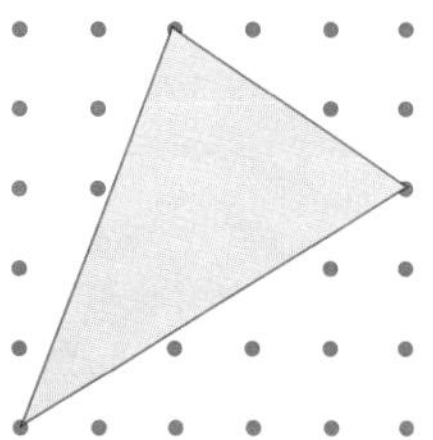

12. Mosi works in a grocery store after school. He stacked grapefruit in the shape of a square pyramid. There was one grapefruit on the top level, four on the next level, and nine on the next level. If there were eight levels in all, how many grapefruit did Mosi stack?

13. What are the whole-number dimensions of the rectangular prism with a volume of 12 cubic units and the greatest possible surface area for such a prism?

14. Kevin went to the grocery store with exactly 90¢ in change. He did not have any pennies.

a. What is the least number of coins he could have?

b. What is the greatest number of coins he could have?

15. Pilar's birthday cake is in the shape of a cube, with icing on the top and four sides. She cut it as shown.

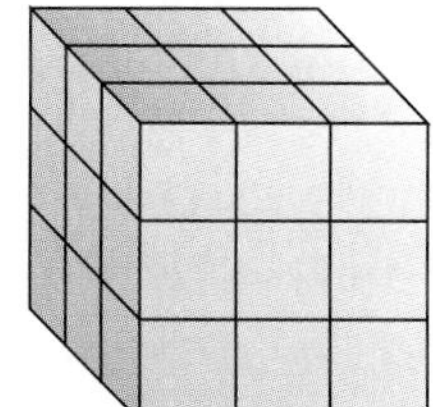

a. How many cuts did Pilar make?

b. How many pieces did she cut the cake into?

c. How many of the pieces don't have any icing?

16. **Choose A, B, or C.** Which piece of wrapping paper shown below can you *not* use to wrap the box shown without cutting?

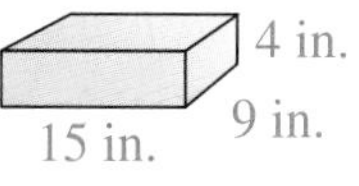

A. 20 in.

B. 18 in.

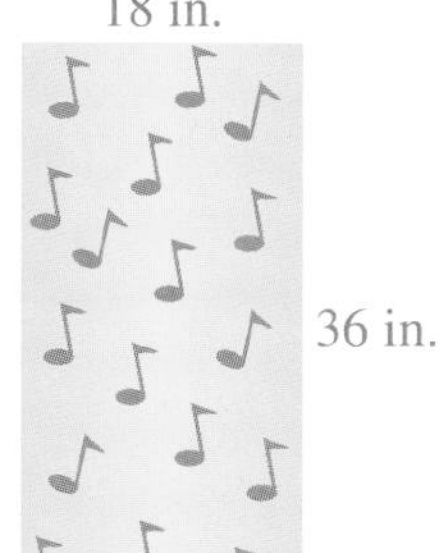

C. 14 in.

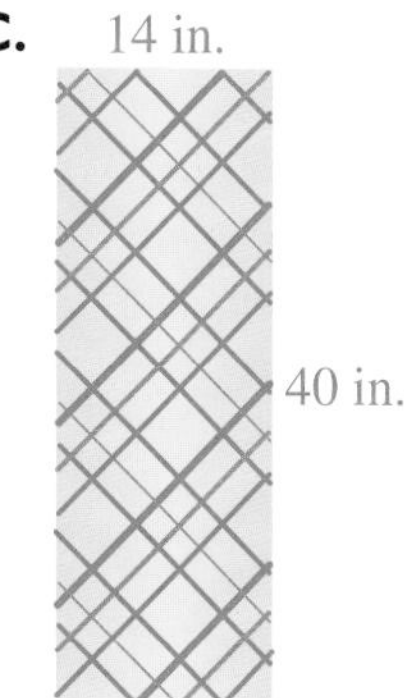

Mixed REVIEW

Write using an exponent.

1. $6 \times 6 \times 6 \times 6$

2. $22 \times 22 \times 22$

Find the volume of each rectangular prism.

3. $l = 7$ cm, $w = 2$ cm, and $h = 4$ cm

4. $l = 5$ ft, $w = 3$ ft, and $h = 7$ ft

5. A collector buys a stamp for $25, sells it for $30, buys it back for $33, and finally sells it for $35. How much money did he make or lose in buying and selling this stamp?

CHAPTER 6

Wrap Up

Perimeter and Area of Polygons — 6-1, 6-2, 6-3

Perimeter is the distance around a figure.

Area is the number of square units inside a figure.

1. Estimate the area of the figure. Assume each square stands for 1 m^2.

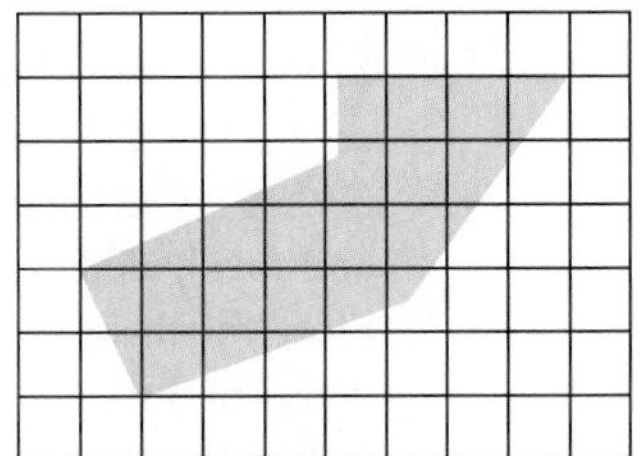

2. Find the area and perimeter of the figure.

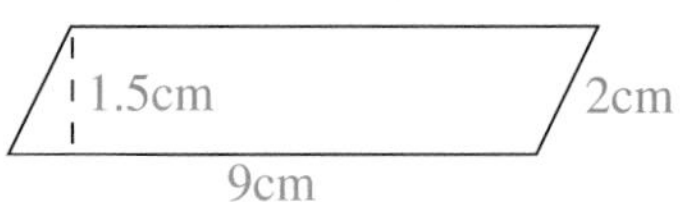

3. A rectangular yard has an area of 72 m^2. One side is 8 m long. How much fence do you need to enclose the entire yard?

4. Find the area of a triangle with a base 12 cm and height 7.6 cm.

Circumference and Area of Circles — 6-4, 6-5

We use the symbol π to stand for the quotient of the circumference and diameter of a circle. The formula for area of a circle is $A = \pi r^2$.

Find the circumference and area of a circle with the given radius or diameter. Use 3.14 for π. Round to a convenient place.

5. $r = 6$ in.

6. $r = 3.8$ m

7. $d = 24.5$ cm

8. $d = 37.6$ ft

Calculator **Find the circumference and area of each circle. Round to a convenient place.**

9.

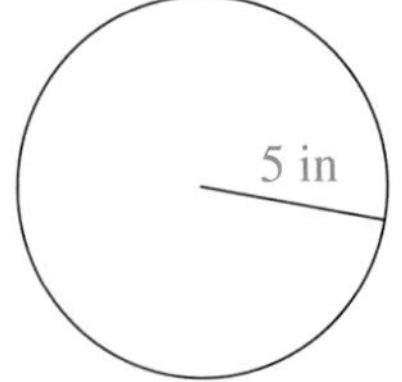

10.

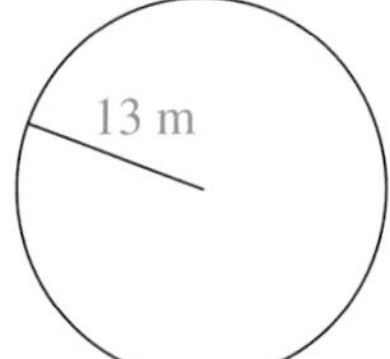

11.

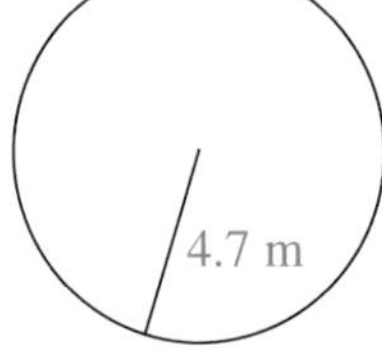

Three-Dimensional Figures 6-6

Three dimensional figures are figures such as boxes, cans, and baseballs that do not lie in a plane. Some three-dimensional figures have flat, polygonal surfaces called ***faces.*** When two faces intersect, the resulting segment is called an ***edge.*** Each point where edges meet is a ***vertex.***

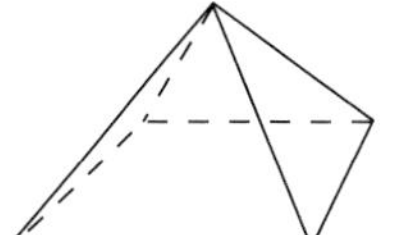

12. **a.** Identify the figure.

b. Find the number of faces, edges, and vertices.

13. **Writing** Give a description of a sphere.

Surface Area and Volume 6-7, 6-8

The sum of the areas of the faces of a three-dimensional prism or pyramid is the ***surface area*** of the figure.

The ***volume*** of a three-dimensional figure is the number of cubic units needed to fill the space inside the figure. The volume of a rectangular prism is $V = lwh$.

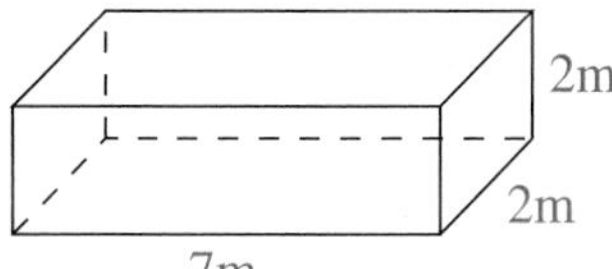

14. Find the surface area and the volume of the rectangular prism.

15. **Choose A, B, C, or D.** Which could not be dimensions for a rectangular prism with a volume of 60 m^3?

A. 1 m by 1 m by 60 m **B.** 4 m by 15 m by 2 m

C. 3 m by 4 m by 5 m **D.** 1 m by 6 m by 10 m

Strategies and Applications 2-7

Sometimes a physical model can help you solve a problem.

16. You have 12 square tables. One person can sit on each side. You need to arrange the tables so that at least one side is touching another table. How many people can you seat?

17. Design a box to hold 4 cube-shaped candles. Use the least possible amount of material. Each candle has 4 in. sides.

GETTING READY FOR CHAPTER 7

Tell whether each number is divisible by 2, 5, or 10.

1. 72 **2.** 40 **3.** 47 **4.** 55 **5.** 1,000 **6.** 129

PUTTING IT ALL TOGETHER

Follow Up

Patterns and Squares

In this chapter you have learned about areas and perimeters of figures. You have learned to solve problems by making models. Have you learned anything to change your mind about Orlando's claims about tile squares? Take another look at the decision you reached regarding his claims. If necessary, revise your decision. Then write a short paper explaining how you reached your decision. The following are suggestions to help you support your reasoning.

✓ Use patterns.
✓ Make a model.
✓ Draw a graph.

The problems preceded by the magnifying glass (p. 236, # 30; p. 249, # 25; and p. 258, # 17) will help you complete the investigation.

Excursion: Suppose Orlando had investigated triangles instead of squares.

How many tiles would he need to build an 8-triangle from a 7-triangle?

Do this with your group. You will need a protractor and compass.

Prepare a circle graph that represents how your time is spent during a typical school day. You should round your time to the nearest quarter hour. Divide your circle into fractions that represent the time spent on each activity.

Some things to think about: How many hours are represented by the circle graph? How can you use the measurement of a circle (360 degrees) to determine what fraction is needed to represent a part of the school day?

Rules:

- Three or more players may play.
- You will need twenty-four 3" x 5" index cards.
- Choose 6 space figures. Write their names twice, once each onto 12 cards.
- Draw the shape of each space figure twice, once each onto the 12 remaining cards. Shuffle the cards and arrange them face down.
- Take turns turning over two cards. If a name card and its matching picture card are turned over, the player keeps the cards and takes another turn. If the name and picture cards do not match, play continues to the left. The game is over when all the cards are gone. The player with the most cards wins.

Boxed In

You and a partner have been hired by the Crumbly Cookie Company to design a box for their latest product. The box must have a volume of 24 cm^3. The design you create has to use as little cardboard as possible. Use graph paper to plan your design. Show where the box would be folded to make each side. Explain how you know that your design is 24 cm^3 and uses the least amount of cardboard possible.

WHAT'S ON YOUR MIND

Rules:

- Two players may play.
- One player thinks of a space figure.
- The other player asks questions that can only be answered with a yes or a no, to determine what figure the player is thinking about. Players should use the words *base, side, vertex, face, angle,* and so on when asking their questions.
- The number of guesses that it takes a player to determine the space figure is that player's score. After playing an equal number of rounds, the player with the least amount of points wins.

CHAPTER 6

Assessment

1. Find the area of the figure. Assume each square represents 1 cm^2.

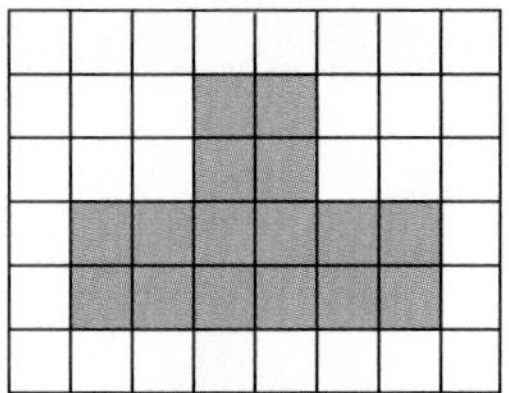

2. Find the area and perimeter of a square with sides 6 m.

3. The perimeter of a rectangle is 32 ft. One dimension is 9 ft. Find the area.

4. Find the area of the figure below.

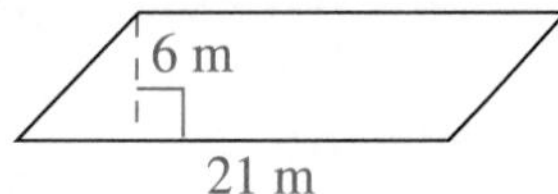

5. Find the area of a parallelogram with base 12 cm and height 7 cm.

6. Find the area of a triangle with base 9.2 m and height 19.3 m.

7. Find the area of the triangle below.

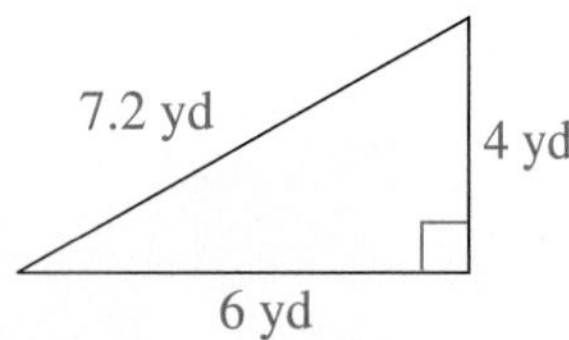

8. **Writing** Which is larger: a pie plate with a radius of 5 in. or a pie plate with a diameter of 9 in.? Explain.

9. What is the surface area of a box with length 8 ft, width 5 ft, and height 4 ft?

10. Find the circumference and area of a circle with the given radius or diameter. Round to the nearest tenth.

    a. $r = 10$ km **b.** $d = 12$ cm

    c. $d = 7.4$ yd **d.** $r = 27$ m

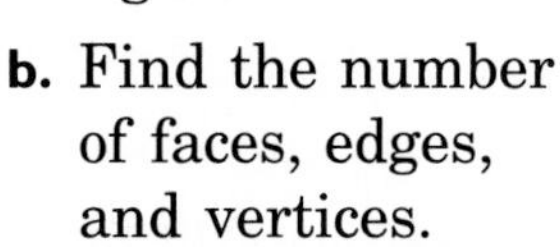

11. **a.** Identify the figure.

    b. Find the number of faces, edges, and vertices.

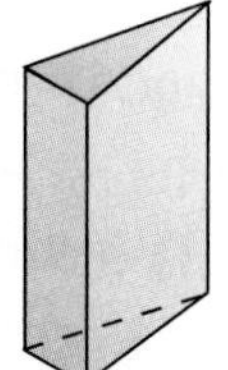

12. A rectangular prism is 17 m long, 3 m wide, and 5 m high. Find its volume.

13. The volume of a rectangular prism is 504 cm^3. The area of the base is 72 cm^2. Find the height of the prism.

14. The volume and two dimensions of a rectangular prism are given. Find the third dimension.

    a. $V = 189$ cm^3, $h = 7$ cm, $w = 3$ cm

    b. $V = 1{,}080$ $in.^3$, $h = 15$ in., $w = 6$ in.

    c. $V = 360$ ft^3, $h = 9$ ft, $w = 4$ ft

15. **Choose A, B, C, or D.** Which could be a net for a rectangular prism?

A. 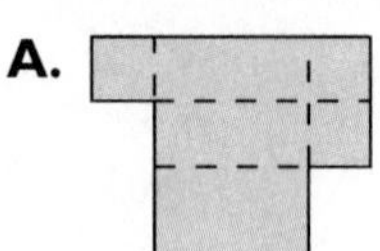

B. 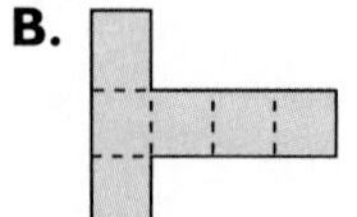

C. 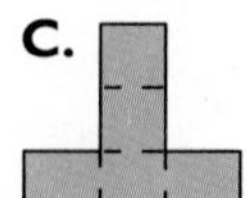

D. 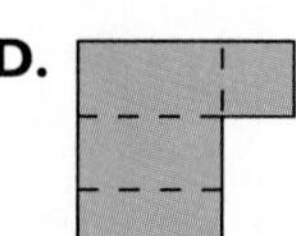

Cumulative Review

Choose A, B, C, or D.

1. What is the area of a circle whose diameter is 6 cm?
   A. 36 cm^2 B. 6 cm^2
   C. 28 cm^2 D. 12 cm^2

2. What is the median cost of peanut butter per serving?
   A. 20 cents B. 20.5 cents
   C. 21 cents D. 22 cents

Peanut Butter Prices (3 tbsp serving)

Brand	Price	Brand	Price
Sticky Stuff	22¢	Grandma's Choice	20¢
Shop Along	19¢	All Natural	22¢
Cityside	14¢	Nutty Taste	22¢

3. What do you do first to evaluate the expression $3.9 + 4.1 \times 16 - 6 \div 4.8$?
   A. Add 3.9 and 4.1.
   B. Multiply 4.1 by 16.
   C. Subtract 6 from 16.
   D. Divide 6 by 4.8.

4. Find the volume of the open box made by folding the sides of the net shown.
   A. 90 $in.^3$ B. 66 $in.^3$
   C. 165 $in.^3$ D. 14 $in.^3$

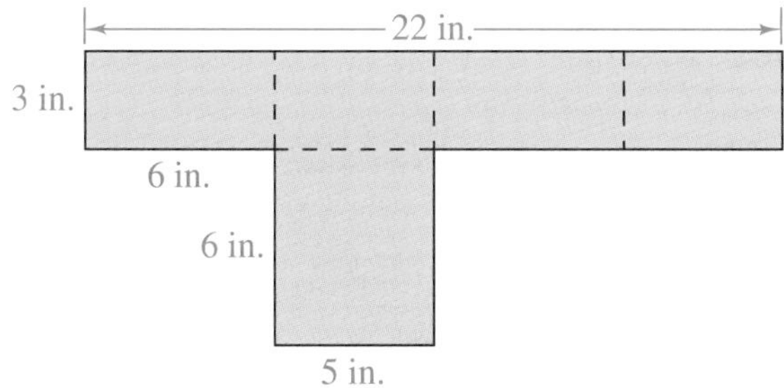

5. If you continue the pattern which figure will have 51 blocks?
   A. the 26th B. the 25th
   C. the 50th D. the 100th

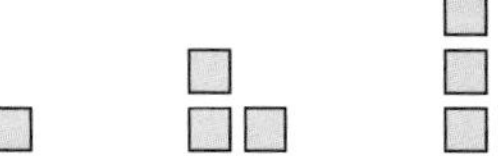

6. A 13.5 mi high speed train will cost \$622 million. About how much is that per mile?
   A. \$460,000 B. \$4.6 million
   C. \$46 million D. \$460 million

7. Which equation is *not* an example of the distributive property?
   A. $12(6.2) + 12(3.8) = 12(6.2 + 3.8)$
   B. $0.75(8.869) + 0.25(8.869) = 8.869$
   C. $19.1(80) = 19.1(100) - 19.1(20)$
   D. $8.1(1.9 + 3.5) = (8.1 + 1.9)(3.5)$

8. Which data display would you use to compare the salaries of nurses?
   A. line plot B. bar graph
   C. line graph D. circle graph

9. A triangle and a rectangle have equal bases and equal heights. How do their perimeters compare?
   A. The perimeter of the triangle is greater.
   B. The perimeter of the rectangle is greater.
   C. The perimeters are equal.
   D. It is impossible to tell.

CHAPTER 7

Fraction Concepts

The highest tsunami was about 278 ft. It appeared off Ishigaki Island, Japan on April 24, 1771. The tsunami tossed an 826.7–t block of coral more than 1.3 mi.

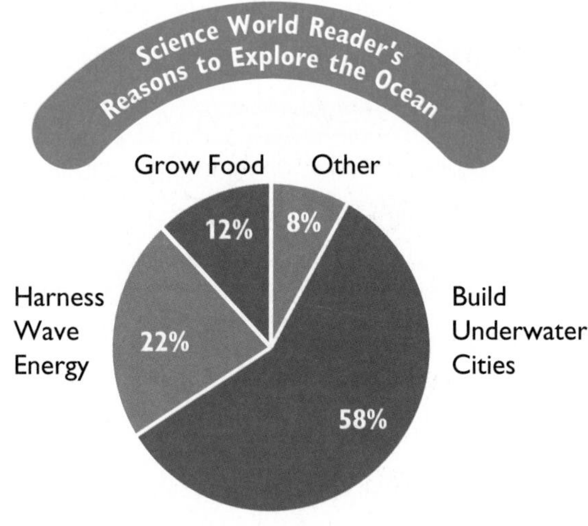

Source: *Science World*

A *tsunami* is an unusually large wave caused by a volcanic eruption on the ocean floor. The speed of a tsunami and the distance between crests relate to the depth of the ocean. The diagram shows that a wave in 18,000 ft of water will travel up to 519 mi/h. More shallow water slows the bottom of a wave. The top continues to push forward. This causes the wave to grow higher and higher until it hits the shore with tremendous force.

sea level

speed (mi/h)	519
depth (feet)	18,000

WHAT YOU WILL LEARN

- how to model, compare, and order fractions
- how to use technology to simplify fractions
- how to solve problems by working backward

The *tidal range* measures the difference between water level at high tide and low tide.

Tidal Ranges

Location	Average tidal range (ft)
Bay of Fundy, Canada	39.4
Boston, MA, USA	9.5
Galveston, TX USA	1.0
Rio de Janeiro, Brazil	2.5
Sunrise, Cook Inlet, AK USA	30.3
Darwin, Australia	14.4
Rangoon, Burma	12.8
Hamburg, Germany	7.3

Source: *Collier's Encyclopedia*

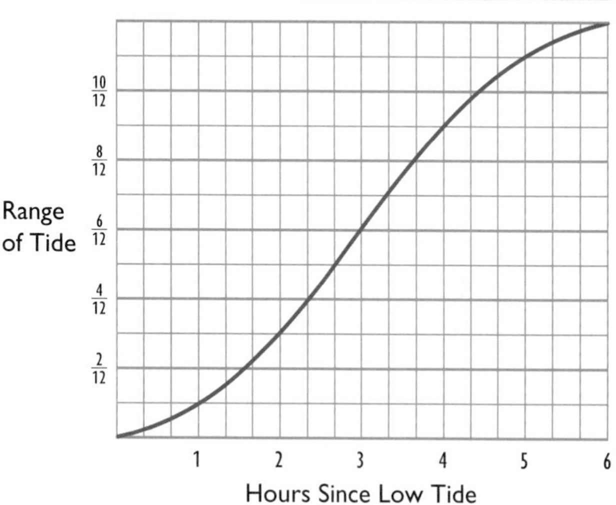

When a tsunami gets closer to land where the water is shallower, the wavelength becomes narrower. The tsunami may hit the coast with a wall of water up to 125 ft high.

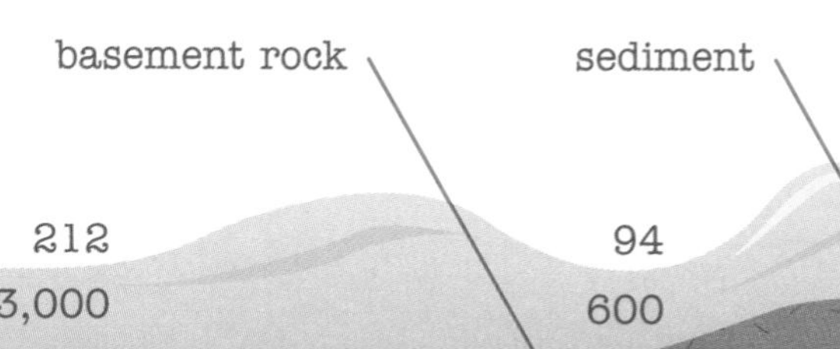

investigation

Project File

Memo

Every culture develops ways of representing numbers. The Hottentots of southern Africa used only the numbers 1 and 2, which they represented by holding up one or two fingers. Anything greater than 2 they referred to as "many."

There are many ways to represent numbers visually. The illustration shows five ways to represent the number 6.

What other objects besides a snowflake can you think of that you could use to represent the number 6?

Mayan numeration system

VI

Roman numeration system

6

Arabic numeration system

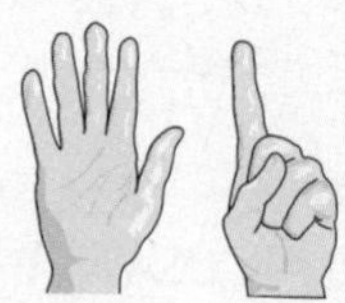

Hand system

Snowflake system

Mission: Make a list of objects you could use to represent whole numbers 0 through 9. Anyone looking at an object should easily understand the number it represents. Decide how to use the objects to represent the numbers 10 through 20. Make a poster displaying your own personalized numeration system.

Leads to Follow

- ✓ Would a snowflake be an appropriate choice for representing the number 6 in your system? Why or why not?
- ✓ Suppose you can think of several objects to represent a number. How can you decide which object is best?

What's Ahead

- Exploring divisibility using mental math

7-1 Mental Math: Divisibility

THINK AND DISCUSS

What's so important about *divisibility*? Is it the ability to completely disappear? No, that's *invisibility*. **Divisibility** is the ability of one number to divide into another with no remainder. You'll use divisibility many times working with and understanding fractions.

1. Look at the numbers in the table below.

Divisible by 2	Not divisible by 2
10 14 202 5,756 798 80 120	9 13 467 4,005 99 42,975

a. Give two more numbers that are divisible by 2. Give two more numbers that are not divisible by 2.

b. **Discussion** Give a rule for divisibility by 2.

c. Which of the numbers in the table that are divisible by 2 are also divisible by 5? divisible by 10?

d. Which of the numbers in the table that are not divisible by 2 are divisible by 5? divisible by 10?

e. **Discussion** Give rules for divisibility by 5 and divisibility by 10.

Enjoying an ear of corn *can be a mathematical experience! An ear of corn always has an even number of rows.* ***By what number is the number of rows divisible?***

The rules for divisibility can help you save time finding the divisibility of a number. One of the fun things about mathematics is that there are a lot of patterns that lead to great shortcuts. The chart below shows some facts about divisibility.

Divisible By	Rule
1	All numbers are divisible by 1.
2	All even numbers are divisible by 2.
5	Numbers ending in 5 or 0 are divisible by 5.
10	Numbers ending in 0 are divisible by 10.

You can determine whether a number is divisible by 3 by adding up the digits. Then determine whether the sum is divisible by 3.

Example 1 Is 2,571 divisible by 3?

- Find the sum of the digits.
  $2 + 5 + 7 + 1 = 15$

  Determine whether the sum is divisible by 3.
  $15 \div 3 = 5$

The sum of the digits is divisible by 3, so 2,571 is divisible by 3.

The divisibility rule for 9 is like the divisibility rule for 3.

2. **a.** Mental Math Is 99 divisible by 9?

b. What is the sum of the digits of the number 99? Is this sum divisible by 9?

c. Mental Math Is 66 divisible by 9?

d. What is the sum of the digits of the number 66? Is this sum divisible by 9?

e. Discussion Give a rule for divisibility by 9.

WHO? A Greek mathematician named Plato (427?–348 B.C.) wrote about the number 5,040 in his work *The Laws.* He stated that 5,040 is divisible by 60 numbers, including 1 through 10.

Source: *Number Theory*

Example 2 Is 27,216 divisible by 1, 2, 3, 5, 9, or 10?

1	Yes, all numbers are divisible by 1.
2	Yes, it is an even number.
3	Yes, the sum of the digits is divisible by 3.
5	No, it does not end in 5 or 0.
9	Yes, the sum of the digits is divisible by 9.
10	No, it does not end in zero.

TRY THESE

Mental Math **Determine whether the first number is divisible by the second.**

3. 525; 5 **4.** 848,960; 10 **5.** 2,385; 10 **6.** 36,928; 1

7. 60,714; 3 **8.** 757,503; 9 **9.** 4,673; 2 **10.** 333,335; 3

ON YOUR OWN

Mental Math **State whether each number is divisible by 1, 2, 3, 5, 9, or 10.**

11. 105 **12.** 15,345 **13.** 40,020 **14.** 8,516

15. 356,002 **16.** 12,345 **17.** 2,021,112 **18.** 70,641

Find the digit to make each number divisible by 9.

19. 34,76■ **20.** ■7,302 **21.** 2■6,555 **22.** 19,76■,228

Find a number that satisfies the given conditions.

23. a three-digit number divisible by 1, 2, 3, and 5

24. a four-digit number divisible by 1, 2, 3, 5, 9, and 10

25. a number greater than 1 billion divisible by 1, 2, and 3

26. Critical Thinking If a number is divisible by 5, must it be divisible by 10? Use an example to support your answer.

27. **Choose A, B, C, or D.** The five sides of the Pentagon are congruent. The perimeter of the building is divisible by 5 and 10. What is the length of each side?

A. 351 ft **B.** 353 ft **C.** 352 ft **D.** 357 ft

28. Writing Describe how you can use your calculator to tell if one number is divisible by another. To determine divisibility by 1, 2, 3, 5, 9, or 10, do you think it is easier to use mental math or a calculator? Explain.

29. Use the numbers at the right.

a. Use the divisibility rules to tell which numbers are divisible by both 2 and 3.

b. Calculator Which numbers are divisible by 6?

c. Use your results to write a divisibility rule for 6.

78 154 237
8,010 21,822

30. Elissa and eight of her friends went to lunch at a Thai restaurant. The total amount of the check was $56.61.

a. Can the group split the check into equal parts?

b. Do you think divisibility rules hold for decimal numbers? Use examples to support your answer.

Suppose it takes 27 number cubes to fill a clear cubical box.

1. How many number cubes will be touching the bottom of the box?
2. How many number cubes will be touching the sides of the box?
3. How many number cubes will not be visible?

Solve.

4. $a - 7 = 23$
5. $35 = 19 + c$
6. $54 = 3t$
7. $\frac{y}{9} = 30$

What's Ahead

- Recognizing prime and composite numbers
- Finding the prime factorization of a composite number

WHAT YOU'LL NEED

✓ Square tiles

✓ Graph paper

7-2 Prime Factorization

THINK AND DISCUSS

You can build all the rectangles shown at the right using exactly 12 square tiles.

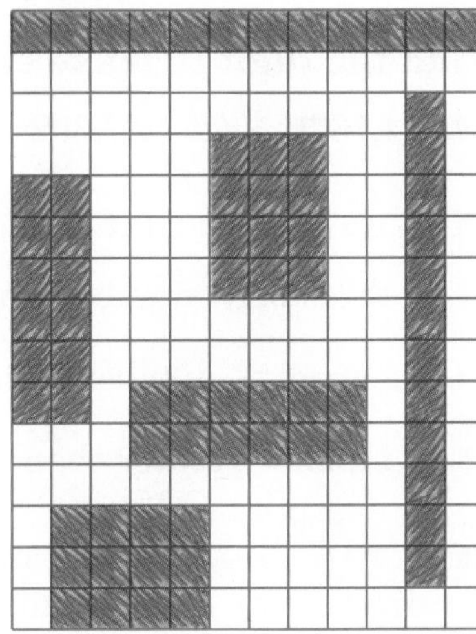

1. **Discussion** Does a 4 by 3 rectangle have the same shape as a 3 by 4 rectangle? Explain.
2. How many rectangles with different shapes can you build using exactly 12 square tiles? What are their dimensions?

The numbers 1, 2, 3, 4, 6, and 12 are *factors* of 12. One number is a **factor** of another if it divides that number with no remainder.

3. **Discussion** How are the dimensions of the rectangles built using exactly 12 tiles related to the factors of 12?
4. Use square tiles to find all the factors of 17 and of 20.

You call a number that has exactly two factors, 1 and itself, a **prime number.** A number that has more than two factors is called a **composite number.**

5. How many rectangles with different shapes can you build using a prime number of square tiles?
6. Describe the number of rectangles with different shapes you can build using a composite number of tiles.
7. **Discussion** Why is the number 1 considered to be neither prime nor composite?

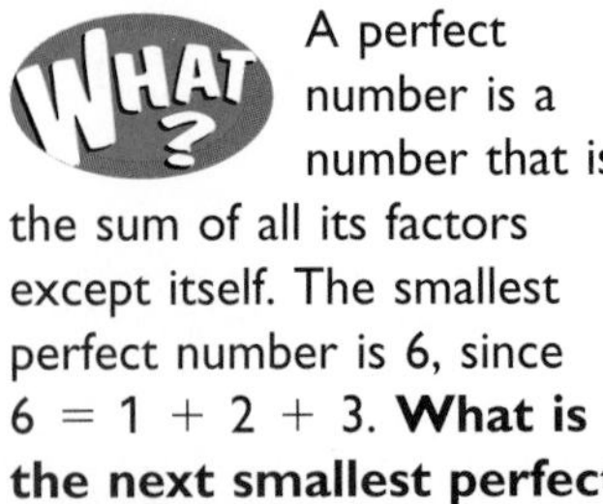

A perfect number is a number that is the sum of all its factors except itself. The smallest perfect number is 6, since 6 = 1 + 2 + 3. **What is the next smallest perfect number?**

Source: *More Joy of Mathematics*

Example 1 Tell whether 9 is prime or composite.

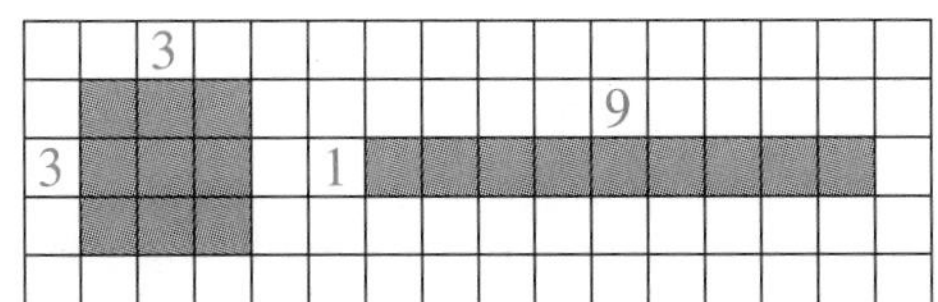

The dimensions of the rectangles show that the factors of 9 are 1, 3, and 9. So, 9 is composite.

A composite number is divisible by its prime factors. You can find these prime factors using a **factor tree.** Two factor trees for the number 36 are shown below.

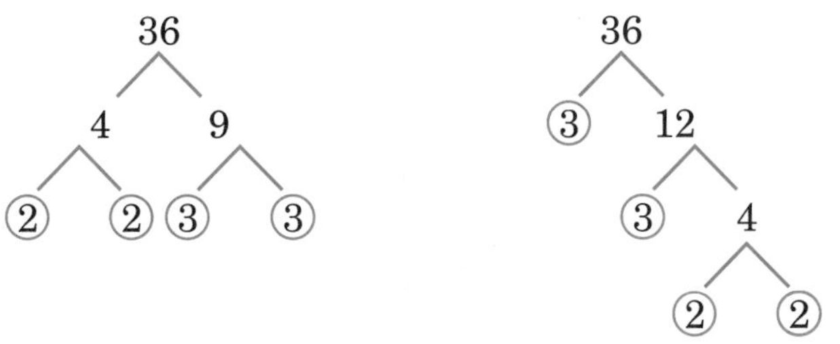

8. a. **Discussion** How are the two factor trees alike? How are they different?
   b. Name the prime factors of 36.

9. **Discussion** How can you use divisibility rules to begin a factor tree?

You can write a composite number as a product of its prime factors. This product is the **prime factorization** of the number.

Example 2 Find the prime factorization of 75 using a factor tree.

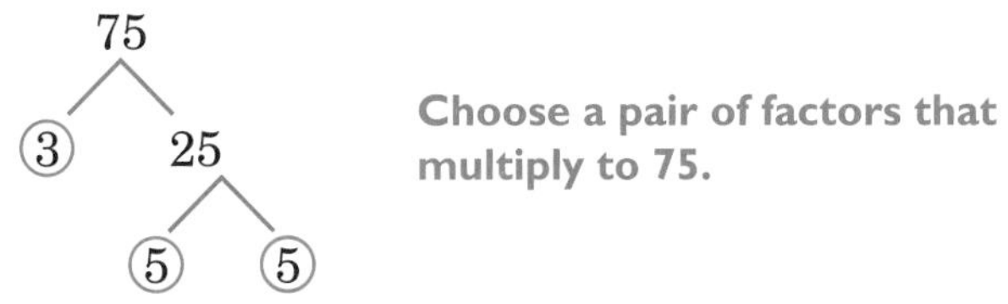

The prime factorization of 75 is $3 \times 5 \times 5$.

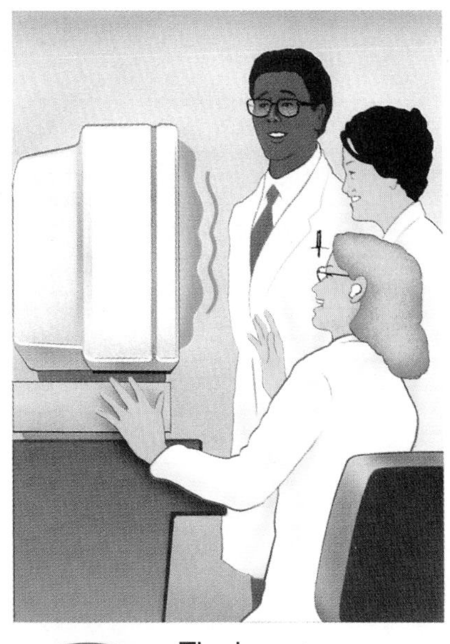

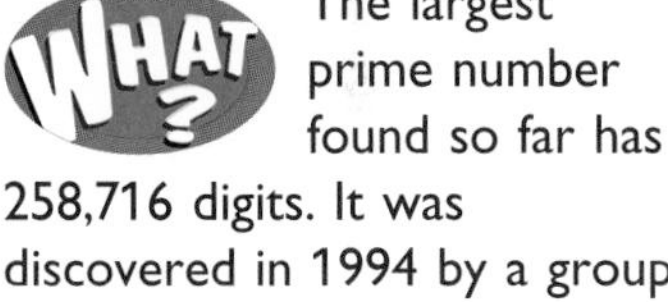

The largest prime number found so far has 258,716 digits. It was discovered in 1994 by a group of computer scientists.

Problem Solving Hint

It is helpful to circle each prime factor as soon as it appears in your factor tree.

1	2	3	4	5	6
7	8	9	10	11	12
13	14	15	16	17	18
19	20	21	22	23	24
25	26	27	28	29	30
31	32	33	34	35	36
37	38	39	40	41	42
43	44	45	46	47	48
49	50				

WORK TOGETHER

Work with a partner to find prime numbers using a method called a *sieve*. List the numbers 1 to 50 as shown at the left.

10. Mark out 1, since it's not prime. Circle 2, since it is prime. Mark out every multiple of 2. What pattern do you notice for the multiples of 2?

11. Circle the first number after 2 that is unmarked. This is the next prime number. Mark out all of its multiples. What pattern do you notice for these multiples?

12. The next prime number is 5. Circle it and mark out all of its multiples. Describe the pattern formed by the multiples of 5.

13. What is the next prime number? Circle it and mark out all of its multiples.

14. Circle 11 because it is prime. Why have you already marked out all of the multiples of 11 in the table?

15. What do you notice about the rest of the unmarked numbers? List the prime numbers less than 50.

WHAT? The Sieve of Eratosthenes allows you to determine all prime numbers less than a given value. This procedure was established by Eratosthenes (c. 276–195 B.C.), a Greek mathematician.

Source: *The Joy of Mathematics*

TRY THESE

16. The rectangles that can be formed using exactly 16 square tiles are shown below. List all the factors of 16.

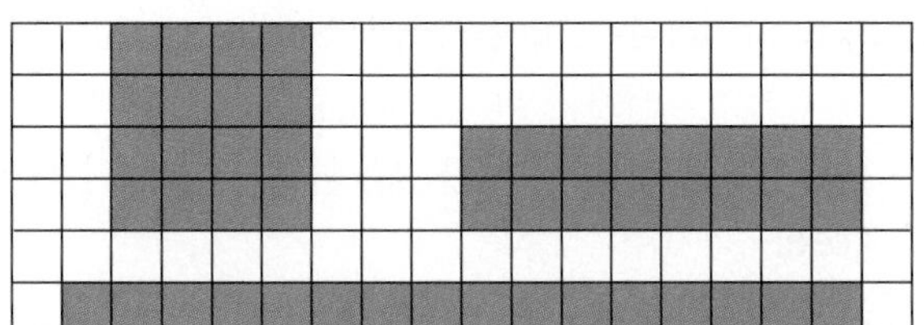

List all the factors of each number. Tell whether each number is prime or composite.

17. 55 **18.** 51 **19.** 103 **20.** 100

Find the prime factorization using a factor tree.

21. 30 **22.** 63 **23.** 120 **24.** 275

ON YOUR OWN

25. **Writing** Sketch all the rectangles with different shapes that can be formed using exactly 8 square tiles. Explain how to use your diagram to find the factors of 8 and to tell if 8 is a prime or composite number.

Christian Goldbach (1690–1764) believed that every even number could be written as the sum of two prime numbers. His belief has never been proven or disproven. **How can you write the number 24 as the sum of two primes?**

Source: *The I Hate Mathematics Book*

Sketch all the rectangles with different shapes that can be formed using exactly the given number of square tiles. List all the factors of each number. Tell whether each number is prime or composite.

26. 15 27. 3 28. 28 29. 21

Tell whether each number is prime or composite.

30. 36 31. 19 32. 72 33. 90

34. 44 35. 7 36. 80 37. 86

38. 93 39. 71 40. 150 41. 56

Copy and complete each factor tree.

42. 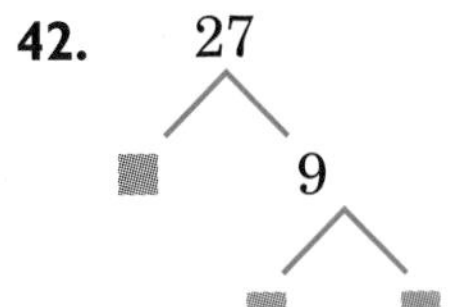

43. 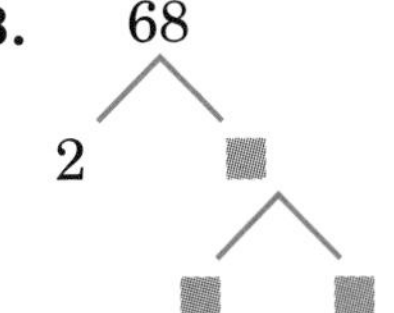

44. 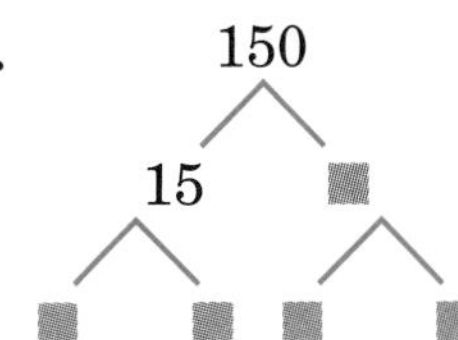

Find the prime factorization using a factor tree.

45. 50 46. 32 47. 45 48. 90

49. 143 50. 160 51. 108 52. 531

Calculator **Find the number with the given prime factorization.**

53. $3 \times 17 \times 17 \times 17 \times 47$ 54. $7 \times 7 \times 17 \times 23 \times 23$

55. Two prime numbers that differ by 2, such as 3 and 5, are called *twin primes.* Find all twin primes that are less than 100.

56. How can you use exponents to write the prime factorization $2 \times 2 \times 2 \times 3 \times 3 \times 5$?

Determine whether each number is divisible by 3, 5, or 9.

1. 378 2. 6,480
3. 4,095 4. 3,003

Find the area.

5. 8 m, 10 m, 6 m

6. 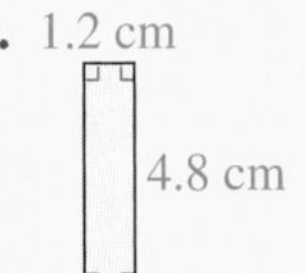

7. Find the sum of the whole numbers from 25 through 50.

What's Ahead

- Finding the greatest common factor of two or more numbers

7-3 Greatest Common Factor

WORK TOGETHER

At a Collectors Club meeting, the sponsor announces that two sets of stamps have been donated. The sponsor is planning to distribute each set equally among the members present at the meeting. Suppose one set contains 18 stamps and the other set contains 24 stamps. Let's find the greatest number of members that can be present at the meeting.

The stamps above are a sample of those that have been printed to honor mathematicians.

1. Is it possible only five members are present? Explain.
2. Is it possible only three members are present? Explain.
3. What must be true about the number of members present?
4. List all the possible numbers of members that can be present at the meeting. What is the largest number of members that can be present?

THINK AND DISCUSS

The factors that are the same for two or more numbers are their **common factors.** The **greatest common factor** (GCF) of two or more numbers is the greatest number that is a factor of each number. You can find the GCF of two numbers by making a list.

Example 1 Find the GCF of 18 and 30.

- Make a list of factors for each number. Then circle the factors the numbers have in common.

18: 1, 2, 3, 6, 9, 18

30: 1, 2, 3, 5, 6, 10, 15, 30

The GCF of 18 and 30 is 6, since it is the greatest of their common factors.

5. **Discussion** Explain how you can find the GCF of three or more numbers.

You can also use prime factorization to find the GCF of a set of numbers.

Example 2 Find the GCF of 42 and 90.

- Make a factor tree for each number.

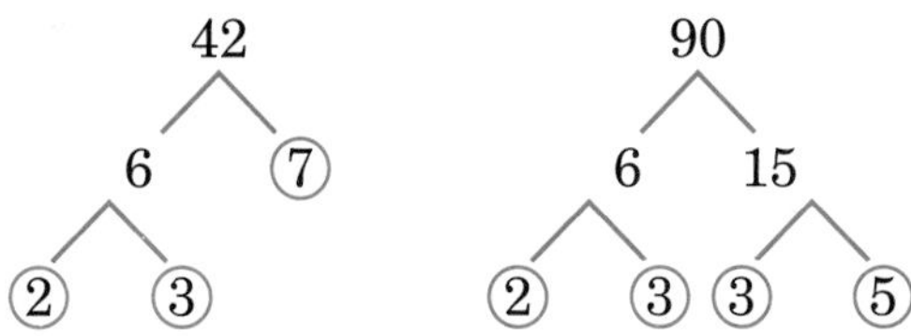

- Write the prime factorization for each number. Then identify common factors.

$42 = 2 \times 3 \times 7$

$90 = 2 \times 3 \times 3 \times 5$

- Multiply the common factors together.

$2 \times 3 = 6$

The GCF of 42 and 90 is 6.

6. a. Make a list to find the GCF of 28 and 33.

b. Use prime factorization to find the GCF of 28 and 33. Explain why the GCF is not easily recognized using this method.

c. **Discussion** How will you know that the GCF of a set of numbers is 1 when you use prime factorization?

I think the one lesson I have learned is that there is no substitute for paying attention.

—Diane Sawyer (1945–)

TRY THESE

Mental Math **Find the GCF of each set of numbers.**

7. 14, 21

8. 6, 18

9. 10, 15, 20

10. 13, 17

11. a. Name all the factors of 36 and of 56.

b. Name all the common factors of 36 and 56.

c. Find the GCF of 36 and 56.

12. **Critical Thinking** The GCF of 18 and some number is 6. What are three possible values for the number?

Mixed REVIEW

Write the prime factorization.

1. 324
2. 600

Use graph paper to model each decimal.

3. 0.75
4. 0.7

Find the area of each circle. Use 3.14 for π.

5. radius = 7 m
6. diameter = 16 in.

7. The bus from Montreal to Toronto is scheduled to leave at 5:43 A.M. and arrive at 4:54 P.M. How long is the trip if the bus passes through one time zone, gaining an hour?

ON YOUR OWN

Make a list to find the GCF of each set of numbers.

13. 14, 35 **14.** 24, 25 **15.** 12, 15, 21

16. 26, 34 **17.** 11, 23 **18.** 6, 8, 12

Use prime factorization to find the GCF of each set of numbers.

19. 22, 104 **20.** 64, 125 **21.** 6, 57, 102

22. 13, 120 **23.** 17, 85 **24.** 150, 240

25. Writing What is the GCF of any two prime numbers? Explain why this is true.

26. The graph shows the GCF of a number x and 4.

a. Describe the pattern in the graph.

b. What is the GCF of 8 and 4?

c. Use the graph to predict the GCF of 18 and 4.

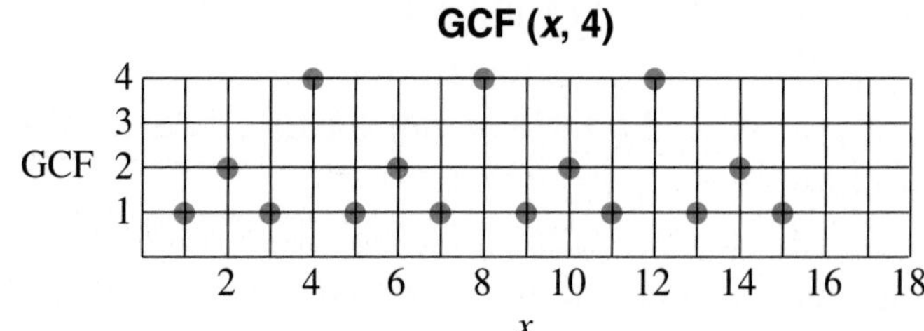

CHECKPOINT

Mental Math **State whether each number is divisible by 1, 2, 3, 5, 9, or 10.**

1. 960 **2.** 243 **3.** 2,310 **4.** 5,070

Find the prime factorization using a factor tree.

5. 960 **6.** 243 **7.** 2,310 **8.** 5,070

Find the GCF of each set of numbers.

9. 48, 56 **10.** 24, 42, 72 **11.** 300, 450

Problem Solving Practice

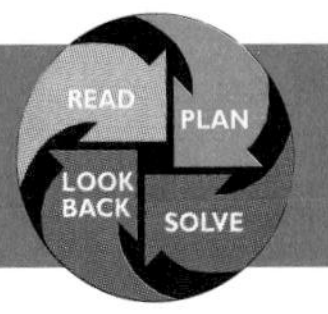

PROBLEM SOLVING STRATEGIES

Make a Table
Use Logical Reasoning
Solve a Simpler Problem
Too Much or Too Little Information
Look for a Pattern
Make a Model
Work Backward
Draw a Diagram
Guess and Test
Simulate a Problem
Use Multiple Strategies

Solve. The list at the left shows some possible strategies you can use.

1. Alicia and Brad are at the library today. Alicia goes to the library every 6 days and Brad goes to the library every 8 days. How many times in the next 12 weeks will Alicia and Brad be at the library on the same day?

2. In how many different ways can Latosha, Pang-Ni, and Charles stand in line at the bookstore?

3. **Health** After a health screening in her homeroom, Ms. Kato reported the results. Of the 25 students in the class, a total of 11 needed a dental check-up, 17 needed an eye exam, and 5 students needed neither a dental check-up nor an eye exam. How many students needed both?

4. **Money** Taesha has \$1.35 in nickels and dimes. She has a total of 15 coins. How many of each coin does she have?

5. Each time Aretha's grandmother visits, she doubles the amount of money Aretha has saved and gives her \$3 extra to spend. After her grandmother's first visit, Aretha had a total of \$19. How much had Aretha saved before her grandmother's visit?

6. Box A has 9 green balls and 4 red balls. Box B has 12 green balls and 5 red balls. You want the fraction of green balls in Box A to equal the fraction of red balls in Box B. How many green balls must move from Box A to Box B?

7. How many days old are you?

8. **Entertainment** At the grand opening of the Plex Cinema, every 15th person to buy a ticket got a free ticket for a future feature. Every 10th person got a coupon for a free box of popcorn. Of the 418 ticket buyers, how many received both prizes?

9. Alaina is watching a football game at school. Alaina's piano recital begins at 7:00 P.M. It takes her 15 min to get home, 20 min to eat supper, 25 min to change, and 10 min to get there. What time should she leave the game?

Shigechiyo Izumi holds the record for the longest living person. Shigechiyo lived 120 years, 237 days. **About how many minutes is that?**

Source: *Guinness Book of World Records*

What's Ahead

- Exploring fractions and equivalent fractions using models
- Estimating fractions

WHAT YOU'LL NEED

✓ Fraction bars 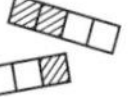

7-4 Exploring Fractions

THINK AND DISCUSS

You can model fractions using *fraction bars*. **Fraction bars** represent fractions as shaded parts of a region.

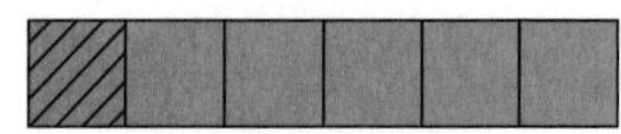

1. a. How does the model represent the numerator (1) and denominator (6)?
   b. How would $\frac{5}{6}$ be represented using this type of model?

2. Name the fraction modeled by each fraction bar.
   a. 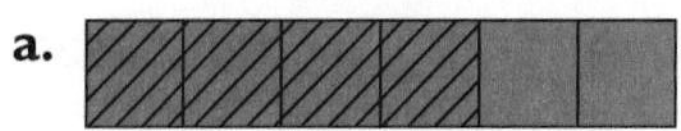
   b. 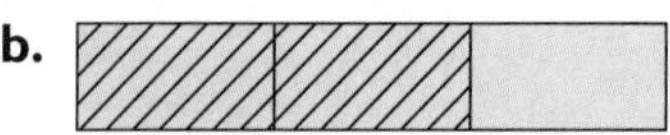

3. Find a fraction bar that models each fraction.
   a. $\frac{2}{6}$ b. $\frac{3}{4}$ c. $\frac{6}{10}$ d. $\frac{2}{5}$

4. **Discussion** What number is represented when all the regions are shaded in a fraction bar? Explain.

The fraction bars at the right show equivalent fractions. **Equivalent fractions** are fractions that represent the same part of a whole.

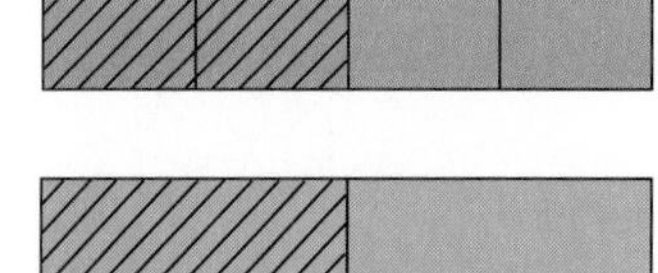

5. a. What fraction is modeled by the blue fraction bar? the green fraction bar?
   b. Compare the area shaded in the blue fraction bar with the area shaded in the green fraction bar.
   c. Find two other fraction bars that show the same shaded area as the fraction bars shown above.
   d. Name three fractions that are equivalent to $\frac{1}{2}$.

6. Find a fraction bar that models $\frac{4}{6}$. Name two other fraction bars that show an equivalent fraction.

***A flash of lightning** lasts for about $\frac{3}{100}$ of a second. That's quicker than the blink of an eye!*

WORK TOGETHER

Work with a partner to write rules for estimating fractions.

7. The fractions at the right are close to 0. Write a rule to tell when a fraction is close to 0. $\frac{1}{14}$ $\frac{3}{17}$ $\frac{2}{25}$ $\frac{7}{125}$

8. The fractions at the right are close to $\frac{1}{2}$. Write a rule to tell when a fraction is close to $\frac{1}{2}$. $\frac{3}{8}$ $\frac{8}{14}$ $\frac{11}{23}$ $\frac{55}{100}$

9. The fractions at the right are close to 1. Write a rule to tell when a fraction is close to 1. $\frac{99}{100}$ $\frac{3}{4}$ $\frac{45}{50}$ $\frac{79}{91}$

10. Use your rules to write three fractions that are close to 0, three fractions that are close to $\frac{1}{2}$, and three fractions that are close to 1. Then exchange with your partner to see if he or she can estimate each fraction.

Mixed REVIEW

Find the GCF.

1. 18, 24
2. 30, 45
3. 36, 56, 72

Write a variable expression.

4. 10 less than a number
5. the sum of twice a number and 5
6. the product of a number and 6

7. Find the length and width of a rectangle whose area is 48 m^2 and whose perimeter is 32 m.

ON YOUR OWN

Name the fraction modeled by each fraction bar.

11.

12.

Find a fraction bar that models each fraction. Name other fraction bars that show an equivalent fraction.

13. $\frac{1}{2}$ 14. $\frac{9}{12}$ 15. $\frac{2}{3}$ 16. $\frac{2}{6}$

17. **Writing** Use the models at the right to explain why the fractions $\frac{2}{4}$ and $\frac{1}{3}$ are not equivalent.

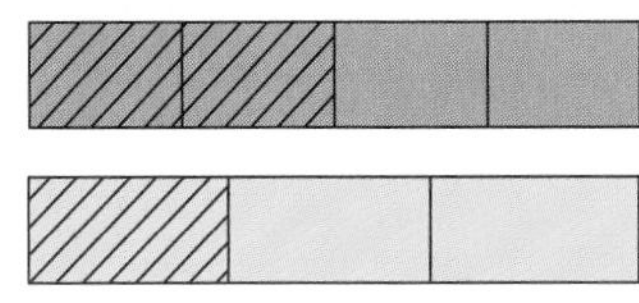

18. **Estimation** Tell whether each fraction at the right is close to 0, close to $\frac{1}{2}$, or close to 1.

$\frac{3}{30}$	$\frac{7}{9}$	$\frac{1}{10}$
$\frac{38}{45}$	$\frac{17}{40}$	$\frac{45}{100}$
$\frac{35}{80}$	$\frac{5}{99}$	$\frac{75}{80}$

19. **Critical Thinking** Write three fractions that are close to 0, three fractions that are close to $\frac{1}{2}$, and three fractions that are close to 1.

What's Ahead

- Finding equivalent fractions
- Expressing fractions in simplest form

WHAT YOU'LL NEED

✓ Fraction bars 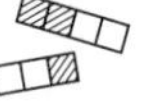

7-5 Equivalent Fractions

THINK AND DISCUSS

The area shaded in the red fraction bar is equal to the area shaded in the yellow fraction bar. Therefore, the models represent equivalent fractions.

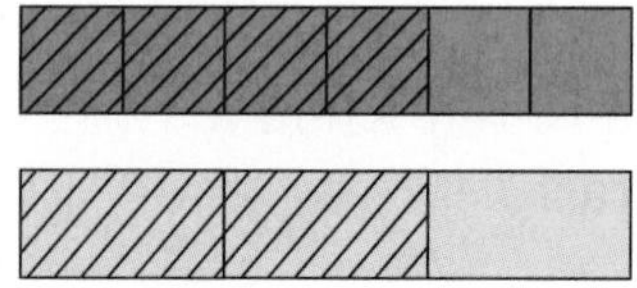

1. a. Name the pair of equivalent fractions that are modeled.
   b. Find another fraction bar that represents a fraction equivalent to those modeled above. What fraction is represented?

2. **Discussion** Model the fractions $\frac{3}{5}$ and $\frac{3}{4}$ using fraction bars. Use the model to explain why the fractions are not equivalent.

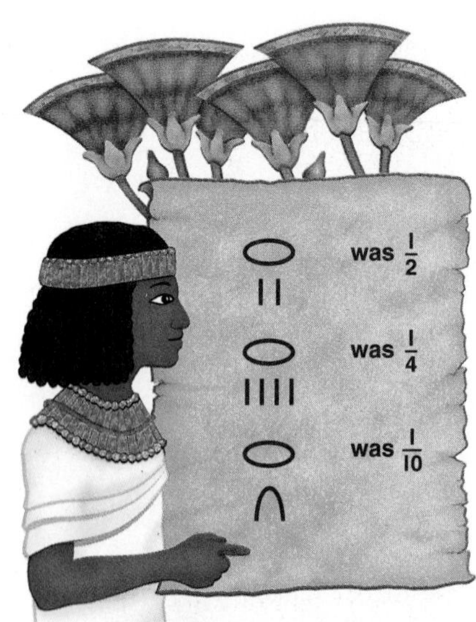

The Egyptians in Africa wrote fractions by placing an oval above the symbols for their numbers.

Source: *The History of Mathematics*

You can form equivalent fractions by multiplying or dividing the numerator and denominator by the same nonzero number.

3. The fractions $\frac{3}{4}$ and $\frac{9}{12}$ are modeled below.

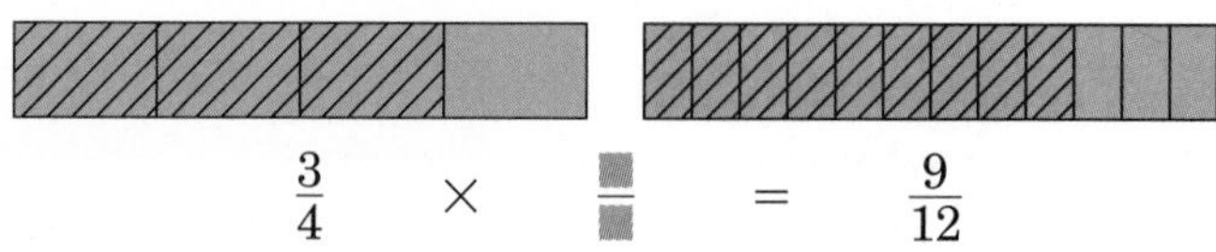

$$\frac{3}{4} \times \frac{■}{■} = \frac{9}{12}$$

   a. What number can you multiply both the numerator and denominator of $\frac{3}{4}$ by to get $\frac{9}{12}$?
   b. Explain how multiplication by this number is shown in the models.
   c. **Discussion** What whole number are you actually multiplying $\frac{3}{4}$ by to get $\frac{9}{12}$? Explain.
   d. Use multiplication to find two other fractions equivalent to $\frac{3}{4}$.

4. The fractions $\frac{6}{12}$ and $\frac{2}{4}$ are modeled below.

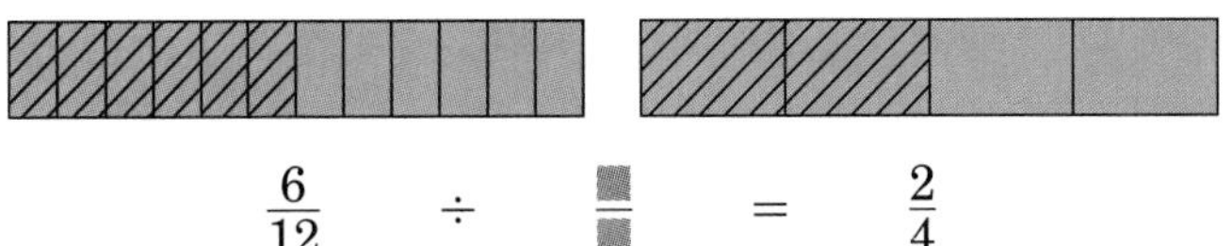

$$\frac{6}{12} \div \frac{\blacksquare}{\blacksquare} = \frac{2}{4}$$

a. What number can you divide both the numerator and denominator of $\frac{6}{12}$ by to get $\frac{2}{4}$?

b. Explain how division by this number is modeled.

c. **Discussion** What whole number are you actually dividing $\frac{6}{12}$ by to get $\frac{2}{4}$? Explain.

d. Use division to find two other fractions equivalent to $\frac{6}{12}$.

When you divide both the numerator and denominator of a fraction by the greatest common factor (GCF), the fraction is in **simplest form.**

Example 1 Write $\frac{20}{28}$ in simplest form.

- Make a list of factors for the numerator and denominator. Circle the common factors and identify the GCF.

  20: (1,) (2,) (4,) 5, 10, 20

  28: (1,) (2,) (4,) 7, 14, 28 ← The GCF is 4

- Divide both the numerator and denominator of $\frac{20}{28}$ by their GCF of 4.

$$\frac{20}{28} \div \frac{4}{4} = \frac{5}{7}$$

The fraction $\frac{20}{28}$ written in simplest form is $\frac{5}{7}$.

Can you imagine stacking up one billion dollars worth of $100 bills? You would build a tower $\frac{6}{10}$ of a mile high! **What is the height in simplest form?**

Source: *Junior Fact Finder*

TRY THESE

5. Model equivalent fractions $\frac{3}{5}$ and $\frac{6}{10}$ using fraction bars.

Write two fractions equivalent to each fraction.

6. $\frac{1}{4}$ 7. $\frac{10}{20}$ 8. $\frac{4}{5}$ 9. $\frac{15}{45}$

Mental Math **Write each fraction in simplest form.**

10. $\frac{16}{18}$ 11. $\frac{12}{16}$ 12. $\frac{21}{24}$ 13. $\frac{120}{150}$

Marlee Matlin, who is hearing impaired, won an Oscar award for Best Actress for her role in the movie "Children of a Lesser God."

ON YOUR OWN

Write a fraction for each sentence.

14. **Money** It costs the United States government about four-fifths of a cent to make one penny.

15. **Entertainment** Best Director and Best Picture Oscars have gone to the same film 47 out of 64 times.

Name the fractions modeled. Tell whether they are equivalent.

16.

17. 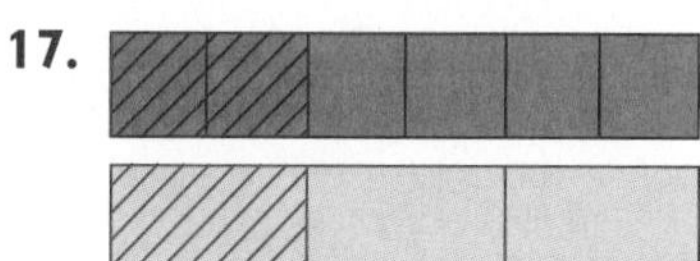

Replace each ■ with the appropriate number.

18. $\frac{2}{5} \times \frac{■}{■} = \frac{8}{20}$ 19. $\frac{40}{50} \div \frac{■}{■} = \frac{8}{10}$ 20. $\frac{4}{16} \div \frac{4}{4} = \frac{■}{■}$

Write two fractions equivalent to each fraction.

21. $\frac{4}{8}$ 22. $\frac{1}{6}$ 23. $\frac{6}{18}$ 24. $\frac{7}{21}$

State whether each fraction is in simplest form. If not, write it in simplest form.

25. $\frac{24}{56}$ 26. $\frac{21}{77}$ 27. $\frac{25}{150}$ 28. $\frac{3}{50}$

29. $\frac{45}{135}$ 30. $\frac{17}{51}$ 31. $\frac{10}{65}$ 32. $\frac{126}{153}$

33. **Writing** Can you write a fraction in simplest form if you divide the numerator and denominator by a number other than the GCF? Explain.

34. What is the only common factor of the numerator and denominator when a fraction is written in simplest form?

35. **Critical Thinking** Use the numbers 2, 6, 4, and 12 to write two pairs of equivalent fractions.

36. **Data File 7 (pp. 272–273)** Four hours after low tide, what part of the tidal range will be covered? Express your answer in simplest form.

Mixed REVIEW

Tell whether each fraction is close to 0, $\frac{1}{2}$, or 1.

1. $\frac{23}{25}$ 2. $\frac{3}{40}$ 3. $\frac{37}{80}$

Find the surface area.

4. a cube with a side of 10 cm

5. a rectangular prism with a height of 4 in., a length of 6 in., and a width of 5 in.

6. A swim team can line up in 6 lanes with an equal number of swimmers in each lane. If only 5 lanes are used, two lanes have an extra person. What is the least number of people on the swim team?

Practice

Mental Math **Decide whether each number is divisible by 1, 2, 3, 5, 9, or 10.**

1. 124 **2.** 365 **3.** 480 **4.** 7,083 **5.** 3,498

Tell whether each number is prime or composite.

6. 2 **7.** 24 **8.** 31 **9.** 51 **10.** 17

Find the prime factorization using a factor tree.

11. 35 **12.** 148 **13.** 273 **14.** 75 **15.** 144

Find the GCF of each set of numbers.

16. 18, 24 **17.** 25, 35 **18.** 13, 19 **19.** 56, 63 **20.** 14, 8, 24

Name the fraction modeled by each fraction bar.

21. **22.** **23.**

Find a fraction bar that models each fraction. Name other fraction bars that show an equivalent fraction.

24. $\frac{2}{3}$ **25.** $\frac{3}{4}$ **26.** $\frac{1}{2}$ **27.** $\frac{2}{5}$ **28.** $\frac{1}{4}$

Write two fractions equivalent to each fraction.

29. $\frac{1}{6}$ **30.** $\frac{9}{16}$ **31.** $\frac{2}{8}$ **32.** $\frac{3}{5}$ **33.** $\frac{11}{12}$

Name the fractions modeled. Tell whether they are equivalent.

34. 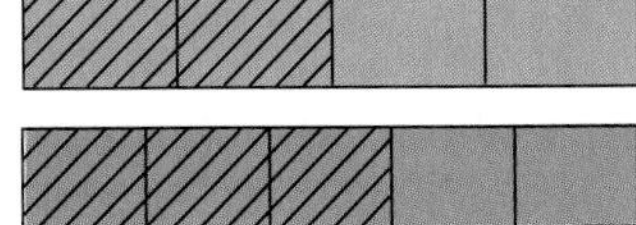

35. 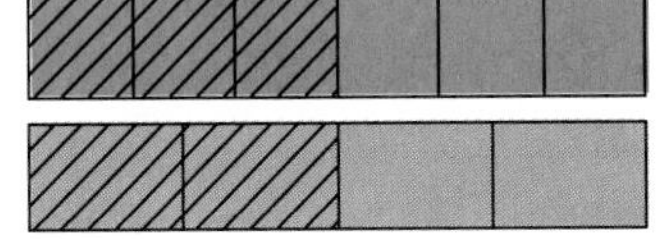

36. 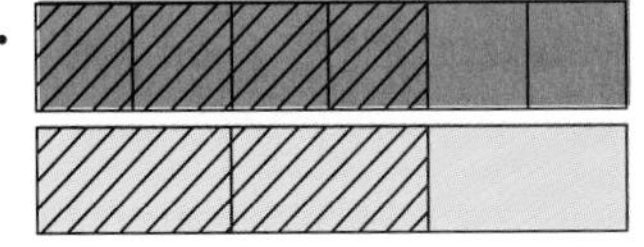

Write each fraction in simplest form.

37. $\frac{12}{18}$ **38.** $\frac{24}{60}$ **39.** $\frac{15}{90}$ **40.** $\frac{14}{35}$ **41.** $\frac{33}{77}$

What's Ahead

- Using a calculator to simplify fractions

TECHNOLOGY

7-6 Simplifying Fractions

WHAT YOU'LL NEED

✓ Calculator 

THINK AND DISCUSS

You can use a fraction calculator to simplify a fraction. The fraction calculator divides the numerator and denominator by a common factor and rewrites the fraction. You repeat the process until the fraction is in simplest form.

Example Use a fraction calculator to simplify $\frac{9}{27}$.

Press	Display	
9 [/] 27	9/27	Enter the fraction.
[Simp]	SIMP N/D→n/d 9/27	
[=]	N/D→n/d 3/9	The fraction is simplified once.
[Simp]	SIMP N/D→n/d 3/9	
[=]	1/3	The fraction is in simplest form.

1. By what common factor were the numerator, 9, and the denominator, 27, first divided?

2. Critical Thinking The display N/D→n/d could be written $\frac{N}{D} \rightarrow \frac{n}{d}$. What do the n's and the d's represent?

*A **fruit salad** with 10 c of fruit contains 2 c of strawberries. So $\frac{2}{10}$ or $\frac{1}{5}$ of the salad is strawberries.*

WORK TOGETHER

Work with a partner to simplify fractions using a calculator. Each person should copy the table that appears on the following page. You may work with your partner to simplify the first fraction, $\frac{12}{20}$. Then, work separately on the remaining fractions. The person with the most points wins.

Step 1 Guess the GCF of the numerator and denominator of the fraction. Record your guess in your table.

Step 2 Enter the fraction into the calculator using the [/] key.

Step 3 Press [Simp]. Enter your guess for the GCF of the numerator and denominator of the fraction. Press [=].

Step 4 If N/D→n/d is not displayed, you chose the GCF of the numerator and denominator of the fraction. Give yourself 3 points and go on to the next fraction.

If N/D→n/d is displayed, the factor you chose is not the GCF of the numerator and denominator of the fraction. Re-enter the fraction and try again. After three tries, you do not receive any points.

	Fraction	First Guess (3 points)	Second Guess (2 points)	Third Guess (1 point)	Points	Simplified Form
3.	$\frac{12}{20}$	■	■	■	■	■
4.	$\frac{15}{25}$	■	■	■	■	■
5.	$\frac{21}{24}$	■	■	■	■	■
6.	$\frac{5}{40}$	■	■	■	■	■
7.	$\frac{27}{81}$	■	■	■	■	■

TRY THESE

Calculator Use a calculator to simplify each fraction.

8. $\frac{4}{12}$ **9.** $\frac{30}{45}$ **10.** $\frac{18}{54}$ **11.** $\frac{16}{48}$

ON YOUR OWN

Choose Use a calculator, paper and pencil, or mental math to simplify each fraction.

12. $\frac{8}{24}$ **13.** $\frac{20}{65}$ **14.** $\frac{17}{68}$ **15.** $\frac{14}{35}$

16. $\frac{105}{180}$ **17.** $\frac{35}{56}$ **18.** $\frac{24}{64}$ **19.** $\frac{39}{117}$

20. a. Calculator Simplify $\frac{19}{57}$.

b. Writing Press the [x⇄y] key. What number appears in the display? Why?

Mixed REVIEW

Replace each ■ with = or ≠.

1. $\frac{7}{10}$ ■ $\frac{2}{3}$

2. $\frac{5}{15}$ ■ $\frac{24}{72}$

Simplify using the order of operations.

3. $5 + 2 \times 8 - 1$

4. $16 \div 2 \times 3 - 20$

5. $3^2 - 2^3$

6. $6 \times (8 - 3)^2 - 10^2$

7. A mischievous child got off the elevator at the 9th floor. She had already gone down 5, up 6, and down 3 floors. On what floor did she first enter the elevator?

What's Ahead

- Writing mixed numbers and improper fractions using models and computation

7-7 Mixed Numbers and Improper Fractions

WORK TOGETHER

Work with a partner to explore the fractions modeled below.

$\frac{4}{4}$ 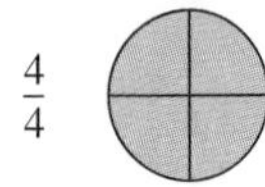

$\frac{5}{2}$ 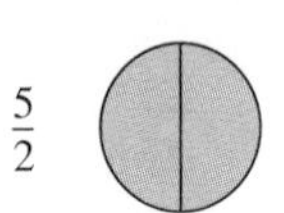 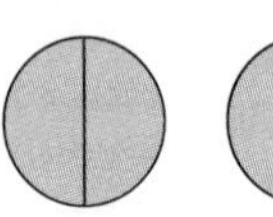

$\frac{1}{6}$ 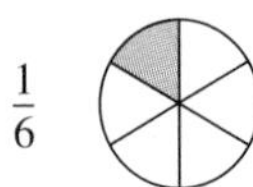

$\frac{1}{2}$ 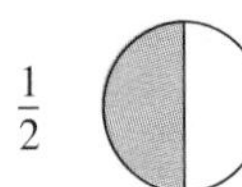

$\frac{11}{8}$ 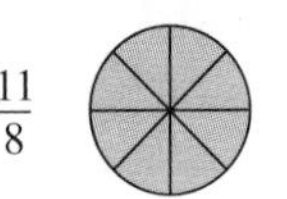 

$\frac{3}{3}$ 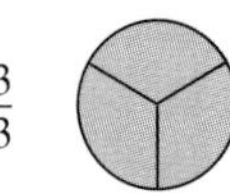

The next time** you're in a car, watch for mixed numbers! They are often on signs indicating distances to various destinations. **What mixed numbers appear on the road signs above?

1. a. What fractions name a number equal to 1?
   b. Compare the numerator and denominator of a fraction that is equal to 1. (*Hint:* Use >, <, or =.)
2. a. What fractions name a number less than 1?
   b. Compare the numerator and denominator of a fraction that is less than 1.
3. a. What fractions name a number greater than 1?
   b. Compare the numerator and denominator of a fraction that is greater than 1.

THINK AND DISCUSS

A fraction whose numerator is greater than its denominator is called an **improper fraction.** You can write an improper fraction as a *mixed number.* A **mixed number** shows the sum of a whole number and a fraction.

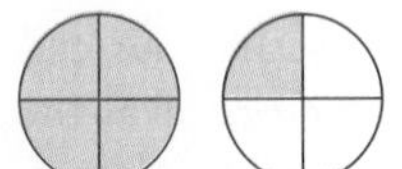

4. a. What improper fraction is modeled at the left?
   b. How many whole circles are shaded?
   c. What additional fraction of a circle is shaded?
   d. **Discussion** The mixed number $1\frac{1}{4}$ describes the shaded portion. How does this number show the sum of a whole number and a fraction?

5. Describe the shaded region at the right using an improper fraction and using a mixed number.

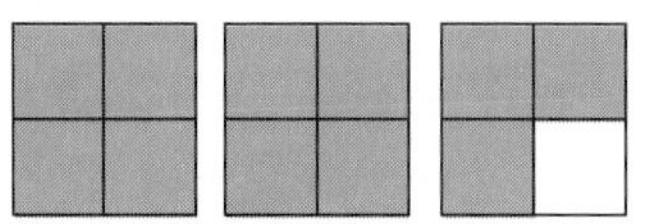

You can use a model to help you write a mixed number as an improper fraction.

Example 1 Write $2\frac{1}{4}$ as an improper fraction.

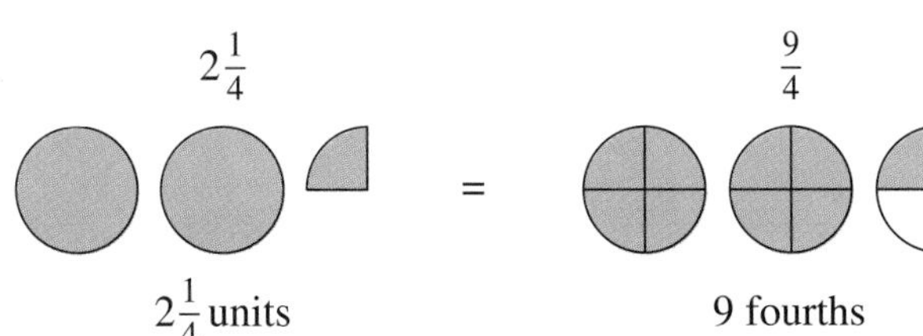

The mixed number $2\frac{1}{4}$ can be written as $\frac{9}{4}$.

Problem Solving Hint

To write a mixed number as an improper fraction, you can multiply the whole number by the denominator and add the numerator. Then write the result over the denominator.

You can use division to write an improper fraction as a mixed number.

Example 2 Write $\frac{11}{5}$ as a mixed number.

$5\overline{)11}$ = 2 R1 — **Divide 11 by 5.**

$2\frac{1}{5}$ — **Express the remainder as a fraction.**

The fraction $\frac{11}{5}$ can be written as $2\frac{1}{5}$.

TRY THESE

6. Is an improper fraction greater than, less than, or equal to one? Use a model to support your answer.

Use the diagram at the right. Describe each shaded region using an improper fraction and a mixed number.

7. 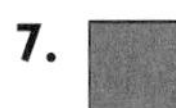 
8. 
9. 

Write each improper fraction as a mixed number. Write each mixed number as an improper fraction.

10. $5\frac{1}{2}$
11. $\frac{9}{4}$
12. $\frac{17}{7}$
13. $4\frac{3}{5}$

Gifts from the Sea

Pearls are the only gems that come from the sea. They are also the only gem that is made by a living thing—a clam. The largest pearl was found in the Philippines in 1934 in the shell of a giant clam. It was $9\frac{1}{2}$ in. long by $5\frac{1}{2}$ in. in diameter and weighed 14 lb 1 oz. This pearl is called The Pearl of Lao-tze and is valued at about $42 million.

ON YOUR OWN

14. Identify the mixed numbers in the article at the left. Write each mixed number as an improper fraction.

15. Choose A, B, C, or D. What mixed number represents the amount shaded?

A. $4\frac{3}{4}$ **B.** $3\frac{3}{4}$

C. $3\frac{15}{16}$ **D.** $3\frac{1}{4}$

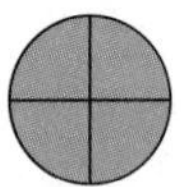
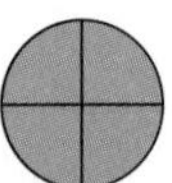
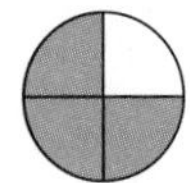

Write each improper fraction as a mixed number.

16. $\frac{17}{5}$ **17.** $\frac{13}{7}$ **18.** $\frac{27}{5}$ **19.** $\frac{37}{12}$ **20.** $\frac{53}{23}$

Write each mixed number as an improper fraction.

21. $6\frac{3}{5}$ **22.** $2\frac{7}{8}$ **23.** $4\frac{1}{2}$ **24.** $3\frac{1}{4}$

25. **Data File 11 (pp. 447–448)** What improper fraction is in the formula used to change from degrees Celsius to degrees Fahrenheit? Write the improper fraction as a mixed number.

26. **Investigation (p. 274)** The illustration shows five ways to represent visually the number 6. Choose any whole number other than 6 and list at least five ways to represent visually that number.

27. Writing Describe two situations in which you have used mixed numbers.

Mixed REVIEW

Write in simplest form.

1. $\frac{45}{60}$ **2.** $\frac{36}{64}$

Find the volume.

3. a cube with a side length equal to 12 cm

4. a rectangular prism with a height of 10 cm and a base with an area of 18 cm^2

5. Replace each ■ with +, −, ×, or ÷.

4 ■ 4 ■ 4 = 20

CHECKPOINT

Write each fraction in simplest form.

1. $\frac{12}{16}$ **2.** $\frac{64}{96}$ **3.** $\frac{21}{27}$ **4.** $\frac{9}{54}$ **5.** $\frac{18}{36}$

Write each improper fraction as a mixed number.

6. $\frac{49}{5}$ **7.** $\frac{21}{8}$ **8.** $\frac{49}{6}$ **9.** $\frac{17}{4}$ **10.** $\frac{5}{2}$

Write each mixed number as an improper fraction.

11. $5\frac{2}{3}$ **12.** $12\frac{3}{4}$ **13.** $8\frac{5}{6}$ **14.** $10\frac{1}{2}$

What's Ahead

- Finding the least common multiple of two or three numbers

7-8 Least Common Multiple

Under magnification, *you can see the "split ends" of a human hair. Regular haircuts can prevent this from happening.*

THINK AND DISCUSS

Pam and Teresa get their hair cut at the same place on Saturdays. Pam gets a haircut every six weeks, and Teresa gets a haircut every four weeks. One Saturday Pam sees Teresa getting a haircut.

Here's a list of Pam and Teresa's haircut schedules.

Pam, every 6 weeks: 6, 12, 18, 24, 30, 36, 42, 48, 54, . . . weeks
Teresa, every 4 weeks: 4, 8, 12, 16, 20, 24, 28, 32, 36, . . . weeks

In 18 weeks Pam will have had 3 haircuts. The number 18 is a *multiple* of 6. A **multiple** of a number is the product of that number and a nonzero whole number.

1. List the weeks that Pam and Teresa will get haircuts on the same day.

These numbers are multiples of both 6 and 4, so they are **common multiples.** The smallest common multiple of two or more numbers is the **least common multiple (LCM).** The LCM of 6 and 4 is 12.

You can also use the prime factorization of each number to find the LCM of the numbers.

Example Find the LCM of 15, 18, and 20.

- Write the prime factorizations.

$15 = 3 \times \textcircled{5}$

$18 = 2 \times \boxed{3 \times 3}$

$20 = \boxed{2 \times 2} \times 5$

Circle all the different factors where they appear the greatest number of times.

- Multiply the circled factors.

$2 \times 2 \times 3 \times 3 \times 5 = 180$

The LCM is 180.

Mixed REVIEW

Change to a whole or a mixed number.

1. $\frac{15}{6}$
2. $\frac{63}{8}$
3. $\frac{27}{4}$
4. $\frac{42}{3}$

Find the area and perimeter.

5. Rectangle: 4.8 cm by 2.4 cm
6. Square: 15 m by 15 m

7. Mugsy is tied with a 20-ft-long rope to a stake in the ground. Draw a diagram and find the approximate area of the dog's play space.

TRY THESE

2. a. List the multiples of each number to find the LCM of 30, 40, and 50.
   b. Use prime factorization to find the LCM of 30, 40, and 50.
   c. **Writing** Which method do you think is more efficient? Explain your choice.
3. I lift weights every third day and swim every fourth day. I did both this morning. When will be the next time I do both exercise activities?

ON YOUR OWN

Find the LCM of each set of numbers.

4. 75, 100
5. 22, 55, 60
6. 4, 12
7. 12, 20
8. 5, 6, 10
9. 14, 33

GREAT EXPECTATIONS

Amusement Park Designer

I want to be an amusement park designer. This career interests me because I like to make things and I have good ideas to make things. I want to learn more about this because it uses math and I'm good at math. If I do become an amusement park designer it would be fun. My interest started in this when I first rode on a roller coaster and tried to find another ride I would like. I couldn't find one, so I said to myself that if I become someone who makes rides, I can make rides that I like. There was one time when I went to a park and I wanted a ride that was fast and would get me wet. I got wet on it, but it wasn't fast enough. I make models, which would help me learn how to build models of the parks before they were made.

Stephen Horel

10. **Critical Thinking** A number has both 8 and 10 as factors.

   a. What is the smallest the number could be?

   b. Name four other factors of the number.

11. **Travel** Two ships sail back and forth between Boston and London. One ship makes a round trip in 12 days. The other ship makes a round trip in 16 days. They are both in London today. In how many days will both ships be in London again?

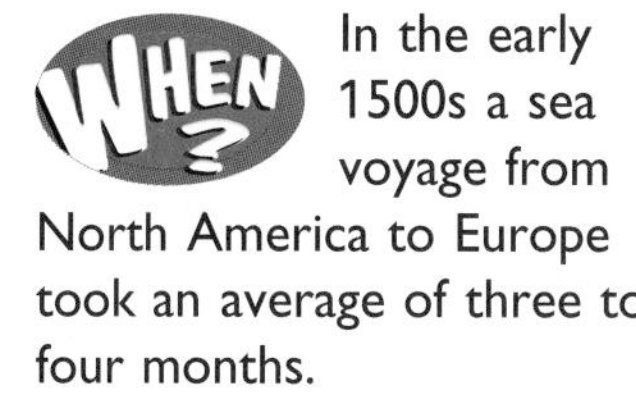

In the early 1500s a sea voyage from North America to Europe took an average of three to four months.

12. For each pair of numbers, find the GCF, the LCM, the product of the two numbers, and the product of the GCF and LCM.

   a. 12 and 18 b. 20 and 25 c. 24 and 28

   d. **Writing** Look over your results. Describe the pattern.

13. **Choose A, B, C, or D.** The LCM of a number and 15 is 120. What is the number?

   A. 20 **B.** 12 **C.** 6 **D.** 24

Dear Stephen,

Yes, it certainly is fun developing theme park attractions. When I help design a new ride, it is surprising how much math and physics I use. I think of ratio and capacity when I try to figure out how fast the ride will go and how many people should be on it at one time. Most roller coaster attractions run two trains with an average of 32 seats on each train. Each ride takes approximately two minutes. We allow one minute to load guests and one minute to unload them. We call this a cycle of four minutes. If thirty-two guests ride every cycle, in one hour with two trains leaving the station every two minutes, there are thirty cycles. Now we see that our roller coaster has a capacity of 960 guests per hour.

Hugh Darley
Design and Entertainment, Paramount Parks

What's Ahead

- Comparing and ordering fractions

7-9

Comparing and Ordering Fractions

WORK TOGETHER

WHAT YOU'LL NEED

✓ Fraction bars 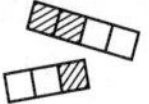

Work in groups. Use fraction bars to compare each pair of fractions. First, find the appropriate bars. Then, line up the left edges of the two fraction bars and compare the shaded regions. The fraction bars at the left show that $\frac{3}{10} < \frac{1}{3}$.

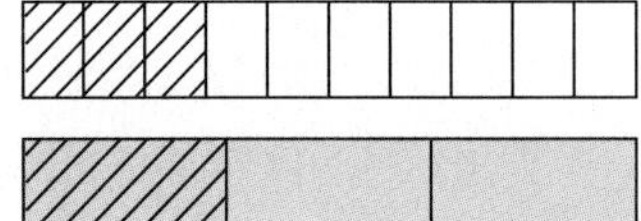

1. Compare using <, >, or =.

a. $\frac{3}{5}$ ■ $\frac{4}{5}$ **b.** $\frac{3}{4}$ ■ $\frac{3}{5}$ **c.** $\frac{3}{12}$ ■ $\frac{1}{4}$

d. $\frac{9}{10}$ ■ $\frac{7}{10}$ **e.** $\frac{1}{4}$ ■ $\frac{2}{5}$ **f.** $\frac{2}{3}$ ■ $\frac{8}{12}$

g. $\frac{2}{6}$ ■ $\frac{4}{12}$ **h.** $\frac{7}{10}$ ■ $\frac{3}{5}$ **i.** $\frac{1}{3}$ ■ $\frac{2}{5}$

THINK AND DISCUSS

You used fraction bars to *compare* fractions. You can also use fraction bars to *order* fractions.

2. Use fraction bars to order each set of fractions from least to greatest.

a. $\frac{7}{10}, \frac{1}{10}, \frac{3}{10}$ **b.** $\frac{3}{4}, \frac{3}{5}, \frac{3}{10}, \frac{3}{12}$

c. How are the fractions in part (a) alike? Without using fraction bars, how can you tell which fraction is the greatest?

d. How are the fractions in part (b) alike? Without using fraction bars, how can you tell which fraction is the greatest?

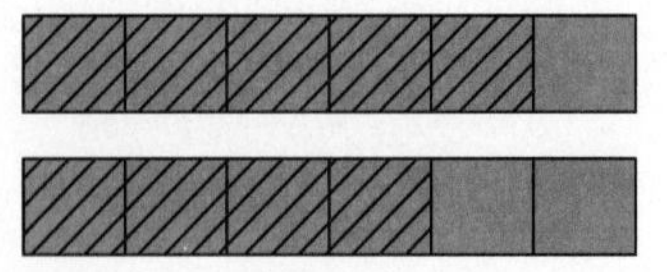

It is easy to compare fractions with the same denominator. The parts of the whole are the same size, so the fraction with the larger numerator is greater. For example, $\frac{5}{6} > \frac{4}{6}$ because the numerator $5 > 4$. The fraction bars at the left confirm this result.

Suppose you want to compare two fractions with different denominators. You can use equivalent fractions to find a *common denominator* of the two fractions. A common denominator must be a multiple of each of the original denominators. The **least common denominator (LCD)** is the least common multiple (LCM) of the original denominators.

To write equivalent fractions, multiply the numerator and the denominator by the same nonzero factor.

Example 1 Compare $\frac{7}{24}$ and $\frac{5}{18}$. Use <, >, or =.

- The LCM of 24 and 18 is 72. So the LCD is 72.
- Write equivalent fractions using the LCD.

$$\frac{7}{24} = \frac{7}{24} \times \frac{3}{3} = \frac{21}{72} \qquad \frac{5}{18} = \frac{5}{18} \times \frac{4}{4} = \frac{20}{72}$$

- Compare the numerators.

$$21 > 20$$

Since $\frac{21}{72} > \frac{20}{72}$, then $\frac{7}{24} > \frac{5}{18}$.

When comparing mixed numbers, first compare the quantity of each whole number. Decide which number is greater. If the whole number part of each mixed number is the same, then compare the fraction part of each number as in Example 1.

3. Compare using <, >, or =.

a. $3\frac{2}{5}$ ■ $2\frac{4}{5}$ **b.** $1\frac{2}{3}$ ■ $1\frac{5}{9}$ **c.** $5\frac{7}{8}$ ■ $6\frac{5}{6}$

d. $2\frac{4}{7}$ ■ $2\frac{12}{21}$ **e.** $4\frac{2}{5}$ ■ $4\frac{3}{7}$ **f.** $3\frac{8}{12}$ ■ $3\frac{3}{4}$

To order three or more fractions, find the LCD. Use the LCD to write equivalent fractions. Then order the numerators.

Example 2 Order from least to greatest: $\frac{3}{8}$, $\frac{2}{5}$, $\frac{7}{20}$.

- The LCM of 8, 5, and 20 is 40. So the LCD is 40.
- Write equivalent fractions using the LCD.

$$\frac{3}{8} = \frac{15}{40} \qquad \frac{2}{5} = \frac{16}{40} \qquad \frac{7}{20} = \frac{14}{40}$$

- Put the numerators in order.

$$14 < 15 < 16$$

Since $\frac{14}{40} < \frac{15}{40} < \frac{16}{40}$, then $\frac{7}{20} < \frac{3}{8} < \frac{2}{5}$.

4. Order from least to greatest: $\frac{2}{6}$, $\frac{8}{21}$, $\frac{4}{14}$.

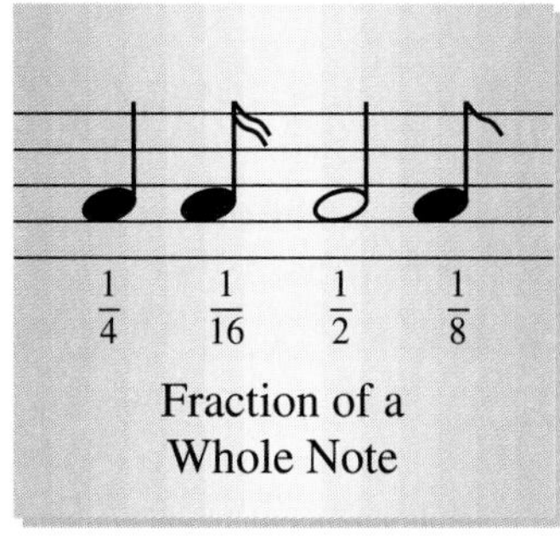

***Musical notes** are based on fractions of a whole note.* **Order these notes from least to greatest.**

Torta Garfagnana
$\frac{1}{2}$ cup sweet almonds
$2\frac{2}{3}$ cups flour
1 teaspoon baking soda
$\frac{3}{4}$ cup butter
1 tablespoon aniseed
$\frac{2}{3}$ cup milk

TRY THESE

Compare using <, >, or =.

5. $2\frac{11}{19} \blacksquare 1\frac{13}{19}$ 6. $\frac{13}{20} \blacksquare \frac{1}{4}$ 7. $\frac{9}{24} \blacksquare \frac{3}{8}$ 8. $\frac{15}{17} \blacksquare \frac{9}{10}$

Order each set of fractions from least to greatest.

9. $\frac{11}{24}, \frac{5}{8}, \frac{5}{12}$ 10. $\frac{11}{15}, \frac{2}{3}, \frac{7}{12}$ 11. $\frac{5}{7}, \frac{11}{14}, \frac{3}{4}$

12. **Cooking** Compare the recipe amounts for sweet almonds, butter, and milk. Which is the greatest? the least?

ON YOUR OWN

Compare using <, >, or =.

13. $5\frac{4}{7} \blacksquare 5\frac{5}{7}$ 14. $\frac{3}{11} \blacksquare \frac{1}{4}$ 15. $3\frac{1}{4} \blacksquare 3\frac{1}{5}$ 16. $\frac{2}{9} \blacksquare \frac{4}{15}$

17. Timothy ran $1\frac{3}{4}$ mi. Wenona ran $1\frac{7}{10}$ mi. Who ran farther?

Order each set of numbers from least to greatest.

18. $\frac{1}{5}, \frac{1}{8}, \frac{7}{40}, \frac{3}{10}$ 19. $\frac{7}{12}, \frac{23}{40}, \frac{8}{15}, \frac{19}{30}$ 20. $1\frac{8}{11}, 2\frac{1}{4}, 1\frac{3}{4}$

21. **Data File 8 (pp. 316–317)** Order the Women's Olympic Long Jump Winners from least to greatest distance.

22. Tell whether each fraction is greater than, less than, or equal to $\frac{1}{2}$.
 a. $\frac{3}{5}$ b. $\frac{5}{12}$ c. $\frac{5}{8}$ d. $\frac{2}{3}$
 e. **Writing** How can you use your results to compare $\frac{3}{5}$ and $\frac{5}{12}$? Is it possible to use the results above to compare $\frac{3}{5}$ and $\frac{5}{8}$? Why or why not?

23. **Choose A, B, C, or D.** To compare $\frac{9}{24}$ and $\frac{5}{15}$, which would you do first and why?
 A. Find the LCM of 24 and 15.
 B. Simplify each fraction.
 C. Find the prime factorization of 24 and 15.
 D. Multiply 24×15 to find a common denominator.

Mixed REVIEW

Find the LCM of each set of numbers.

1. 8, 12, 6 2. 5, 6, 15
3. 9, 15, 18 4. 36, 40

Use the distributive property to simplify.

5. $7(100 - 2)$
6. $8(50 + 3)$

7. What is the ratio of the circumference of a circle to its diameter?

7-10 Fractions and Decimals

What's Ahead

- Modeling fractions and decimals
- Writing decimals as fractions
- Writing fractions as decimals

WHAT YOU'LL NEED

✓ Calculator 

✓ Decimal squares 

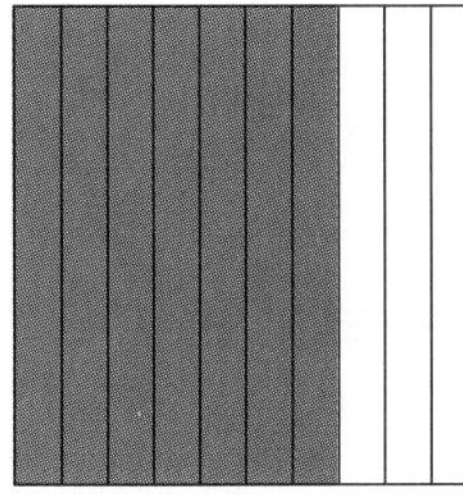

WORK TOGETHER

Work with a partner.

1. **a.** What decimal does the model at the left represent?
   b. Say the decimal out loud.
   c. Have your partner write the decimal as a fraction.
   d. Complete this statement using the decimal and the fraction: ■ = ■.
2. **a.** Find a decimal square that models 0.05.
   b. Have your partner read the decimal out loud.
   c. Write the decimal as a fraction.
   d. Simplify the fraction. Complete this statement using the fraction and the decimal: ■ = ■.
3. **a.** **Discussion** List the steps you need to follow to write a decimal as a fraction.
   b. Do you need to use a model? Give an example to support your answer.

THINK AND DISCUSS

FLASHBACK

You read 0.225 as "two hundred twenty-five thousandths."

To express a decimal as a fraction, write the fraction as you would say the decimal. Then simplify the fraction.

Example 1 Write 0.225 as a fraction in simplest form.

$$0.225 = \frac{225}{1000}$$

$$= \frac{225 \div 25}{1000 \div 25}$$ **Simplify. The GCF of 225 and 1000 is 25.**

$$0.225 = \frac{9}{40}$$

4. Write each decimal as a fraction in simplest form.
   a. 0.6 **b.** 0.35 **c.** 0.130

If a decimal is greater than one, it can be written as a mixed number.

Example 2 Write 1.32 as a fraction in simplest form.

$1.32 = 1\frac{32}{100}$ Keep the whole number 1.

$= 1\frac{32 \div 4}{100 \div 4}$ Simplify. The GCF of 32 and 100 is 4.

$1.32 = 1\frac{8}{25}$

One way to express a fraction as a decimal is to divide the numerator by the denominator. The fraction symbol itself means division. For example, here's how to write $\frac{3}{4}$ as a decimal using a calculator.

3 [÷] 4 [=] 0.75 ← $\frac{3}{4} = 0.75$

If there is no remainder, the quotient is a **terminating decimal.** Sometimes the quotient does have a remainder. A quotient that repeats digits and does not end is a **repeating decimal.** The number 0.4444 . . . is an example of a repeating decimal. You write the decimal as $0.\overline{4}$. The bar over the 4 means that the digit 4 repeats.

FLASHBACK
Annex zeros to the dividend.

Example 3 Write the fraction $\frac{4}{15}$ as a decimal.

$$\frac{4}{15} \rightarrow \begin{array}{r} 0.266 \\ 15\overline{)4.000} \\ -\ 3\,0 \\ \hline 100 \\ -\ 90 \\ \hline 100 \\ -\ 90 \\ \hline 1 \end{array}$$

The digit 6 repeats.

$\frac{4}{15} = 0.2\overline{6}$

You can show repeating decimals using a calculator.

Example 4 Write the fraction $\frac{8}{11}$ as a decimal.

- Divide the numerator by the denominator.

  8 [÷] 11 [=] 0.7272727

- Notice which digits repeat: 72.
- Write the decimal using a bar over these digits.

  $\frac{8}{11} = 0.\overline{72}$

5. Write each fraction as a decimal. Use a bar to show repeating decimals.

a. $\frac{5}{9}$ **b.** $\frac{2}{3}$ **c.** $\frac{5}{11}$

6. a. How would you write $\frac{1}{3}$ as a decimal?

b. How would you write 2 as a decimal?

c. How can you use your results from parts (a) and (b) to write $2\frac{1}{3}$ as a decimal? Explain.

TRY THESE

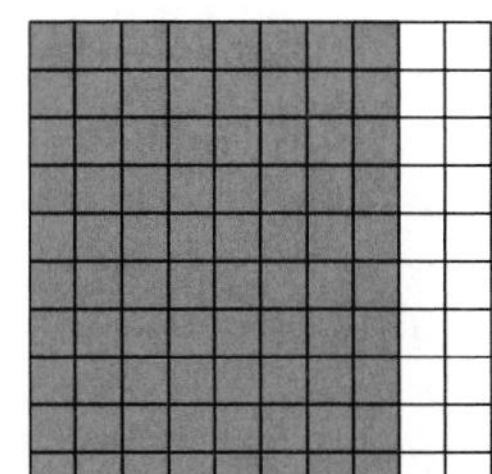

7. a. What decimal does the model at the right represent?

b. Write this number as a fraction in simplest form.

8. a. Draw a decimal square to show 0.68.

b. Write 0.68 as a fraction in simplest form.

Write each decimal as a fraction in simplest form. Write each fraction as a decimal.

9. 0.3 **10.** $\frac{9}{20}$ **11.** $\frac{11}{8}$ **12.** 0.004

13. 2.625 **14.** $\frac{5}{6}$ **15.** 0.075 **16.** $\frac{5}{12}$

ON YOUR OWN

Write each decimal as a fraction in simplest form. Write each fraction as a decimal.

17. 0.565 **18.** 1.62 **19.** 0.07 **20.** 0.064

21. $1\frac{1}{9}$ **22.** $\frac{14}{25}$ **23.** $\frac{7}{15}$ **24.** $4\frac{7}{10}$

25. $\frac{5}{24}$ **26.** $\frac{7}{16}$ **27.** $3\frac{4}{11}$ **28.** $\frac{7}{20}$

29. **Shopping** Pallaton took the bus to the grocery store to buy sliced turkey to make sandwiches for his school lunches. He orders a quarter pound ($\frac{1}{4}$ lb) of turkey at the delicatessen. What decimal should Pallaton see on the digital scale?

In the space shuttle a typical lunch is corned beef with asparagus, strawberries, and an almond crunch bar.

Source: *How in the World?*

30. **Data File 7 (pp. 272–273)** It's been four hours since low tide. Find the range of tide as a fraction and a decimal.

31. Channa has \$1 to spend. She buys a package of sunflower seeds for \$.55. What fraction of her money did she spend?

32. **Investigation (p. 274)** Use your personal numeration system to write a number as a fraction and a decimal.

33. a. **Calculator** Write each fraction as a decimal: $\frac{17}{50}$, $\frac{1}{3}$, $\frac{8}{25}$, $\frac{26}{75}$.
    b. Arrange the fractions in order from least to greatest.
    c. Would you prefer to use equivalent fractions with a common denominator to order the numbers in part (a)? Why or why not?

34. Order each set of numbers from least to greatest.
    a. $\frac{7}{8}$, 0.8, $\frac{9}{11}$, 0.87
    b. 1.65, $1\frac{2}{3}$, $1\frac{3}{5}$, 1.7

35. a. **Writing** Explain the steps you would use to write 0.8 as a fraction in simplest form.
    b. **Writing** Explain the steps you would use to write $\frac{2}{9}$ as a decimal.

Mixed REVIEW

Order from least to greatest.

1. $\frac{3}{4}$, $\frac{2}{3}$, $\frac{7}{10}$
2. $\frac{1}{5}$, $\frac{1}{6}$, $\frac{3}{10}$
3. $3\frac{3}{8}$, $\frac{32}{10}$, $\frac{7}{2}$

Write three equivalent fractions for each.

4. $\frac{9}{10}$
5. $\frac{3}{4}$

6. Jan and Leah both earn money running errands for elderly neighbors. Leah earns \$1.25 more an hour than Jan. If together they earned \$15.75 for 3 hours of work, how much did each earn per hour?

CHECKPOINT

Find the LCM of each set of numbers.

1. 16, 24, 32
2. 28, 56, 63
3. 40, 36, 18

Write each fraction as a decimal.

4. $\frac{2}{5}$
5. $\frac{7}{100}$
6. $\frac{3}{8}$
7. $\frac{1}{6}$

Write each decimal as a fraction in simplest form.

8. 0.52
9. 0.04
10. 0.75
11. 15.025

12. **Choose A, B, C, or D.** Which set of numbers is in order from greatest to least?
    A. 0.56, 0.055, 0.53, 0.52
    B. 1.75, $\frac{3}{2}$, 1.25, 2.0
    C. 3.47, $3\frac{1}{2}$, 3.6, $\frac{8}{3}$
    D. $\frac{7}{8}$, 0.8, 0.75, $\frac{8}{11}$

PROBLEM SOLVING

7-11 Work Backward

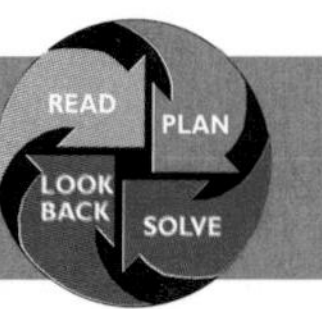

What's Ahead

- Solving problems by working backward

Sometimes you need to work backward from a known result to find a fact at the beginning.

> A teacher lends pencils to students. At the end of one day she has 16 pencils. She remembers giving out 7 pencils in the morning, collecting 5 before lunch, and giving out 3 after lunch. How many pencils did the teacher have at the start of the day?

READ

Read and understand the given information. Summarize the problem.

1. How many pencils does the teacher have at the end of the day?
2. How many times did the teacher give out pencils? collect pencils?
3. Do you think she had *more than* or *fewer than* 16 pencils at the start of the day? Why?

PLAN

Decide on a strategy to solve the problem.

In this problem you know that there were 16 pencils at the *end* of the day. Work backward to find out how many pencils the teacher had at the *start* of the day. Add or subtract each time the teacher gave out or collected pencils.

SOLVE

Try out the strategy.

4. What was the teacher's last action with pencils before the end of the day? How many pencils did she have just before that action?
5. Continue working backward to find the number of pencils the teacher had at the start of the day.

LOOK BACK

Think about how you solved this problem.

6. Check by starting with your answer and working *forward.* Did you get 16 pencils for the end of the day?
7. **Writing** Some people might prefer to solve using the strategy "guess and check." Solve the problem using 18 as your guess. Which strategy do you prefer? Why?

TRY THESE

Work backward to solve each problem.

8. **Money** At the first store in the mall, I spent half my money. At a second store, I spent half my remaining money and $6 more. Then I had just $2. How much money did I have when I arrived at the mall?

9. I'm thinking of a number. If I multiply by 3 and then add 5, the result is 38. What is the number?

10. **Hobbies** Horace decided to sell all the cards in his baseball card collection to some friends. He sold Juanita half his cards plus 1 card. Next he sold Ethan half the remaining cards. Then he sold Erica 13 cards. Finally, he sold the remaining 9 cards to Cleon. How many cards were in Horace's collection at the start?

Leroy "Satchel" Paige was the first African American pitcher to enter major league baseball when he played for the Cleveland Indians. A 1953 *Tops* baseball card of Paige costs over $100.

Source: *The Book of Lists*

ON YOUR OWN

Use any strategy to solve each problem. Show your work.

11. **Sports** Olivia won a chess tournament by winning three games. At each round the loser is eliminated and the winner advances to the next round. How many players were in the tournament?

12. I'm thinking of two numbers. Their greatest common factor is 6, and their least common multiple is 18. What are the two numbers?

13. Kathy and Bill baked some muffins. They put half of them away for the next day and divided the remaining muffins among their 3 sisters, each of whom received 3 muffins. How many muffins did Kathy and Bill bake?

14. **Sports** In a box of sporting equipment there are twice as many bats as softballs and two more golf clubs than bats. Six items are either golf clubs or golf balls. There are two golf balls. How many softballs are in the box?

15. The last Thursday of a certain month is the 27th day of that month. What day of the week is the first day of the month?

16. Aaron has a track meet at 4:00 P.M. It takes him 5 min to change his clothes and 10 min to get to the track. Before the start of the race, Aaron needs to meet with his coach for 10 min and stretch for 15 min. When school is over, he plans to spend some time in the library.

a. When should Aaron leave the library?

b. If school lets out at 2:50 P.M., how much time can Aaron spend in the library?

17. Critical Thinking Suppose you are stranded on a desert island with only a 3-qt container and a 5-qt container. Without marking the odd-shaped containers, explain how you can measure exactly 1 qt of water.

18. Music I owned some CDs. I received a shipment of 12 more, but my sister borrowed 4 of them. Later she returned 2 CDs. Now I have 30 CDs. How many did I have before the shipment arrived?

19. Writing Why is it sometimes necessary to use inverse operations when working backward? Explain.

20. Find a number between 1 and 100 that satisfies these conditions. If it is divided by 3 or 5, the remainder is 1. If it is divided by 7, the remainder is 4.

21. Investigation (p. 274) Use your personalized numeration system to write the number 10. What would the number 7 look like?

22. What is the greatest number of 3 in. by 5 in. index cards that can be cut from a rectangular sheet of construction paper that measures 2 ft by $2\frac{1}{2}$ ft?

23. A bacterial population grows rapidly, doubling in size every 6 min. A teaspoon of bacteria is placed in a jar, and in 2 h the jar is filled. How long did it take for the jar to be half full?

24. On January 27th, Eldridge's aunt and grandmother came to visit. His aunt visits every four days, and his grandmother visits every six days. What was the first date in January that both visited Eldridge on the same day?

Over 632,487 units of Stevie Wonder's "Jungle Fever" have been sold. A Gold Award is given for sales of 500,000 units. Units include tapes, CDs, and albums.

Mixed REVIEW

Write each fraction as a decimal.

1. $\frac{17}{20}$
2. $\frac{3}{25}$

Write each decimal as a fraction in simplest form.

3. 0.48
4. 0.06
5. 0.95
6. 0.152

7. Kale counted 12 wheels on the cycles in the Annual Homecoming Parade. His sister Leilani counted 7 cycles in all. The only cycles allowed were unicycles, bicycles, and tricycles. How many cycles of each type were in the parade?

CHAPTER 7

Wrap Up

Divisibility and Prime Factorization 7-1, 7-2

The rules for divisibility can help you find factors. A ***prime number*** has exactly two factors, 1 and itself, while a ***composite number*** has more than two factors.

When a composite number is written as a product of its prime factors, it is called the ***prime factorization.***

State whether each number is divisible by 1, 2, 3, 5, 9, or 10.

1. 69 **2.** 146 **3.** 837 **4.** 405 **5.** 628 **6.** 32, 870

7. Choose A, B, C, or D. Which number is a prime number?

A. 519 **B.** 523 **C.** 525 **D.** 530

Find the prime factorization using a factor tree.

8. 72 **9.** 120 **10.** 33 **11.** 80 **12.** 234 **13.** 345

GCF, LCM, and Simplifying Fractions 7-3, 7-6, 7-8

The ***greatest common factor*** (GCF) of two or more numbers is the greatest number that is a factor of each number.

To simplify a fraction, divide both the numerator and the denominator of the fraction by the GCF. You can also use a fraction calculator to simplify fractions.

The ***least common multiple*** (LCM) of two or more numbers is the smallest number that is a multiple of each number.

Find the GCF and the LCM of each set of numbers.

14. 40, 140 **15.** 28, 33 **16.** 24, 9 **17.** 15, 25 **18.** 18, 42, 60 **19.** 10, 12, 16

Write each fraction in simplest form.

20. $\frac{16}{18}$ **21.** $\frac{24}{60}$ **22.** $\frac{15}{50}$ **23.** $\frac{27}{72}$ **24.** $\frac{16}{44}$ **25.** $\frac{6}{21}$

Equivalent Fractions 7-4, 7-5

You form ***equivalent fractions*** by multiplying or dividing the numerator and denominator by the same nonzero number.

Write two fractions equivalent to each fraction.

26. $\frac{1}{8}$ **27.** $\frac{2}{10}$ **28.** $\frac{5}{25}$ **29.** $\frac{3}{5}$ **30.** $\frac{14}{28}$ **31.** $\frac{30}{50}$

Comparing and Ordering Fractions and Mixed Numbers 7-7, 7-9

An ***improper fraction*** has a numerator greater than its denominator. A ***mixed number*** shows the sum of a whole number and a fraction. Compare fractions by finding a common denominator.

Write each improper fraction as a mixed number. Write each mixed number as an improper fraction.

32. $4\frac{3}{4}$ **33.** $\frac{22}{5}$ **34.** $\frac{57}{7}$ **35.** $2\frac{3}{7}$ **36.** $\frac{30}{14}$ **37.** $5\frac{2}{11}$

38. Order from least to greatest: $1\frac{5}{6}$, $1\frac{7}{9}$, $\frac{35}{36}$, $1\frac{3}{4}$.

Fractions and Decimals; Strategies 7-10, 7-11

To express a decimal as a fraction, write the fraction as you would say the decimal. Then simplify the fraction. To write a decimal as a fraction, divide the numerator by the denominator. Write a bar over the digit or digits that repeat.

Write each decimal as a fraction in simplest form. Write each fraction as a decimal.

39. 0.04 **40.** 3.875 **41.** 2.14 **42.** $\frac{17}{40}$ **43.** $\frac{8}{9}$ **44.** $\frac{6}{11}$

45. At the first store Tina spent \$7. At the next store she spent half of her remaining money. At the last store she spent half of her remaining money and \$3 more. Tina had \$5 left. How much money did she have before shopping?

GETTING READY FOR CHAPTER 8

Tell whether each fraction is close to 0, to $\frac{1}{2}$, or to 1.

1. $\frac{54}{98}$ **2.** $\frac{11}{12}$ **3.** $\frac{1}{6}$ **4.** $\frac{2}{9}$ **5.** $\frac{19}{40}$ **6.** $\frac{5}{11}$

PUTTING IT ALL TOGETHER

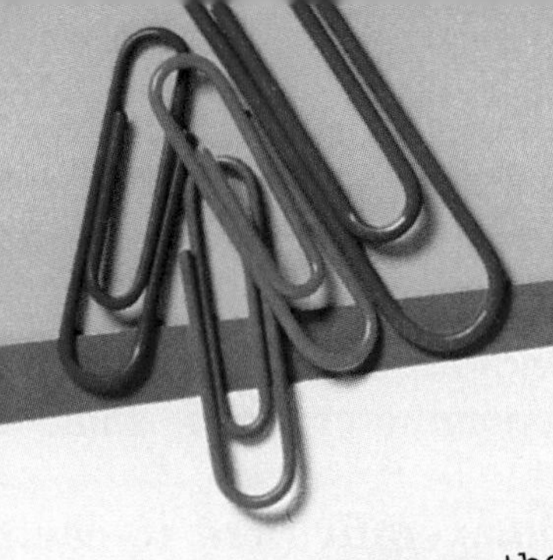

Follow Up

Representing Numbers

The theme of this month's Math Competition is "fraction concepts." Look again at the objects you chose to represent whole numbers. Make any changes you feel are necessary. Then, using your finalized personalized numeration system, create a display illustrating the competition theme. The problems preceded by the magnifying glass (p. 296, # 26; p. 306, # 32; and p. 309, # 21) will help you prepare your display.

Excursion: The Greek mathematician Pythagoras was interested in numbers like 1, 3, and 6 that can be represented visually as triangles.

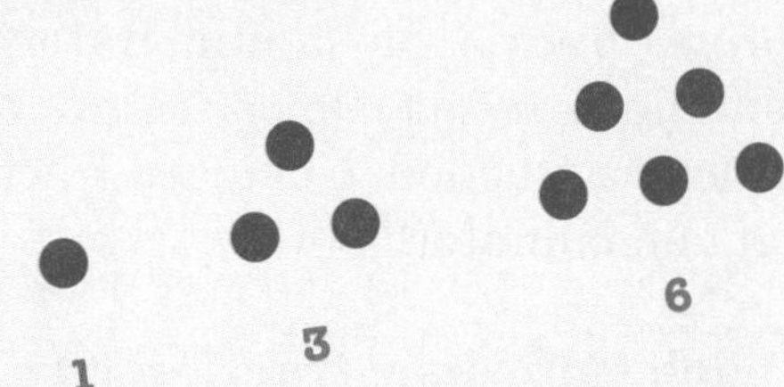

Write the next 8 triangular numbers. What patterns can you find in the numbers? What conclusions about triangular numbers can you draw?

Prime Puzzler

I am a number between 300 and 500. My prime factors are 2, 3 and 13. What number am I?

Write a Prime Puzzler of your own. Challenge a partner to solve your puzzle.

Excursion: Can you make a Prime Puzzler with more than one possible answer?

Two of a Kind

Rules:

- *Play with three or more players*
- *You will need at least thirty index cards or 3 x 5 cards cut from heavy pieces of paper. On one card write a fraction and on another card write its equivalent decimal. Continue doing this until you have written 15 different fractions and their decimal equivalents.*
- *Arrange the cards face down in rows. Take turns flipping over two cards to find a match, a fraction and its equivalent decimal. If a player is correct, the player can keep the cards. The game is over when all the cards are gone. The player with the most cards wins.*

Excursion: Instead of matching the cards, state whether the first card flipped over is <, >, or = to the second card flipped over. If a player is correct, the player can keep the cards. The game is over when all the cards are gone. The player with the most cards wins.

The Write Stuff

Write a word problem that includes the following fractions and decimals:

$$\mathbf{0.5},\ \frac{3}{4},\ 2\frac{1}{12},\ \text{and } \mathbf{0.64}.$$

Check to make sure your word problem makes sense and can be solved. Challenge a partner to solve your word problem.

To Be or Not to Be

It is impossible for 3 people to each eat $\frac{1}{2}$ of the same pie. Yet it is possible for 3 people to play $\frac{1}{4}$ of a softball game. Write a list of 5 impossible fraction situations and a list of 5 possible fraction situations.

Excursion: Challenge another group to determine which items on your list are impossible and those items that are possible.

CHAPTER 7

Assessment

1. **Writing** Is 24,357 divisible by 9? Explain your answer.

2. **Choose A, B, C, or D.** Which number is divisible by 2, 3, and 10?

   A. 375 B. 430
   C. 2,328 D. 5,430

3. List all the factors of each number. Tell whether each number is prime or composite.

   a. 33 b. 54
   c. 19 d. 102

4. Find the GCF of each set of numbers.

   a. 24, 36 b. 20, 25, 30
   c. 45, 105 d. 7, 19

5. Find the prime factorization of each number.

   a. 132 b. 360

6. Name the fraction modeled.

   a. 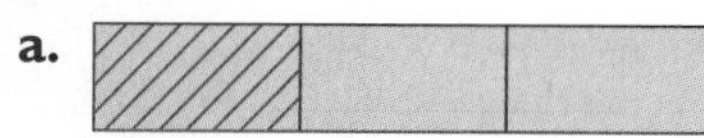

   b. 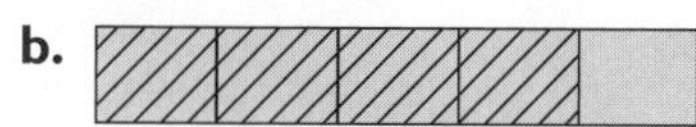

7. **Estimation** Classify each fraction as close to 0, close to $\frac{1}{2}$, or close to 1.

   a. $\frac{12}{16}$ b. $\frac{2}{20}$
   c. $\frac{24}{50}$ d. $\frac{40}{75}$

8. Name two fractions that are equivalent to $\frac{6}{18}$.

9. Write each fraction in simplest form.

   a. $\frac{5}{45}$ b. $\frac{34}{51}$
   c. $\frac{56}{128}$ d. $\frac{120}{180}$

10. Find the LCM of each set of numbers.

    a. 4, 8 b. 6, 11
    c. 18, 45 d. 10, 12, 15

11. Compare. Fill in the ■ with <, >, or =.

    a. $1\frac{2}{5}$ ■ $1\frac{1}{5}$ b. $\frac{15}{4}$ ■ $\frac{17}{5}$
    c. $\frac{7}{14}$ ■ $\frac{1}{2}$ d. $2\frac{3}{5}$ ■ $2\frac{7}{11}$

12. **Choose A, B, or C.** Lee jogged $\frac{1}{2}$ mi, Mary jogged $\frac{2}{3}$ mi, and Rosalinda jogged $\frac{3}{8}$ mi. Who jogged the longest distance?

    A. Lee B. Mary C. Rosalinda

13. Order each set of numbers from least to greatest.

    a. $5\frac{3}{4}, 5\frac{1}{8}, 5\frac{2}{4}$ b. $4\frac{4}{5}, 3\frac{7}{10}, 3\frac{3}{5}$
    c. $2\frac{1}{4}, 1\frac{3}{4}, 3\frac{2}{4}$ d. $\frac{2}{9}, \frac{7}{63}, \frac{5}{18}, \frac{1}{2}$

14. Write each decimal as a fraction in simplest form.

    a. 0.4 b. 0.82 c. 0.025

15. Write each fraction as a decimal. Use a bar to show repeating decimals.

    a. $\frac{5}{8}$ b. $\frac{6}{11}$ c. $\frac{15}{45}$

16. Solve the following puzzle. When I add 2 to a number, subtract 5, and then multiply by 3, my result is 24. What is my number?

Cumulative Review

Choose A, B, C, or D.

1. In which polygon can three diagonals be drawn from one vertex?
   A. quadrilateral **B.** hexagon
   C. 7-sided polygon **D.** pentagon

2. Which number pattern can be described by the following rule: *Start with the number 12 and subtract 4 repeatedly?*
   A. 12, 8, 4, . . . **B.** 12, 8, 10, . . .
   C. 12, 16, 24, . . . **D.** 12, 24, 20, . . .

3. Which angle does not appear to be a right angle? Classify the angle as acute, obtuse, or straight.
   A. $\angle COD$
   B. $\angle DOE$
   C. $\angle AOB$
   D. $\angle CEO$

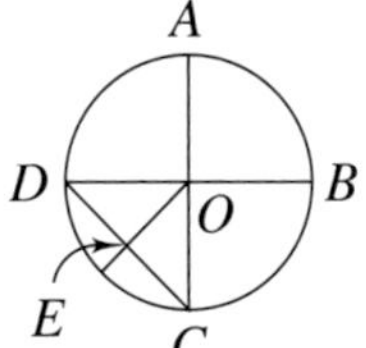

4. Which expression has a value of 13?
   A. $3 + (2)^2$ **B.** $(3 + 2)^2$
   C. $3^2 + 2^2$ **D.** $3^3 + 2^2$

5. Which of the pairs of triangles appear to be similar but *not* congruent?

A.
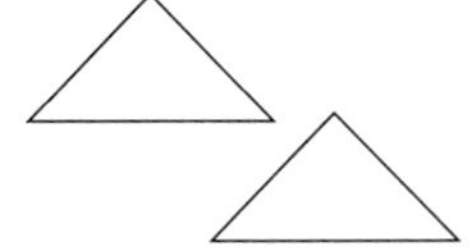
B.
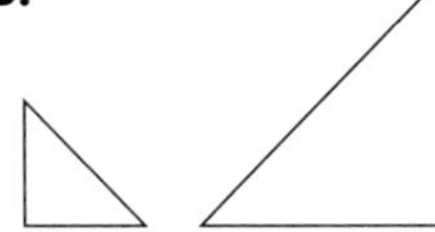
C.
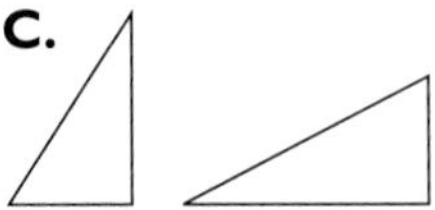
D.
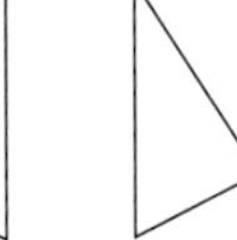

6. Which decimal is equivalent to $\frac{3}{8}$?
   A. 0.037 **B.** 0.38 **C.** 0.375 **D.** 3.75

7. Which word phrase describes the variable expression $2b - 8$?
   A. eight minus two times b
   B. two times b
   C. two minus eight times b
   D. two times b minus eight

8. Which set of numbers has a GCF of 8?
   A. 24, 36, 48 **B.** 56, 63, 42
   C. 64, 24, 56 **D.** 56, 36, 28

9. Which fraction model does *not* equal $\frac{2}{3}$?
   A. **B.**
   C. **D.**

10. Which name best describes the quadrilateral?
    A. parallelogram
    B. square
    C. rhombus
    D. rectangle

11. Which fraction is *not* equivalent to 0.125?
    A. $\frac{5}{40}$ **B.** $\frac{125}{1000}$ **C.** $\frac{1}{8}$ **D.** $\frac{15}{200}$

CHAPTER **8**

Fraction Operations

Barcelona, Spain, hosted the 1992 Summer Olympics. More than 14,000 athletes represented 172 nations. The athletes competed for medals in 257 events.

Carl Lewis received the gold medal for the long jump at the 1992 Summer Olympics.

Top Medal Winners in the 1992 Summer Olympics

Country	Number of Gold	Number of Silver	Number of Bronze	Total Medals
Unified Team	45	38	29	112
United States of America	37	34	37	108
Germany	33	21	28	82
People's Republic of China	16	22	16	54
Cuba	14	6	11	31
Hungary	11	12	7	30
South Korea	12	5	12	29
France	8	5	16	29
Australia	7	9	11	27
Spain	13	7	2	22
Japan	3	8	11	22
Great Britain	5	3	12	20

Source: *United States Olympic Committee*

Nations Participating in Summer Olympic Games, 1956–1992

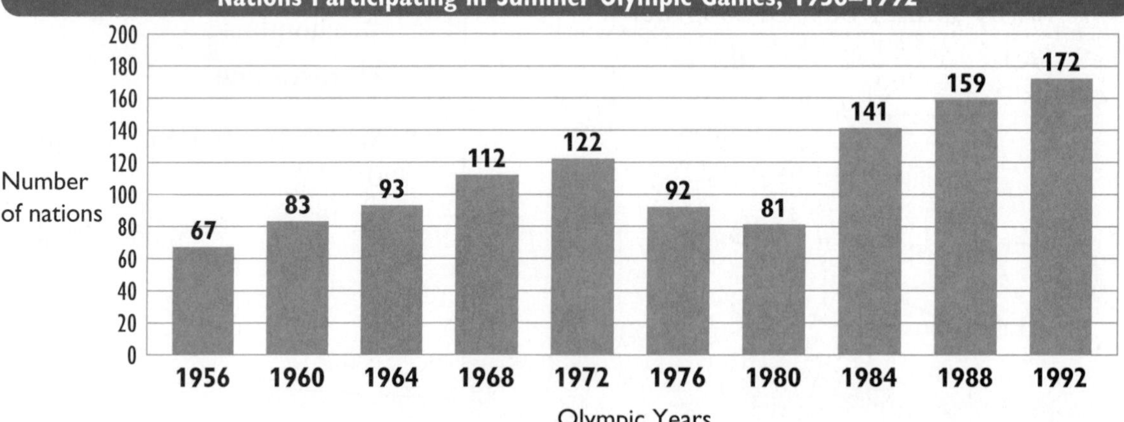

Source: *Runner's World*

Data File 8

WHAT YOU WILL LEARN

- how to estimate with fractions
- how to model fraction concepts and operations
- how to use technology to explore patterns
- how to solve problems by drawing a diagram

Women's Olympic Long Jump Winners

Year		Distance
1956	Elzibieta Krzesinska *Poland*	20 ft 10 in.
1960	Vyera Krepkina *USSR*	20 ft $10\frac{3}{4}$ in.
1964	Mary Rand *Great Britain*	22 ft $2\frac{1}{4}$ in.
1968	Viorica Viscopoleanu *Romania*	22 ft $4\frac{1}{4}$ in.
1972	Heidemarie Rosendahl *W. Germany*	22 ft 3 in.
1976	Angela Voigt *E. Germany*	22 ft $\frac{3}{4}$ in.
1980	Tatiana Kolpakova *USSR*	23 ft 2 in.
1984	Anisoara Cusmir-Stanciu *Romania*	22 ft 10 in.
1988	Jackie Joyner-Kersee *United States*	24 ft $3\frac{1}{2}$ in.
1992	Heike Drechsler *Germany*	23 ft $5\frac{1}{4}$ in.

Sources: *United States Olympic Committee*

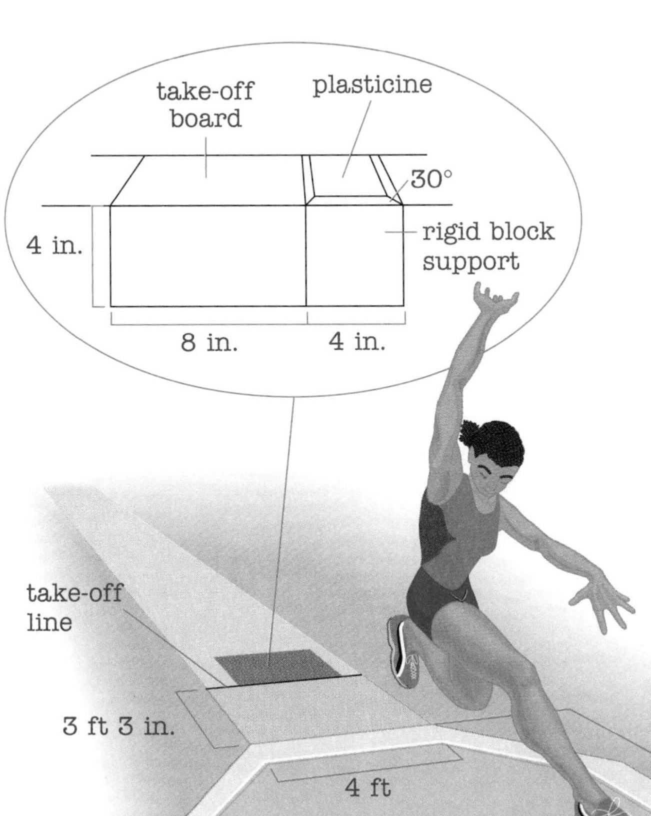

LONG JUMP TAKE-OFF BOARD

A take-off board is built into the runway where runners begin long jumps. The edge nearest the landing area is known as the take-off line. Athletes cannot step past this line. A clay-like substance is on the edge of the board. If athletes step past the line, their footprint can be seen in the clay.

Source: *Rules of the Game*

investigation

Project File

Memo

A **nomograph** is a tool you can make to add fractions. The nomograph shown is a simple one for adding thirds.

The three lines are number lines spaced equal distances apart. The middle number line shows twice as many numbers as the outer two. Fractions to be added are found on the outer lines. A line connecting them intersects the middle line at the sum of the fractions.

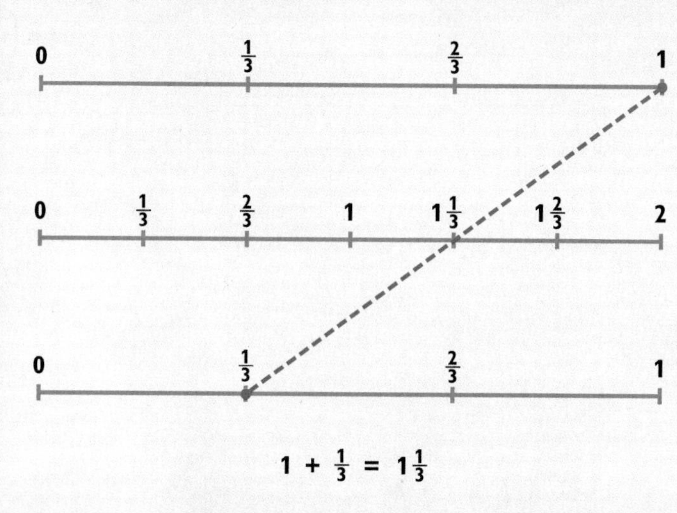

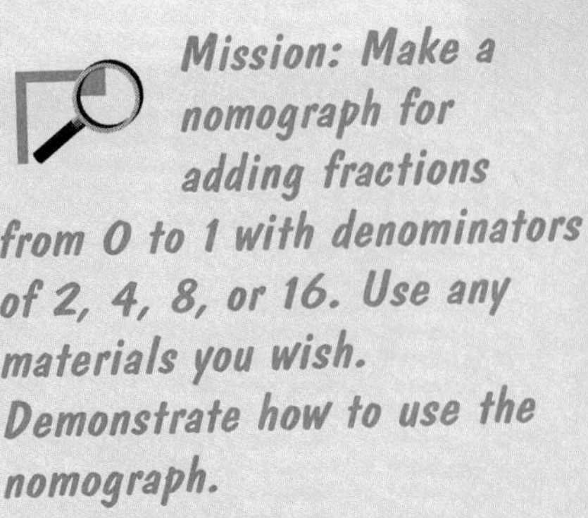

Mission: Make a nomograph for adding fractions from 0 to 1 with denominators of 2, 4, 8, or 16. Use any materials you wish. Demonstrate how to use the nomograph.

- ✓ What divisions should you have on your number lines?
- ✓ How will your nomograph differ from the nomograph for adding thirds?

What's Ahead

- Rounding fractions and mixed numbers
- Estimating sums and differences of fractions and mixed numbers

WHAT YOU'LL NEED

✓ Ruler

8-1 Estimating Sums and Differences

WORK TOGETHER

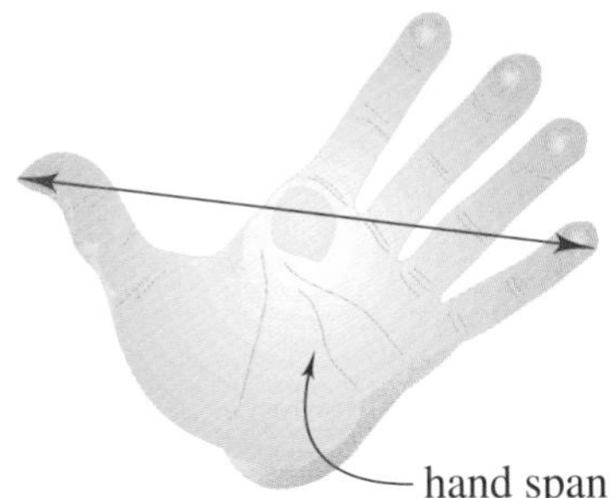

Use a ruler to measure the hand span of each member of your group. Record each measurement to the nearest half inch. What is the range of hand spans within your group?

THINK AND DISCUSS

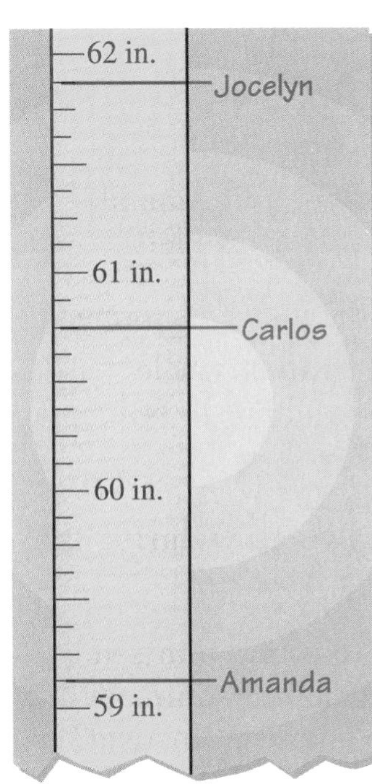

At the beginning of the summer, Jocelyn, Carlos, and Amanda measured their heights. See the growth chart at the left.

1. Round each height to the nearest half inch.

   a. Jocelyn: $61\frac{7}{8}$ in. **b.** Carlos: $60\frac{3}{4}$ in. **c.** Amanda: $59\frac{1}{8}$ in.

2. **Discussion** How do you round to the nearest half inch? Did you round when measuring your hand spans?

When you round a measurement to the nearest half inch, you decide if the fraction is closest to 0, $\frac{1}{2}$, or 1.

3. Is each fraction closest to 0, $\frac{1}{2}$, or 1?

   a. $\frac{1}{10}$ **b.** $\frac{7}{9}$ **c.** $\frac{5}{12}$ **d.** $\frac{1}{4}$

4. **Discussion** Does $\frac{1}{4}$ round to 0 or $\frac{1}{2}$? Why?

You can use models to round a fraction.

5. Write the fraction represented by the model. Then round to the nearest $\frac{1}{2}$.

   a.

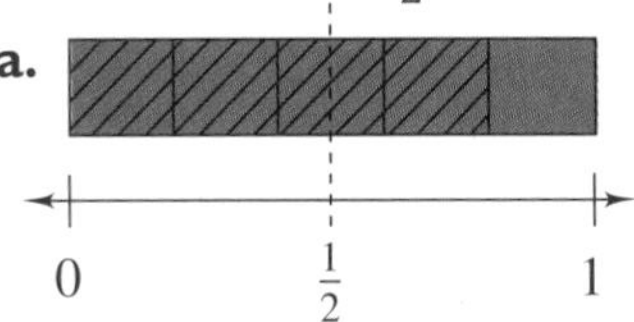

   b.

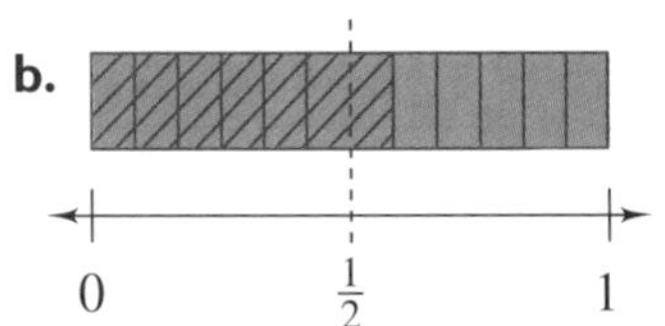

6. Represent each fraction or mixed number with a model. Use fraction bars, rulers, number lines, or decimal squares. Then round to the nearest $\frac{1}{2}$.

a. $\frac{6}{10}$ **b.** $1\frac{1}{3}$ **c.** $2\frac{3}{4}$ **d.** $\frac{1}{100}$

To estimate a sum or difference of fractions, you can round each fraction to the nearest $\frac{1}{2}$. Then add or subtract.

7. Estimate the sum $\frac{7}{12} + \frac{4}{5}$.

   a. Round each fraction to the nearest $\frac{1}{2}$. So round $\frac{7}{12}$ to ■, and round $\frac{4}{5}$ to ■.

   b. Add the rounded fractions: ■ + ■ = ■.

8. Estimate the difference $\frac{9}{10} - \frac{3}{7}$.

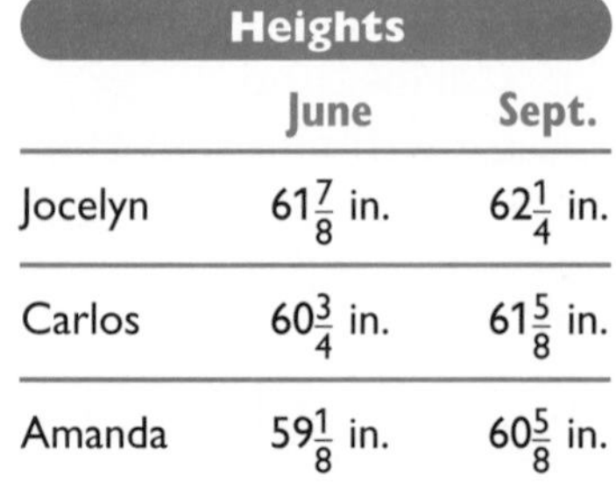

Heights	June	Sept.
Jocelyn	$61\frac{7}{8}$ in.	$62\frac{1}{4}$ in.
Carlos	$60\frac{3}{4}$ in.	$61\frac{5}{8}$ in.
Amanda	$59\frac{1}{8}$ in.	$60\frac{5}{8}$ in.

At the end of the summer, Carlos, Jocelyn, and Amanda measured their heights again. See the table at the left.

9. About how much did Amanda grow during the summer?

   a. Round each mixed number to the nearest whole number. So round $59\frac{1}{8}$ to ■, and round $60\frac{5}{8}$ to ■.

   b. Subtract the whole numbers: ■ − ■ = ■.

10. About how much did Carlos and Jocelyn grow during the summer? Which of the three grew the most?

11. **Discussion** Why does it make sense to round a mixed number to the nearest *whole number* before adding or subtracting? Could you round to the nearest $\frac{1}{2}$ instead?

ON YOUR OWN

Round each measurement to the nearest half inch.

12. $6\frac{5}{8}$ in. 13. $10\frac{3}{16}$ in. 14. $1\frac{7}{8}$ in. 15. $100\frac{1}{4}$ in.

16. Round each measurement in Exercises 12–15 to the nearest inch.

17. **Estimation** About how many innings did David Wells of the Toronto Blue Jays pitch in the 1992 World Series? Use the information at the left.

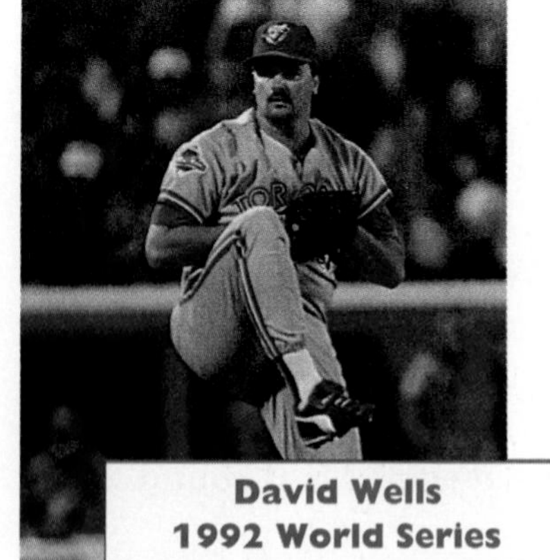

David Wells
1992 World Series

Game	1	2	3	4	5	6
Innings Pitched	1	$1\frac{2}{3}$	—	—	$1\frac{1}{3}$	$\frac{1}{3}$

18. **Choose A, B, C, or D.** Which number is closest to 5?

A. $4\frac{3}{4}$ **B.** $4\frac{2}{6}$ **C.** $4\frac{7}{8}$ **D.** $4\frac{1}{3}$

Write the fraction modeled by the fraction bar. Then round to the nearest $\frac{1}{2}$.

19. 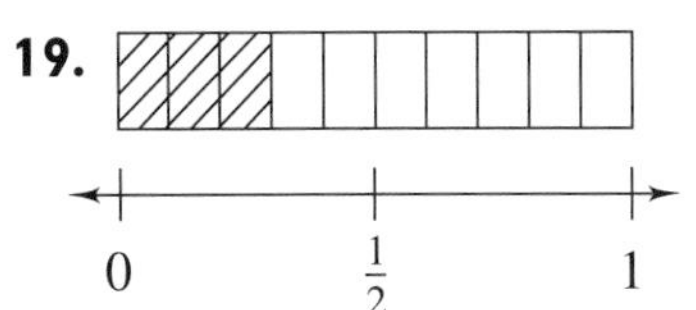

20. 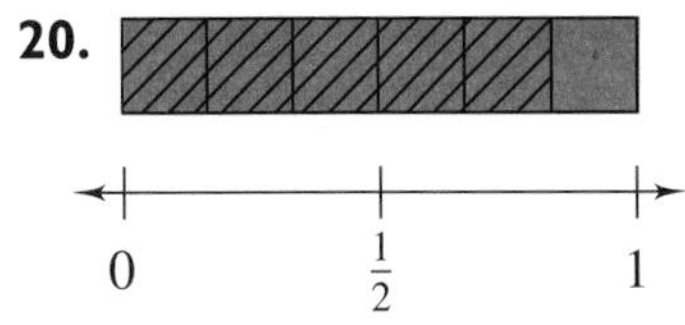

Use the information at the right.

21. **Estimation** About how much did the Kudzu plant grow from Day 1 to Day 2?

22. Estimate the average growth per day for the Kudzu plant.

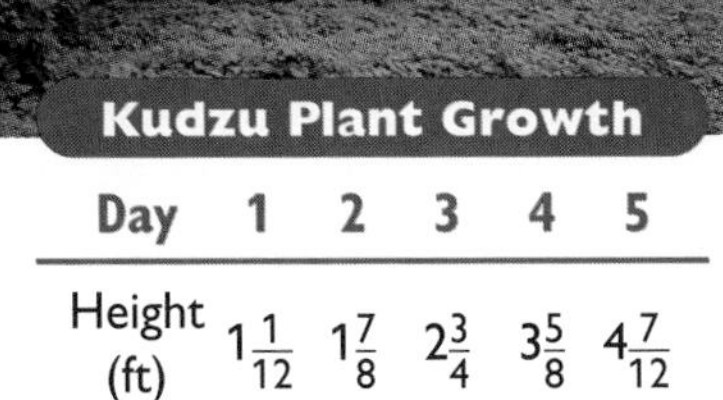

Kudzu Plant Growth

Day	1	2	3	4	5
Height (ft)	$1\frac{1}{12}$	$1\frac{7}{8}$	$2\frac{3}{4}$	$3\frac{5}{8}$	$4\frac{7}{12}$

Estimate each sum or difference.

23. $\frac{7}{8} + \frac{5}{12}$ **24.** $\frac{9}{10} - \frac{3}{8}$ **25.** $3\frac{3}{4} - 1\frac{2}{5}$

26. $\frac{9}{16} + \frac{5}{8}$ **27.** $7\frac{8}{12} + 4\frac{10}{12}$ **28.** $4\frac{8}{12} - \frac{5}{6}$

29. Think of three fractions with a sum of about 1.

30. Think of two mixed numbers with a difference of about 5.

31. **Critical Thinking** Will the sum of many fractions less than $\frac{1}{4}$ ever be greater than 1? Support your answer.

32. **Writing** Suppose you are a finalist in a contest to build the tallest tower of recycled cans. Your tower is $7\frac{7}{8}$ ft. The other towers are $7\frac{3}{4}$ ft and $7\frac{15}{16}$ ft. If you round each height, will you be able to tell who wins? Explain.

33. **Estimation** You plan to put a fence around your garden, shown at the right. About how much fence will you need?

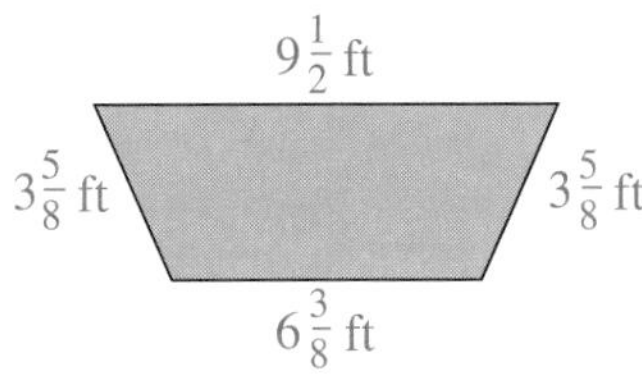

34. **Sewing** Bonita is making a quilt. Material costs $4.96 per yard. She needs $1\frac{5}{8}$ yd of a solid material and $\frac{3}{4}$ of a print material. About how much will the material cost?

Mixed REVIEW

Round to the place of the underlined digit.

1. 0.0̲93 **2.** 5.618̲4

3. The last Friday of a certain month is the 28th day of the month. What day of the week is the first day of the month?

4. When I divide a number by 8, add 6, and then multiply by 2, my result is 18. What is my number?

5. Find the information needed to answer: Ajayi bought 3 juices. How much did he pay for them?

What's Ahead

- Modeling addition and subtraction of fractions with like denominators
- Adding and subtracting fractions with like denominators

WHAT YOU'LL NEED

✓ Fraction bars 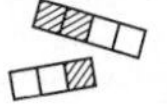

8-2 Adding and Subtracting Fractions

THINK AND DISCUSS

Suppose you and a friend order a pizza for dinner. The pizza is cut into eight equal pieces. You eat two pieces, and your friend eats three pieces. What portion of the pizza is eaten? What portion of the pizza is left? You can model this problem.

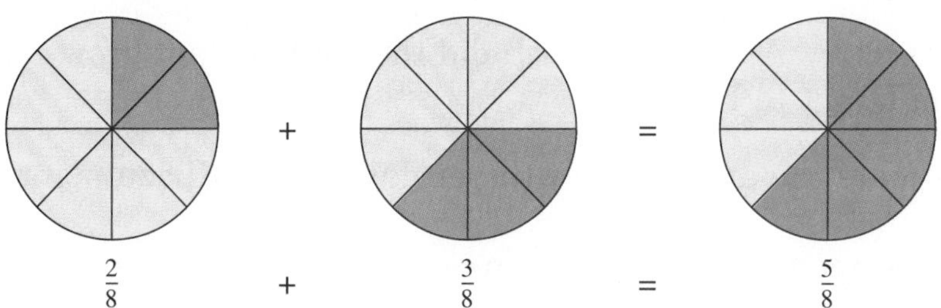

$\frac{2}{8} + \frac{3}{8} = \frac{5}{8}$

1. What fraction represents the amount of pizza you have eaten? What fraction represents the amount of pizza your friend has eaten? What portion of the pizza is eaten?

2. What fraction represents the whole pizza? What portion of the pizza is left?

You can use fraction bars to model addition problems.

3. Write the addition sentence for each model.

a. 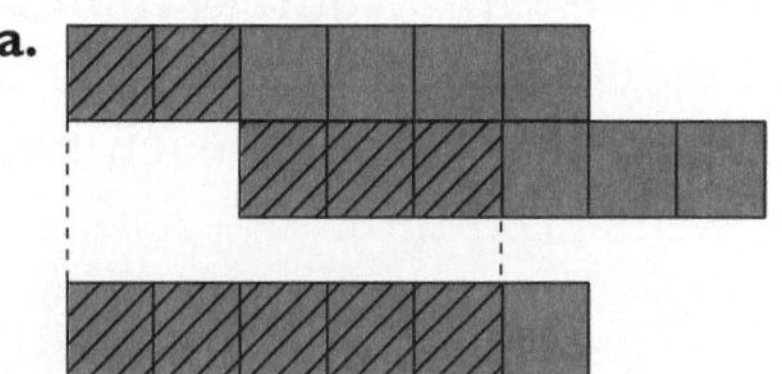

b. 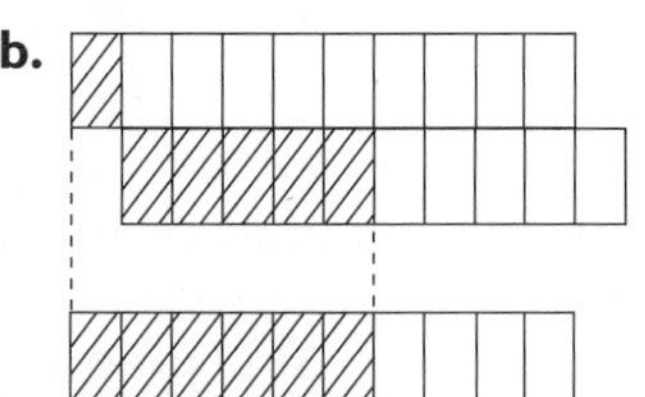

FLASHBACK

To write a fraction in simplest form, divide the numerator and the denominator by the GCF. Or, use a fraction calculator to simplify.

4. In Exercise 3b. the sum $\frac{6}{10}$ is not in simplest form. Write $\frac{6}{10}$ in simplest form. Use fraction bars to show that the two fractions are equivalent.

5. Draw a model and write the sum in simplest form.

   a. $\frac{2}{5} + \frac{1}{5}$ b. $\frac{1}{6} + \frac{1}{6}$ c. $\frac{3}{10} + \frac{7}{10}$

The sum of fractions is sometimes greater than 1.

6. Write the addition sentence for the model shown below. Write the sum as a mixed number in lowest terms.

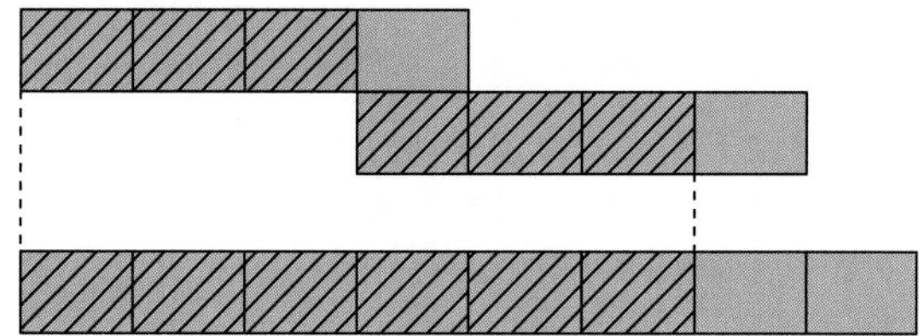

FLASHBACK

To write an improper fraction as a mixed number, divide the numerator by the denominator.

7. Draw a model to represent $\frac{4}{5} + \frac{3}{5} = \frac{7}{5}$. Write $\frac{7}{5}$ as a mixed number. Does the result match your model?

You can model subtraction problems. Suppose there are 3 pieces of a pizza. You eat 1 piece. The circles show what's left.

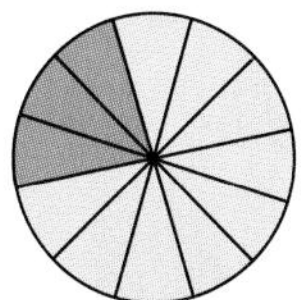 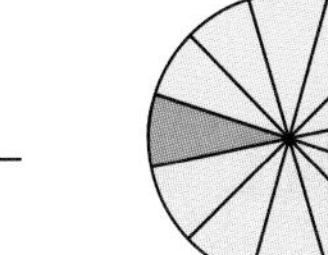 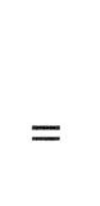 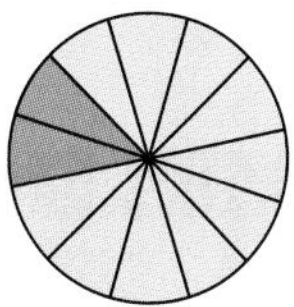

***Pizza originated** in Naples, Italy. The first pizza restaurant in the United States opened in 1905 in New York City.*

8. Use the model to write a subtraction sentence for the problem. What portion of the pizza is left?

9. **Discussion** You can also use fraction bars to model this problem. Do you prefer circles or fraction bars? Why?

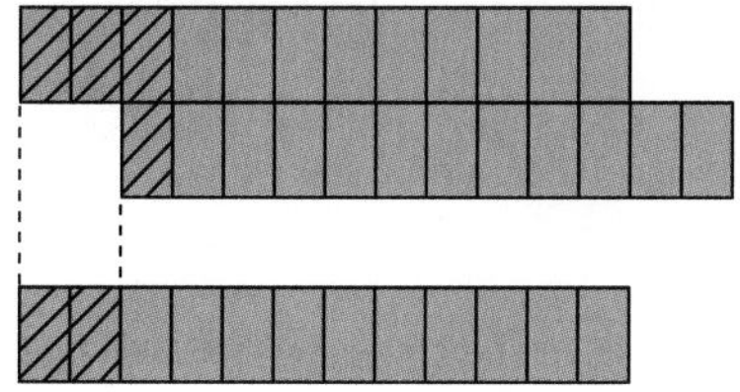

10. Write the subtraction sentence for each model.

a.

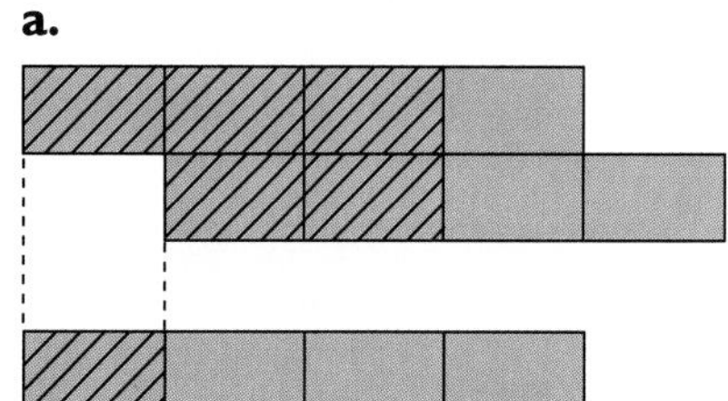

b.

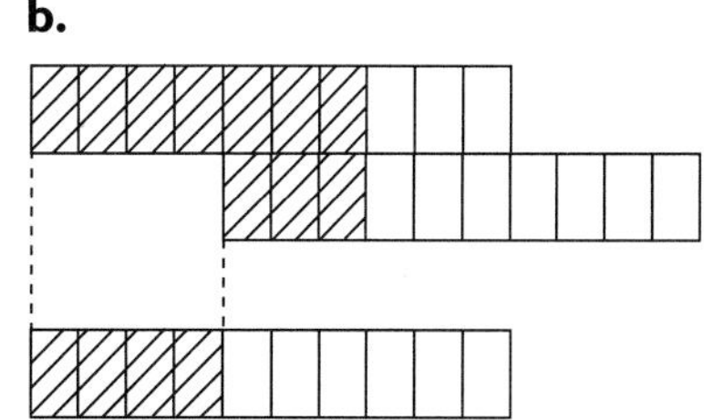

11. Draw a model and write the difference in simplest form.

a. $\frac{5}{6} - \frac{1}{6}$ **b.** $\frac{3}{8} - \frac{1}{8}$ **c.** $\frac{9}{10} - \frac{7}{10}$

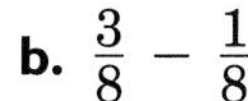

12. **Discussion** How can you add or subtract fractions without using a model? Develop a rule for adding and subtracting fractions with like denominators.

You can use an equation to solve some fraction problems. Suppose you and a friend order a pizza with eight equal pieces. Your friend eats three pieces and asks how many you have eaten. You do not remember! You both look at the pizza and see that two pieces are left. What portion of the pizza did you eat?

13. To solve this problem, write the equation $\frac{3}{8} + x = \frac{8}{8} - \frac{2}{8}$. What does each part of the equation represent?

14. Solve for x. What portion of the pizza did you eat?

15. **Discussion** Think of another way to solve this problem.

WORK TOGETHER

Work with a partner. Draw a diagram of a pizza. Make your pizza rectangular or circular. Divide the pizza into as many equal pieces as you wish. Write a problem about yourselves and your pizza. Make sure the problem uses addition or subtraction of fractions. Write a complete solution to your problem. Draw a model or a diagram to show the problem and your solution.

ON YOUR OWN

Write an addition sentence for each model.

16.

17.

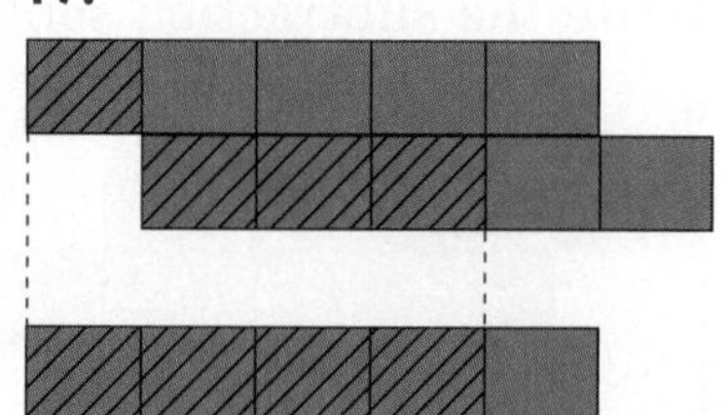

18. 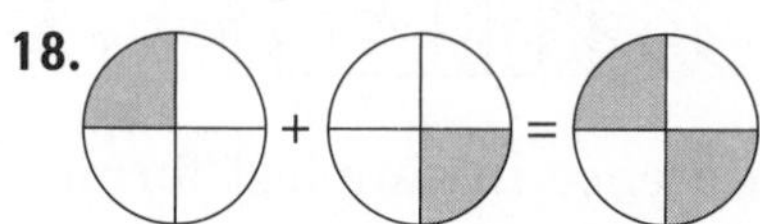

19. 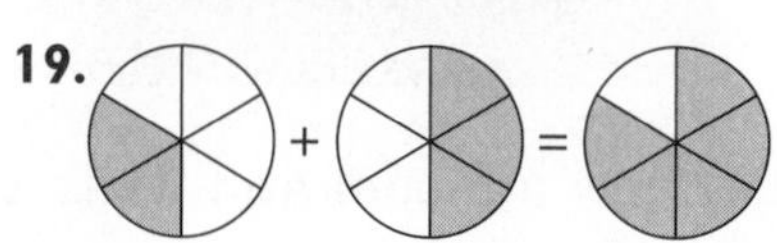

Mixed REVIEW

Name each space figure. Give the number of faces, edges, and vertices.

1. 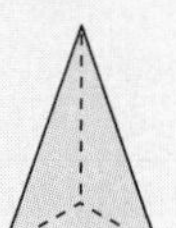

2. 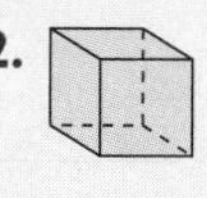

Estimate each sum or difference.

3. $\frac{9}{10} + \frac{3}{4}$

4. $6\frac{7}{12} - 2\frac{11}{12}$

5. Akira spent one third of his money, then spent \$6, then spent half the money he had left to leave him with exactly \$4. How much money did he start with?

Write a subtraction sentence for each model.

20. 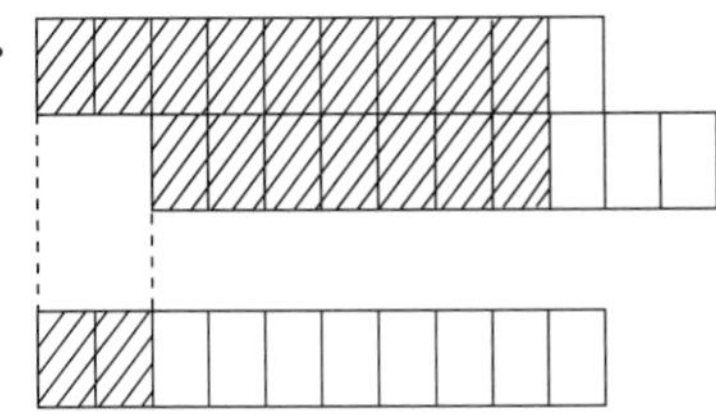

21. 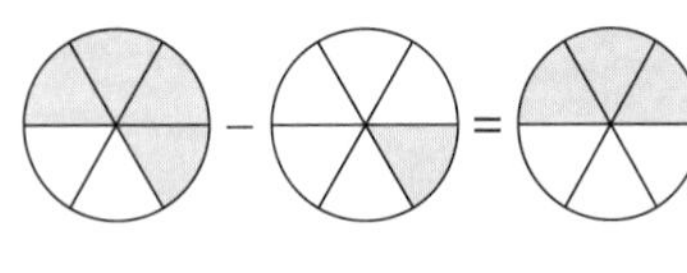

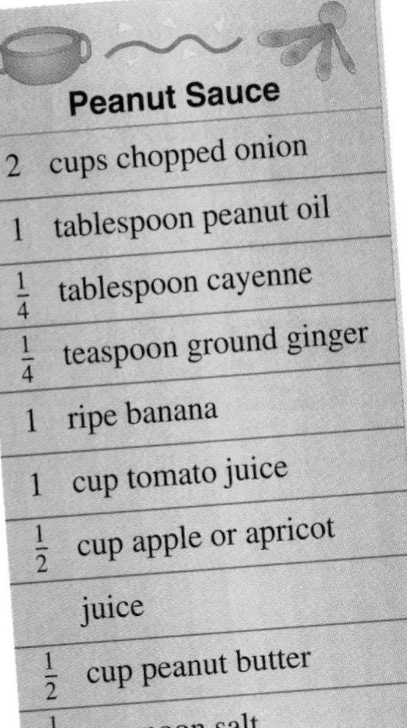

Peanut Sauce

2	cups chopped onion
1	tablespoon peanut oil
$\frac{1}{4}$	tablespoon cayenne
$\frac{1}{4}$	teaspoon ground ginger
1	ripe banana
1	cup tomato juice
$\frac{1}{2}$	cup apple or apricot juice
$\frac{1}{2}$	cup peanut butter
$\frac{1}{2}$	teaspoon salt

Draw a model and find each sum or difference.

22. $\frac{1}{3} + \frac{1}{3} = \blacksquare$

23. $\frac{9}{10} - \frac{1}{10} = \blacksquare$

24. $\frac{4}{7} + \frac{6}{7} = \blacksquare$

25. **Cooking** Peanut sauce is commonly used as a base for stews and soups in Nigeria, Ghana, and Sierra Leone.
   a. To make the sauce spicier, you decide to double the amount of cayenne. How much cayenne will you use?
   b. You decide to use an equal amount of apple and apricot juices. How much of each type of juice will you use?

Mental Math **Decide if the answer will be greater than 1. Write *yes* or *no*. Then add or subtract.**

26. $\frac{4}{7} + \frac{2}{7}$

27. $\frac{4}{5} - \frac{2}{5}$

28. $\frac{7}{10} + \frac{4}{10}$

29. $\frac{8}{9} - \frac{4}{9}$

30. $\frac{5}{6} + \frac{4}{6}$

31. $\frac{3}{3} - \frac{1}{3}$

Is each answer correct? Write *yes* or *no*. If *no*, write the correct answer. Write answers in simplest form.

32. $\frac{3}{10} + \frac{3}{10} = \frac{4}{5}$

33. $\frac{7}{12} - \frac{3}{12} = \frac{4}{12}$

34. $\frac{5}{6} + \frac{4}{6} = 1\frac{1}{2}$

Writing **The flag of Thailand is at the right. Describe what each equation can represent in the flag.**

35. $\frac{1}{6} + \frac{1}{6} = \frac{2}{6}$

36. $\frac{6}{6} - \frac{4}{6} = \frac{2}{6}$

37. $\frac{1}{3} + \frac{1}{3} = \frac{2}{3}$

Mental Math **Find x. Do not write in simplest form.**

38. $\frac{5}{6} - \frac{1}{6} = x$

39. $\frac{3}{10} + x = \frac{8}{10}$

40. $x + \frac{2}{5} = \frac{4}{5}$

41. $x = \frac{2}{8} + \frac{5}{8}$

42. $\frac{6}{7} - x = \frac{4}{7}$

43. $x - \frac{1}{3} = \frac{1}{3}$

44. **Sports** In an archery tournament, Zwena hit the target 9 times out of 12. What portion of Zwena's arrows did not hit the target? Draw a model to show your solution.

45. **Investigation (p. 318)** Make a nomograph to add $\frac{2}{6}$ and $\frac{3}{6}$.

What's Ahead

• Using a variety of methods to add and subtract fractions with unlike denominators

8-3 Unlike Denominators

WHAT YOU'LL NEED

✓ Fraction bars

✓ Calculator

WORK TOGETHER

Work with a partner to solve the problem below. Try to think of several different ways to solve it. Use fraction bars, circle models, number lines, rulers, or any other materials.

1. Shika is preparing a display of crystals and rocks for the science fair. She needs $\frac{1}{4}$ yd of black velvet for the crystals and $\frac{5}{12}$ yd for the rocks. How many yards of black velvet does Shika need for the display?

2. **Writing** Explain how you solved the problem. How is this problem different from problems in the previous lesson?

THINK AND DISCUSS

There are many different ways to solve problems like the one above. You can use fraction bars even when the denominators are not the same.

Example 1 Find the sum $\frac{1}{4} + \frac{2}{3}$.

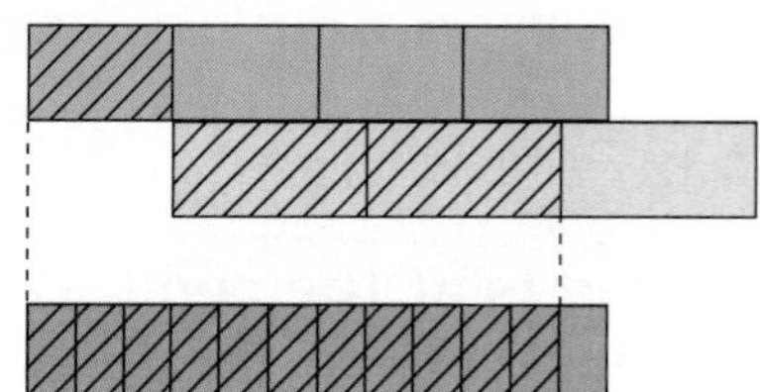

Use the fraction bar for $\frac{1}{4}$.

Use the fraction bar for $\frac{2}{3}$.

Find a fraction bar with an area equal to the sum.

$$\frac{1}{4} + \frac{2}{3} = \frac{11}{12}$$

Quartz crystals are used in clocks. Because of the electric current that passes through the crystal, quartz clocks keep time within 1 second each year.

Source: *Did You Know?*

3. **Discussion** Why does the sum of $\frac{1}{4}$ and $\frac{2}{3}$ not have a denominator of 4 or 3?

4. **Discussion** Draw circle models for $\frac{1}{4}$ and $\frac{2}{3}$. How can you use the models to find the sum $\frac{1}{4} + \frac{2}{3}$?

5. Use models to find each sum or difference.

   a. $\frac{1}{2} + \frac{1}{3}$ b. $\frac{4}{5} - \frac{1}{2}$ c. $\frac{5}{6} + \frac{1}{9}$ d. $\frac{1}{2} - \frac{1}{4}$

You can use fraction bars another way. Find equivalent fractions with the same denominator, then add or subtract.

Example 2 Find the difference $\frac{1}{2} - \frac{1}{3}$.

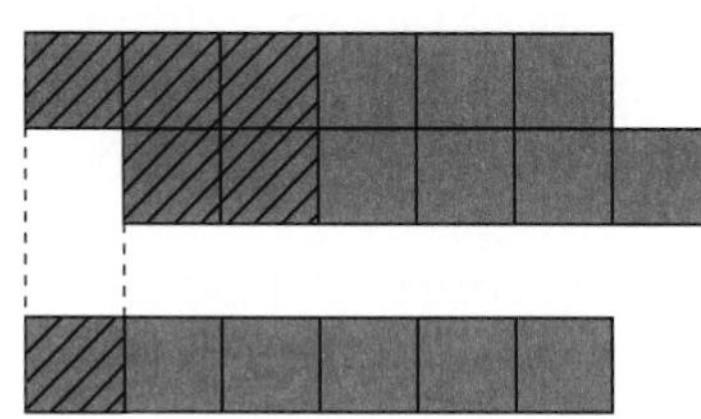

Use the $\frac{3}{6}$ fraction bar for $\frac{1}{2}$.

Use the $\frac{2}{6}$ fraction bar for $\frac{1}{3}$.

Subtract: $\frac{3}{6} - \frac{2}{6}$.

$$\frac{1}{2} - \frac{1}{3} = \frac{3}{6} - \frac{2}{6} = \frac{1}{6}$$

6. What is the least common denominator (LCD) of $\frac{1}{2}$ and $\frac{1}{3}$?

7. Draw circle models for $\frac{1}{2}$ and $\frac{1}{3}$. Then divide each circle into six equal parts. Use the models to find the difference.

FLASHBACK

The least common denominator (LCD) is the least common multiple (LCM) of the denominators.

8. Add or subtract. Use models and equivalent fractions.
   a. $\frac{3}{5} + \frac{1}{10}$ b. $\frac{5}{6} - \frac{2}{3}$ c. $\frac{1}{3} + \frac{1}{4}$ d. $\frac{5}{12} - \frac{1}{4}$

FLASHBACK

To write equivalent fractions, multiply the numerator and the denominator by the same non-zero factor.

You can use equivalent fractions without models.

Example 3 Find the sum $\frac{7}{8} + \frac{1}{6}$.

Estimate: $1 + 0 = 1$ Round to the nearest $\frac{1}{2}$.

The LCD is 24. Find the LCD of 8 and 6.

$\frac{7}{8} = \frac{21}{24}$ $\frac{1}{6} = \frac{4}{24}$ Write equivalent fractions.

$\frac{7}{8} + \frac{1}{6} = \frac{21}{24} + \frac{4}{24} = \frac{25}{24} = 1\frac{1}{24}$ Add. Write a mixed number.

You can use a fraction calculator to compute.

Example 4 Find the difference $\frac{13}{16} - \frac{5}{8}$.

Estimate: $1 - \frac{1}{2} = \frac{1}{2}$

Press 13 [/] 16 [−] 5 [/] 8 [=] 3/16

$$\frac{13}{16} - \frac{5}{8} = \frac{3}{16}$$

9. **Discussion** Suppose you have a calculator that does not compute fractions. How can you use the calculator to find a sum or difference of fractions?

A fossil is a rock that contains the preserved remains of a plant or animal. Scientists often date rocks by finding the age of the remains in the rock.

Source: *Rocks and Minerals*

Sometimes you can use estimation to solve a fraction problem.

Example 5 Two students explore a fossil rock ledge along an old road. One student explores $\frac{1}{3}$ mi of the ledge, while the other explores $\frac{1}{4}$ mi of the ledge. Do they explore at least 1 mi of the ledge altogether?

Since $\frac{1}{3}$ is less than $\frac{1}{2}$, and $\frac{1}{4}$ is less than $\frac{1}{2}$, the sum $\frac{1}{3} + \frac{1}{4}$ must be less than 1. So the students do *not* explore at least 1 mi of the ledge altogether.

10. **Discussion** Describe all the different ways you can solve problems that involve adding or subtracting fractions. Which methods do you prefer? Why?

TRY THESE

Write a number sentence for each model shown.

11. 12.

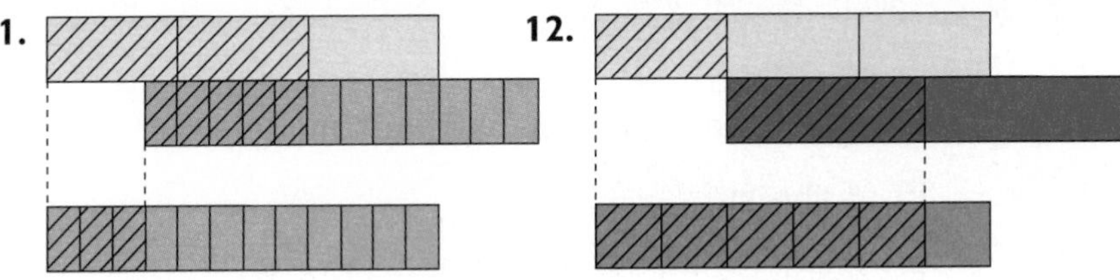

Draw a model for each equation.

13. $\frac{5}{6} - \frac{1}{3} = \frac{3}{6}$
14. $\frac{3}{8} + \frac{1}{2} = \frac{7}{8}$
15. $\frac{3}{4} + \frac{1}{3} = 1\frac{1}{12}$

Write the LCD. Then add or subtract.

16. $\frac{1}{3} + \frac{5}{8}$
17. $\frac{9}{10} - \frac{2}{5}$
18. $\frac{5}{6} - \frac{1}{10}$

Calculator Add or subtract. Write in simplest form.

19. $\frac{7}{10} - \frac{1}{8}$
20. $\frac{9}{16} + \frac{3}{4}$
21. $\frac{1}{2} + \frac{1}{3} + \frac{1}{4}$

Estimation Is the answer greater or less than 1?

22. $\frac{1}{8} + \frac{1}{4}$
23. $\frac{4}{5} - \frac{1}{2}$
24. $\frac{1}{2} + \frac{3}{4}$

25. **Art** Suppose you use $\frac{3}{4}$ yd of felt on the top of a bulletin board display. Then you use another $\frac{2}{3}$ yd on the bottom of the display. How much felt do you use altogether?

Mixed REVIEW

Solve. Write the answer in simplest form.

1. $\frac{4}{9} + \frac{2}{9}$
2. $\frac{13}{18} - \frac{11}{18}$

Solve. Use models if they help you.

3. $2.6 + 0.4$
4. $3.17 - 1.26$

5. Wahkuna, Alma, and Yuji are a pharmacist, a teacher, and a stock broker. Wahkuna met the teacher and the stock broker at a fund-raiser. The teacher went to college with Alma. Match each person with the correct occupation.

ON YOUR OWN

Write a number sentence for each model.

26.

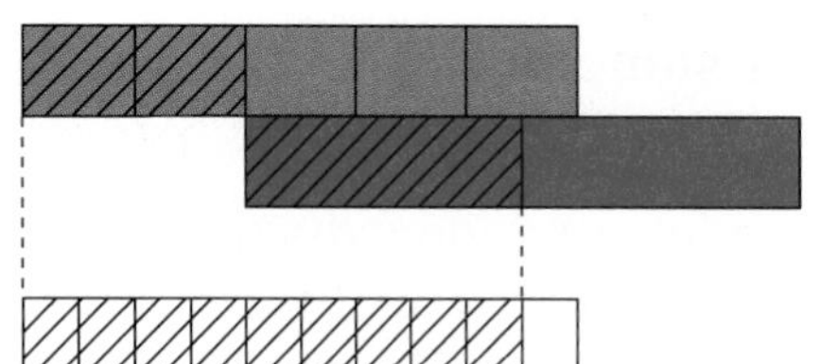

27.

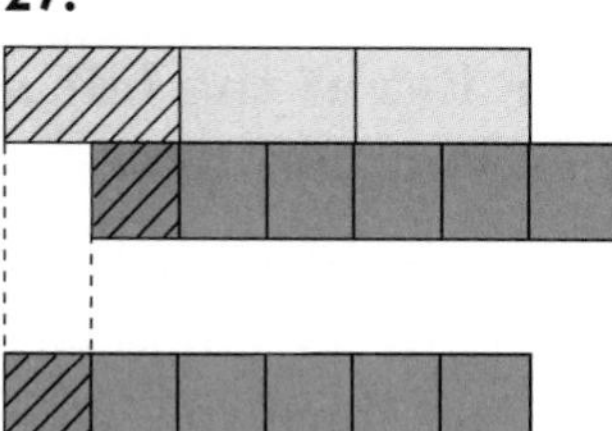

Social Studies **Use the data at the right.**

28. Order the countries from least to greatest population.

29. Is the population of Costa Rica and Nicaragua together greater than or less than the population of Honduras?

30. Do the fractions add to 1? Why or why not?

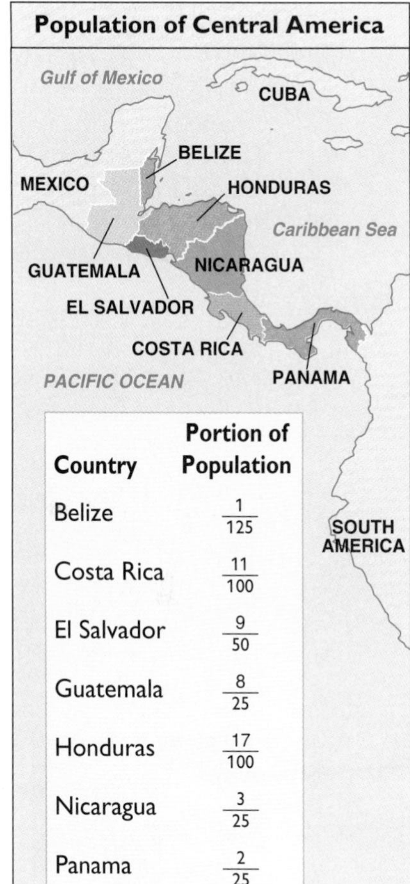

Country	Portion of Population
Belize	$\frac{1}{125}$
Costa Rica	$\frac{11}{100}$
El Salvador	$\frac{9}{50}$
Guatemala	$\frac{8}{25}$
Honduras	$\frac{17}{100}$
Nicaragua	$\frac{3}{25}$
Panama	$\frac{2}{25}$

Choose **Use any method to add or subtract.**

31. $\frac{5}{8} + \frac{9}{12}$ **32.** $\frac{11}{30} - \frac{1}{5}$ **33.** $\frac{2}{5} + \frac{1}{2}$

34. $\frac{3}{4} - \frac{1}{3}$ **35.** $\frac{1}{3} + \frac{1}{2}$ **36.** $\frac{9}{10} - \frac{7}{8}$

37. Writing Explain four different ways to find the sum $\frac{1}{2} + \frac{3}{4}$.

Find x. Write the answer in simplest form.

38. $x = \frac{1}{6} + \frac{1}{2}$ **39.** $\frac{2}{5} - \frac{3}{10} = x$ **40.** $x = \frac{2}{3} + \frac{7}{12}$

41. You and a friend order a pizza with eight equal pieces. You eat half the pizza and take the rest home. The next day you eat one piece. What portion of the pizza is left? Draw a model that shows the problem and your solution.

42. Data File 7 (pp. 272–273) Compute the fraction of the tide covered between hours 1 and 2, 2 and 3, 3 and 4, 4 and 5, and 5 and 6. Describe any patterns you see.

43. A package of sliced ham weighs $\frac{1}{2}$ lb. Another package of sliced ham weighs $\frac{3}{4}$ lb. You buy both packages. Do you have enough ham for each of four persons to get $\frac{1}{3}$ lb?

44. Investigation (p. 318) Make a nomograph to add $\frac{2}{3}$ and $\frac{1}{6}$.

Problem Solving Practice

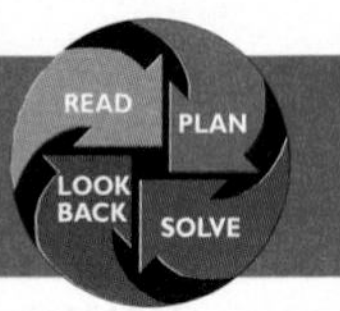

PROBLEM SOLVING STRATEGIES

Make a Table
Use Logical Reasoning
Solve a Simpler Problem
Too Much or Too Little Information
Look for a Pattern
Make a Model
Work Backward
Draw a Diagram
Guess and Test
Simulate a Problem
Use Multiple Strategies

Solve. The list at the left shows some possible strategies you can use.

1. A store owner is stacking boxes for a window display. The top row will have one box. The second row will have three boxes. The third row will have five boxes. If this pattern continues, how many boxes will the tenth row have?

2. Kyle is sewing a square pillow. He cut out thirteen pieces of material. Then he forgot how to place the pieces to make the pillow! There are eight isosceles right triangles and five squares. All the triangles are the same size, and all the squares are the same size. The area of two triangles equals the area of one square. Think of at least one way Kyle can place all the pieces to make the square pillow.

3. William drives about 24 mi total to and from work each day. He works five days each week and takes two weeks of vacation each year. About how many miles does William drive to and from work in one year?

4. Three cousins shared a relative's inheritance. Amina got $\frac{1}{2}$ of the money. Kareem got $\frac{1}{5}$ of the money. Ahmed got \$3,000. How much money was the total inheritance?

5. Britta needs to get to work by 9:30 A.M. She must drive her son to school, which takes 12 min. She will also drop off some dry cleaning. From school to the dry cleaners takes about 15 min. From the dry cleaners to work takes about 18 min. By what time should Britta leave home?

6. Juan is making sandwiches for a party. Each sandwich has one type of bread, one type of cheese, and one type of meat. There are two choices for bread, for cheese, and for meat. How many different sandwiches can Juan make?

7. **Sports** A basketball team sold 496 raffle tickets and collected \$396.80. Expenses totaled \$75.98. How much did each ticket cost?

***The National** Wheelchair Athletic Association was founded in 1957 and has about 1,500 members.*

TECHNOLOGY

8-4 Exploring Patterns in Fraction Sums

What's Ahead

- Exploring series
- Using spreadsheets to list and graph fraction sums

WHAT YOU'LL NEED

✓  

✓ Spreadsheet software 

✓ Calculator 

Reward B

A piece of gold every minute for the rest of your life in the pattern described below.

1st piece: $\frac{1}{2}$ oz

2nd piece: $\frac{1}{4}$ oz

3rd piece: $\frac{1}{8}$ oz

THINK AND DISCUSS

Alarms scream out from a jewelry store. A car screeches away. You see the license plate and memorize the number. Thanks to your memory and a computer search, the stolen jewels are returned. The jeweler offers you a choice between the two rewards described at the left. Which reward will you choose?

1. **Discussion** Which reward seems to be the better choice?
2. With reward B, how much will the 4th piece of gold weigh? How much will the 5th piece of gold weigh?
3. With reward B, how many ounces of gold will you have after you receive the second piece?

You can use a table to analyze reward B.

		Total Ounces	
Piece	**Ounces**	**Expression**	
1	$\frac{1}{2}$	$\frac{1}{2}$	$\frac{1}{2}$
2	$\frac{1}{4}$	$\frac{1}{2} + \frac{1}{4}$	■
3	$\frac{1}{8}$	$\frac{1}{2} + \frac{1}{4} + \frac{1}{8}$	■

4. **Discussion** What does each column in the table show?
5. **Discussion** Describe the pattern in the "Ounces" column.
6. **Calculator** Copy and complete the table above. Add another row.
7. **Discussion** Analyze the fractions in the "Sum" column. Describe any patterns you see in the numerators or denominators of the fractions.
8. How much gold will you have after you get piece 5? First use the pattern to make a prediction, then calculate.

Mixed REVIEW

Solve. Write the answer in simplest form.

1. $\frac{5}{6} + \frac{9}{10}$
2. $\frac{9}{16} - \frac{2}{6}$

Name each of the following for circle O.

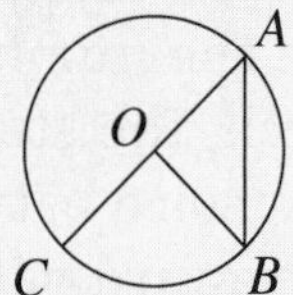
A
O
C
B

3. a diameter
4. two radii
5. **Data File 2 (pp. 38–39)** Find the total time you would expect to spend at Space Mountain in Walt Disney World.

You can use a spreadsheet to see what happens as you continue to get more pieces of gold with reward B.

9. **Computer** Set up a spreadsheet like the one below. Which columns of the table you made will you use?

	A	B	C	D
1	Piece	Numerator of the Sum	Denominator of the Sum	Sum as a Decimal
2	1	1	2	0.500
3	2	3	4	0.750

10. Use the patterns you described in Exercise 7 to write formulas for columns B and C.
11. Use columns B and C to write a formula for column D.
12. **Computer** Fill in the spreadsheet for the first 10 pieces of gold. What do you notice about the values in column D?
13. **Discussion** Now that you have analyzed reward B, which reward is the better choice? Are you surprised?
14. **Computer** Draw a line graph of the values in columns A and D. How does the graph show the pattern of reward B?

WORK TOGETHER

Suppose you are offered a third choice. Reward C is described at the left. Work in small groups to analyze reward C.

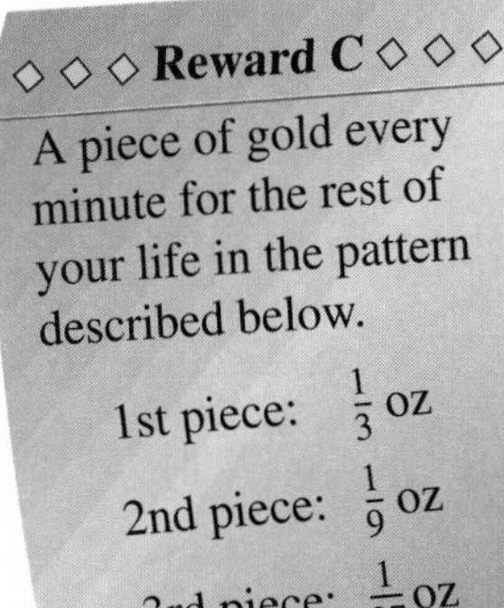
◇ ◇ ◇ Reward C ◇ ◇ ◇
A piece of gold every minute for the rest of your life in the pattern described below.
1st piece: $\frac{1}{3}$ oz
2nd piece: $\frac{1}{9}$ oz
3rd piece: $\frac{1}{27}$ oz

15. Complete a table that shows at least four pieces of gold.
16. **Computer** Use a spreadsheet to see what happens as you get more and more pieces of gold.
17. Draw a graph that shows the pattern of reward C.
18. **Critical Thinking** Do you think there is a limit to how much gold you will get with reward C? Support your answer.
19. **Writing** How are rewards B and C similar? How are they different? Which is the better choice between the two?

ON YOUR OWN

Use the pattern of fraction sums at the right.

Expression	Sum
$\frac{1}{4}$	$\frac{1}{4}$
$\frac{1}{4} + \frac{1}{16}$	■
$\frac{1}{4} + \frac{1}{16} + \frac{1}{64}$	■

20. Analyze the "Expression" column. Write the next expression in the pattern.

21. Calculator Copy and complete the table. Add another row.

22. Writing Add more rows to the table until you see a pattern in the sum. Describe the pattern.

23. Computer Make a spreadsheet like the one on the previous page. Fill in values for the first ten sums. Then draw a line graph of the sums.

24. Critical Thinking If this pattern continues forever, do you think the sum will ever reach $\frac{3}{8}$? Why or why not?

25. Reward D is described at the right. Which of the rewards A, B, C, or D is the best choice? Explain.

Reward D

A piece of gold every minute for the rest of your life in the pattern described below.

1st piece: $\frac{1}{2}$ oz

2nd piece: $\frac{1}{4}$ oz

3rd piece: $\frac{1}{6}$ oz

26. Suppose you start at your school and walk 1 mi north, then $\frac{1}{2}$ mi south, then $\frac{1}{4}$ mi north, $\frac{1}{8}$ mi south, and so on. About how far from your school will you end up?

CHECKPOINT

Write the fraction modeled by the fraction bar. Then round to the nearest $\frac{1}{2}$.

1. 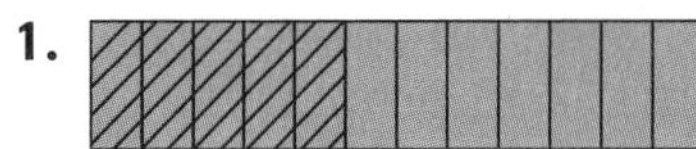

 **2.** 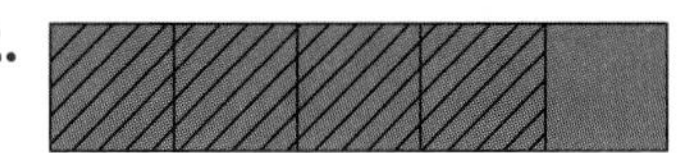

Find each sum or difference. Then write the answer in simplest form.

3. $\frac{2}{7} + \frac{4}{7}$ **4.** $\frac{3}{8} + \frac{1}{8}$ **5.** $\frac{5}{9} - \frac{2}{9}$ **6.** $\frac{7}{12} - \frac{6}{12}$

7. $\frac{4}{9} + \frac{2}{5}$ **8.** $\frac{3}{8} + \frac{3}{4}$ **9.** $\frac{7}{10} - \frac{1}{4}$ **10.** $\frac{2}{3} - \frac{6}{13}$

11. Use the pattern of fraction sums at the right.

a. Copy and complete the table.

b. Add another row.

c. Writing Describe the pattern in the sum.

Expression	Sum
$\frac{1}{5}$	$\frac{1}{5}$
$\frac{1}{5} + \frac{1}{25}$	■
$\frac{1}{5} + \frac{1}{25} + \frac{1}{125}$	■

What's Ahead

- Solving problems that involve adding and subtracting mixed numbers

8-5 Adding & Subtracting Mixed Numbers

WHAT YOU'LL NEED

✓ Ruler 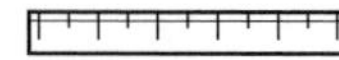

✓ Scissors 

✓ String 

THINK AND DISCUSS

The giant tortoise is one of the slowest moving animals. Suppose a giant tortoise travels $8\frac{1}{4}$ yd in one minute, and $7\frac{1}{2}$ yd the next minute. How far did the giant tortoise travel during these two minutes?

1. Solve the problem above. Explain your solution.
2. **Discussion** Think of several different ways to find $8\frac{1}{4} + 7\frac{1}{2}$.

The slowest giant male tortoise ever recorded crawled only 15 feet in 43.5 seconds!

Source: *Guinness Book of World Records*

One way to add or subtract mixed numbers is to compute the whole number and fraction parts separately.

Example 1 Calculate $8\frac{1}{4}$ yd + $7\frac{1}{2}$ yd to find the distance the giant tortoise traveled.

$8 + 7 = 15$ **Add whole numbers.**

$\frac{1}{4} + \frac{1}{2} = \frac{3}{4}$ **Add fractions.**

$15 + \frac{3}{4} = 15\frac{3}{4}$ **Combine whole number and fraction parts.**

The giant tortoise traveled $15\frac{3}{4}$ yd.

3. Use the method in Example 1 to find the sum $10\frac{1}{8} + 6\frac{3}{16}$.

Divide to rename an improper fraction as a mixed number.

Sometimes the sum of the fraction part is improper. So rename it as a mixed number.

Example 2 After traveling $15\frac{3}{4}$ yd, the giant tortoise traveled another $3\frac{1}{2}$ yd. How far did the tortoise travel?

$15 + 3 = 18$ **Add whole numbers.**

$\frac{3}{4} + \frac{1}{2} = \frac{3}{4} + \frac{2}{4} = \frac{5}{4}$ **Add fractions.**

$18 + \frac{5}{4} = 18 + 1\frac{1}{4} = 19\frac{1}{4}$ **Rename the improper fraction as a mixed number and combine.**

The giant tortoise traveled $19\frac{1}{4}$ yd.

Sometimes you need to rename before you subtract.

4. An antelope ran $4\frac{1}{2}$ yd while a cheetah ran $6\frac{1}{4}$ yd. Write a subtraction expression to show how much farther the cheetah ran than the antelope. Can you subtract $\frac{1}{2}$ from $\frac{1}{4}$?

***The cheetah** is the fastest animal on land for distances up to 350 yd. The prong-horned antelope is faster than the cheetah after 350 yd.*

Example 3 Calculate $6\frac{1}{4}$ yd $-$ $4\frac{1}{2}$ yd to find how much farther the cheetah ran than the antelope.

Since you cannot subtract $\frac{1}{4} - \frac{1}{2}$, rename $6\frac{1}{4}$.

$6\frac{1}{4} = 5 + 1\frac{1}{4} = 5 + \frac{5}{4} = 5\frac{5}{4}$ **Rename the mixed number.**

$5 - 4 = 1$ **Subtract whole numbers.**

$\frac{5}{4} - \frac{1}{2} = \frac{5}{4} - \frac{2}{4} = \frac{3}{4}$ **Subtract fractions.**

$5\frac{5}{4} - 4\frac{1}{2} = 1\frac{3}{4}$ **Combine.**

The cheetah ran $1\frac{3}{4}$ yd farther than the antelope.

5. Look at the addition equation $4\frac{1}{2} + x = 6\frac{1}{4}$. Can you use this equation to solve the problem above? If so, how?

Example 4 Solve the equation $4\frac{1}{2} + x = 6\frac{1}{4}$.

Think: What must you add to $4\frac{1}{2}$ to get $6\frac{1}{4}$?

$4\frac{1}{2} + \frac{1}{2} + 1 + \frac{1}{4} = 6\frac{1}{4}$

So $x = \frac{1}{2} + 1 + \frac{1}{4} = 1\frac{3}{4}$.

6. Use the method in Example 4 to find the difference between $5\frac{3}{8}$ yd and $2\frac{3}{4}$ yd. Then subtract to compare.

You can use a fraction calculator with mixed numbers. First estimate the answer. Write the answer in simplest form.

FLASHBACK

To estimate, round each mixed number to the nearest whole number. Then add or subtract.

Example 5 Find the sum $8\frac{11}{16} + 5\frac{3}{8}$.

Estimate: $9 + 5 = 14$

Press: 8 Unit 11 / 16 + 5 Unit 3 / 8 =

Display: 13 U 17 / 16

$8\frac{11}{16} + 5\frac{3}{8} = 13\frac{17}{16} = 14\frac{1}{16}$

WORK TOGETHER

Work with a partner. Cut a piece of string each length: $1\frac{3}{8}$ in., $2\frac{1}{4}$ in., $1\frac{7}{8}$ in., $3\frac{1}{8}$ in., $5\frac{3}{4}$ in. Select two pieces of string.

- Make a line with the two pieces and measure its length.
- Write an addition equation for the two pieces and the length.
- Find the sum and compare it to the measured length.

Repeat several times by selecting two other pieces of string.

TRY THESE

Complete to rename each mixed number.

7. $3\frac{1}{10} = 2\frac{■}{10}$ **8.** $5\frac{5}{6} = 4\frac{■}{6}$ **9.** $1\frac{3}{4} = \frac{■}{4}$

Estimate each sum or difference.

10. $6\frac{1}{4} + 2\frac{3}{5}$ **11.** $2\frac{5}{16} + 1\frac{1}{4}$ **12.** $8\frac{1}{5} - 3\frac{3}{4}$

Find each sum or difference.

13. $1\frac{1}{4} + 6\frac{1}{2}$ **14.** $3\frac{1}{3} + 1\frac{5}{6}$ **15.** $9\frac{1}{2} - 4\frac{7}{8}$

16. Explain how you can mentally find $9\frac{1}{4} + 6\frac{3}{4}$.

17. Cooking A recipe lists $1\frac{3}{4}$ c milk, and another recipe lists $1\frac{1}{2}$ c milk. You measure the milk in your refrigerator. You have about 3 c. Do you have enough milk for both recipes?

Coyote

$2\frac{1}{2}$ in.

2 in.

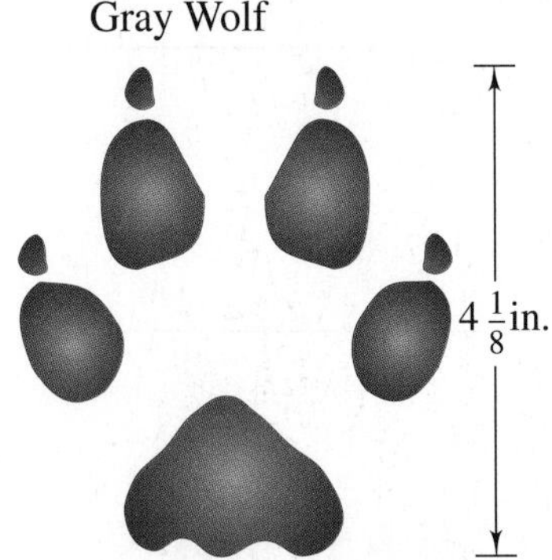

Red Fox

$2\frac{1}{4}$ in.

$2\frac{1}{8}$ in.

ON YOUR OWN

Biology **Use the scale drawings of animal tracks.**

18. How much wider is the gray wolf's track than the red fox's track?

19. Which is longer, the coyote's track or the red fox's track? How much longer?

20. Is the length or the width of the gray wolf's track larger? by how much?

Mental Math **Add or subtract mentally.**

21. $9\frac{2}{3} - 5\frac{2}{3}$ 22. $1 - \frac{1}{6}$ 23. $3 + 1\frac{2}{3}$ 24. $4\frac{1}{2} + 4\frac{1}{2}$

Biology **Use the data at the right.**

25. Rewrite the table showing the lengths of the cones from shortest to longest.

26. Find the difference in length between the shortest cone and the longest cone.

27. **Estimation** Which two cones differ in length by about $\frac{1}{2}$ in.?

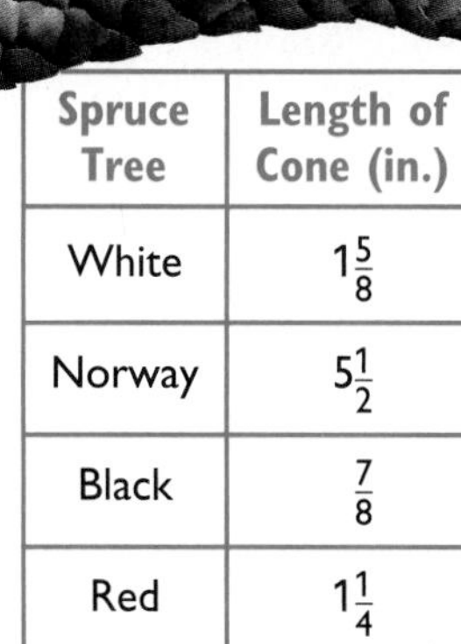

Spruce Tree	Length of Cone (in.)
White	$1\frac{5}{8}$
Norway	$5\frac{1}{2}$
Black	$\frac{7}{8}$
Red	$1\frac{1}{4}$

Choose **Use any method to add or subtract.**

28. $7\frac{1}{10} + 3\frac{2}{5}$ 29. $1\frac{7}{8} + 1\frac{1}{4}$ 30. $4\frac{5}{12} - 1\frac{1}{2}$ 31. $6\frac{4}{5} - 2\frac{1}{3}$

32. $8 - 1\frac{2}{3}$ 33. $4\frac{5}{8} - 1\frac{3}{8}$ 34. $3\frac{1}{6} - 2$ 35. $10\frac{1}{4} + 3\frac{1}{3}$

36. **Estimation** The sides of a triangle have lengths $5\frac{1}{2}$ in., $3\frac{7}{8}$ in., and $2\frac{1}{4}$ in. Is a 12-in. piece of string long enough to go around the triangle?

37. **Gardening** Paul plans to fence a rectangular flower garden that measures $4\frac{1}{2}$ ft by $3\frac{1}{4}$ ft. Fencing costs \$5/ft. How much will the fence for the flower garden cost?

38. **Writing** Explain how you can mentally find the sum $5\frac{1}{3} + 3\frac{4}{5} + 2\frac{2}{3} + 6\frac{1}{5}$.

39. **Data File 8 (pp. 316–317)** How much farther did Jackie Joyner-Kersee jump than Heike Drechsler?

40. **Choose A, B, C, or D.** Which two mixed numbers are equivalent to $3\frac{1}{5}$?

   A. $3\frac{1}{10}$ and $2\frac{6}{5}$ **B.** $3\frac{2}{10}$ and $2\frac{6}{5}$

   C. $3\frac{2}{10}$ and $3\frac{6}{5}$ **D.** $3\frac{3}{5}$ and $2\frac{5}{5}$

41. **Critical Thinking** Write the next two numbers in the pattern: $9\frac{1}{3}$, $8\frac{1}{6}$, 7, $5\frac{5}{6}$, $4\frac{2}{3}$, ■, ■.

42. **Investigation (p. 318)** Explain how you can use a nomograph to add any two mixed numbers. Make a nomograph to add $2\frac{5}{6}$ and $1\frac{1}{3}$.

Mixed REVIEW

Look for a pattern. Then write the next three numbers.

1. $\frac{1}{5}$, $\frac{3}{5}$, 1, ■, ■, ■

2. 1, $\frac{9}{10}$, $\frac{4}{5}$, ■, ■, ■

Classify each triangle as scalene, isosceles, or equilateral.

3. side lengths of 7, 7, 7

4. side lengths of 3, 5, 3

5. The rotary club has \$140 in savings. The dues from 8 new members raised the amount to \$198. Find the dues from each member.

PROBLEM SOLVING

What's Ahead

- Solving a problem by drawing a diagram

8-6 Draw a Diagram

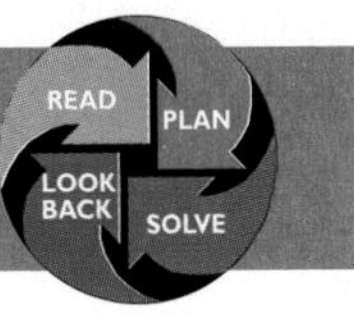

Drawing a diagram is a strategy you can use to solve many problems. A diagram helps you to see a problem and its solution more clearly.

Prehistoric Zuni design of a turkey

> An artist is creating a tiled wall for the Native American wing of a museum. The wall will display scenes of Native American life in the past and present. The border will be tiles containing Native American picture writing. Each border tile will have a different symbol. Each tile is a square that measures $\frac{1}{2}$ ft on a side. The tiled wall, including the border, will be 6 ft high by 10 ft wide. How many border tiles does the artist need to make?

READ

Read and understand the given information. Summarize the problem.

Identify the information you need to use to solve the problem.

1. What size and shape are the border tiles? Sketch one tile.
2. What size and shape is the tiled wall? Sketch the wall. Do the dimensions include the border?
3. Is the problem asking you to find the total number of tiles the artist needs to make for the tiled wall?

PLAN

Decide on a strategy to solve the problem.

If you draw a diagram of the tiled wall, you can then draw in the border. You may want to use grid paper, then count the number of border tiles needed.

4. Suppose you let one unit on the grid paper represent 1 ft. How many tiles will fit across the top of the wall?
5. Instead you let one square on the grid paper represent one tile. How many tiles will fit across the top of the wall?
6. Experiment with the two methods described in Exercises 4 and 5. Which do you prefer? Why?

Draw a diagram to "see" the problem and its solution.

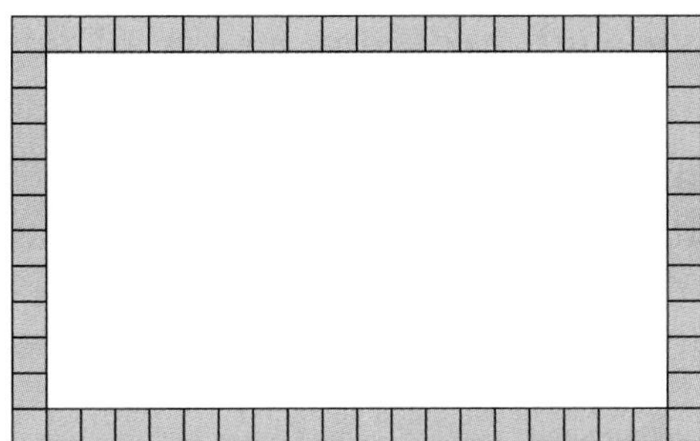

1 square = 1 tile

SOLVE

Try out the strategy.

7. Use the diagram to find the number of border tiles the artist needs to make. Explain why your answer is correct.

8. **Discussion** As soon as the diagram was drawn, was this problem easy to solve?

9. **Discussion** Do you think this problem would be difficult to solve without drawing a diagram?

10. **Discussion** Instead of drawing a diagram, one student did the following. Find the number of border tiles needed for each side of the wall: top, 20; bottom, 20; left side, 12; right side, 12. Then add: 20 + 20 + 12 + 12 = 64 border tiles. What is wrong with this solution?

LOOK BACK

Think about how you solved this problem.

TRY THESE

Draw a diagram to solve each problem.

11. **Carpentry** Barbara is making a bookcase with wood that is $\frac{3}{4}$ in. thick. The bookcase has four shelves. One shelf is used for the top of the bookcase, and one is used for the bottom. The space between shelves is 12 in. Find the total height of the bookcase.

12. **Gardening** Hahnee is planting flowers along the edge of a circular flower bed. He will place the plants 6 in. apart. The diameter of the circle measures about 7 ft. How many plants will Hahnee need?

13. **Pets** Joseph has 24 ft of fence for a rectangular dog kennel. Each side will be a whole number of feet (no fractions). List all possible dimensions for the kennel. Which will give Joseph's dog the greatest area?

"*A picture shows me at a glance what it takes dozens of pages of a book to expound.*
—Ivan Sergeyevich Turgenev (1818–1883)"

ON YOUR OWN

Use any strategy to solve each problem. Show all your work.

14. Elisheba has a rug that is 12 ft by 18 ft in her living room. She wants to cut it into two smaller rectangular rugs that can be placed in other rooms. Show how she can make one cut and end up with two rugs the same size and shape.

15. To celebrate its opening day, a store is offering a free gift to every 15th customer. The store manager expects about 100 customers each hour. About how many gifts will the store offer by the end of its 12-h opening day?

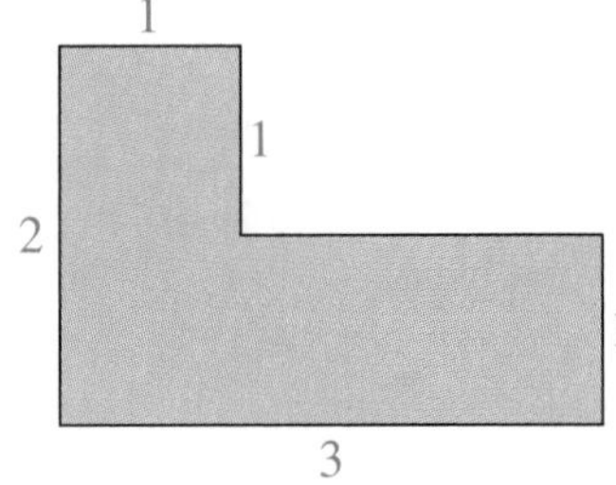

16. **Writing** Write a problem that can be solved using the diagram at the left. Solve your problem.

17. An artist created four rectangular wooden panels for a gallery floor. Each panel measures $5\frac{1}{2}$ ft by 4 ft. The panels will be placed end-to-end along the 4-ft side. There will be 3 ft of space between the center two panels. Will the panels fit on the gallery floor, which is 25 ft long?

18. Suppose your class is setting up the Recycling Relay Race for your school's celebration of Earth Day. You are using a rectangular area that is 15 ft by 40 ft. You will hammer a pole into the ground every 5 ft along the perimeter of the rectangular area. How many poles will you need?

19. Six flags are evenly spaced around a circular track. LaWanda times herself as she runs around the track. It takes her 10 s to run from the first flag to the third flag. At this pace, how long will it take LaWanda to run around the entire track?

20. There are four containers on a shelf. The shapes of the containers are circular, square, oval, and rectangular. The colors are blue, white, green, and red. The blue container is neither square nor rectangular. The containers with a curved surface are blue or green. The green container is neither square nor round. The square container is not red. What color is each container?

21. A rectangle has an area of 3,000 sq. ft. One side is 40 ft. Find the perimeter of the rectangle.

Mixed REVIEW

Find each sum or difference.

1. $2\frac{3}{7} + 4\frac{3}{14}$
2. $6\frac{2}{3} - 4\frac{1}{6}$

Use the data. Math Test Grades: A, C, B, B, C, F, A, A, C, D.

3. Make a line plot.
4. How many students received a grade of C or better?
5. Eight people are attending a meeting. Each person shakes hands with each of the others exactly once. What is the total number of handshakes exchanged?

Practice

Estimate each sum or difference.

1. $\frac{5}{7} + \frac{6}{11}$ **2.** $4\frac{1}{4} - 2\frac{6}{7}$ **3.** $\frac{7}{16} + \frac{5}{32}$ **4.** $\frac{7}{10} - \frac{2}{5}$

Round each measurement to the nearest half inch.

5. $7\frac{3}{4}$ in. **6.** $1\frac{6}{7}$ in. **7.** $3\frac{1}{3}$ in. **8.** $99\frac{2}{5}$ in. **9.** $10\frac{2}{15}$ in.

Draw a model and find each sum or difference.

10. $\frac{1}{7} + \frac{1}{7}$ **11.** $\frac{7}{8} - \frac{3}{8}$ **12.** $\frac{1}{10} + \frac{3}{10}$ **13.** $\frac{3}{4} - \frac{1}{4}$

Use any method to add or subtract.

14. $\frac{1}{4} + \frac{1}{3}$ **15.** $\frac{1}{5} - \frac{1}{10}$ **16.** $\frac{7}{8} - \frac{3}{4}$ **17.** $\frac{1}{6} + \frac{1}{7} + \frac{1}{8}$

18. $\frac{5}{6} - \frac{5}{8}$ **19.** $\frac{7}{12} - \frac{3}{10}$ **20.** $\frac{3}{4} + \frac{1}{3}$ **21.** $\frac{3}{10} + \frac{4}{5}$

22. Analyze the "Expression" column. Fill in the sums, then write the next expression in the pattern.

Expression	Sum
$\frac{1}{1}$	$\frac{1}{1}$
$\frac{1}{1} + \frac{1}{4}$	■
$\frac{1}{1} + \frac{1}{4} + \frac{1}{9}$	■

Find each sum or difference.

23. $5\frac{2}{3} + 2\frac{1}{2}$ **24.** $4\frac{1}{2} - 3\frac{3}{4}$ **25.** $1\frac{2}{3} + 1\frac{1}{4}$ **26.** $7\frac{3}{5} - 3\frac{2}{3}$

27. $2\frac{3}{4} + 6\frac{5}{16}$ **28.** $9\frac{4}{7} - 5\frac{1}{14}$ **29.** $8\frac{3}{8} + 6\frac{3}{4}$ **30.** $10\frac{1}{10} - 3\frac{3}{20}$

31. Stanley rides his bicycle half way to school and then gets a flat tire. He walks his bike the next quarter mile. At that point, Mrs. Chan picks Stanley up and drives him the remaining $\frac{1}{2}$ mile to school. Find the distance between Stanley's house and the school.

32. Consuela throws her hat up a 20-ft tree. The hat lands $\frac{3}{4}$ of the way up. She climbs the tree half way and reaches 4 ft for her hat. Can she get her hat back this way? Why or why not?

What's Ahead

• Multiplying fractions and mixed numbers

8-7 Multiplying Fractions & Mixed Numbers

WORK TOGETHER

WHAT YOU'LL NEED

✓ Fraction bars 

✓ Calculator 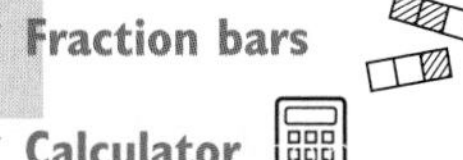

Work with a partner. Use a fraction calculator. Experiment to see what happens when you multiply by a fraction less than 1. Start with a fraction such as $\frac{1}{2}$. Multiply several different numbers by $\frac{1}{2}$. Use whole numbers, mixed numbers, decimals, and fractions. Make a table like the one at the left.

Number	Fraction	Product
10	$\frac{1}{2}$	5
5	$\frac{1}{2}$	■
3.8	$\frac{1}{2}$	■
$9\frac{1}{4}$	$\frac{1}{2}$	■
■	$\frac{1}{4}$	■

1. When you multiply a number by a fraction less than 1, is the product greater than or less than the number? Why?

THINK AND DISCUSS

Suppose your community is given a square tract of land for a park. The planning board wants to use $\frac{1}{2}$ of the land for ball fields and $\frac{1}{2}$ of the land for a picnic/play area. One third of the picnic/play area will have playground equipment. What portion of the park will have playground equipment? You can use models or multiplication to solve this problem.

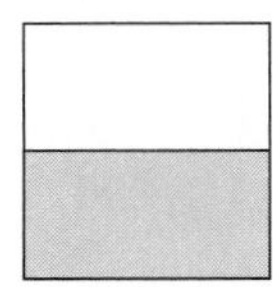

2. Use the square at the left to represent the park. The shaded area represents the picnic/play area. What portion of the park is the picnic/play area? Write a fraction.

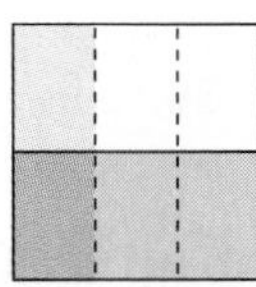

3. Now divide the square into thirds, as shown at the left. Which area on the square represents the area of the park that will have playground equipment? What portion of the square (park) is this? Write a fraction.

4. The portion of the park that has playground equipment is $\frac{1}{3}$ of $\frac{1}{2}$ of the park. How does the model show this?

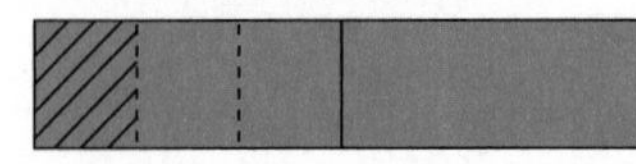

5. Does the fraction bar at the left represent $\frac{1}{3}$ of $\frac{1}{2}$? Explain.

You can multiply to find $\frac{1}{3}$ of $\frac{1}{2}$. The word "of" means multiply.

$$\frac{1}{3} \text{ of } \frac{1}{2} = \frac{1}{3} \times \frac{1}{2} = \frac{1 \times 1}{3 \times 2} = \frac{1}{6}$$

6. Use models and multiplication to find $\frac{2}{3}$ of $\frac{3}{4}$, or $\frac{2}{3} \times \frac{3}{4}$.

To solve some problems, you will multiply a fraction and a whole number.

Example 1 Suppose 12 schools in your county enter a science-math competition. Two-thirds of the schools will advance to the second round of competition. How many schools will advance to the second round?

Find $\frac{2}{3}$ of 12. So multiply $\frac{2}{3} \times 12$. *"Of" means multiply.*

$\frac{2}{3} \times 12 = \frac{2}{3} \times \frac{12}{1} = \frac{2 \times 12}{3 \times 1} = \frac{24}{3} = 8$ *Write 12 as $\frac{12}{1}$.*

So 8 schools will advance to the second round.

7. Does the model at the right represent $\frac{2}{3}$ of 12? Explain.

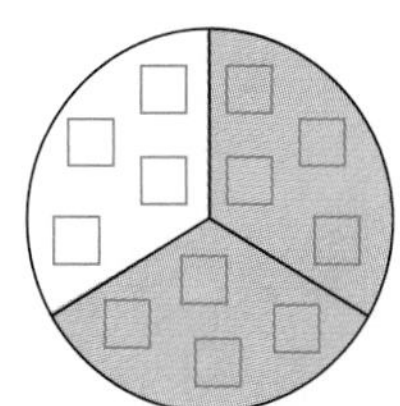

Sometimes you can simplify before multiplying. Divide the numerator and the denominator by a common factor.

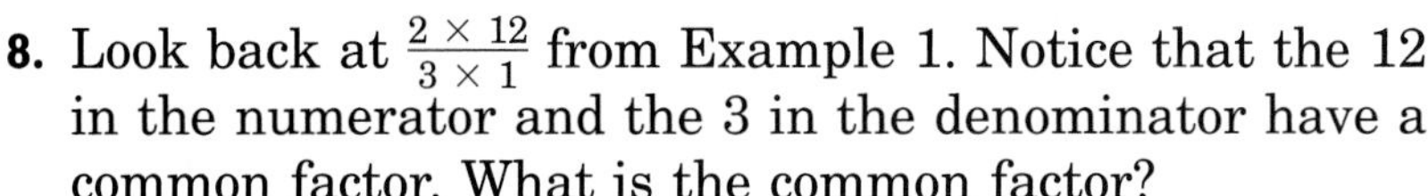

8. Look back at $\frac{2 \times 12}{3 \times 1}$ from Example 1. Notice that the 12 in the numerator and the 3 in the denominator have a common factor. What is the common factor?

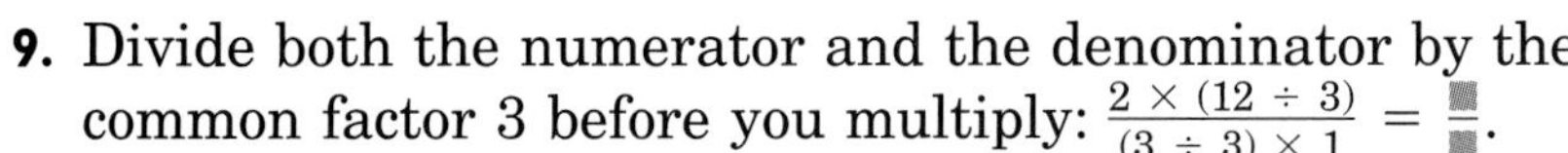

9. Divide both the numerator and the denominator by the common factor 3 before you multiply: $\frac{2 \times (12 \div 3)}{(3 \div 3) \times 1} = \frac{■}{■}$.

10. Use this method to find $\frac{4}{5} \times \frac{1}{2}$. What is the common factor? Check your answer.

FLASHBACK

To write a mixed number as an improper fraction, multiply the whole number by the denominator and add the numerator. Then write the result over the denominator.

When you multiply with mixed numbers, first write each mixed number as an improper fraction.

Example 2 What is the area of the rectangle?

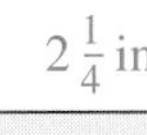

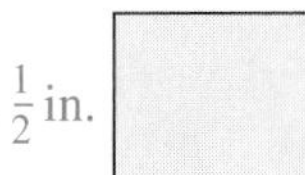

Estimate: $2 \times 2 = 4$

Write $2\frac{1}{4}$ as $\frac{9}{4}$ and $1\frac{1}{2}$ as $\frac{3}{2}$.

$2\frac{1}{4} \times 1\frac{1}{2} = \frac{9}{4} \times \frac{3}{2} = \frac{9 \times 3}{4 \times 2} = \frac{27}{8} = 3\frac{3}{8}$

The area of the rectangle is $3\frac{3}{8}$ sq. in.

FLASHBACK

To estimate with fractions, round to the nearest $\frac{1}{2}$. To estimate with mixed numbers, round to the nearest whole number.

11. List the steps for finding $6\frac{2}{3} \times 1\frac{1}{5}$. Then multiply.

TRY THESE

Draw a model to represent each product.

12. $\frac{1}{4}$ of $\frac{1}{3}$ **13.** $\frac{1}{2}$ of $\frac{3}{4}$ **14.** $\frac{3}{4}$ of 16 **15.** $\frac{1}{5}$ of $\frac{5}{8}$

Estimate. Then find the product.

16. $3\frac{1}{2} \times 1\frac{1}{4}$ **17.** $\frac{2}{3} \times \frac{1}{3}$ **18.** $\frac{3}{4} \times 9$ **19.** $15 \times \frac{1}{5}$

Explain how to simplify. Then find the product.

20. $\frac{3}{16} \times \frac{4}{5}$ **21.** $3\frac{1}{5} \times \frac{3}{4}$ **22.** $5\frac{1}{3} \times 2\frac{1}{2}$ **23.** $12 \times \frac{5}{6}$

ON YOUR OWN

24. Choose A, B, C, or D. Which product does the model represent?

A. $\frac{3}{4} \times \frac{2}{3}$ **B.** $\frac{1}{3} \times \frac{1}{3}$

C. $\frac{3}{4} \times \frac{1}{3}$ **D.** $\frac{1}{3} \times \frac{2}{3}$

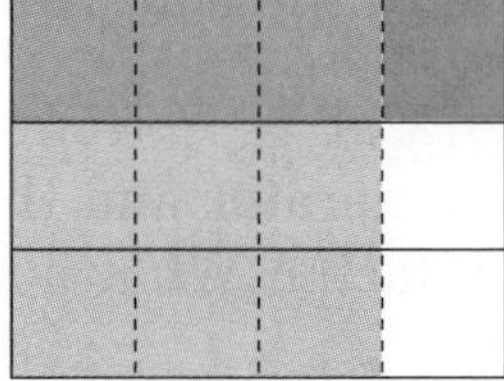

Estimate each product.

25. $2\frac{3}{4} \times 6\frac{1}{8}$ **26.** $5\frac{1}{2} \times 1\frac{3}{10}$ **27.** $9\frac{4}{5} \times 5\frac{7}{12}$ **28.** $\frac{4}{7} \times 1\frac{1}{3}$

A piece of lumber called a "2 by 4" does not measure 2 in. by 4 in. A "2 by 4" is actually $1\frac{1}{2}$ in. thick and $3\frac{1}{2}$ in. wide.

Lumber Name	Thickness (in.)	Width (in.)
1 by 4	$\frac{3}{4}$	$3\frac{1}{2}$
2 by 2	$1\frac{1}{2}$	$1\frac{1}{2}$
2 by 4	$1\frac{1}{2}$	$3\frac{1}{2}$
2 by 6	$1\frac{1}{2}$	$5\frac{1}{2}$

Use the information at the left.

29. Carpentry Zahara is building the floor of a deck. She will place 32 "2 by 4" boards side by side with $\frac{1}{4}$ in. space between each board. How wide is the floor of the deck?

30. Carpentry Simon loaded his truck with boards. He placed all the boards in a single stack. The stack had three "2 by 6" boards and six "2 by 2" boards. How high is the stack?

31. Writing When you multiply two fractions that are each less than 1, will the product *always, sometimes,* or *never* be less than either of the fractions? Explain your answer.

32. Sewing A quilt pattern shows a square with $4\frac{1}{2}$ in. sides. Patty wants to reduce each side to $\frac{2}{3}$ the length shown on the pattern. Find the dimensions of the reduced square. Solve two different ways, using models and multiplication.

Find each product.

33. $\frac{5}{8} \times 16$ 34. $\frac{2}{3} \times \frac{9}{10}$ 35. $6 \times \frac{2}{3}$ 36. $8\frac{1}{2} \times 8\frac{1}{2}$

37. $4\frac{1}{9} \times 3\frac{3}{8}$ 38. $\frac{1}{5} \times 100$ 39. $\frac{2}{5} \times \frac{1}{6}$ 40. $2\frac{1}{3} \times 10$

Read the news article below. Use for Exercises 41–44.

Almost Half Barely Literate

Ninety million U.S. adults do not have adequate literacy skills, according to the recent National Adult Literacy Survey. From the U.S. adult population of about 191 million, a random sample of about 16,000 people 16 and older were surveyed. The study, funded by the Department of Education, placed adults in five levels of proficiency. About $\frac{1}{4}$ of the 90 million adults at low literacy levels are immigrants learning English as a second language. Of the estimated 40 million adults at the lowest of the five levels, about 37% are illiterate, not able to complete the survey.

But this is a solvable problem, according to advocates of literacy programs. In 1980, 2 million adults were enrolled in a literacy program. Today, there are 3.8 million enrolled, an increase of nearly 90%. At least $\frac{1}{3}$ of the current population of enrolled adults are learning English as a second language.

How can you help? If you would like to find out about literacy programs in your area, or if you would like to volunteer, call the Contact Literacy Center hotline at 1 (800) 228-8813 or TT1 (800) 552-9097 for the hearing impaired.

41. What numbers in the news article support the claim in the title that *almost half* are barely literate?

42. How many of the 90 million adults at low literacy levels are immigrants learning English as a second language? What portion of the entire U.S. adult population is this?

43. How many immigrants learning English as a second language are enrolled in a literacy program today? What portion of the immigrants at low literacy levels is this?

44. What portion of the U.S. adult population is illiterate? How many people is this?

Mixed REVIEW

Simplify.

1. $8 + 3 \times 6$
2. $12 \div 4 + 8 \times 2 - 1$
3. How many tournament games will the champion have to play if there are 32 teams competing in a single-elimination tournament?
4. The lengths of three rods are 4 mm, 6 mm, and 9 mm. How can you arrange these rods to measure a length of 11 mm?
5. A clock chimes every hour. How many times will it chime in the month of July?

What's Ahead

- Dividing fractions and mixed numbers

8-8 Dividing Fractions & Mixed Numbers

WORK TOGETHER

WHAT YOU'LL NEED

✓ Fraction bars

✓ Calculator

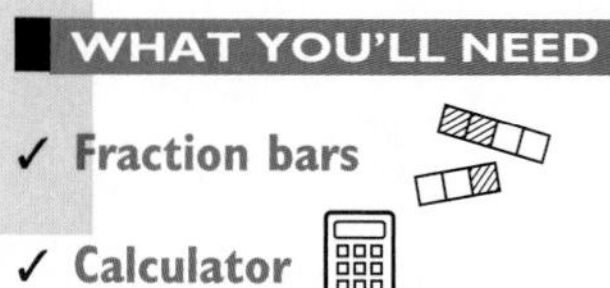

Number	Fraction	Quotient
10	$\frac{1}{2}$	■
5	$\frac{1}{2}$	■
3.8	$\frac{1}{2}$	■
$9\frac{1}{4}$	$\frac{1}{2}$	■
■	$\frac{1}{4}$	■

Work with a partner. Use a fraction calculator. Experiment to see what happens when you divide by a fraction less than 1. Start with a fraction such as $\frac{1}{2}$. Divide several different numbers by $\frac{1}{2}$. Use whole numbers, mixed numbers, decimals, and fractions. Make a table like the one at the left.

1. When you divide a number by a fraction less than 1, is the quotient greater than or less than the number? Why?

THINK AND DISCUSS

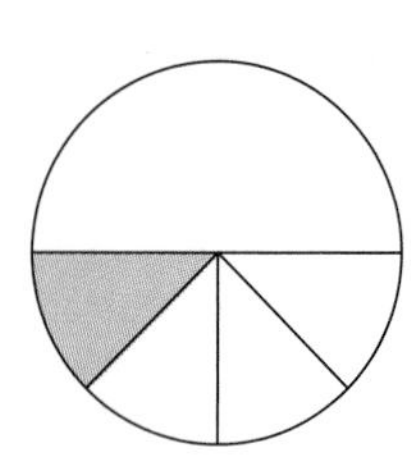

Suppose your family and some friends order a jumbo-sized pizza. You and three friends equally share $\frac{1}{2}$ of the pizza. What portion of the pizza does each friend get to eat? You can use models, multiplication, or division to solve this problem.

2. Use the circle at the left to represent the pizza. Since four of you will share $\frac{1}{2}$ the pizza, divide $\frac{1}{2}$ the pizza into four equal pieces. What portion of the pizza does each friend get to eat? Look at the model!
3. To use multiplication to solve this problem, think about how much each friend gets. Each friend gets $\frac{1}{4}$ of $\frac{1}{2}$ of the pizza. So multiply to find $\frac{1}{4} \times \frac{1}{2}$.
4. To use division to solve this problem, think about $\frac{1}{2}$ of the pizza shared by four friends. What portion will each friend get if $\frac{1}{2}$ of the pizza is divided by 4 people? So divide to find $\frac{1}{2} \div 4$.
5. **Discussion** Compare the three different ways to solve this problem. Which do you prefer? Do your answers agree?
6. Compare the multiplication and division expressions used to solve this problem. They result in the same answer, so they must be equal. Do you agree that $\frac{1}{2} \div 4 = \frac{1}{2} \times \frac{1}{4}$?

The numbers 4 and $\frac{1}{4}$ are *reciprocals* because their product is 1. Dividing by a number is the same as multiplying by the reciprocal of that number. You saw this in Exercise 6.

7. Find each product. What do you notice?

a. $\frac{1}{2} \times \frac{2}{1}$ **b.** $\frac{2}{3} \times \frac{3}{2}$ **c.** $\frac{1}{7} \times \frac{7}{1}$ **d.** $8 \times \frac{1}{8}$ **e.** $\frac{9}{2} \times \frac{2}{9}$

8. Write the reciprocal of each number.

a. $\frac{2}{3}$ **b.** $\frac{1}{9}$ **c.** 5 **d.** 1 **e.** $\frac{7}{4}$

Rhythmic gymnastics *is an Olympic event. Gymnasts dance while holding a piece of equipment such as a ribbon, hoop, rope, club, or ball.*

You will use reciprocals to divide with fractions.

Example 1 Nancy has 3 yd of ribbon. It takes $\frac{3}{8}$ yd to make one bow. How many bows can Nancy make if she uses all the ribbon?

$3 \div \frac{3}{8}$ — Divide 3 by $\frac{3}{8}$.

$= 3 \times \frac{8}{3}$ — Multiply 3 by the reciprocal of $\frac{3}{8}$.

$= \frac{3 \times 8}{1 \times 3} = 8$

Nancy can make 8 bows with 3 yd of ribbon.

LOOK BACK How can you check that the answer makes sense?

9. Draw a model for the problem and solution in Example 1.

10. Discussion To divide by a number, you can multiply by its ■ instead. Why does this work?

When you divide with mixed numbers, first write each mixed number as an improper fraction.

Example 2 Leroy made 30 c of soup. How many $1\frac{1}{4}$-c servings of soup does he have?

Divide: $30 \div 1\frac{1}{4}$

$30 \div \frac{5}{4} = 30 \times \frac{4}{5}$ — Write $1\frac{1}{4}$ as $\frac{5}{4}$.

$= \frac{30 \times 4}{1 \times 5}$

$= \frac{(30 \div 5) \times 4}{1 \times (5 \div 5)}$ — Simplify before you multiply.

$= 6 \times 4 = 24$

Leroy has 24 $1\frac{1}{4}$-c servings of soup.

TRY THESE

Write the reciprocal of each number.

11. $\frac{4}{5}$ 12. 3 13. $\frac{2}{10}$ 14. $\frac{1}{5}$ 15. $3\frac{1}{2}$ 16. $2\frac{5}{6}$

17. Draw a diagram to show how many $\frac{1}{3}$-ft pieces of string you can cut from a piece that is $3\frac{1}{3}$ ft long.

18. You have a 15-lb bag of bird seed. If the birds you feed eat $1\frac{1}{2}$ lb of seed each day, how many days will your seed last?

Divide. Write each answer in simplest form.

19. $\frac{3}{8} \div 5$ 20. $\frac{7}{8} \div \frac{3}{4}$ 21. $4 \div \frac{3}{4}$ 22. $\frac{1}{5} \div \frac{1}{3}$

23. $4\frac{1}{6} \div 10$ 24. $\frac{2}{3} \div 1\frac{1}{2}$ 25. $2\frac{5}{8} \div \frac{3}{4}$ 26. $3\frac{1}{5} \div 1\frac{1}{3}$

Mt. Kilimanjaro, Kenya

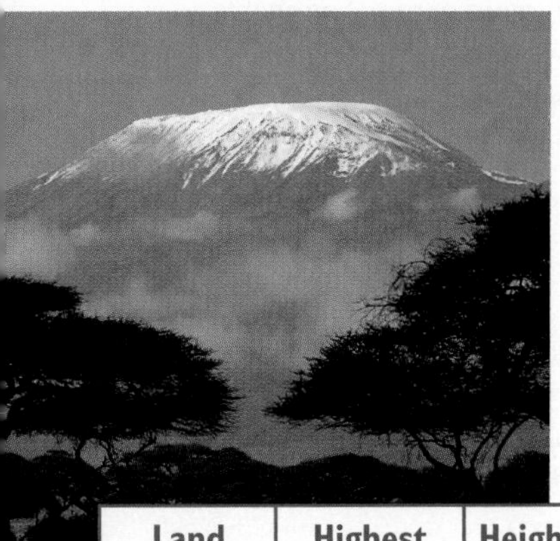

Land Mass	Highest Peak	Height (mi)
Africa	Kilimanjaro	$3\frac{7}{10}$
Asia	Everest	$5\frac{1}{2}$
Australia	Kosciusko	$1\frac{4}{10}$
Antarctica	Vinson Massif	$3\frac{1}{5}$
Europe	El'brus	$3\frac{1}{2}$
South America	Aconcaqua	$4\frac{3}{10}$
North America	McKinley	$3\frac{8}{10}$

ON YOUR OWN

27. Samuel is cutting canvas into pieces. The canvas is $\frac{3}{4}$ yd long. How many $\frac{1}{8}$-yd pieces can he cut?

28. How many $\frac{1}{4}$ in. are in $\frac{1}{2}$ ft? Draw a model that shows the problem and your solution.

The chart at the left shows the highest peaks on each of the seven major land masses on Earth.

29. How much higher is Mt. Everest than Mt. McKinley?

30. Mt. Kilimanjaro is $\frac{2}{3}$ the height of which mountain peak?

31. Which mountain peak is $\frac{3}{10}$ mi higher than Mt. El'brus?

32. Which peak is about 3 times as high as Mt. Kosciusko?

Divide. Write each answer in simplest form.

33. $\frac{2}{3} \div \frac{1}{3}$ 34. $\frac{1}{8} \div \frac{1}{4}$ 35. $\frac{3}{4} \div \frac{2}{3}$ 36. $\frac{9}{10} \div \frac{3}{5}$

37. $\frac{5}{6} \div \frac{5}{9}$ 38. $2 \div \frac{1}{2}$ 39. $\frac{4}{5} \div 6$ 40. $\frac{2}{10} \div \frac{1}{7}$

Mental Math **Find each quotient mentally.**

41. $6 \div \frac{1}{2}$ 42. $5 \div \frac{1}{3}$ 43. $3 \div \frac{1}{8}$ 44. $7 \div \frac{1}{5}$

45. **Writing** Write a problem that can be solved by dividing 10 by $\frac{1}{3}$. Solve your problem at least two different ways.

46. **Choose A, B, C, or D.** Which quotient is greater than 1?

A. $\frac{3}{5} \div \frac{3}{5}$ **B.** $\frac{1}{4} \div \frac{3}{4}$ **C.** $\frac{1}{3} \div 4$ **D.** $2 \div \frac{1}{4}$

47. How many $\frac{1}{2}$-c servings are in an 8-c pitcher of juice?

48. Alejandro decides to use a $\frac{1}{4}$-gal jar to fill a 5-gal jug. How many times must Alejandro pour liquid from the jar into the jug to fill it?

49. Luella cut 3 apples into eighths. How many pieces of apple does she have?

50. How many $\frac{1}{2}$-in. thick cookies can you slice from a roll of cookie dough 1 ft long?

Divide. Write each answer in simplest form.

51. $5\frac{5}{6} \div \frac{7}{8}$ 52. $9 \div 2\frac{1}{7}$ 53. $9\frac{1}{2} \div 3\frac{1}{2}$ 54. $2\frac{1}{3} \div 7$

55. $1\frac{3}{4} \div 4\frac{3}{8}$ 56. $2\frac{2}{5} \div \frac{1}{5}$ 57. $6 \div 3\frac{1}{2}$ 58. $6\frac{1}{3} \div 1\frac{1}{6}$

CHECKPOINT

1. Naomi cut a board in half. Then she cut each piece in half again. Then Naomi cut each of these pieces in half again. How many pieces are there?

2. What is the reciprocal of $\frac{7}{8}$? of 4? of $\frac{1}{3}$? of $2\frac{1}{6}$?

Find the product or quotient. Write each answer in simplest form.

3. $2\frac{4}{5} \times 3\frac{1}{8}$ 4. $\frac{5}{12} \times 1\frac{7}{9}$ 5. $3 \times \frac{3}{4}$ 6. $\frac{2}{9} \times 27$

7. $\frac{2}{3} \div 6$ 8. $\frac{7}{36} \div \frac{1}{8}$ 9. $6\frac{1}{4} \div \frac{3}{8}$ 10. $5\frac{4}{7} \div 3\frac{3}{14}$

11. **Choose A, B, C, or D.** Which quotient is less than 1?

A. $\frac{2}{5} \div \frac{1}{6}$ **B.** $1\frac{1}{3} \div \frac{2}{3}$ **C.** $2\frac{1}{9} \div 3\frac{4}{5}$ **D.** $\frac{2}{3} \div \frac{2}{3}$

Mixed REVIEW

Write a decimal for the given words.

1. five hundredths
2. forty-seven thousandths

Find each product. Write the answer in simplest form.

3. $4\frac{4}{5} \times 2\frac{1}{3}$
4. $6\frac{2}{3} \times 4\frac{1}{5}$
5. In a class of 40 students, 29 wore jeans, 18 wore sneakers, and 10 wore both jeans and sneakers. How many wore neither jeans nor sneakers?

MATH AND MEASUREMENT

8-9 The Customary System

What's Ahead

- Solving problems that involve changing units of length, weight, and capacity in the customary system

Customary Units of Length
12 inches (in.) = 1 foot (ft)
36 inches = 1 yard (yd)
3 feet = 1 yard
5,280 feet = 1 mile (mi)

Customary Units of Weight
16 ounces (oz) = 1 pound (lb)
2,000 pounds = 1 ton (T)

Customary Units of Capacity
8 fluid ounces (fl oz) = 1 cup
2 cups (c) = 1 pint (pt)
2 pints = 1 quart (qt)
4 quarts = 1 gallon (gal)

THINK AND DISCUSS

Fractions and mixed numbers are commonly used with the customary system of measurement. For example, you may need $1\frac{1}{4}$ c of flour for a recipe. Or you may buy $\frac{1}{2}$ gal of milk for your family.

1. **Discussion** Look at the list of customary units at the left. For each unit, think of something you would measure with that unit. Give examples from your daily life.

You can multiply or divide to change units of measurement.

2. **a.** How many inches are in 2 ft?
   b. How many tons are 10,000 lb?
   c. Eighteen pints is the same amount as how many quarts?
   d. How many yards are in 90 ft?
3. **Discussion** Look back at your answers for Exercise 2. How did you know whether to multiply or divide?

To solve many problems, you change units of measurements.

Example 1 Pat needs $8\frac{1}{2}$ ft of fabric for a sewing project. Fabric is sold in $\frac{1}{8}$-yd lengths. How many yards of fabric should Pat buy?

Think: $8\frac{1}{2}$ ft is how many yards?

Divide: $8\frac{1}{2} \div 3$

$$= \frac{17}{2} \times \frac{1}{3}$$

$$= \frac{17}{6} = 2\frac{5}{6}$$

Round $2\frac{5}{6}$ yd up to the next $\frac{1}{8}$-yd: $2\frac{7}{8}$.

Pat should buy $2\frac{7}{8}$ yd of fabric.

For some problems you need to change units of measurement in order to decide if you have enough of something.

As part of the Friendship Festival, 75,000 people attended the world's largest birthday party to celebrate the 215th birthday of the United States. **How much fruit punch would you need to serve the 75,000 guests?**

Example 2 Suppose you are planning a party. You invite 24 guests. You want to serve at least 2 c of fruit punch to each guest. You fill your punch bowl, which holds $3\frac{1}{2}$ gal. Do you have enough punch?

Think: How much punch do you need?
24 guests $\times$ 2 c per guest $=$ 48 c

Think: How many cups are in $3\frac{1}{2}$ gal?

Change gallons to quarts. $3\frac{1}{2}$ gal $=$ ■ qt **1 gal = 4 qt**

$3\frac{1}{2} \times 4 = \frac{7}{2} \times 4 = 14$ qt

Change quarts to pints. 14 qt $=$ ■ pt **1 qt = 2 pt**
$14 \times 2 = 28$ pt

Change pints to cups. 28 pt $=$ ■ c **1 pt = 2 c**
$28 \times 2 = 56$ c

There are 56 c in $3\frac{1}{2}$ gal. You need only 48 c, so you have enough punch.

4. **Discussion** Solve the problem in Example 2 another way. Think: How many gallons are in 48 c?

TRY THESE

Complete.

5. 30 oz $=$ ■ lb
6. $5\frac{1}{2}$ ft $=$ ■ in.
7. 27 qt $=$ ■ gal
8. What operation do you use to change:
   a. inches to feet? **b.** yards to feet? **c.** gallons to cups?

Compare using $<$, $>$, or $=$.

9. 85 in. ■ 8 ft
10. $3\frac{1}{2}$ lb ■ 56 oz
11. $2\frac{1}{2}$ gal ■ 25 pt
12. A regular hexagon has sides that are 9 in. long. Find the perimeter of the hexagon in feet.
13. In some parts of Alaska, moose actually cause traffic jams. A moose weighs about 1,000 lb. How many tons is a moose?

ON YOUR OWN

Complete.

14. $6\frac{1}{4}$ ft = ■ yd **15.** $1\frac{3}{4}$ mi = ■ ft **16.** $2\frac{1}{2}$ qt = ■ pt

17. 24 oz = ■ lb **18.** $3\frac{1}{2}$ T = ■ lb **19.** $4\frac{1}{4}$ c = ■ fl oz

20. **Cooking** Light Cranberry "Mousse" requires 32 oz nonfat plain yogurt. Mary will use a measuring cup for this amount. How many cups of yogurt should she measure?

Avocado Cream

a sauce for quesadillas, salads, and tortilla chips

1 ripe avocado
juice of 1 lime
$\frac{1}{2}$ cup nonfat plain yogurt

21. **Cooking** Use the recipe at the left. Odetta bought a 6-oz container of nonfat plain yogurt. Did Odetta buy enough yogurt for Avocado Cream?

22. **Nutrition** The American Heart Association recommends that an adult eat no more than 6 oz of cooked poultry, fish, or lean red meat each day. Scott is serving six adults a $2\frac{1}{2}$ lb roast beef for dinner. Each adult will eat about the same amount. Should they eat the whole roast? Explain.

Write >, <, or =.

23. $6\frac{1}{2}$ pt ■ 2 qt **24.** 24 fl oz ■ 3 c **25.** 6,750 lb ■ $3\frac{3}{4}$ T

GREAT EXPECTATIONS

Veterinarian

I want to be a veterinarian because I love animals. At my house I have a fish, dog, cat, bird, and a mouse. Almost every day I walk down my lane that has 6 dogs, 5 cats, 3 donkeys, 1 mule, 1 horse, 16 geese, 4 goats and 1 pig.

A personal experience I had that made me want to become a vet was when my dog died. The veterinarian could not do anything to save him. It made me want to be a vet, so maybe that won't happen to someone else's pet. I also want to help rescue animals, like after an oil spill. I want to help save endangered species, too.

Lisa Mollmann

26. Writing Describe a situation from daily life in which you need to change from one unit of measure to another.

27. The Washington Monument in Washington, D.C., is 555 ft $5\frac{1}{8}$ in. tall. How many inches tall is the monument?

28. The Mont Blanc Tunnel goes through a mountain and connects Italy and France. Its length is 7.2 miles. What is the length of the tunnel in feet?

29. La Grande Complexe is a hydroelectric power facility in Canada. One of its dams, LG2, has a spillway that allows 750,000 gal of water to pass through per second.

a. How many gallons pass through LG2 in 1 min?

b. A gallon of water weighs about 8 lb. About how many tons of water pass through the dam's spillway in 1 s?

Add or subtract. Rename when necessary.

Sample

$$\begin{array}{r} 8 \text{ lb } 3 \text{ oz} \\ -\ 4 \text{ lb } 7 \text{ oz} \\ \hline \end{array} \qquad \begin{array}{r} 7 \text{ lb } 19 \text{ oz} \\ -\ 4 \text{ lb } \ 7 \text{ oz} \\ \hline 3 \text{ lb } 12 \text{ oz} \end{array}$$

Rename 1 lb as 16 oz.
16 oz + 3 oz = 19 oz

30. $\begin{array}{r} 4 \text{ ft } 10 \text{ in.} \\ +1 \text{ ft } \ 9 \text{ in.} \\ \hline \end{array}$

31. $\begin{array}{r} 5 \text{ yd } 1 \text{ ft} \\ -\ 1 \text{ yd } 2 \text{ ft} \\ \hline \end{array}$

32. $\begin{array}{r} 3 \text{ gal } 3 \text{ qt} \\ +\ 2 \text{ gal } 5 \text{ qt} \\ \hline \end{array}$

Mixed REVIEW

Find the GCF of each set of numbers.

1. 36, 27
2. 24, 60, 72

Find each quotient. Write the answer in simplest form.

3. $\frac{7}{8} \div \frac{1}{4}$
4. $\frac{2}{7} \div \frac{14}{15}$
5. Linda bought 4 tickets to the movies. Each ticket cost $4.25. She paid with a $20 bill. How much did it cost Linda for the tickets?

Dear Lisa,

I also love helping animals. I decided that I wanted to spend my time keeping them healthy and helping them when they became ill. I have two cats, a rabbit, a parrot, two parakeets, and fish—as well as a husband and two little girls.

Working hours can be long if you live and practice in a small town. You may get an emergency call in the middle of the night and not get home before office hours start the next morning. Larger cities have emergency clinics available for problems on the weekends or holidays.

It is sad that animals do not live as long as people. We see diseases that we cannot cure today. However, many veterinarians participate in research to discover new treatments for both animal and human illnesses. The more we learn, the easier it will be to save pets in the future.

Dr. Chris Stone Payne, DVM
Small Animal Veterinarian

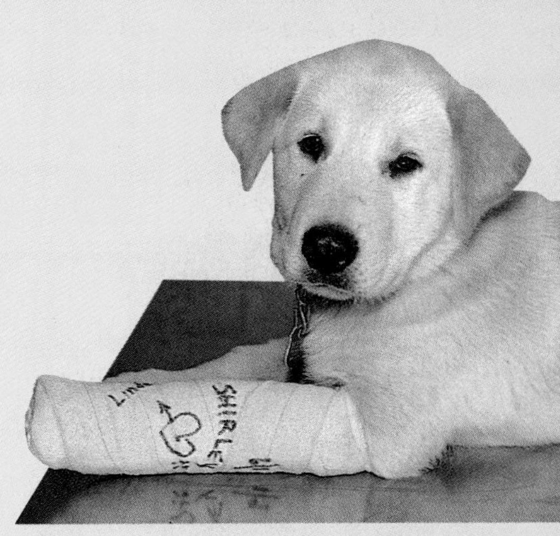

CHAPTER 8

Wrap Up

Estimating Sums and Differences 8-1

You can estimate the sum or difference of fractions by rounding each fraction to the nearest $\frac{1}{2}$. To estimate the sum or difference of mixed numbers, round each mixed number to the nearest whole number.

Estimate each sum or difference.

1. $\frac{15}{16} - \frac{7}{12}$
2. $\frac{6}{11} + \frac{7}{8}$
3. $7\frac{3}{5} - 3\frac{1}{6}$
4. $4\frac{4}{9} + 1\frac{8}{15}$

Adding and Subtracting Fractions 8-2, 8-3, 8-5

You can use models to add or subtract fractions.

To add or subtract fractions first find a common denominator and then add or subtract the numerators.

5. Write an addition sentence to describe the model.

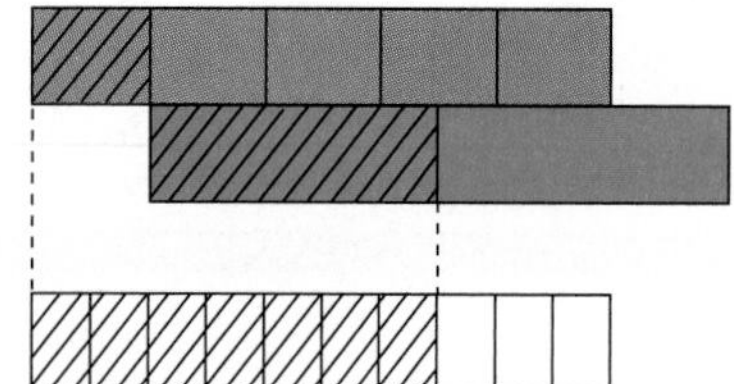

6. Write a subtraction sentence to describe the model.

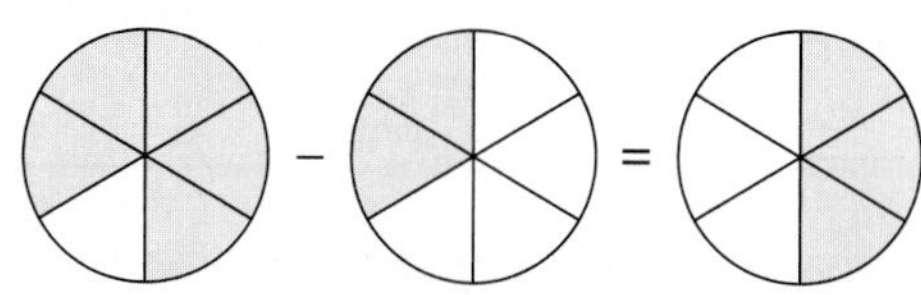

Find each sum or difference.

7. $\frac{7}{9} - \frac{2}{9}$
8. $4\frac{5}{6} - 2\frac{1}{3}$
9. $\frac{1}{3} + \frac{3}{4}$
10. $\frac{4}{7} + \frac{5}{7}$
11. $\frac{7}{16} + \frac{1}{4}$
12. $6\frac{2}{5} - 2\frac{3}{4}$
13. $3\frac{7}{8} + 1\frac{2}{12}$
14. $\frac{9}{10} - \frac{5}{6}$

Exploring Patterns in Fraction Sums 8-4

15. Copy and complete the table. Add more rows to the table until you see a pattern in the sum. Describe the pattern.

Expression	Sum
$\frac{1}{3}$	$\frac{1}{3}$
$\frac{1}{3} + \frac{1}{6}$	■
$\frac{1}{3} + \frac{1}{6} + \frac{1}{12}$	■

Multiplying and Dividing Fractions 8-7, 8-8

Sometimes you can simplify before multiplying. Divide the numerator and the denominator by any common factors.

To multiply fractions, you multiply their numerators and then multiply their denominators. To divide fractions, you multiply by the reciprocal of the divisor. To find $\frac{2}{3} \div \frac{5}{6}$, multiply $\frac{2}{3} \times \frac{6}{5}$.

When you multiply or divide with mixed numbers, first write each mixed number as an improper fraction.

Find each product or quotient.

16. $\frac{3}{5} \times \frac{10}{12}$ **17.** $\frac{2}{3} \div 8$ **18.** $2\frac{1}{6} \times 3\frac{3}{4}$ **19.** $2\frac{3}{8} \div 2\frac{1}{2}$

20. $\frac{4}{7} \div \frac{4}{7}$ **21.** $4\frac{1}{7} \times 6$ **22.** $8 \times \frac{3}{4}$ **23.** $8 \div 3\frac{1}{5}$

Strategies and Applications 8-6, 8-9

Sometimes it's helpful to draw a diagram when solving a problem.

24. Mrs. Cruz bought a rectangular piece of carpet, 12 ft wide and 18 ft long. She expects to carpet her rectangular living room, square dining room, and a hallway measuring 4 ft wide and 18 ft long.

a. Draw a diagram to show how she can make the three carpets with two cuts.

b. Find the dimensions of the living room and dining room.

c. Find the area of each room and the combined area of all three rooms.

25. In baseball, the distance from the pitcher to the batter is 60 ft. How far is this in yards?

26. You can make 6 whole wheat pancakes with $\frac{1}{2}$ c milk. How many pancakes can you make with $\frac{1}{2}$ gal milk?

GETTING READY FOR CHAPTER 9

Use equivalent fractions to fill in the ■.

1. $\frac{1}{2} = \frac{■}{14}$ **2.** $\frac{6}{18} = \frac{2}{■}$ **3.** $\frac{3}{5} = \frac{■}{30}$ **4.** $\frac{16}{56} = \frac{■}{7}$

PUTTING IT ALL TOGETHER

Follow Up

The Nomograph

At the beginning of the chapter you constructed a nomograph for adding fractions with denominators of 2, 4, 8, or 16. Now you have been hired by a company that plans to manufacture nomographs. Your job is to write a description of the design for a nomograph capable of adding two fractions with possible denominators of 2 through 10. You should explain the operation of the nomograph and tell how to use it to add mixed numbers as well as simple fractions. The problems preceded by the magnifying glass (p. 325, # 45; p. 329, # 44; and p. 337, # 42) will help you write your description.

Calculating devices have been known since ancient times. The **abacus** was probably the first such device. Until recently, engineers and scientists used the **slide rule** extensively, but it has been replaced by the calculator and the computer.

Excursion: Find out how an abacus works. Make a simple abacus and demonstrate how it is used.

Where to Look:

- an encyclopedia

Travel Time

For two days, keep a record of the amount of time you spend traveling. This includes time spent riding in a car or bus, walking, or riding your bicycle. Make a table that shows the day, the activity, the minutes of time spent traveling, and the fractional parts of an hour spent traveling. For example, if you ride your bicycle for 25 min, you would record this as 25/60. At the end of the two days, total your travel time in hours and minutes. How could you represent this information as a fraction? Do you need to round times to the nearest hour?

How Many More?

Try this with your group.

Measure something in your classroom that is longer than 3 ft, such as the width of the door opening or the height of a wall. Record this measurement in feet and inches. Then write several different forms of the same length using fractions. For example, some of the ways $3\frac{1}{2}$ ft can be written as fractions are $3\frac{6}{12}$ ft, $\frac{7}{2}$ ft, and $1\frac{1}{6}$ yd.

On a Roll

Rules:

- **2 or more players**
- **Prepare 3 number cubes. On two number cubes, write a mixed number on each side. On the third number cube, write three plus and three minus signs.**
- **Players take turns rolling the number cubes. If a player rolls two mixed numbers and a plus sign, the player adds the mixed numbers. If a player rolls two mixed numbers and a minus sign, the player subtracts the lesser mixed number from the greater one. (Players can use scratch paper.)**
- **Each correct answer is the player's score. Players should keep a running tally of their scores to simplify adding. If a player does not give a correct answer, the player receives no score for that round. After an equal number of rounds, the player with the highest score wins.**

CHAPTER 8

Assessment

1. Kelsey tutored for $3\frac{3}{4}$ h on Tuesday and $7\frac{1}{3}$ h on Saturday.
   a. About how many more hours did Kelsey tutor on Saturday than on Tuesday?
   b. About how much time did Kelsey tutor altogether?

2. Draw a model to find each sum or difference.
   a. $\frac{1}{4} + \frac{1}{4}$
   b. $\frac{11}{12} - \frac{5}{12}$

3. Find each sum. Then write the answer in simplest form.
   a. $\frac{3}{5} + \frac{11}{15}$
   b. $\frac{7}{12} + \frac{3}{8}$
   c. $\frac{6}{15} + \frac{4}{9}$
   d. $\frac{1}{2} + \frac{6}{7}$

4. Find each difference. Then write the answer in simplest form.
   a. $\frac{3}{4} - \frac{2}{5}$
   b. $\frac{5}{6} - \frac{4}{15}$
   c. $\frac{7}{8} - \frac{17}{32}$
   d. $\frac{6}{7} - \frac{3}{5}$

5. Use the pattern of fraction sums given at the right.

Expression	Sum
$\frac{1}{3}$	$\frac{1}{3}$
$\frac{1}{3} + \frac{1}{9}$	■
$\frac{1}{3} + \frac{1}{9} + \frac{1}{27}$	■

   a. Copy and complete the table.
   b. Add another row.
   c. **Writing** Describe the pattern you see in the "Sum" column.

6. Explain how you can mentally find the sum $3\frac{1}{4} + 2\frac{2}{3} + 5\frac{3}{4} + 1\frac{1}{3}$.

7. Roscoe grew $4\frac{1}{4}$ in. over a two-year period. If he grew $2\frac{1}{2}$ in. the first year, how many inches did Roscoe grow during the second year?

8. Four students are waiting in line. Bayo is behind Sarah, David is in front of Max, and Sarah is behind Max. Find the order of the four students.

9. **Choose A, B, C, or D.** A sales representative completed $\frac{4}{7}$ of a 1,394-mi business trip. About how many miles of the trip remain?
   A. about 100 mi
   B. about 700 mi
   C. about 400 mi
   D. about 1000 mi

10. Tung has an income of $2,640 each month. He spends $\frac{1}{5}$ of his income on rent. How much does Tung spend on rent each month?

11. A doll maker uses $1\frac{7}{8}$ yd of material to make one doll. How many dolls can be made from a piece of material that is 45 yd long?

12. Write $>$, $<$, or $=$.
   a. $3\frac{1}{2}$ yd ■ 7 ft
   b. 34 oz ■ $2\frac{3}{4}$ qt
   c. $5\frac{1}{4}$ c ■ 42 oz

13. Complete.
   a. 28 oz = ■ lb
   b. $5\frac{3}{4}$ ft = ■ in.
   c. $9\frac{1}{4}$ gal = ■ qt = ■ pt

CHAPTER 8

Cumulative Review

Choose A, B, C, or D.

1. Which is *not* equivalent to five tenths?

A. 0.05 **B.** $\frac{5}{10}$ **C.** 0.5

D. fifty hundredths

2. Summer vacation is 68 days. If $\frac{3}{4}$ of vacation has gone by, how many days are left?

A. 12 days **B.** 51 days

C. 23 days **D.** 17 days

3. The perimeter of a rectangle is 36 ft. One dimension is 12 ft. Find the area.

A. 72 ft^2 **B.** 6 ft^2

C. 60 ft^2 **D.** 3 ft^2

4. Which set of numbers is in order from least to greatest?

A. 0.67, $\frac{2}{3}$, $\frac{7}{10}$, $\frac{3}{4}$ **B.** $\frac{1}{4}$, $\frac{6}{25}$, 0.23, $\frac{2}{9}$

C. $1\frac{1}{4}$, $1\frac{2}{7}$, 1.3, $1\frac{1}{3}$ **D.** 0.37, $\frac{3}{8}$, $\frac{1}{3}$, 0.4

5. Which is *not* a true statement?

A. $0.04 > 0.01$ **B.** $0.48 < 0.4798$

C. $0.014 < 0.02$ **D.** $29.6 > 29.06$

6. A box is 24 cm long, 12 cm wide, and 11 cm high. Find its surface area.

A. 288 cm^2 **B.** 1,368 cm^2

C. 792 cm^2 **D.** 47 cm^2

7. Jeremiah bought a radio for $18.64. Sales tax is $1.49. How much does he need to buy the radio?

A. $19.03 **B.** $17.15

C. $33.54 **D.** $20.13

8. Find the circumference and area of a circle with a diameter of 4.6 m. Round to the nearest tenth.

A. $C = 16.6, A = 14.4$

B. $C = 28.9, A = 66.4$

C. $C = 14.4, A = 16.6$

D. $C = 4.6, A = 5.29$

9. Which set of numbers has a GCF of 3?

A. 15, 30, 45 **B.** 6, 30, 24

C. 24, 36, 9 **D.** 36, 27, 18

10. How many hours are in $\frac{5}{6}$ of a day?

A. 20 **B.** 4 **C.** 9 **D.** 18

11. A relay team is competing in a $\frac{1}{2}$-mi race. Each person runs $\frac{1}{8}$ mi. How many team members are there?

A. 16 **B.** 2 **C.** 8 **D.** 4

12. Find the prime factorization of 300?

A. $2 \times 2 \times 3 \times 5$

B. $2 \times 5 \times 5 \times 7$

C. $2 \times 3 \times 3 \times 5 \times 5$

D. $2 \times 2 \times 3 \times 5 \times 5$

13. The freshman car wash earned $214.35. The sophomore car wash earned $189.76. How much money did the two classes make altogether?

A. $404.11 **B.** $403.01

C. $393.01 **D.** $24.59

CHAPTER 9

Ratio, Proportion, and Percent

Data File 9

In Prague, the capital of the Czech Republic, membership to a fitness club costs about \$18 per month. That's about $\frac{1}{9}$ of the average salary there. In Budapest, the capital of Hungary, membership costs almost \$36 a month or about $\frac{1}{6}$ of the average salary in Budapest.

Derek Turnbull made history in 1992 when he ran in a series of masters races. To compete as a master you must be at least 40 years old. Derek was a 65-year-old sheep farmer from New Zealand. He broke the world record for his age group in every race.

Derek Turnbull's Record

Event	Old Record	Turnbull in 1992
800 m	2:20.5	2:17.8
1500 m	4:41.82	4:39.8
One mile	5:05.61	4:56.4
3,000 m	10:10.2	9:47.4
5,000 m	17:43.4	16:38.8
10,000 m	36:03	34:42.8
Marathon (26 mi)	2:42:29	2:41:57

Source: *Runner's World*

Exercise Participation for Teens, Ages 12–15*

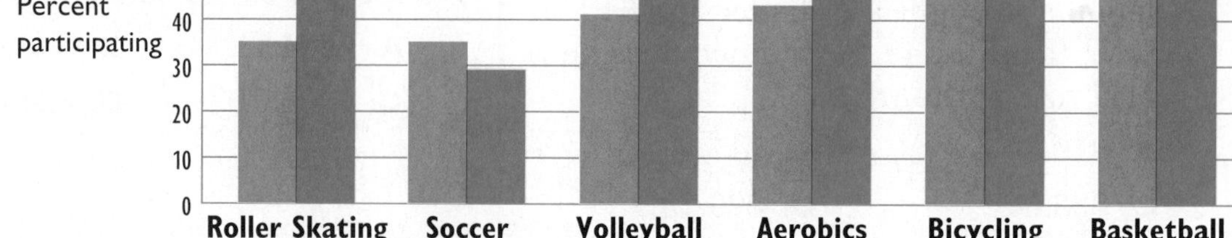

*based on 549 males and 523 females surveyed

Source: Teenage Research Unlimited

WHAT YOU WILL LEARN

- how to model and use ratios and proportions
- how to relate fractions, decimals, and percents
- how to use technology to investigate similar figures
- how to solve problems using guess and test

Aerobic Fitness

This chart shows the results of the 1989 one-mile walk/run test. It gives the percent of girls and boys in each age category who met the goal.

Age (years)	Goal time (min) (boys)	Goal time (min) (girls)	Percent passed (boys)	Percent passed (girls)
6	15:00	16:00	76	91
7	14:00	15:00	74	63
8	13:00	14:00	72	69
9	12:00	13:00	70	74
10–11	11:00	12:00	73	71
12	10:00	12:00	69	75
13	9:30	11:30	68	66
14–16	8:30	10:30	73	50

Source: *U.S. News & World Report*

Sit-ups

The goals listed below are the number of sit-ups per minute. In the 1989 study, 76% of the boys and 72% of the girls met the goals.

Children ages 5–7	20/min
Children ages 8–9	25/min
Children ages 10–11	30/min
Boys ages 12–13	35/min
Girls ages 12–13	30/min
Boys ages 14–16	40/min
Girls ages 14–16	35/min

Source: *U.S. News & World Report*

STANDARD TRACK

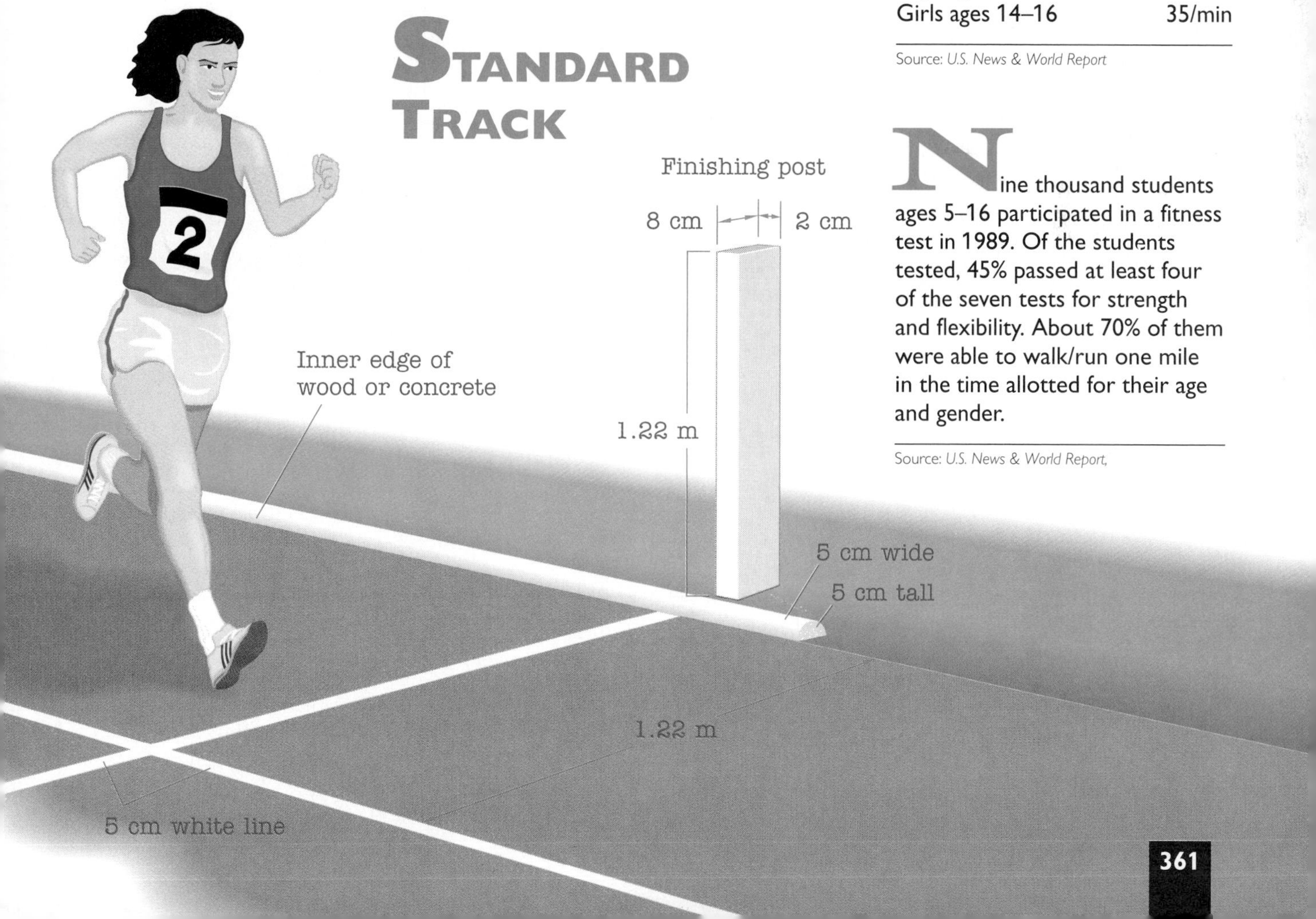

Finishing post

8 cm

2 cm

1.22 m

Inner edge of wood or concrete

5 cm wide

5 cm tall

1.22 m

5 cm white line

Nine thousand students ages 5–16 participated in a fitness test in 1989. Of the students tested, 45% passed at least four of the seven tests for strength and flexibility. About 70% of them were able to walk/run one mile in the time allotted for their age and gender.

Source: *U.S. News & World Report*,

investigation

Project File

Memo

The Astro County Science Museum is raising funds to build a scale model of the solar system in the museum lobby. The lobby is 50 ft long. A brochure put out by the museum states that in the model, the sun will be the size of a basketball. According to the brochure, "Everyone committed to furthering the cause of science education in Astro County should donate to this worthy project." Would you give money for the model of the solar system?

	Diameter (mi)	Mean Distance from Sun (millions of miles)
Sun	865,120	0
Mercury	3,030	36.0
Venus	7,520	67.2
Earth	7,926	3.0
Mars	4,216	141.7
Jupiter	88,724	483.9
Saturn	74,560	885.0
Uranus	31,600	1,781.6
Neptune	30,600	2,790.2
Pluto	1,860	3,670.7

Mission: Design your own model of the solar system with a sun the size of a basketball. Your design should include estimates of the sizes of the planets and their distances from the sun. Then decide whether you should donate money to the science museum.

Leads to Follow

- ✓ About how many times the size of Jupiter is the sun? About how many times the size of Pluto is the sun?
- ✓ How can you estimate the overall size of the model?
- ✓ What do you need to know in order to decide whether to give money to the museum?

What's Ahead

• Exploring the meaning of ratio

9-1 Exploring Ratios

THINK AND DISCUSS

WHAT YOU'LL NEED

✓ Pattern blocks 

"There are 3 times as many peanuts as almonds in the mixture." "There are 2 counselors for every 9 campers." "Combine 1 part ginger ale to 2 parts fruit juice." Each statement involves a *ratio.* A **ratio** compares two numbers by division.

You can write the ratio of ginger ale to fruit juice in three ways.

$$1 \text{ to } 2 \qquad 1 : 2 \qquad \frac{1}{2} \leftarrow \frac{\text{ginger ale}}{\text{fruit juice}}$$

1. For your class, write each ratio in three different ways.

a. boys to girls **b.** girls to boys

c. boys to all students **d.** girls to all students

2. **Discussion** Name two situations where you might use ratios.

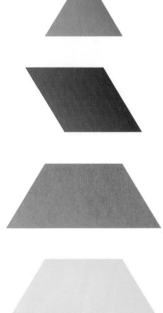

WORK TOGETHER

Work in groups. Use pattern blocks to explore ratios. Write a ratio to compare the areas of the following figures.

3. triangle : rhombus **4.** triangle : triangle

5. triangle : trapezoid **6.** triangle : hexagon

7. Copy and complete each table.

a.

Figure	triangle	trapezoid	hexagon
Area	1	■	■

b.

Figure	trapezoid	hexagon
Area	1	■

c. Write two ratios that compare the area of the trapezoid to the area of the hexagon.

d. Write two ratios that compare the area of the rhombus to the area of the hexagon.

Mixed REVIEW

The radius of a circle is 4 cm. Use 3.14 for π.

1. Find the circumference.

2. Find the area.

Find the perimeter of a rectangle with the following dimensions.

3. $\frac{1}{2}$ ft by 8 in.

4. 3 in. by $\frac{1}{4}$ ft

Write two equivalent fractions.

5. $\frac{2}{3}$ **6.** $\frac{3}{5}$

7. Eight birds and squirrels are at the backyard feeder. You count 22 legs. How many birds and how many squirrels are there?

ON YOUR OWN

Write a ratio in three ways to compare each.

8. plates to bowls

9. cups to bowls

10. bowls to cups

11. plates to cups

Write a ratio to represent each comparison.

12. sunglasses to caps

13. bats to balls

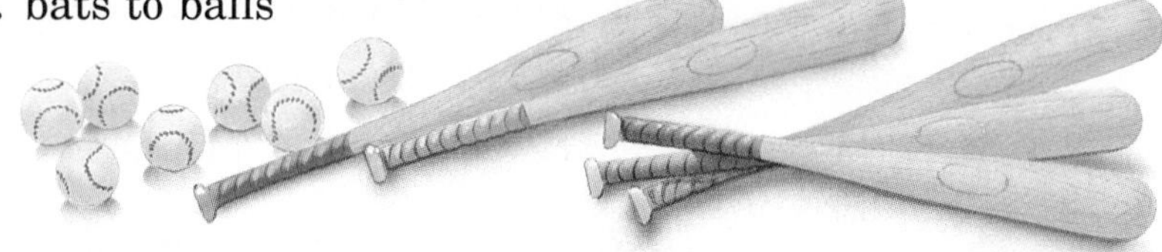

14. the number of vowels to consonants in the alphabet

15. the number of vowels to consonants in your name

Draw a picture to represent each ratio.

16. 4 stars to 8 moons

17. $\frac{\text{2 apples}}{\text{6 bananas}}$

18. 3 big tiles : 7 small tiles

19. 3 shirts to 5 shorts

Name two pattern blocks with areas in the following ratio.

20. 1 : 2 **21.** $\frac{6}{1}$ **22.** 2 to 3 **23.** $\frac{3}{1}$

24. Writing In Anna's class, 12 out of 16 students received a grade of B or better. Anna said that 1 out of 4 received less than a B. Is she correct? Explain your reasoning.

25. Activity Look in a newspaper and find two examples of ratios. You might try the sports pages or look in a supermarket ad.

What's Ahead

- Finding equal ratios
- Finding unit rates

WHAT YOU'LL NEED

✓ Stopwatch

9-2 Ratios and Rates

THINK AND DISCUSS

A ratio of 1 c of unpopped corn will pop to about 8 qt of popcorn. How much popcorn can you expect from 3 c of unpopped corn?

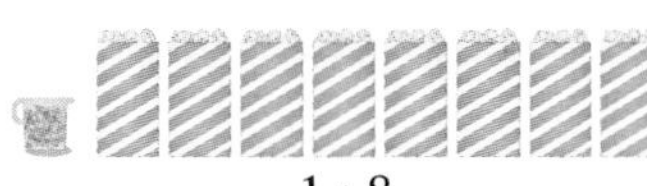

1 : 8

Model the problem by showing 1 c of unpopped corn for 8 qt of popped corn.

2 : 16

There is 1 c of unpopped corn for every 8 qt of popped corn. You can expect about 16 qt of popcorn from 2 c of unpopped corn.

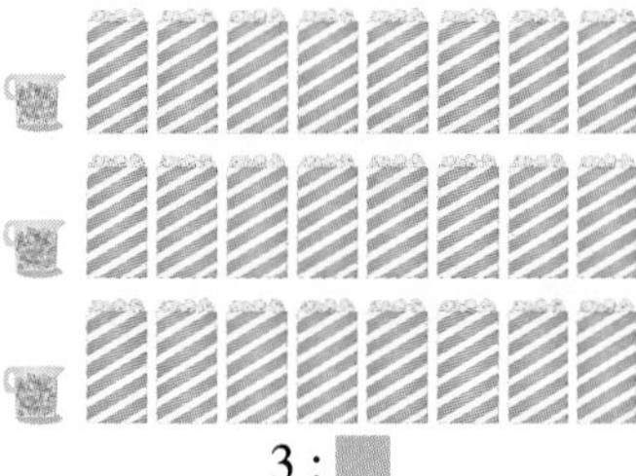

3 : ■

For every 3 c of unpopped corn you would expect about ■ of popcorn.

FLASHBACK

Multiplying or dividing the numerator and the denominator of a fraction by the same number is the same as multiplying or dividing by 1.

The ratios 1 : 8, 2 : 16, and 3 : 24 are **equal ratios** since they are names for the same number. You can find equal ratios by multiplying or dividing each term in a ratio by the same nonzero number.

$$\frac{1}{8} \overset{\times 2}{=} \frac{2}{16} \qquad \frac{3}{24} \overset{\div 3}{=} \frac{1}{8}$$

1. Use multiplication and division to write two equal ratios.

a. 6 : 8 **b.** 10 to 35 **c.** $\frac{21}{42}$ **d.** 12 : 18

WHO? Michael Jordan, wore a new pair of sneakers for each game. After each game he signed the sneakers and donated them to charity. Even in one game the shoes got a workout. On average Michael ran 4.5 mi/game.

Source: *3-2-1 Contact*

We commonly write ratios in simplest form.

2. a. Write the fraction $\frac{25}{75}$ in simplest form.
   b. How would you write the ratio $\frac{50}{150}$ in simplest form?
3. **Discussion** Do equal ratios have the same simplest form? Support your answer using an example.

We call a ratio that compares two items with different units a **rate.** For example, $\frac{46 \text{ mi}}{2 \text{ h}}$ compares miles traveled to hours of travel. A **unit rate** compares a quantity to a unit of one.

Example A car traveled 300 mi on 12 gal of gas. Find the unit rate in miles per gallon (mi/gal).

- $\frac{\text{miles}}{\text{gallons}} \rightarrow \frac{300}{12}$ **Write the comparison as a ratio.**
- $\frac{300}{12} = \frac{25}{1}$ (÷ 12 numerator and denominator) **Divide the numerator and the denominator by the GCF, 12.**

The unit rate is $\frac{25 \text{ mi}}{1 \text{ gal}}$, or 25 mi/gal. You read this unit rate as "25 miles per gallon."

LOOK BACK How could you use a model to find the unit rate?

WORK TOGETHER

- Have a partner time you for 10 s as you print the uppercase letters of the alphabet in order from A to Z.
- Switch roles and time your partner. Count the number of letters each partner printed.

4. a. Find your writing rates. Compare the number of letters each wrote to the time allowed.
   b. How can you use multiplication to find each unit rate for one minute? Show your work.
5. Tashia's writing rate is $\frac{24 \text{ letters}}{15 \text{ s}}$. Carol's rate is $\frac{18 \text{ letters}}{10 \text{ s}}$. Who has the faster writing rate?

TRY THESE

Write three equal ratios for each given ratio.

6. 6 : 18 **7.** $\frac{4}{24}$ **8.** 8 to 10 **9.** 30 : 40

10. Sports The team won 8 games out of 12 games played. Write the ratio of games won to games played in simplest form.

Find the unit rate for each situation.

11. \$19.50 for 3 shirts **12.** 300 mi in 12 h

13. read 66 pages in 2 h **14.** type 110 words in 5 min

***A woodpecker** can pound its beak against wood at a rate of 20 pecks/s.*

ON YOUR OWN

Write three equal ratios.

15. $\frac{50}{100}$ **16.** 9 to 81 **17.** 8 : 14 **18.** $\frac{14}{42}$

Find the value that makes the ratios equal.

19. $\frac{5}{10}, \frac{■}{20}$ **20.** 25 : 75, 1 : ■ **21.** 6 to 9, ■ to 3

22. $\frac{8}{■}, \frac{2}{20}$ **23.** 7 : ■, 14 : 42 **24.** $\frac{■}{15}, \frac{25}{75}$

25. Critical Thinking Carlos tells you he ate $\frac{1}{3}$ of a pizza. Raylene says she ate $\frac{9}{27}$, and Maggie says she ate $\frac{2}{6}$. Which of these forms do you find easier to use? Explain your answer.

Write each ratio in simplest form.

26. squares : circles **27.** squares : triangles

28. triangles : squares **29.** hexagons : circles

Write the unit rate for each situation.

30. 16 mi in 4 h **31.** 175 mi in 7 da

32. \$24 for 8 toys **33.** 10 pears for 5 children

34. 36 balloons for 3 bunches **35.** 144 players on 12 teams

Did you know you can use the digits 1 to 9 to write the ratio 4 : 5?

9876 : 12345 = 4 : 5

Source: *Curious and Interesting Numbers*

36. La Crystal is taking swimming lessons. She will pay $126 for 28 lessons. Bill will pay $30 for 6 lessons.

a. Write a unit rate for La Crystal's and for Bill's lesson.

b. Who is paying more per lesson? How much more?

Sign On the Dotted Line

Do you have an autograph of your favorite celebrity? Well, if you do, hold on to it. Someday it might be worth something.

Autographs of stars from the past are sometimes worth big money. Clark Gable's autograph is worth $100. Lucille Ball's is worth $75. President Harry Truman's is worth $40 and Hillary Clinton's is worth $100.

The signature of Button Gwinnett, a signer of the Declaration of Independence, recently sold for $100,000. Only 40 of his signatures are still around.

Use the article above. Write each ratio in simplest form.

37. the price of President Truman's autograph compared to Clark Gable's

38. the price of Lucille Ball's autograph compared to Button Gwinnett's

39. the price of Lucille Ball's autograph compared to Hillary Clinton's

40. Critical Thinking The ratio of water to land in Earth's southern hemisphere is 4 : 1. The ratio in the northern hemisphere is 3 : 2. Estimate Earth's ratio of water to land.

41. Data File 9 (pp. 360–361) Write each of Derek Turnbull's 1992 records as a rate. Compare distance to time.

42. Writing Explain how ratios and rates are similar and how they are different. Give an example of each.

Find each answer.

1. $\frac{2}{3} \times \frac{3}{5}$ **2.** $9\frac{1}{2} \times \frac{3}{8}$

3. There are 24 students in Mr. Alvarez's class. Twelve students have brown eyes and four have blue eyes.

a. Find the ratio of brown-eyed students to blue-eyed students.

b. Write a ratio comparing the number of blue-eyed students to all students.

4. You have 5 coins with a total value $.75. Two of the coins are quarters. What are the other coins?

What's Ahead

- Recognizing proportions
- Solving proportions

9-3 Solving Proportions

WORK TOGETHER

A **proportion** is an equation stating that two ratios are equal. For example 1 : 2 and 4 : 8 are equal. They form the proportion $\frac{1}{2} = \frac{4}{8}$.

Work with a partner to explore the proportions below. Use a calculator and any operations on the numerators and denominators. Describe as many relationships as you can.

$$\frac{180}{42} = \frac{30}{7} \qquad \frac{7}{8} = \frac{21}{24} \qquad \frac{16}{30} = \frac{8}{15}$$

1. a. Is each statement above true? How do you know?
   b. Follow these steps for each statement. Multiply the red numbers. Then multiply the blue numbers.
   c. What do you notice about the products?

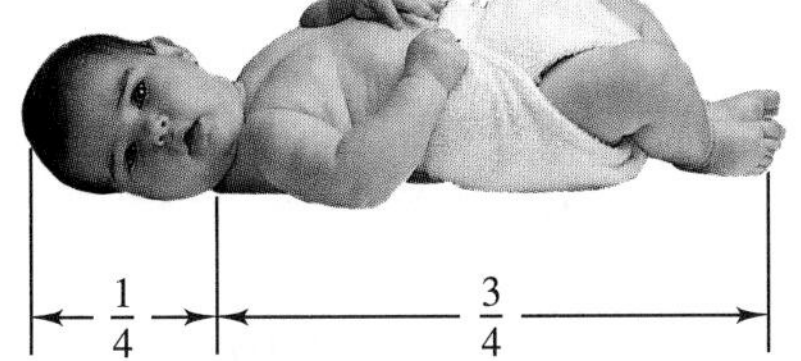

WHO? Fra Filippo Lippi (1406–1469) was the first to draw babies using the correct proportions. Earlier artists drew babies with their heads $\frac{1}{6}$ as long as their bodies. While $\frac{1}{6}$ is correct for an adult, a baby's head is $\frac{1}{4}$ the length of its body.

Source: *The Macmillan Illustrated Almanac For Kids*

THINK AND DISCUSS

2. a. Look at the proportion $\frac{3}{4} = \frac{6}{8}$. Describe a way to tell if the proportion is true.
   b. Look at the proportion $\frac{12}{20} = \frac{21}{35}$. Describe a way to tell if the proportion is true.
   c. For which proportion above did you find it easier to show equality? Explain your reasoning.
3. a. Examine the ratios $\frac{1}{3}$ and $\frac{4}{5}$. Multiply the red numbers. Multiply the blue numbers. What do you notice?
   b. Do the ratios form a proportion? Why or why not?

You can use *cross products* to tell if two ratios form a proportion. The cross products of a proportion are *always* equal.

4. The cross products of the proportion $\frac{3}{4} = \frac{9}{12}$ are $3 \times ■$ and $4 \times ■$.

Example 1 Do the ratios $\frac{4}{10}$ and $\frac{20}{50}$ form a proportion?

$$\frac{4}{10} \stackrel{?}{=} \frac{20}{50}$$ Circle the cross products.

$4 \times 50 \stackrel{?}{=} 10 \times 20$ Write the cross products.

$200 = 200$ Simplify.

Yes, the ratios form a proportion.

You can use cross products to help you find the missing term in a proportion.

Example 2 Find the value of n in $\frac{n}{312} = \frac{5}{24}$.

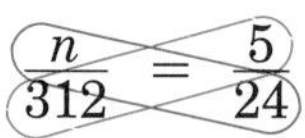

Circle the cross products.

$n \times 24 = 312 \times 5$ Write the cross products.

$24n = 1{,}560$ Simplify.

$\frac{24n}{24} = \frac{1{,}560}{24}$ Divide both sides by 24.

$n = 65$

You can also multiply or divide by a fraction equal to 1 to find a missing term in a proportion.

5. Use division by 1 to find the value of y in $\frac{9}{39} = \frac{3}{y}$.

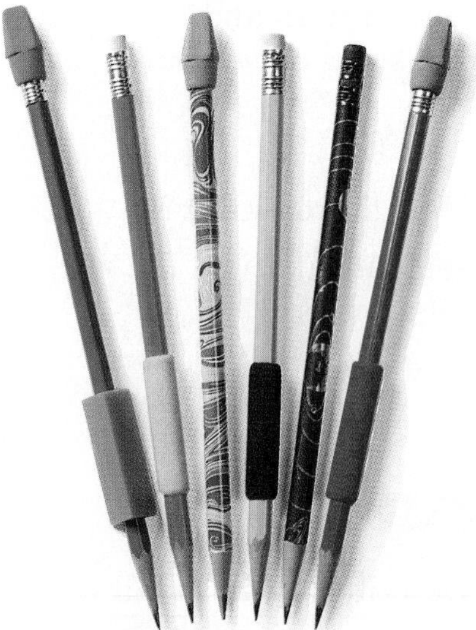

WHAT? The familiar eraser on the end of a pencil wasn't introduced until about 1860. Some teachers objected because they felt that students would make more errors if they were easy to correct.

Proportions can help you solve problems involving rates.

Example 3 Pencils at the school store are 2 for \$.15. Find the cost of buying 21 pencils.

$\frac{\text{pencils}}{\$} \begin{matrix}\rightarrow \\ \rightarrow\end{matrix} \frac{2}{0.15} = \frac{21}{c}$ Let c represent the cost.

$2 \times c = 0.15 \times 21$ Write the cross products.

.15 [×] 21 [÷] 2 [=] 1.575 Use a calculator to solve.

$c = 1.575$

Round to the next cent. The pencils cost \$1.58.

LOOK BACK How could you use a pattern to find the cost of the pencils?

TRY THESE

Choose Use a calculator, paper and pencil, or mental math. Determine whether each pair of ratios forms a proportion.

6. $\frac{3}{9}, \frac{6}{18}$ 7. $\frac{9}{10}, \frac{18}{30}$ 8. $\frac{1}{2}, \frac{50}{100}$ 9. $\frac{10}{20}, \frac{30}{40}$

Mental Math Find the value of y.

10. $\frac{48}{y} = \frac{4}{7}$ 11. $\frac{9}{32} = \frac{y}{48}$ 12. $\frac{4}{18} = \frac{6}{y}$ 13. $\frac{y}{55} = \frac{18}{22}$

14. A certain flavor of frozen yogurt contains 65 calories for 2 oz. How many calories are in 10 oz of the frozen yogurt?

ON YOUR OWN

Choose Use a calculator, paper and pencil, or mental math. Determine whether the pairs of ratios form a proportion.

15. $\frac{33}{39}, \frac{55}{65}$ 16. $\frac{4}{12}, \frac{6}{8}$ 17. $\frac{42}{6}, \frac{504}{72}$ 18. $\frac{9}{11}, \frac{63}{77}$

Find the value of the variable.

19. $\frac{2}{9} = \frac{25}{x}$ 20. $\frac{93}{60} = \frac{m}{40}$ 21. $\frac{18}{n} = \frac{6}{3}$ 22. $\frac{k}{17} = \frac{20}{34}$

23. Use the digits 2, 5, 6, and 15. Write as many proportions as possible.

24. Marva gets paid $7.00 for 2 h of babysitting. Saturday she babysat for the Fields. They paid her $17.50. How long did she babysit?

25. Writing In your own words, define *proportion.* Write and solve a problem that uses proportions.

26. Calculator A piano has 88 keys. The ratio of white keys to black keys is 52 to 36. A piano maker has 676 white keys.
    a. How many black keys does the piano maker need to have the correct ratio of white keys to black keys?
    b. How many pianos can be built? Explain how you got your answer.

Mixed REVIEW

Find the GCF.

1. 18, 27 2. 52, 78
3. 84, 28

Write two equal ratios.

4. 14 : 35 5. $\frac{6}{8}$
6. 8 to 20

7. Julio, Stella, and Ted ate tuna, roast beef, or chicken for lunch. Ted didn't have roast beef or chicken. Stella didn't have roast beef. What did each person have?

The first piano was built in 1720. The largest piano ever built weighs $1\frac{1}{3}$ T or about 2,700 lb.

27. **Sports** Youth soccer teams in Hopkinton have 22 players and 3 coaches. On sign-up day, 196 students show up to play. How many coaches are needed?

28. At the Habra's cookout the guests ate 3 hamburgers for every 2 hot dogs. They ate 18 hamburgers. How many hot dogs did they eat?

29. **Data File 5 (pp. 182–183)** Suppose the alarm goes off in 220 households. About how many of these people get up?

$C = \pi d$

$\pi \approx 3.14$

30. **Investigation (p. 362)** Find the diameter of a basketball. Research the size of at least three other game balls used in sports. Write ratios comparing the diameters.

CHECKPOINT

1. **Choose A, B, C, or D.** Lavalle's bookstore sold 24 paperbacks, 6 hardcovers, 38 magazines, and 5 calendars. What was the ratio of magazines sold to paperbacks sold?

   A. 24 : 38 **B.** 19 to 31 **C.** $\frac{19}{12}$ **D.** 12 : 24

Write two equal ratios for each.

2. $\frac{10}{15}$ 3. 20 to 34 4. 18 : 40 5. $\frac{23}{44}$

Write each ratio in simplest form.

6. $\frac{28}{38}$ 7. 22 : 60 8. $\frac{18}{54}$ 9. 90 : 190

Find each unit rate.

10. You can buy 3 tacos for $2.67.

11. A package of 6 batteries costs $2.10.

Determine whether the pairs of ratios form a proportion.

12. $\frac{8}{9}, \frac{64}{88}$ 13. $\frac{2}{3}, \frac{28}{42}$ 14. $\frac{7}{12}, \frac{9}{16}$ 15. $\frac{23}{30}, \frac{6}{8}$

16. **Science** A glacier moves about 12 in. every 8 h. About how far will a glacier move in 72 h?

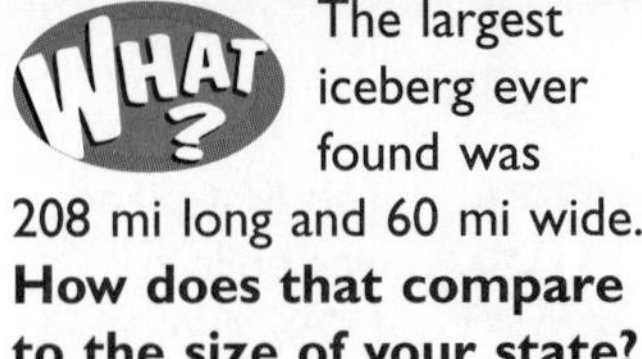

The largest iceberg ever found was 208 mi long and 60 mi wide. **How does that compare to the size of your state?**

Source: *3-2-1 Contact*

9-4 Guess and Test

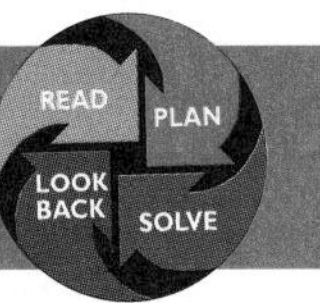

What's Ahead

- Solving problems by using guess and test

A good problem solving strategy is *Guess and Test.* First make a reasonable guess and then test it against the information you are given in the problem. If your guess is incorrect, keep trying until you find the correct answer.

> Handmade friendship bracelets use 20 cm of thread. Handmade rings use 8 cm of thread. Marny used a total of 184 cm of thread to make 14 items. **How many friendship bracelets did she make?**

READ

Read and understand the given information. Summarize the problem.

Think about the information you are given and what you are asked to find.

1. a. How much thread is needed to make a friendship bracelet? a ring?
   b. How much thread did Marny use in all?
   c. How many items did Marny make?
2. What does the problem ask you to find?

PLAN

Decide on a strategy to solve the problem.

Guess and Test is a good strategy to use.

3. Suppose you guess that Marny made 4 bracelets.
   a. **Discussion** Why does a guess of 4 bracelets imply that Marny made 10 rings?
   b. How many centimeters of thread are used to make 4 bracelets? 10 rings? Explain how you found each answer.
   c. Does a guess of 4 bracelets result in the correct answer? Why or why not?
   d. Would your next guess for the number of bracelets be higher or lower? Explain.

SOLVE

Try out the strategy.

You can organize your guesses in a table like the one below.

Bracelets	Rings	Thread	High/Low
5 × 20 cm = 100 cm	9 × 8 cm = 72 cm	172 cm	low
8 × 20 cm = 160 cm	6 × 8 cm = 48 cm	208 cm	high
■	■	■	■

4. A guess of 5 bracelets required too little thread and a guess of 8 bracelets required too much thread.
   a. What guesses would be reasonable to make next?
   b. Is one of the guesses more reasonable to make than the other? Explain.
   c. Copy and complete the table above to test your next guess. Keep guessing until you find the correct answer.
   d. How many friendship bracelets did Marny make?

LOOK BACK

Think about how you solved this problem.

Make sure your answer checks against the information given in the problem.

5. Is the total number of bracelets and rings 14? Is the total amount of thread 184 cm?

TRY THESE

Use guess and test to solve each problem.

6. One way parents in Fullerton raise money for the school is by conducting a raffle. Tickets for items are sold and then a drawing is held to determine the winner of the items. You can buy a ticket for a video game for $2 or a remote-control car for $3. On Saturday, $203 was raised by selling 80 raffle tickets. How many remote-control car tickets were sold?

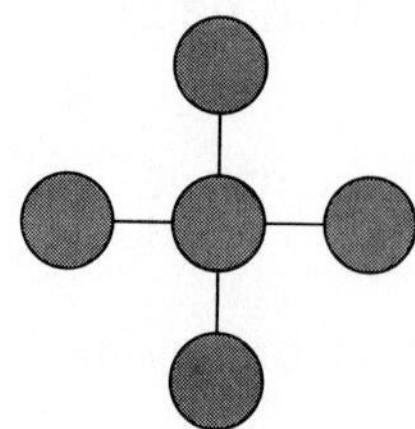

7. Place the digits 2, 3, 4, 6, and 8 in the circles at the left so that the product in both directions is the same. What is the product?

8. Two numbers have a sum of 34 and a product of 285. What are the two numbers?

ON YOUR OWN

Use any strategy to solve. Show your work.

9. Tickets for a movie cost $4.00 for children and $7.00 for adults. On Friday the theater collected $720 by selling 120 tickets. How many adult tickets were sold?

10. The 182 sixth graders at the Fannie Mae Hammer Middle School are taking a trip to the museum. The entrance fee is $1.75 per pupil and $3.25 per adult. The bus fee is $189 per bus. Each bus holds 44 people. What is the total cost for the students and 14 adults to visit the museum?

11. Millie, Bob, and Fran are reading mysteries, fantasies, and biographies. The type of book each is reading does not begin with the same letter as their name. Fran is reading *The Case of the Missing Body.* Who is reading fantasies?

12. Did you know that $\frac{1}{2}$ in. of rain is equal to 4 in. of snow? In April, 1921, 6 ft 4 in. of snow fell during a 24 h period, in Silver Lake, Colorado. How much rain would there have been if it hadn't been cold enough to snow?

13. Place the digits 1 through 9 in the pattern at the right so that the sum is the same in both directions. What is the sum?

14. Making lemonade requires water and lemon juice in the ratio of 3 c water to 2 c lemon juice. You need a total of 10 gal for the fair. How many cups of lemon juice do you need? If you made 10 gal of lemonade for your class, how much would each person get? (*Hint:* 16 c = 1 gal)

Use the pattern at the right. Imagine the pattern continues forever.

Sample 8 ↑ → = ■ Find the number 8 in the pattern. The number above 8 is 13. The number to the right of 13 is 14. So 8 ↑ → = 14.

15. 29 ↓ = ■

16. 13 ← = ■

17. 3 ↑ ↑ = ■

18. 14 → ← = ■

19. 23 ↓ ↓ → = ■

20. 7 ↓ → = ■

21. 18 ■ ■ = 22

22. 2 → ↑ ← ↓ = ■

23. 35 ↓ = ■

Mixed REVIEW

Evaluate.

1. 5 (3 + 8)
2. 3 (14 − 5)

True or False?

3. $\frac{120}{144} = \frac{145}{75}$
4. $\frac{32}{80} = \frac{80}{200}$
5. $\frac{18}{3} = \frac{102}{17}$
6. $\frac{19}{55} = \frac{22}{71}$

7. Hank gets ready for school in 45 min. He can walk to school in 22 min. He needs to be at school by 8:05 A.M. What time should he get up?

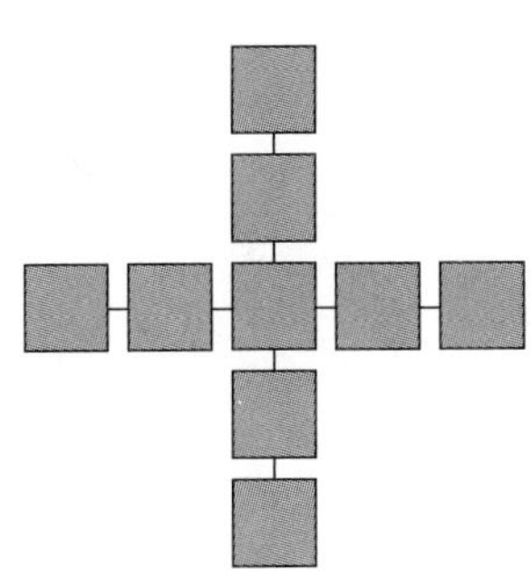

26	27	28	29	30	...
21	22	23	24	25	
16	17	18	19	20	
11	12	13	14	15	
6	7	8	9	10	
1	2	3	4	5	

Problem Solving Practice

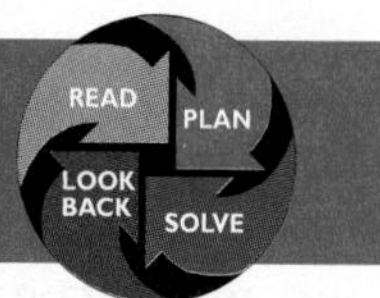

PROBLEM SOLVING STRATEGIES

Make a Table
Use Logical Reasoning
Solve a Simpler Problem
Too Much or Too Little Information
Look for a Pattern
Make a Model
Work Backward
Draw a Diagram
Guess and Test
Simulate a Problem
Use Multiple Strategies

Use any strategy to solve each problem. Show all your work.

1. The product of two consecutive pages in a book is 12,432. The sum is 223. What are the page numbers?

2. The ratio of Peter's height to Rick's height is 5 : 3. The ratio of Rick's height to Sean's height is 1 : 3. What is the ratio of Peter's height to Sean's height?

3. At the sub shop Janet ate two slices of pizza and a small salad. She paid for her meal with a ten-dollar bill. Her change was \$5.11. What was the price of her meal?

4. List the total number of triangles in the figure.

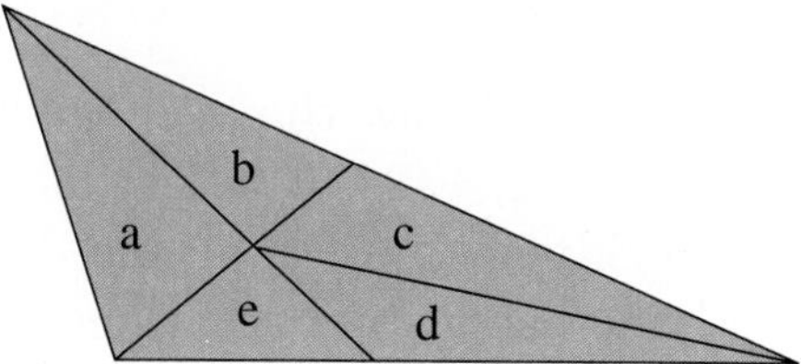

5. The following is *cryptarithm,* a puzzle where each letter represents a different digit. Find the value of each letter. (*Hint:* What is the only possible value for M?)

```
  FUN
+  IS
 MATH
```

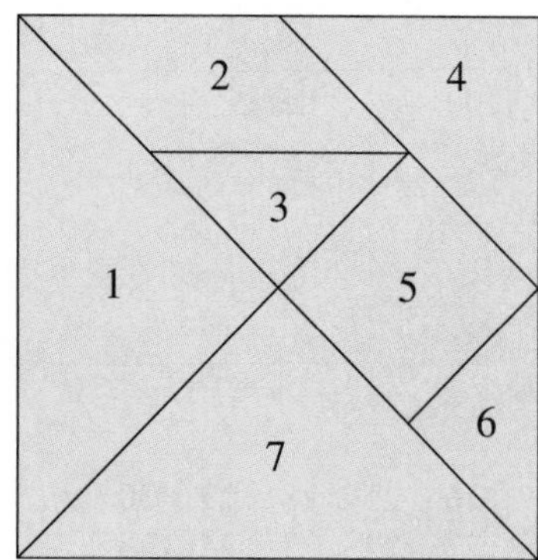

6. Examine the tangram on the left. Using any five pieces, make a rectangle. Is your answer unique? How could you tell?

7. In a race, Jon was behind Marla, but ahead of Noel. Noel was behind Jon, but ahead of Dana. Order the students from fastest to slowest.

8. Maxine saves quarters and dimes in a jar. Last night she counted \$6.75. The number of dimes is one more than the number of quarters. How many quarters are there?

9. The lengths of the sides of a rectangle are in the ratio of 1 : 3. The perimeter is 40 cm. Find the area.

TECHNOLOGY

What's Ahead

- Exploring ratios in corresponding parts of similar figures

9-5 Investigating Similar Figures

WHAT YOU'LL NEED

✓ Computer

✓ Geometry software

✓ Protractor

✓ Metric Ruler

THINK AND DISCUSS

"It's soggy to eat, but fun to watch." That might be your reaction to a cereal that expands when you add milk. Look at the flakes pictured on the box of Tri-Flex.

1. Do the flakes appear to be similar? Explain.

Imagine a bowl of Tri-Flex. The flakes grow as they soak up the milk. The figures show a flake before and after adding milk.

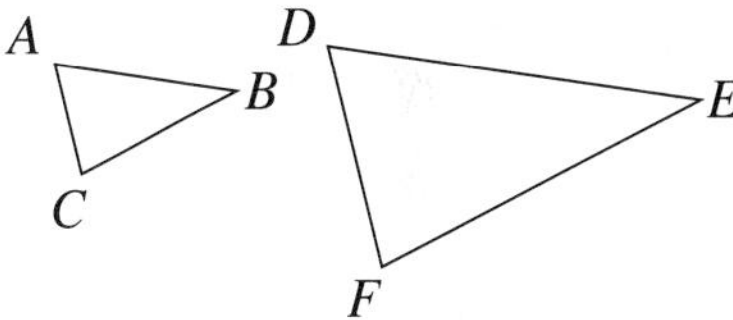

FLASHBACK

Similar figures have the same shape but they can be different sizes.

2. **a.** Do $\triangle ABC$ and $\triangle DEF$ appear to be similar?
   b. Which angle on $\triangle DEF$ used to be $\angle A$?
   c. What seems to be true about the sizes of the angles in $\triangle ABC$ and $\triangle DEF$?
   d. How can you compare the sizes of two angles? Describe at least two different methods.
   e. Use one of your methods to compare the measures of $\angle A$ and $\angle D$, $\angle B$ and $\angle E$, and $\angle C$ and $\angle F$.

3. Match the sides of $\triangle DEF$ with their original sides on $\triangle ABC$. We call matching parts of similar objects **corresponding parts.** Which side of $\triangle DEF$ corresponds to each?
   a. $\overline{AB}$ b. $\overline{BC}$ **c.** $\overline{AC}$

4. Measure the sides of $\triangle ABC$ and $\triangle DEF$.

5. The length of $\overline{AB}$, written AB, is the length from A to B. Compare the ratios.
   a. $\frac{AB}{DE}$ and $\frac{BC}{EF}$ **b.** $\frac{BC}{EF}$ and $\frac{AC}{DF}$ **c.** $\frac{AB}{DE}$ and $\frac{AC}{DF}$

6. a. **Writing** Summarize your results about the ratios that compare the lengths of the sides of $\triangle ABC$ and the lengths of the sides of $\triangle DEF$.

   b. **Discussion** What does it mean to say the lengths of the sides of $\triangle ABC$ and the lengths of the sides of $\triangle DEF$ are in *proportion*?

7. a. **Computer** Use Geometry software to create other pairs of similar triangles and check whether the lengths of their sides are in proportion.

   b. **Writing** Make a conjecture about the lengths of the sides of similar triangles.

WORK TOGETHER

Another cereal maker has come out with expanding flakes in the shape of quadrilaterals.

8. a. Find three pairs of flakes on the box of Fortify that appear similar.

   b. Find three pairs that do not appear to be similar.

9. Look at the BEFORE and AFTER diagram of the Fortify flake shown below. Do quadrilaterals $HIJK$ and $QRST$ appear to be similar?

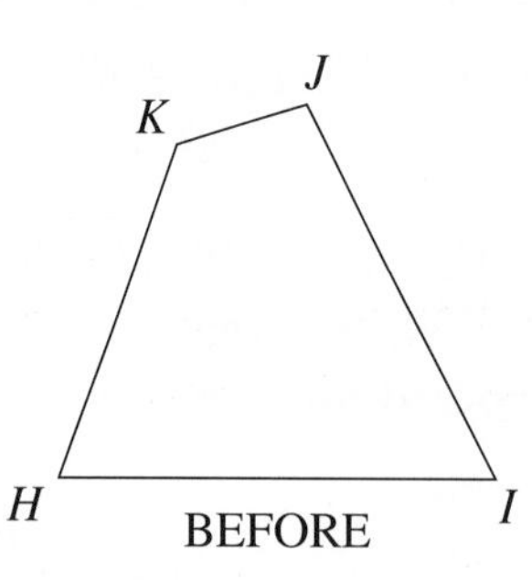

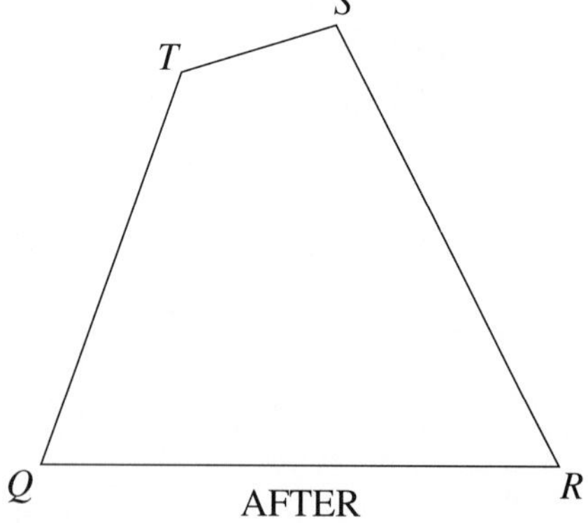

10. a. Measure to see if the sides of the two quadrilaterals are in proportion.

    b. **Computer** Use Geometry software to create other pairs of similar quadrilaterals. Check whether their sides are in proportion.

c. Writing Make a conjecture about the lengths of the sides of similar quadrilaterals.

Use the figure below for 1 and 2.

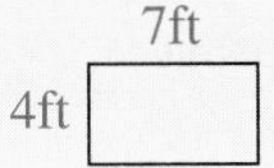

1. Find the perimeter.
2. Find the area.

Solve for n.

3. $\frac{1}{5} = \frac{12}{n}$ 4. $\frac{15}{n} = \frac{3}{25}$

5. The Braxtens have two children. The sum of the children's ages is 21 and the product is 104. How old are the children?

ON YOUR OWN

Try to draw a pair of figures that is not similar. If you think it is not possible, explain why.

11. two rectangles
12. two squares
13. two right triangles
14. two isosceles triangles
15. two equilateral triangles
16. two parallelograms

17. Critical Thinking Imagine quadrilaterals $ABCD$ and $EFGH$. They are not similar, but the following angles have the same measure: $\angle A$ and $\angle E$, $\angle B$ and $\angle F$, $\angle C$ and $\angle G$, and $\angle D$ and $\angle H$. Draw quadrilaterals $ABCD$ and $EFGH$.

18. Computer Use Geometry software. Make and test a conjecture about one of the following.

    a. What can you say about the new triangle formed when you start with a triangle and you connect the midpoints of its sides?

    b. Draw a segment parallel to one side of a triangle to form another smaller triangle. What can you say about the relationship between the new triangle and the original triangle?

    c. Draw a right triangle. Then draw a segment from the vertex of the right angle perpendicular to the opposite side. What can you say about the relationship between the two smaller triangles?

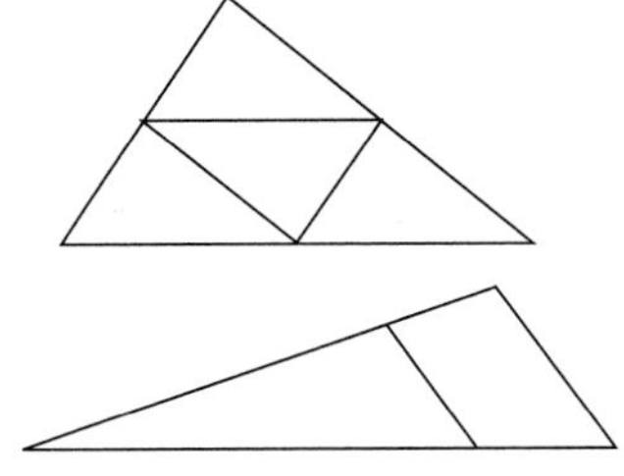

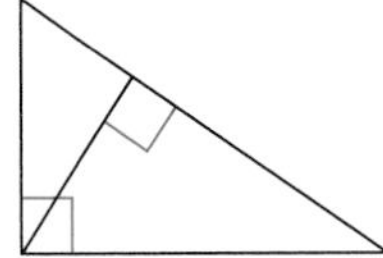

19. Investigation (p. 362) Earlier you collected data on the diameters of four sports balls. Suppose there is a photograph of the four sports balls you researched. The diameter of the basketball in the photo is 1 in. Find the diameters of the other sports balls. Round to the nearest tenth.

MATH AND DESIGN

9-6 Scale Drawings

What's Ahead

- Using scale drawings
- Making scale drawings

WHAT YOU'LL NEED

✓ Ruler

Designers plan objects, clothes, books, and buildings that are attractive, sturdy, and functional. Designers often make drawings, blueprints, 3-D models, and fashion designs created to scale. A **scale** is a ratio that compares a length on a model to the actual length.

THINK AND DISCUSS

Examine the scale drawings below.

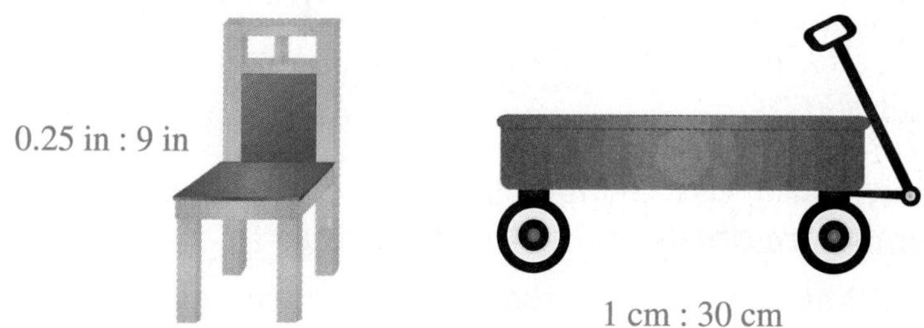

1. Write the scale for each drawing as a ratio in fraction form.

2. **Discussion** Why should a scale drawing show the scale?

You can use the scale on a drawing to calculate the actual size of an object.

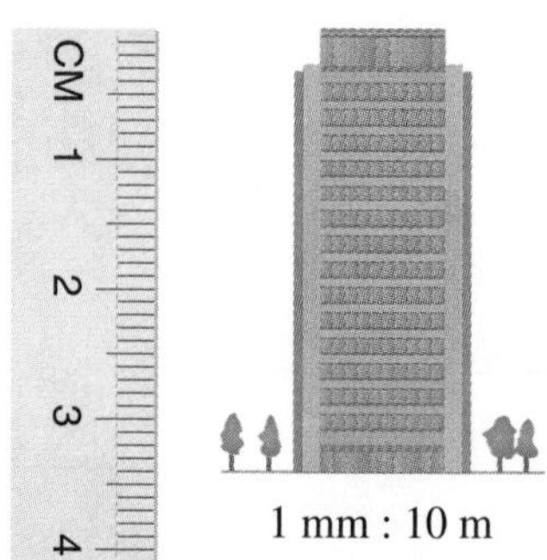

Example Use the scale drawing at the left to find the actual height of the skyscraper.

Measuring the length on the drawing shows the building is 34 mm high.

$\frac{\text{drawing (mm)}}{\text{actual (m)}} \begin{matrix}\rightarrow \\ \rightarrow\end{matrix} \frac{1}{10} = \frac{34}{h}$ — Write the scale as a ratio. Let h represent the actual height.

$1 \times h = 10 \times 34$ — Write cross products.

$h = 340$

The actual height of the skyscraper is about 340 m.

3. **Discussion** Are scale models and drawings and the actual figures they represent examples of similar figures? Give some examples to support your answer.

You can use grid paper to reduce or enlarge designs. The designs below were created on square grids. The design on the right is an enlarged scale drawing of the original design on the left.

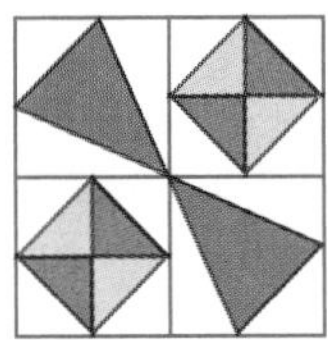

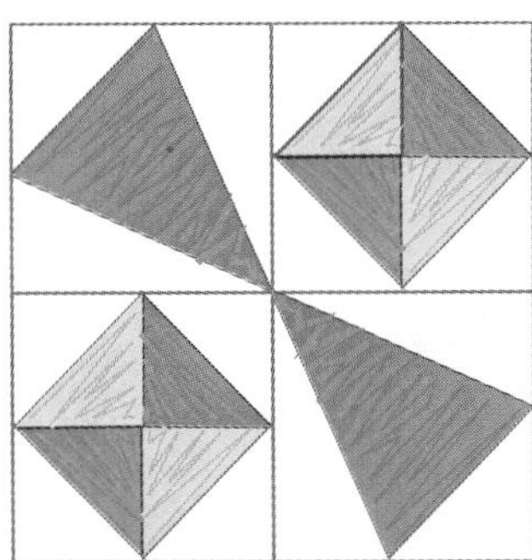

4. Find the dimensions of the grid squares in the grid on the left. Then find the dimensions of the grid squares in the grid on the right. What is the scale of the original design compared to the enlarged design?

5. Bianca used the following method to make an enlarged drawing of the design on the left. She drew a square 4 m × 4 cm. Then, she divided the square into four smaller squares each 2 cm × 2 cm.

   "I started with the bottom right square in the original design. I measured and found that the vertex of the triangle touched the middle of each side. So I measured the square in my grid and made a mark at the halfway point of each side. I used the marks to form the triangle."

   How do you think Bianca made the top right square?

6. a. Make a scale drawing of the original design using a scale of 1 cm to 5 cm.

   b. **Discussion** Explain the steps you followed in making your drawing.

   c. Suppose your scale is 1 cm to 0.5 cm. How would your procedure be different?

Mixed REVIEW

Compare using >, <, or =.

1. 6.8 ■ 6.08
2. 10.412 ■ 10.421

$\triangle ABC \cong \triangle DEF$.

3. $\angle A \cong$ ■, $\angle B \cong$ ■, $\angle C \cong$ ■
4. $\frac{AB}{BC} = \frac{DE}{■}$

Write a ratio for each.

5. 27 compared to 100
6. 56 compared to 100

7. A professional baseball pitcher can pitch at 96 mi/h. Write the rate in feet per second.

TRY THESE

7. The height of a wall in a blueprint is 3 in. The actual wall is 96 in. high. Find the scale of the blueprint.

8. **Writing** Jorge is making a scale model of an airplane. Should he use a scale of 1 in. : 1 yd or 1 yd : 1 in.? Why?

ON YOUR OWN

Use the scale for each drawing to find the actual size.

9. 

whale
1 cm to 3 m

10. 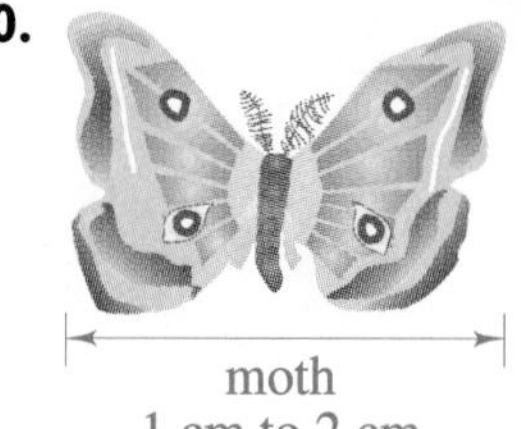

moth
1 cm to 2 cm

11. 

goat
1 mm to 6 cm

12. **Writing** Why would you want to see the blueprint of a house before construction starts?

DECISION MAKING

Borderline

You can distort a design to produce unusual effects. Follow the directions below to learn how to create distortions.

COLLECT DATA

1. Design a border on grid paper. You might look in an art book or a book of geometric tile designs for ideas. Use at least two colors in your drawing. Refer to art books or talk to the art teacher about design considerations.

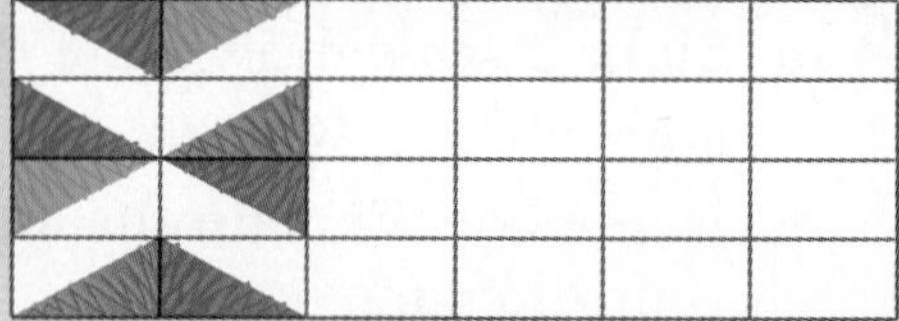

Scaling Down

Have you ever noticed the detail in a toy car? Designers try to make toy cars look real.

A designer chooses a car to model and then selects a size for the toy. Next each piece on the real car is scaled down. To determine the scale the designer uses the ratio $\frac{\text{size of toy car}}{\text{size of real car}}$.

Copy the table. Use the article to complete the table.

	Part	Actual Size	Toy Size
	Car	200 in.	3 in.
13.	Door handle	5 in.	■
14.	Headlights	8 in.	■
15.	Front bumper	6 ft	■
16.	Rear window	4.5 ft	■

ANALYZE DATA

2. In *distortions* the scale is not the same for both dimensions of a design. The original design is on a 4×6 grid. What are the dimensions of the new design? Why is it not in scale with the original?

3. Copy and finish the distortion of the original design. What happens to the shape of the design?

4. What grid dimensions might you use if you want to distort your border design so that it is short and fat?

MAKE DECISIONS

5. Decide on the dimensions of a grid for distorting your design. Predict what the distortion will look like. Draw the new distortion and use it as a border for stationery.

Convex and concave mirrors produce distorted images.

What's Ahead

• Modeling percents

9-7 Percent Sense

WHAT YOU'LL NEED

✓ Metric Ruler

THINK AND DISCUSS

In a survey, 75 out of 100 people said they like to go to the movies. When you compare a number to 100 you are finding a **percent.** You can write the ratio $\frac{75}{100}$ as 75%.

1. **Discussion** Where have you seen or used percents before?

You can think of a percent as a comparison of a number to a set of 100. Study the grid at the right. The amount shaded compared to the whole is 15 out of 100. You can write this as a fraction and as a percent.

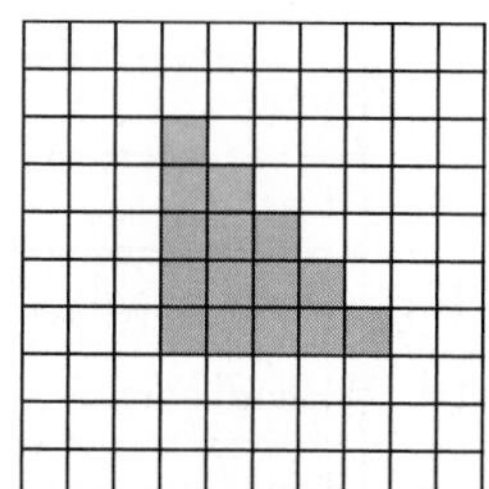

$\frac{15}{100}$ or 15%

2. What percent of each grid is shaded? not shaded?

a. 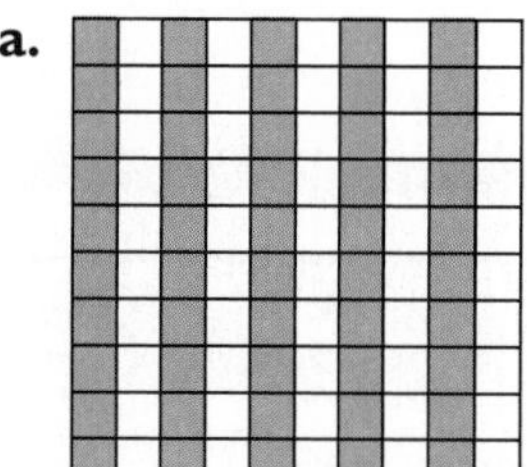

b. 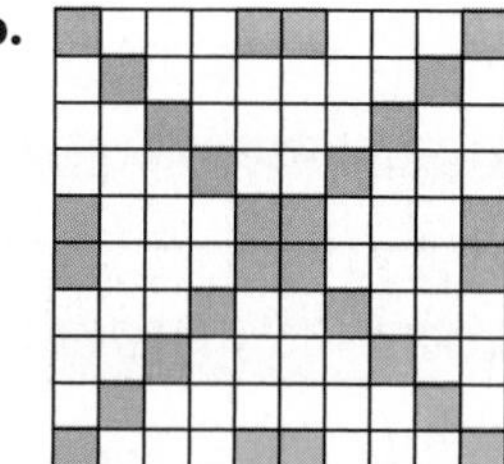

The words *per cento,* meaning *per hundred,* have evolved since the 1400s. The words were abbreviated and eventually changed to the symbol we use today.

3. Think about the equal fraction. Estimate each percent. Choose 25%, 50% or 75%.

   a. About what percent of the glass is full?

   b. About what percent of the pizza is eaten?

   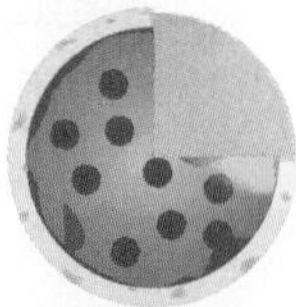

   c. About what percent of the sign is painted?

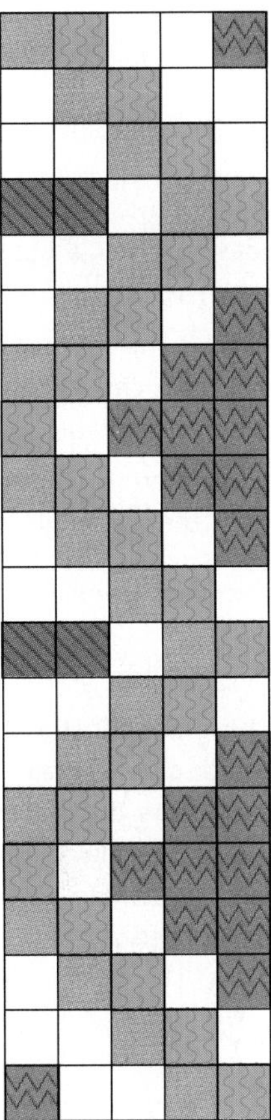

4. Use the design at the right. What percent of the design is made up of each pattern?

   a. b. c. d. e. 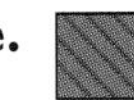

   f. Find the sum of the percents in parts (a) through (e).

5. Draw your own percent design. Use at least three patterns. How many squares should you start with?

6. **Discussion** What's wrong with each spinner?

   a.

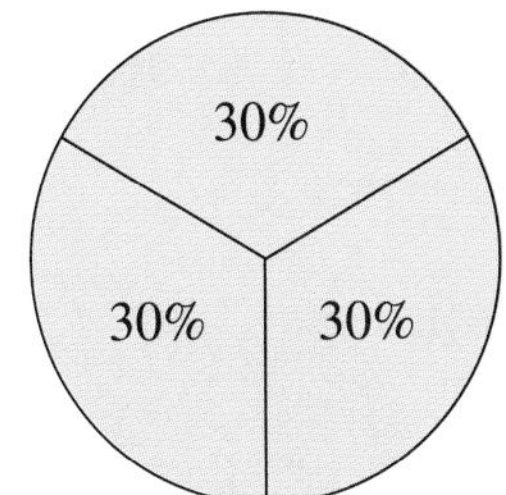

   b.

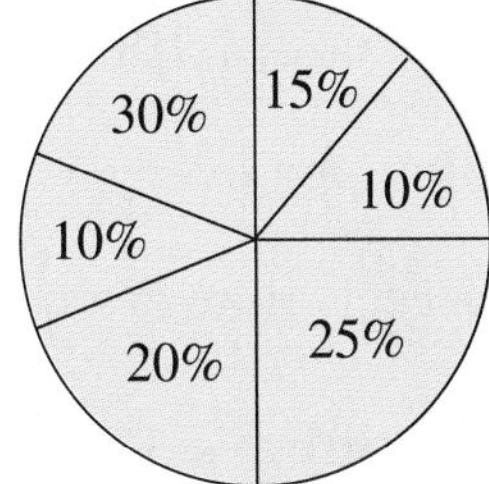

WORK TOGETHER

Work in small groups. Use a centimeter ruler to find each measure. What percent of a meter is each measurement?

a. length of your foot
b. circumference of your head
c. a cubit (distance from tip of middle finger to elbow)
d. your hand span (Spread your fingers. Measure the distance from the tip of your thumb to the tip of your little finger.)
e. width of your smile
f. distance from your knee to the floor

FLASHBACK
100 cm = 1m

7. Why do you think a meter rather than a yard was chosen for the reference set?

ON YOUR OWN

Use a 10 × 10 square grid to model each percent.

8. 5% **9.** 100% **10.** 75% **11.** 37% **12.** 90% **13.** 18%

Mixed REVIEW

Find each answer.

1. $\frac{9}{16} + \frac{12}{16}$ 2. $\frac{6}{8} - \frac{3}{8}$

A drawing has a scale of 1 cm to 2 m.

3. A scale model measures 1 cm × 2.5 cm. What is the size of the table?

4. A window is 12 mm. What is the sill length?

Write as a decimal.

5. $\frac{5}{20}$ 6. $\frac{9}{16}$

7. There are 30 students in a math class. Twelve belong to the computer club, 8 to the hiking club, and 3 to both. How many belong to neither?

FLASHBACK

A prime number has only two factors, one and itself.

Cicely Williams worked for 20 years in West Africa. Her work led to a reduced number of childhood deaths.

14. **Writing** How are 50% of a meter and 50% of \$1 the same? How are they different?

15. **Data File 1 (pp. 2–3)** What percent of people surveyed watch more than 21 hours of TV per week?

Write each as a percent.

16. 98¢ compared to 100¢

17. 11 students out of 100 students are left handed

18. 97 days out of 100 days were sunny last summer

19. 4 radios per every 100 radios arrive damaged

20. 85 correct answers out of 100 questions

Use the numbers 1 through 100.

21. What percent are multiples of 3?

22. What percent are odd?

23. What percent are prime?

24. What percent have at least one 7?

25. What percent are neither prime nor composite?

26. Thirty-five percent of a group surveyed said football was their favorite sport. What percent did not choose football?

27. How much will a sales tax of 5% add to the price of a \$1 item? a \$10 item?

28. Ask 10 people how many hours of TV they watch each week. Use a percent to tell how many watch 10 h or more.

29. **Medicine** In 1790 Dr. Benjamin Rush recorded that 34% of 100 patients died before age 6. Another 41% died before age 26. What percent of his patients lived to age 26 or beyond?

30. **Investigation (p. 362)** Make a scale drawing of Earth and its moon, showing size and distance. Use a diameter of 2 in. for Earth. Round distances to the nearest thousand.

What's Ahead

- Converting percents, fractions, and decimals

WHAT YOU'LL NEED

✓ Graph paper

9-8 Percents, Fractions, and Decimals

WORK TOGETHER

Work in groups to explore percents, fractions, and decimals. Use a 10 × 10 grid for each model.

1. a. Model the percents 30%, 75%, 20%, and 50%.
   b. Model the fractions $\frac{3}{4}$, $\frac{1}{2}$, $\frac{3}{10}$, and $\frac{1}{5}$.
   c. Model the decimals 0.2, 0.5, 0.75, and 0.3.
   d. Match each percent with a fraction and a decimal.

2. Express each shaded area as a percent, as a fraction in simplest form, and as a decimal.

a. 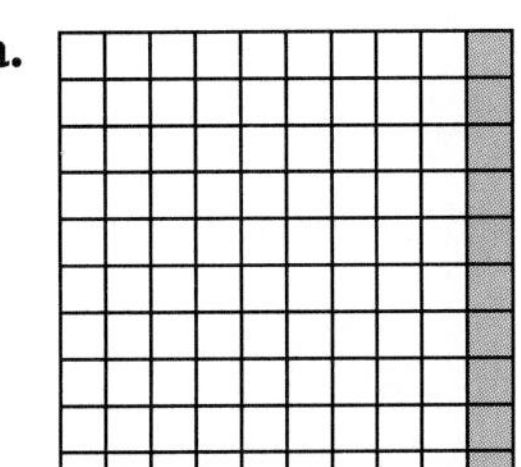

b. 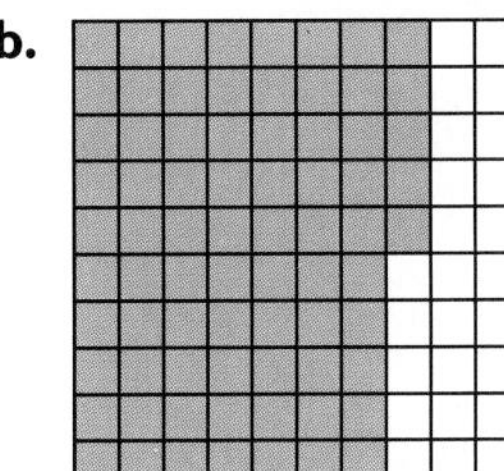

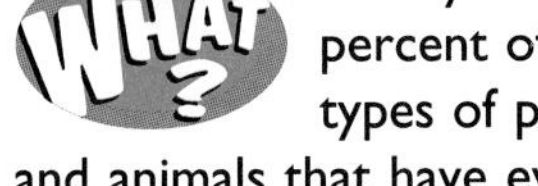

Ninety-nine percent of all types of plants and animals that have ever lived are now extinct.

Source: *The Macmillan Illustrated Almanac For Kids*

THINK AND DISCUSS

You can write a percent as a fraction and as a decimal.

Example 1 Write 36% as a fraction in simplest form and as a decimal.

$36\% = \frac{36}{100}$ — Write the percent as a fraction with a denominator of 100.

$\frac{36}{100} = \frac{9}{25}$ — Write the fraction in simplest form.

$\frac{36}{100} = 0.36$ — Write the fraction as a decimal.

$36\% = \frac{9}{25} = 0.36$

LOOK BACK How could you use a model to show 35% as a fraction and as a decimal?

WHAT? About seven tenths of Earth's surface is covered by water. **Write the decimal as a percent.**

You can also write a fraction as a decimal and as a percent.

Example 2 Write $\frac{3}{10}$ as a decimal and as a percent.

$\frac{3}{10} = \frac{30}{100}$ — **Rewrite the fraction as an equivalent fraction with a denominator of 100.**

$\frac{30}{100} = 0.3$ — **Write the fraction as a decimal.**

$\frac{30}{100} = 30\%$ — **Write the fraction as a percent.**

$\frac{3}{10} = 0.30 = 30\%$

3. **Discussion** How would you write 0.40 as a fraction in simplest form and as a percent?

You can use a fraction calculator to convert fractions, decimals, and percents.

Example 3 Use a fraction calculator to write 50% as a decimal and as a fraction in simplest form.

50 [%] 0.5 — **Use the percent key.**

.5 [F↔D] 5/10 — **Use the fraction to decimal key.**

5/10 [Simp] [=] 1/2 — **Use the Simp key.**

$50\% = 0.5 = \frac{5}{10} = \frac{1}{2}$

4. **Calculator** Write 58% as a decimal and as a fraction in simplest form.

TRY THESE

Shade each amount on a 10 × 10 grid. Describe the shaded area as a fraction in simplest form, as a decimal, and as a percent.

5. 0.8
6. $\frac{11}{20}$
7. 0.72
8. $\frac{2}{5}$
9. 6%

10. The air we breathe is about 80% nitrogen and 20% oxygen. Write each percent as a fraction in simplest form and as a decimal.

ON YOUR OWN

Copy and complete the table below. Write each fraction in simplest form.

	Fraction	Decimal	Percent
11.	■	■	22%
12.	■	0.78	■
13.	$\frac{22}{25}$	■	■
14.	■	0.55	■
15.	$\frac{4}{5}$	■	■

Use the graph at the right.

16. In what percent of lunch boxes are you likely to find fruit?

17. **Choose A, B, C, or D.** Which of the following can you *not* conclude from the graph?
    a. About one fourth of the lunch boxes contained fruit.
    b. Almost 10% of the lunch boxes contained a sandwich.
    c. Fruit was in almost twice as many lunch boxes as cookies.
    d. Students don't take drinks in their lunch boxes.
    e. Take a lunch box survey in your class. Make a graph to show your results.

18. **Writing** How are fractions, decimals, and percents alike? How are they different?

19. a. The table shows the fraction of high school students who graduated from 1940 to 1990. Write each fraction as a percent.

Year	1940	1950	1960	1970	1980	1990
Graduates	$\frac{1}{4}$	$\frac{17}{50}$	$\frac{11}{25}$	$\frac{11}{20}$	$\frac{69}{100}$	$\frac{77}{100}$

Source: *Universal Almanac*

b. Graph the data in the table.
c. Use your graph to predict the percent of high school graduates in the year 2000.

Mixed REVIEW

Evaluate.

1. 13^3
2. 9^3

Write as a percent.

3. 40 out of every 100 teens choose their own clothes.
4. 92 out of every 100 teens help with food shopping.
5. Dwania is saving dimes. The first day she saves 1 dime and the second day 2 dimes. Each day she saves 1 more dime than the day before. How much money will she have after 2 weeks?

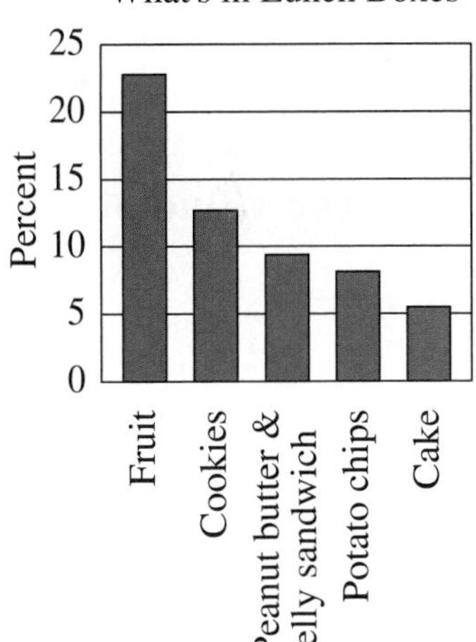

Practice

Write a ratio in three ways using the letters of the word SUPERCALAFRAGALISTICEXPIALIDOCIOUS.

1. the number of A's compared to the total number of letters
2. the number of E's compared to the number of vowels
3. the number of I's compared to the number of S's
4. the number of consonants compared to the total number of letters

Write each ratio as a fraction in simplest form.

5. 20 to 80
6. 15 : 35
7. 33 : 77
8. 14 to 56
9. 17 : 51
10. vowels to consonants in the alphabet
11. vowels to consonants in your first and last name
12. Moira is taking dance lessons. She pays $125 for 10 lessons.
    a. Write the cost of the lessons as a unit rate.
    b. Find the cost of 25 lessons.

Find the value of *n*.

13. $\frac{n}{28} = \frac{9}{12}$
14. $\frac{45}{n} = \frac{30}{48}$
15. $\frac{60}{108} = \frac{n}{9}$
16. $\frac{96}{144} = \frac{4}{n}$
17. $\frac{3}{15} = \frac{12}{n}$

Use a centimeter ruler and the scale drawing at the right.

1 cm : 1 m

18. Find the actual length of the bicycle.
19. Find the actual diameter of the front tire.

Write each as a percent, as a fraction in simplest form, and as a decimal.

20. 24 cm out of 100 cm
21. 55 students out of 100 students
22. 3 hats out of 25 hats
23. 5 pens out of 20 pens
24. 40 heads out of 100 coin tosses
25. 2 days out of 10 days

9-9 Estimating with Percents

What's Ahead

• Estimating a percent of a number

WHAT YOU'LL NEED

✓ Graph paper

Advertisers often use percents. "Save 25% on all cameras." "Our store has expanded. We now offer 40% more merchandise." Knowing how to estimate with percents will help you make sense of such ads.

THINK AND DISCUSS

A jacket is on sale for 60% of the regular price of $49.95. Is $25 enough to buy the jacket? You can use a model to help you visualize the situation. Round $49.95 to $50. Let 100% represent the regular price.

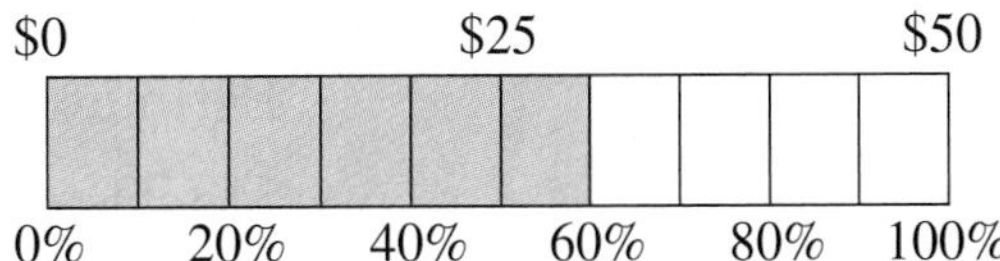

The dollar amounts are above the model and the percentages are below.

1. Why do you think $50 was chosen for the rounded amount? To what might you round $43.99? $55?
2. Why do you think there are ten sections in the model? How many sections are shaded? What percent does each section represent?
3. Copy the model on graph paper. Write dollar amounts above 20%, 40%, 60% and 80%. What is the dollar value of each section?
4. What does the shading in the model represent?
5. Estimate the cost of the jacket. Explain your reasoning.
6. Based on your estimate, is $25 enough to buy the jacket on sale? Why or why not?

Your brain uses about 20% of the calories you eat and about 15% of your blood supply. But your brain accounts for only 2% of your body weight.

You can use mental math to estimate percents.

Example 1 You have breakfast at the Blue Diner. Estimate a 10% tip for a bill of \$6.42.

$\$6.42 \approx \$6.50$	**Round to a convenient place.**
$10\% = 0.10$	**Think of the percent as a decimal.**
$0.10 \times 6.50 = 0.65$	**Multiply mentally.**

The tip is about \$.65.

7. Look at Example 1. Why do you think \$6.42 was rounded to \$6.50 rather than to \$6 or \$7?

8. **Writing** Describe a method for estimating a 15% tip. Include guidelines for rounding the amount of the bill.

Some states charge a sales tax on a variety of things. You can use mental math to estimate the added cost of sales tax.

Example 2 You buy a CD for \$13.99. The sales tax is 3%. Estimate the sales tax and the final cost.

$\$13.99 \approx \$14.00$	**Round to a convenient place.**
3% → 3¢ per dollar	**Think of the percent as cents per dollar.**
$14 \times 3 = 42$	**Multiply mentally.**
$14 + 0.42 = 14.42$	**Add the estimates.**

The sales tax is about \$.42. The final cost is about \$14.42.

9. Look at Example 2. Would you ever want to round the price of an item down before estimating the sales tax? Why or why not?

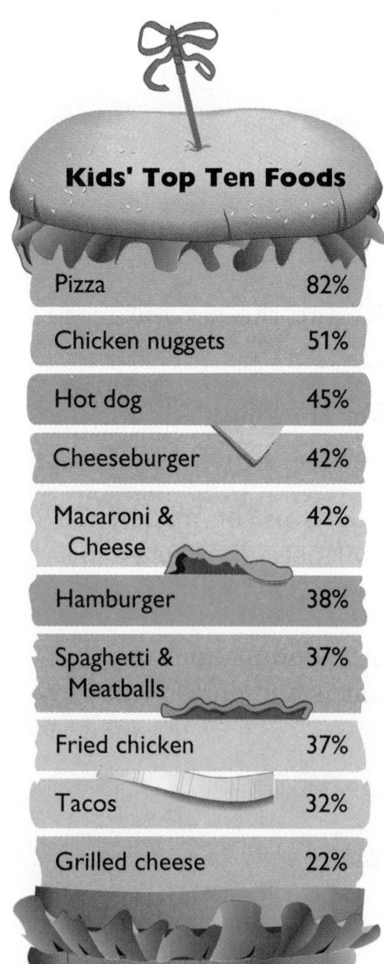

Kids' Top Ten Foods
Pizza 82%
Chicken nuggets 51%
Hot dog 45%
Cheeseburger 42%
Macaroni & Cheese 42%
Hamburger 38%
Spaghetti & Meatballs 37%
Fried chicken 37%
Tacos 32%
Grilled cheese 22%

Source: *Gallup Organization*

WORK TOGETHER

When asked to list their favorite foods, a group of students gave the responses shown at the left. Pizza was the favorite food of 82% of the students.

10. a. **Discussion** Suppose 103 students were surveyed. Would the statement "About 30 students chose tacos." make sense? Why or why not?

b. Suppose 207 students were surveyed. How could you estimate the number of students that chose each food?

11. Use the *Kids Top Ten Foods* chart. Estimate the number of students in your class who will choose pizza as number 1, chicken nuggets as number 2, and so on for all ten foods. You may want to use a model.

12. a. Conduct a survey among your classmates. Have each student rank the foods in the chart from 1 to 10. Write the results as percents.

b. **Writing** How do your survey results compare with your estimates in Exercise 11?

TRY THESE

What dollar amount does the shaded part represent?

13. 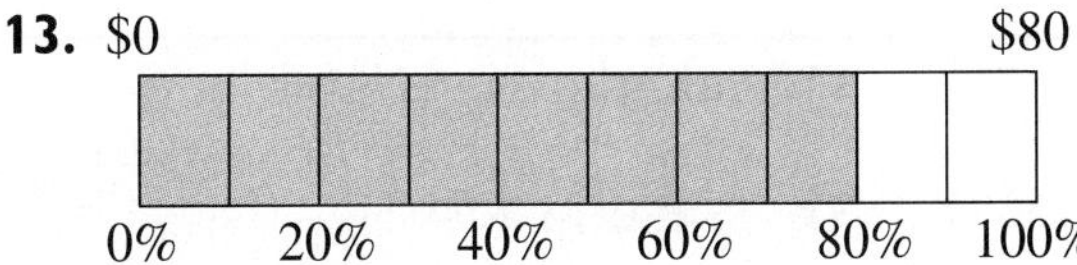

14. 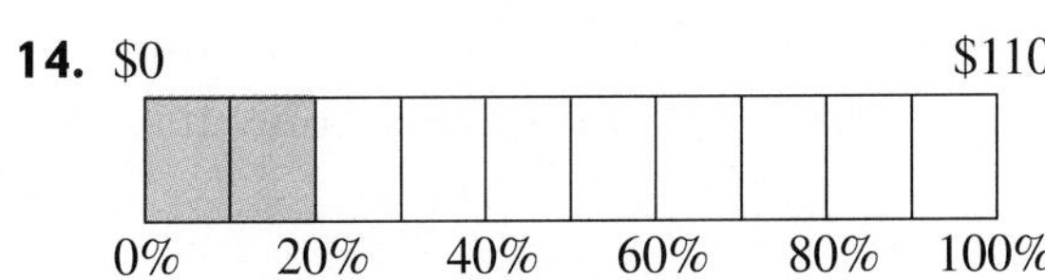

15. The regular price for a pair of boots is $23.99. They are on sale for 80% of the regular price. Estimate the sale price.

16. Estimate a 10% tip, a 15% tip, and a 20% tip for a meal that costs $5.83.

17. Estimate the sales tax and final cost for a hat that costs $18.59 with a sales tax of 5%.

Mixed REVIEW

Evaluate.

1. $\frac{2}{5} + \frac{1}{3}$ 2. $\frac{7}{12} - \frac{3}{8}$

Write as a percent.

3. $\frac{9}{36}$ 4. $\frac{21}{28}$

Write as a fraction.

5. 40% 6. 85%

7. How many 3-digit numbers are divisible by 13? Explain your method.

ON YOUR OWN

Draw a model to help you estimate each amount.

18. 90% of 41 19. 20% of 486 20. 10% of 129

21. 25% of 53 22. 75% of 98 23. 15% of 21

24. A baseball mitt is on sale for 75% of the original price of $39.99. Estimate the sale price of the mitt.

25. **Critical Thinking** The regular price of a chair is $349. Estimate the amount saved for each sale price.

  a. 20% off **b.** 30% off **c.** 75% off

26. By the age of two a child's height is usually about 50% of its full adult height. Estimate the adult height of a 2-year old whose height is 2 ft 9 in.

27. Miguel received the following tips. Estimate the value of each. Which tip was for the greatest amount?

  a. 15% of $4.20 **b.** 10% of $4.75 **c.** 12% of $6.00

Use the sales tax chart at the left. Estimate the sales tax and final cost of the item in each state.

State Sales Tax	
State	**Tax**
Colorado	3%
Florida	6%
Georgia	4%
Massachusetts	5%
New Jersey	7%

Source: *The World Almanac and Book of Facts.*

28. roller blades; $75

29. dictionary; $14.59

30. poster; $9.99

31. calculator; $18.50

32. game; $21.03

33. erasers; $.79

34. **Activity** Find out if there is a sales tax in your state. Then, find out how the state uses the money collected from the sales tax.

35. **Data File 9 (pp. 360–361)** Estimate the number of girls in each age group that passed the aerobic fitness test. Assume 250 girls per age group took the test.

36. **Shopping** A store is having a sale. All items are marked down 30%. Estimate the savings for each item.

  a. a tee-shirt regularly priced at $16.99

  b. a jacket regularly priced at $129

37. Juanita and Tanisha ate lunch at T.J.'s Cantina. The bill was $15.75. They want to add a 15% tip and then share the bill equally. Estimate the amount each should pay.

38. **Investigation (p. 362)** Make a list of objects that might appear in a model of the solar system other than the sun, the Earth, the moon, and the planets.

What's Ahead

• Finding a percent of a number

9-10 Finding a Percent of a Number

THINK AND DISCUSS

Your heart rate or pulse increases when you exercise. A safe exercise range is between 60% and 80% of your maximum *safe heart rate.* You can find your maximum safe heart rate by subtracting your age from 220.

There are at least three different methods you can use to find a person's safe exercise range.

Example Find the safe exercise range for a 12-year-old.

$220 - 12 = 208$ **Find the maximum safe heart rate.**

Method 1 Use a model.

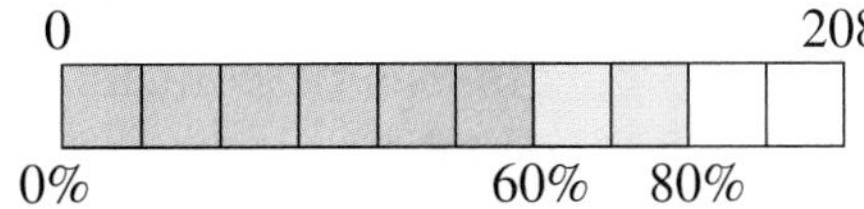

Each section represents 20.8 heart beats.

Method 2 Write the percents as fractions.

$$60\% = \frac{60}{100} \times 208 = \frac{12{,}480}{100} = 124.8 \approx 125$$

$$80\% = \frac{80}{100} \times 208 = \frac{16{,}640}{100} = 166.4 \approx 166$$

Method 3 Write the percent as decimals. Use a calculator.

60 [%] [×] 208 [=] 124.8 ≈ 125

80 [%] [×] 208 [=] 166.4 ≈ 166

Each method gives the same result. The safe exercising range for a 12-year-old is about 125 to 166 heart beats per minute.

1. Find the safe exercise range for a 20-year-old and for a 50-year-old. How does the safe exercise range change as a person grows older?

You can check your heart rate or use the *talk test* to tell whether you are exercising in the right range. If you're so out of breath that you can't talk, slow down. If you can sing, you can pick up the pace. When you can talk comfortably while exercising you are on target.

Source: *Prentice Hall Health*

Sometimes one method is more appropriate or convenient to use than another.

2. Which method would you use to answer each question? Explain your reasons. Use a 24 h day.
   a. Catherine spends 25% of her day in school. How many hours does Catherine spend in school each day?
   b. Ian practices the piano for 5% of the day. For how many hours does Ian practice the piano each day?
   c. **Discussion** Describe a way to calculate each percent using mental math.

TRY THESE

3. Approximately 67% of body weight is water. Suppose a person weighs 114 lb. About how many pounds is water?

4. In the United States, about 46% of the population wears glasses or contact lenses.
   a. How many people would you expect to wear glasses or contact lenses in a group of 85 people?
   b. Explain how you found your answer and why you chose that method.
   c. How many people in your classroom would you expect to wear glasses or contact lenses?

Mixed REVIEW

Compare. Use >, <, or =.

1. $\frac{3}{8}$ ■ $\frac{2}{4}$ 2. $\frac{6}{15}$ ■ $\frac{2}{3}$

Estimate a 15% tip for each amount.

3. $4.00   4. $15.50

Solve for *n*.

5. $\frac{1}{3} = \frac{n}{360}$

6. $\frac{3}{8} = \frac{n}{360}$

7. The chorus director can arrange singers in rows of 10, 12, or 15 with no one left over. What is the least number of singers in the chorus?

ON YOUR OWN

Find each percent. Use any method.

5. 50% of 786   6. 43% of 61   7. 10% of 56

8. 75% of 84   9. 37% of 140   10. 80% of 255

11. 12% of 72   12. 25% of 112   13. 66% of 99

14. **Sports** The Lions won 75% of their 28 games this year. How many games did they win?

15. During the summer Rosa earned $950. She saved 40%. How much money did she save?

16. **Writing** Explain how you would decide when to use each of the three methods in this lesson when finding the percent of a number.

Frequency of Vowels in Written Passages						
Letter	A	E	I	O	U	Y
Frequency	8%	13%	6%	8%	3%	2%

Use the table above to estimate the number of letters you would expect in each passage.

17. the number of E's in a passage of 300 letters

18. the number of A's in a passage of 1400 letters

19. the number of U's in a passage of 235 letters

20. the number of I's in a passage of 695 letters

21. Why don't the percents in the table add to 100%?

22. **a.** Examine a short passage in a book. Count the number of letters in the passage. Use the percents from the table to estimate the number of each vowel to expect.

b. Count the number of A's. Is your count the same as your expected number in (**a.**)? Why or why not?

c. Count the number of B's. Write the number as a percent of the total letters in the passage.

d. Do you think you have enough data to draw any conclusions about the general frequency of the letter B in written passages? Why or why not?

23. Nail biting is a hard habit to kick. About 40% of children and teenagers bite their nails. A town has 1,618 children and teenagers. How many would you expect to be nail biters?

24. The dance club is holding its annual show. The club printed 400 tickets and sold 85% of the tickets. How many tickets did the club sell?

Only two words in the English language use all the vowels a, e, i, o, u, in order. They are *facetious* and *abstemious.* **Find out what each word means.**

Source: *The Macmillan Illustrated Almanac For Kids*

25. **Data File 9 (pp. 360–361)** Use the number of teens surveyed. How many females participate in volleyball? how many males?

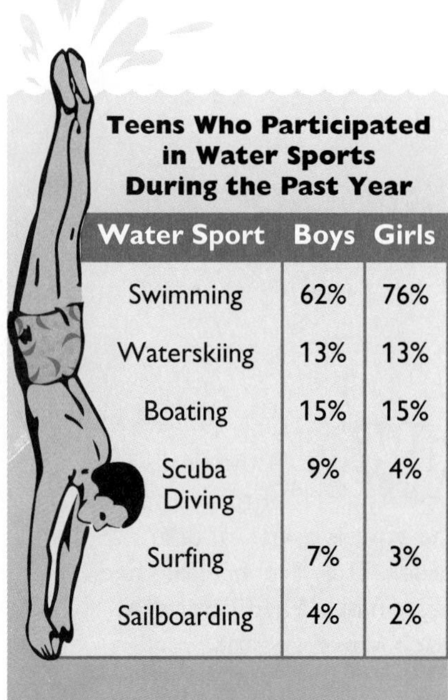

Teens Who Participated in Water Sports During the Past Year

Water Sport	Boys	Girls
Swimming	62%	76%
Waterskiing	13%	13%
Boating	15%	15%
Scuba Diving	9%	4%
Surfing	7%	3%
Sailboarding	4%	2%

Source: *Teenage Research Unlimited*

Use the table at the left.

26. An interviewer talked to 250 males and 250 females between the ages of 12 and 15. How many would you expect to have been swimming in the past year?

CHECKPOINT

1. The average of three consecutive numbers is 9. Their sum is 27. What are the numbers?

2. Find the value of x. The figures are similar.

5, 12; x, 24

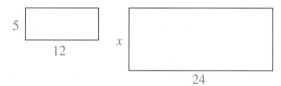

3. A map has a scale of 1 cm : 75 km. The distance on the map from Hondo to Cheyenne is 3.5 cm. What is the actual distance?

Use a 10 × 10 grid to model each percent.

4. 17%　5. 46%　6. 89%　7. 71%

Write as a percent.

8. $\frac{6}{8}$　9. 0.45　10. 0.67　11. $\frac{15}{25}$

12. **Choose A, B, C, or D.** Which of the following is *not* a way to find 88% of 40?

A. 0.88×40　**B.** $\frac{88}{100} \times 40$

C. $\frac{40}{n} = \frac{88}{100}$　**D.** 0.40×88

Find each percent.

13. 58% of 72　14. 86% of 41　15. 8% of 40

What's Ahead

• Making circle graphs.

9-11 Constructing a Circle Graph

WORK TOGETHER

WHAT YOU'LL NEED

✓ Dot paper

✓ Metric Ruler

✓ Scissors

✓ Glue

✓ Compass

✓ Protractor

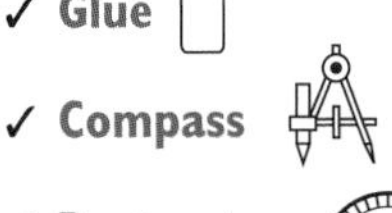

Circle graphs provide a good visual representation of percent data. The table shows the results of a survey of 1,000 adults who were asked to think about the amount of time they spend watching TV. Work with a partner to construct a circle graph for the data.

Too much	Too little	About right	Don't know
49%	18%	31%	2%

Source: *Gallup Organization*

1. Use the data to make a circle graph.
   - draw a strip 10 cm long, leaving a tab at the end. Since 10 cm = 100 mm, each millimeter represents 1%.
   - Mark the strip with the percentages given in the table.

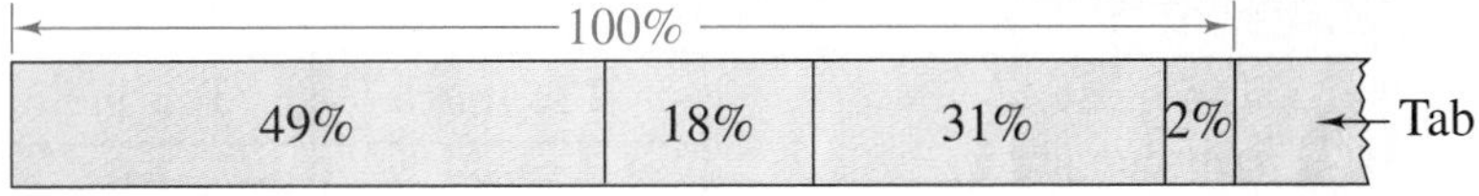

2. Should the percents that make up a circle graph always add to 100%? Why or why not?

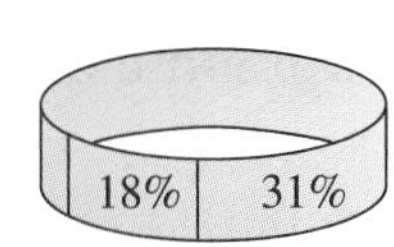

3. Use the strip to form a percent circle. Cut the strip out carefully. Shape the strip into a circle and paste or tape the ends. Make sure to align the beginning and end of the strip.

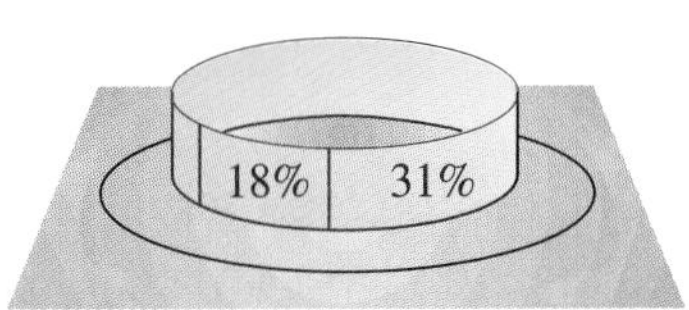

4. Use a compass to draw a circle slightly larger than your percent circle. Place a dot at the center of your circle. Use your percent circle to mark off the percentages around the circumference of the circle. Use a ruler to connect the marks to the center of the circle.

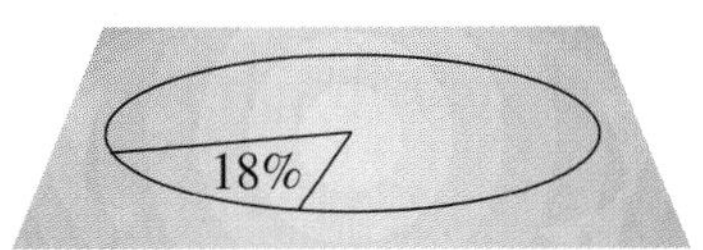

5. Label your graph and give it a title. Does your graph make sense? Use estimation to decide if each section appears to be the correct size.

6. a. Use a protractor to find the measure of each angle on your completed circle graph.

   b. Can you think of another way to find the measure of each angle?

7. Conduct a survey in your classroom to see how your classmates feel about their TV viewing habits. Give the same choice of responses. Make a circle graph of your data.

THINK AND DISCUSS

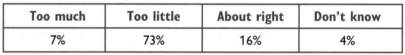

You can also make a circle graph by combining some math skills you already know.

- finding the percent of a number
- the number of degrees in a circle
- using a protractor to draw an angle with a given measure

The most overdue library book in the U.S. was borrowed in 1823. The great-grandson of the borrower returned the book on December 7, 1968. The fine for the overdue book would have been $2,264.

Source: *Guinness Book of Records*

The table below shows the responses of 1,000 adults who were asked whether they spent too much or too little time reading for pleasure.

Too much	Too little	About right	Don't know
7%	73%	16%	4%

Source: *Gallup Organization*

8. **Discussion** Suppose you want to make a circle graph. How could you find the measure of each section using proportions? using percents?

   a. Use a proportion to find the number of degrees for the response "Don't know."

   b. Use a percent to find the number of degrees for the response "Too little."

   c. Use any method to find the number of degrees for the response "About right." Which method do you think is easiest? Why?

   d. Use a compass to draw a circle and a radius. Use your protractor to draw each angle. Label your graph and give it a title.

9. **Discussion** When are circle graphs a better way to display data than tables? Use examples to support your answer.

TRY THESE

10. The graph at the right has the labels in the wrong sections. Tell which section should have each percent label.

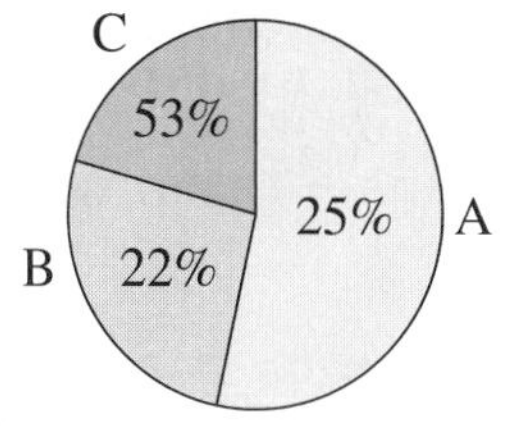

11. La Monte Middle School held several fundraising events. The percent raised from each activity is shown in the table below. Display the data in a circle graph.

Car wash	Paper drive	Book sale	Food stand
42%	28%	18%	12%

ON YOUR OWN

12. a. Construct two circle graphs. One that shows the bus data and another that displays the car pool data. Remember to label your graphs and give them a title.

What Teen Drivers Will Do for Air Quality				
	Very willing	Somewhat willing	Not very willing	Don't know
Use the bus more often	22%	25%	50%	3%
Car pool more often	49%	26%	23%	2%

Source: *Gallup Organization*

b. **Writing** Which option for preserving air quality seems more likely to succeed? Why?

c. Think of another option for preserving air quality. Use the same response choices as in the table and survey 25 students. Make a circle graph to show your results.

13. List the things you do on a Saturday. Estimate the hours you spend on each activity. Write the time as a percent of a 24-hour day. Construct a circle graph.

14. **Data File 1 (pp. 2–3)** Estimate the percent of hours spent on each type of commercial during 604 h of kid's TV.

Mixed REVIEW

Evaluate.

1. $\frac{3}{4} \div \frac{4}{5}$
2. $\frac{8}{15} \div \frac{2}{3}$

Find each percent.

3. 55% of 386
4. 33% of 58
5. Which number doesn't belong? Give a reason for your choice.

2992 1919

4949 2929

CHAPTER 9

Wrap Up

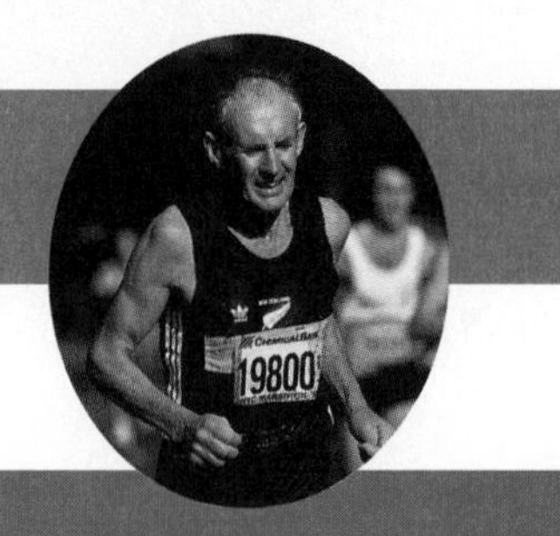

Ratios, Rates, and Proportions 9-1, 9-2, 9-3

A ***ratio*** is a comparison of two numbers.

A ***rate*** is a ratio that compares two measures with different units.

A ***proportion*** is an equation stating that two ratios are equal. You can use cross products to find the missing term in a proportion.

1. A moonrat is a member of the hedgehog family. An adult male's body is about 45 cm long. Write the ratio to compare a moonrat's body length to 1 m in three ways. (1 m = 100 cm)

2. A package of three videotapes is on sale for $5.97. A package of 2 videotapes is on sale for $3.76. Find the unit rate for each. Which tape has the higher unit cost?

Find the value of *n*.

3. $\frac{3}{5} = \frac{n}{35}$ **4.** $\frac{6}{9} = \frac{18}{n}$ **5.** $\frac{n}{6} = \frac{12}{24}$ **6.** $\frac{32}{n} = \frac{8}{4}$ **7.** $\frac{n}{15} = \frac{5}{25}$ **8.** $\frac{17}{51} = \frac{3}{n}$

Similar Figures and Scale Drawings 9-5, 9-6

If two figures are ***similar,*** their corresponding angles are congruent and the ratios of the lengths of their corresponding sides are equal.

A ***scale*** is a ratio that compares length on a drawing or model to the actual length of an object.

9. **Writing** The triangles have equal angle measures. Tell how you would show that the triangles are similar.

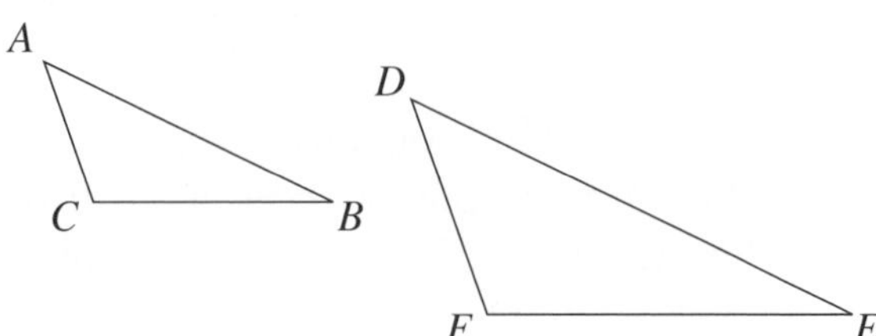

10. A scale on a landscape blueprint is 1 in. : 6 ft. A stone wall is 4 in. long on the blueprint. How long is the wall?

11. A drawing of a leatherback turtle has a scale of 2 cm : 1 m. The drawing of the turtle is 3 cm long. How long is the turtle?

Percents, Fractions, and Decimals 9-7, 9-8, 9-9

A ***percent*** is a ratio that compares a number to 100. You can write a percent as a decimal or as a fraction. You can estimate with a percent.

12. Write 65% as a decimal and as a fraction in simplest form.

13. An office chair is on sale for 80% of the regular price of $87.95. Estimate the sale price.

14. Choose A, B, C, or D. Find the best estimate for 72% of 90.

A. 72 **B.** 45 **C.** 68 **D.** 90

Percent of a Number and Circle Graphs 9-10, 9-11

You can use a model, a fraction, or a decimal to find a percent of a number.

You can make a circle graph to show percent data.

Find each percent.

15. 75% of 40 **16.** 23% of 19 **17.** 60% of 80 **18.** 10% of 235 **19.** 5% of $15.98

20. Use the data at the right to construct a circle graph.

Ways to Get to School

Car	Bus	Bike	Walk
24%	57%	4%	15%

Strategies and Applications 9-4

Sometimes *Guess and Test* is a good strategy to solve problems. Make a reasonable guess, test it against the problem, and keep trying until you find the correct answer.

21. Todd's class is making plastic birdfeeders in two sizes. Small birdfeeders use 2 dowels, large birdfeeders use 3 dowels. The class used 103 dowels to make 38 feeders. How many small birdfeeders did that class make?

GETTING READY FOR CHAPTER 10

22. Lian planned to call her new friend Onida, but the last two digits of her phone number are smudged. How many possibilities are there for Onida's number?

375-04■■

PUTTING IT ALL TOGETHER

Follow Up

Modeling the Solar System

The Astro County Science Museum has begun its final push for donations to help build its model of the solar system. It's time for you to do your part. Write a letter to the editor of the Astro County Gazette. In your letter, explain why you believe local citizens should donate to the project or why they should oppose the project. Explain your reasons for your position. The following are suggestions to help you compose your letter.

- ✓ Use ratios.
- ✓ Use proportions.
- ✓ Use a scale drawing.

The problems preceded by the magnifying glass (p. 372, # 30; p. 379, # 19; p. 386, # 30, and p. 394 # 38) will help you support your argument.

The museum was right to emphasize the importance of science education in its brochure. Surveys regularly reveal that the American public is greatly misinformed about even the most basic science facts. One recent survey showed that 20% of Americans believe that the Sun revolves around the Earth.

Excursion: In a scale model of our galaxy with the Sun the size of a basketball, how far away would the nearest star (after the Sun) appear?

Where to Look:

- an encyclopedia or an astronomy text

ROUND AND ROUND

Do this with your group.

Look through newspapers and magazines for examples of at least 3 circle graphs. For each circle graph, write two words problems that can be solved by using the information displayed in the graph.

Excursion: Look closely at each circle graph. How could the information displayed in any of the circle graphs be displayed by using another kind of graph? Choose one circle graph and make another kind of graph that displays the same information.

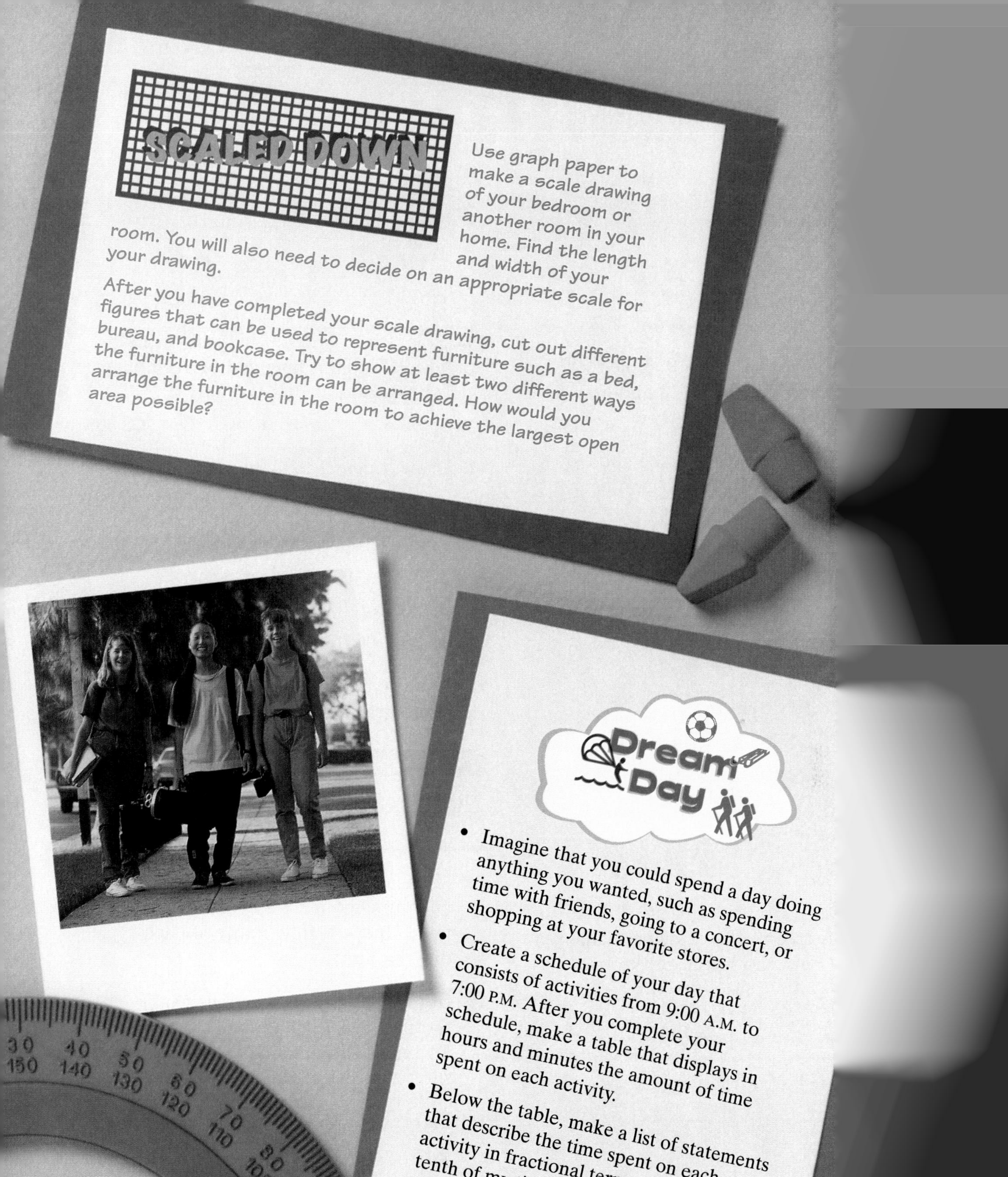
SCALED DOWN
Use graph paper to make a scale drawing of your bedroom or another room in your home. Find the length and width of your room. You will also need to decide on an appropriate scale for your drawing.
After you have completed your scale drawing, cut out different figures that can be used to represent furniture such as a bed, bureau, and bookcase. Try to show at least two different ways the furniture in the room can be arranged. How would you arrange the furniture in the room to achieve the largest open area possible?
Dream Day
• Imagine that you could spend a day doing anything you wanted, such as spending time with friends, going to a concert, or shopping at your favorite stores.
• Create a schedule of your day that consists of activities from 9:00 A.M. to 7:00 P.M. After you complete your schedule, make a table that displays in hours and minutes the amount of time spent on each activity.
• Below the table, make a list of statements that describe the time spent on each activity in fractional terms, such as "One-tenth of my time was spent at a soccer game."

CHAPTER 9

Assessment

1. Which is another way to write the ratio 6 : 3?

   A. 3 : 6 **B.** 6 , 3

   C. $\frac{3}{6}$ **D.** 6 to 3

2. **Writing** Are the ratios 9 apples to 12 apples and 6 apples to 10 apples equal? Explain your answer.

3. Write a ratio comparing the shaded region to the unshaded region as a fraction in lowest terms.

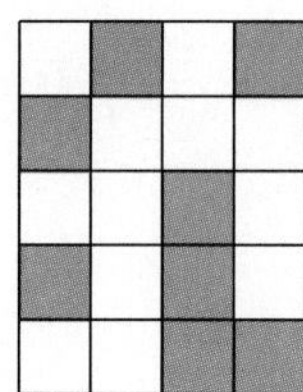

4. Find a ratio equal to $\frac{3}{12}$.

   A. $\frac{9}{24}$ **B.** $\frac{4}{1}$

   C. $\frac{8}{32}$ **D.** $\frac{5}{15}$

5. Solve for n.

   a. $\frac{21}{35} = \frac{9}{n}$ **b.** $\frac{n}{63} = \frac{4}{14}$

6. A scale drawing has a scale of 1 cm to 1.5 m. A tree in the drawing measures 4.5 cm. Find the height of the tree.

7. Write each as a percent.

   a. $\frac{11}{20}$ **b.** 0.7

8. Write each as a fraction in lowest terms.

   a. 38% **b.** 0.62

9. Express each as a decimal.

   a. $\frac{6}{20}$ **b.** 55%

   c. 6% **d.** $\frac{78}{100}$

10. **Estimation** Choose the best estimate for $\frac{5}{12}$. Explain how you arrived at your estimate.

    A. 50% **B.** 40% **C.** 30%

11. Draw a model to show each percent.

    a. 75% of 200 **b.** 30% of 210

12. Find each percent.

    a. 52% of 96

    b. 20% of 400

    c. 38% of 150

13. Use the data in the table to make a circle graph.

Types of Books Preferred

Mysteries	Biographies	Fiction	Humor
22%	13%	55%	10%

14. Marisa spent \$4.25 on stamps. She bought some for \$.29 each and some for \$.35 each. How many of each type did she buy?

15. Gerald bought art supplies that totalled \$15.78. The tax is 3%. Estimate the amount of the tax and the total cost of the art supplies.

16. Estimate a 15% tip on each bill.

    a. \$25.35 **b.** \$9.35

Cumulative Review

Choose A, B, C, or D.

1. What is the ratio of the number of squares to the number of triangles?

   A. 1:1 B. 1:2

   C. 2:1 D. 1:4

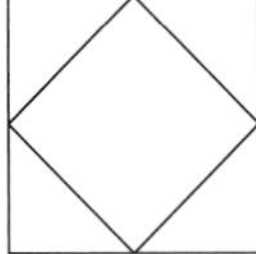

2. A garage charges \$2.00 for the first 90 min and \$1.00 for each additional half hour. Which expression can you use to find the cost of parking for 4h?

   A. 2.00 + 4(1.00)

   B. 2.00 + 2.5(2.00)

   C. 2.00 + 5(1.00)

   D. 4(2.00 + 1.00)

3. Which number is *not* a prime factor of 2,420?

   A. 2 B. 3 C. 5 D. 11

4. What is the best estimate for the area of the shaded region?

   A. 18 square units

   B. 20 square units

   C. 25 square units

   D. 30 square units

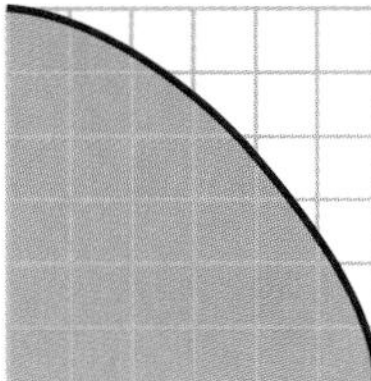

5. Find the value of the expression $3 + b^2$ when $b = 5$.

   A. 64 B. 13

   C. 16 D. 28

6. Which statement is *not* true about points, A, B, and C shown?

   A. A, B, and C are collinear

   B. A, B, and C are coplanar

   C. $\angle ABC$ is acute

   D. A does not lie on $\overleftrightarrow{BC}$

7. What should you do first to find the difference $5\frac{1}{4} - 3\frac{2}{3}$?

   A. Find the difference $5 - 3$

   B. Write $\frac{1}{4}$ and $\frac{2}{3}$ as $\frac{3}{12}$ and $\frac{8}{12}$.

   C. Find the difference $5 - 3\frac{2}{3}$.

   D. Write $5\frac{1}{4}$ as $4\frac{5}{4}$.

8. Sukie boarded the school bus at 7:48 A.M. and arrived at school at 8:13 A.M. How many minutes did she spend on the bus?

   A. 13 min B. 65 min

   C. 25 min D. 15 min

9. Which expression is equivalent to $35 \cdot 10$?

   A. $35\ (100 \div 10)$

   B. $35\ (100 \cdot 10)$

   C. $35 + (100 \cdot 10)$

   D. $35 + (100 + 10)$

10. Find the mean of the allowances: \$4, \$2, \$2.50, \$4, \$3.

    A. \$4.00 B. \$2.50

    C. \$2.75 D. \$3.10

CHAPTER 10

Probability

SHAKE, RATTLE, & ROLL

The map shows the San Andreas fault in California. The numbers at each location show the likelihood of an earthquake and the expected measure on the Richter scale.

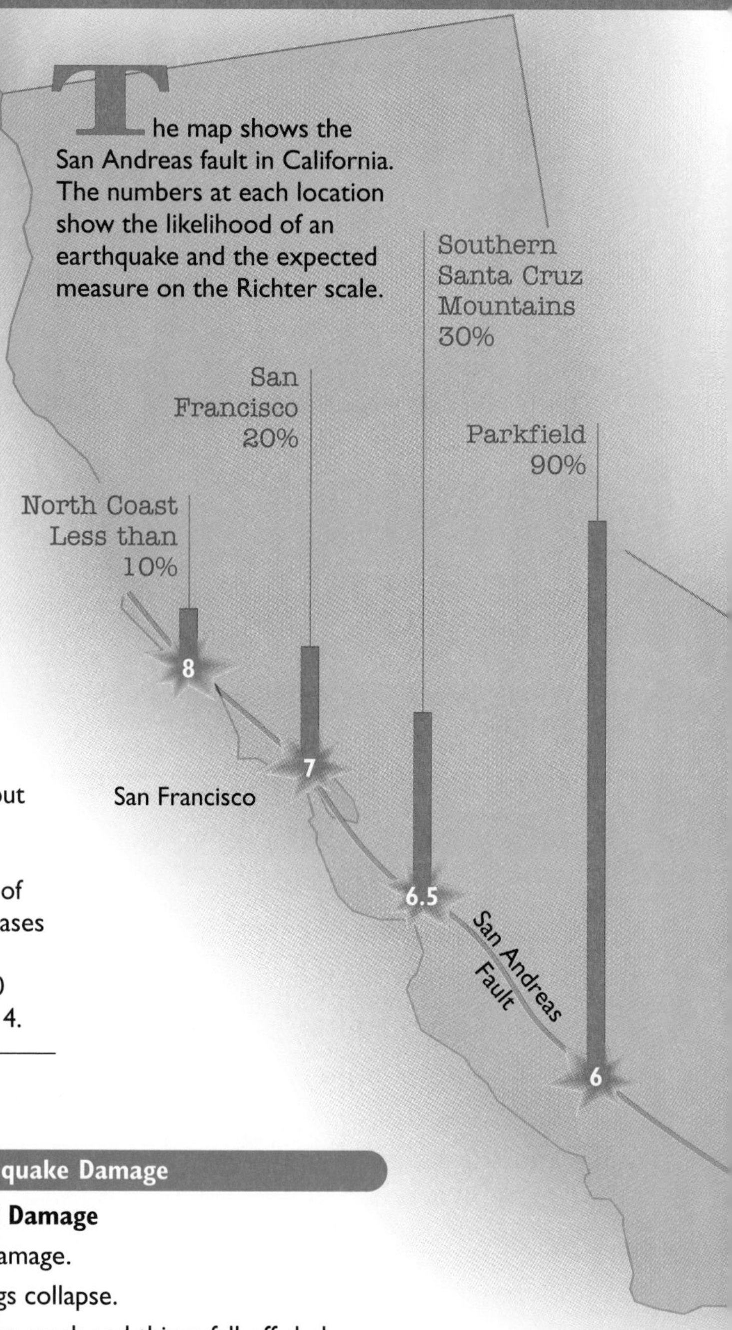

North Coast Less than 10% — 8

San Francisco 20% — 7

Southern Santa Cruz Mountains 30% — 6.5

Parkfield 90% — 6

San Francisco

San Andreas Fault

The Richter Scale

Scientists use the Richter scale to measure the size of an earthquake. Charles F. Richter developed the scale in 1935 to measure the amount of ground motion.

For each increase of one unit on the Richter scale, an earthquake releases about 30 times as much energy. This means it would take 30 earthquakes of magnitude 6 to release the same energy as just one of magnitude 7. An earthquake rating 6 releases about 30 times as much energy as an earthquake rating 5 and about 30^2 or 900 times the energy of an earthquake rating 4.

Source: *Earthquakes,* Bruce A. Bolt

Earthquake Damage

Richter Scale	Typical Damage
8	Total damage.
7	Buildings collapse.
6	Buildings crack and things fall off shelves.
5	Furniture and pictures move.
3–4	People feel a rumble and hear noise.
1–2	Most people don't notice anything.

Source: *Junior Scholastic*

Data File 10

WHAT YOU WILL LEARN

- how to determine fair and unfair games
- how to use tree diagrams and formulas to determine probability
- how to use technology to simulate probability experiments
- how to use probability to make predictions

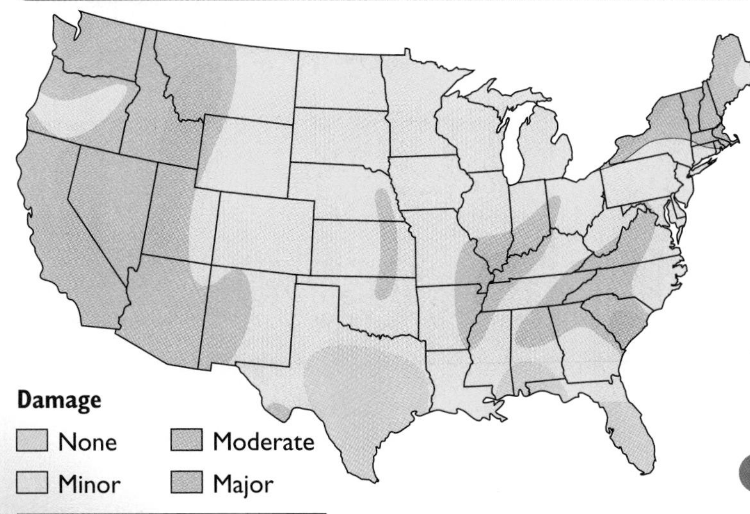

Source: *Earthquakes*, Seymour Simon

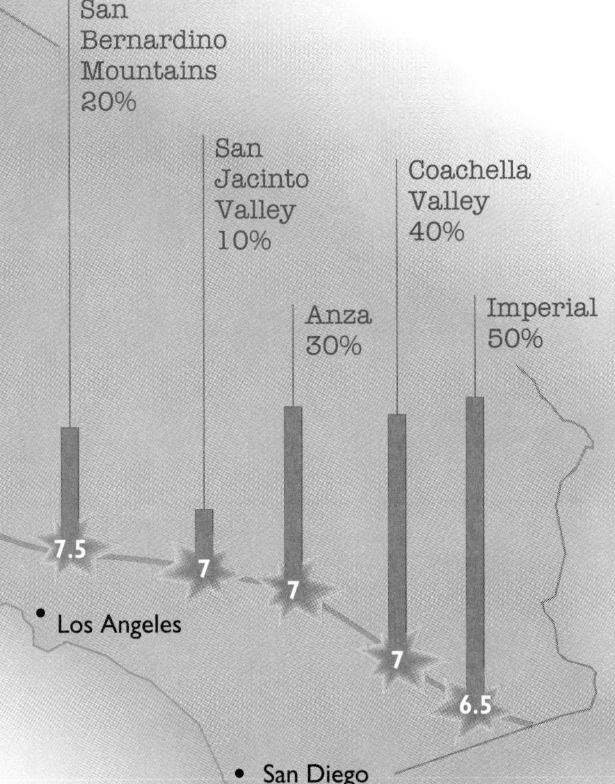

In 1976, more than 240,000 people were reported killed in an earthquake in Tangshan, China. The earthquake measured 8.2 on the Richter scale and was felt up to 800 km away.

Earthquake Waves

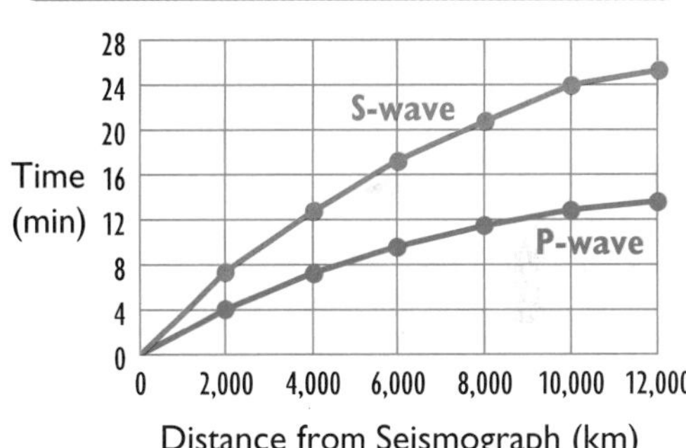

WAVES OF AN EARTHQUAKE

Primary (P) waves travel with a push-pull motion through the earth at a speed of about 7.7 km/s. Secondary (S) waves travel with a side-to-side motion at a slower speed of about 4.4 km/s.

The graphs show the time for P-waves and S-waves to travel a given distance from an earthquake. A seismograph records the wave vibrations and their arrival time. You can use the graph to estimate the distance between the seismograph and the earthquake. Suppose a seismograph is 1,000 km from an earthquake. It would record P-waves after 2 min and S-waves after 4 min.

Source: *Brief Review in Earth Science*, Prentice Hall; *Movers & Shakers*, State Farm Insurance

investigation

Project File

Memo

Forecasting the weather accurately is an extremely difficult challenge. Some weather forecasters use the "butterfly effect" to explain the difficulty of their job. Imagine a butterfly in Brazil fluttering its wings on Monday morning. The fluttering disturbs the air near the butterfly. The disturbance moves on and on, affecting air currents farther and farther away. By Friday afternoon, the disturbance is affecting storm patterns in Chicago.

Now think of all the tiny air movements at any given moment in the world. How is it possible to predict the combined effects they will have on the weather?

Mission: Predict tomorrow's weather. Your prediction should include an estimate of the high and low temperatures, the amount of precipitation, and any other information you consider important. Explain how you arrived at your prediction and estimate how likely it is to come true.

Leads to Follow

- ✓ What information can you gather that might be useful in making your prediction?
- ✓ What are the main forces that affect the weather in your area?

What's Ahead

- Determining if a game is fair or unfair
- Finding experimental probability

10-1 Exploring Fair and Unfair Games

WHAT YOU'LL NEED

✓ Bag or container

✓ Red or blue cubes (or other objects of two colors)

WORK TOGETHER

Play these three games with a partner.

A game is **fair** if each player has the same chance of winning. Players are *equally likely* to win.

1. Before you play Game 1, answer this question: Do you think the game is fair or unfair? If it is unfair, which player is more likely to win?

Game 1 Place 1 red cube and 1 blue cube in a bag. Draw 1 cube from the bag without looking. If the cube is red, player A wins. If the cube is blue, player B wins.

2. Decide who will draw the cubes and who will record data. Play the game 20 times. Record your results in a table.

Number of times player A won	■
Number of times player B won	■
Number of times we played the game	20

3. Does it seem as if the game is fair or unfair? Explain.
4. Complete Questions 1–3 for Games 2 and 3.

Game 2 Place 2 red cubes and 2 blue cubes in a bag. Draw 2 cubes from the bag without looking. If they are the same color, player A wins. If they are not the same color, player B wins.

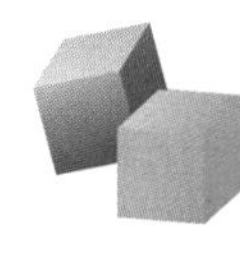

Game 3 Place 3 red cubes and 1 blue cube in a bag. Draw 2 cubes from the bag without looking. If they are the same color, player A wins. If they are not the same color, player B wins.

5. As a class, decide which of the three games are fair and which are unfair.

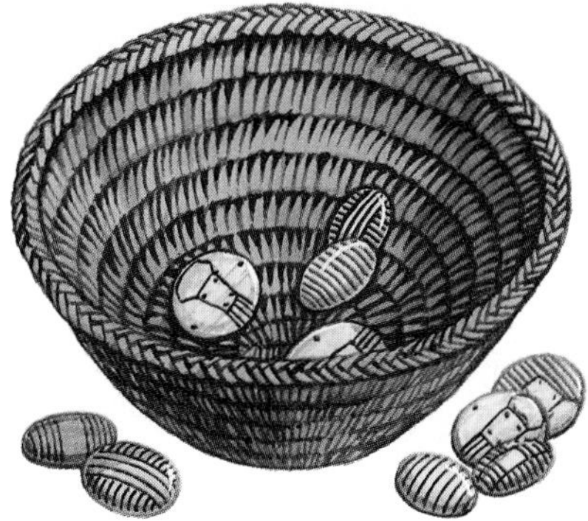

***The Mandan people** along the Missouri River played a game of chance involving tossing decorated bone dice in a basket. The score depended on which sides of the dice landed facing up.*

Mixed REVIEW

Calculate.

1. $\frac{9}{10} + \frac{4}{17}$

2. $2\frac{3}{4} - 1\frac{2}{5}$

3. Construct a circle graph.

Favorite Fruit	
Apples	65%
Oranges	15%
Other	20%

Complete each pattern.

4. 2, 4, 7, 11, ■, ■, ■

5. 0.75, 1.05, 1.35, 1.65, ■, ■, ■

THINK AND DISCUSS

6. Does a fair game always seem fair? Give examples.

7. Si and Karen played Game 1. Karen won 7 times and Si won 13 times. How can this happen if the game is fair?

8. Ki-Jana and Susana played Game 1. The first 3 cubes drawn were blue. Is the fourth cube more likely to be red or blue?

You can use a ratio to show the fraction of the time that a player wins. This ratio is the *experimental probability* of winning the game. You write this ratio as shown below.

$$\text{Probability(A wins)} = \frac{\text{number of times A won}}{\text{total number of times played}}$$

$$\text{Probability(B wins)} = \frac{\text{number of times B won}}{\text{total number of times played}}$$

9. Combine the class data for each game on the previous page. Find Probability(A wins) and Probability(B wins) for each game. What does this tell you about the games?

10. If you play the games tomorrow, will the experimental probabilities be the same as they were today? Explain.

You can decide if a game is fair or unfair by considering all the possible outcomes.

11. In Game 1, the 2 possible outcomes are red and blue. Are they equally likely? How do you know?

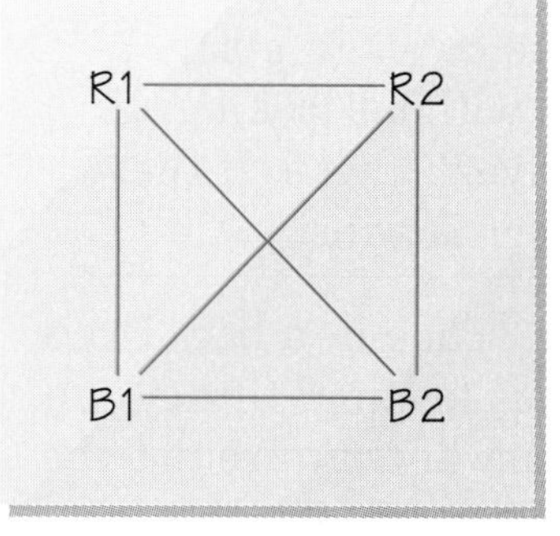

12. For Game 2, Eduardo drew the diagram at the left. Eduardo named the cubes R1, R2, B1, and B2. Each line represents a draw of two cubes.
    a. List all possible outcomes. For example, R1 B1 is one outcome. How many possible outcomes are there?
    b. How many outcomes give player A a win? How many give player B a win? Are A and B equally likely to win?
    c. Is the game fair or unfair? How is this result related to the experimental probabilities you found in Question 9?

13. Draw a diagram for Game 3. List all possible outcomes. Are players A and B equally likely to win? Is the game fair or unfair?

ON YOUR OWN

Game Results	
A wins	卌 ||||
B wins	卌 卌 |
Times played	卌 卌 卌 卌

14. Mia and Jo played a game and completed the table at the right. Find Probability(A wins) and Probability(B wins).

15. If Probability(A wins) = Probability(B wins), what do you know about a game?

16. Leroy rolled 2 dice and found the sum. He played the game many times and recorded the sums in the line plot.

Sum	2	3	4	5	6	7	8	9	10	11	12
	×	×××	×	××	×××××	×××	×××××××	×××××	××	×	

a. Which sum did Leroy get most often?

b. Complete a grid like the one at the right to show all possible outcomes. Which sum is most likely? Compare to your answer in part (a).

c. Use Leroy's data to find Probability(10) and Probability(1).

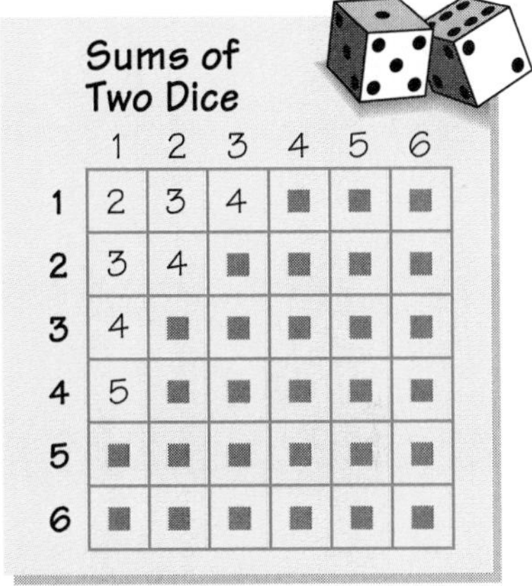

Sums of Two Dice
1 2 3 4 5 6
1 2 3 4 ■ ■ ■
2 3 4 ■ ■ ■ ■
3 4 ■ ■ ■ ■ ■
4 5 ■ ■ ■ ■ ■
5 ■ ■ ■ ■ ■ ■
6 ■ ■ ■ ■ ■ ■

17. Leroy said to Tim, "If the sum of the 2 dice is prime, you win. If the sum is not prime, I win." Use your grid from Exercise 16(b). Is this game fair or unfair? Explain.

FLASHBACK

A prime number has exactly two factors, the number itself and 1. A composite number has more than two factors.

18. a. **Activity** Toss 2 coins at least 25 times. If you toss 2 heads or 2 tails, player A wins. If you toss 1 head and 1 tail, player B wins. Record your results in a table.

b. Does the game seem fair or unfair? Explain.

c. Consider all possible outcomes for the game. Is it fair or unfair? Support your answer without using your recorded data.

19. Bodaway and Litisha played a game 10 times and decided it was unfair. Jaime and Marta played 50 times and decided it was fair. Who do you think is correct? Why?

20. **Writing** You have learned ways to decide if a game seems to be fair or unfair. Which way do you prefer? Why?

21. **Critical Thinking** Design one game that is fair and one that is unfair. Use coins, dice, spinners, or colored cubes.

PROBLEM SOLVING

10-2 Simulate a Problem

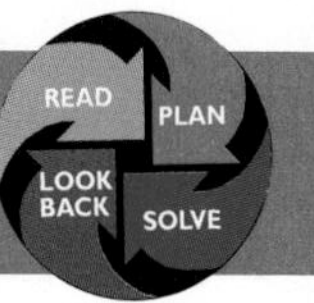

What's Ahead

• Solving problems by simulation

WHAT YOU'LL NEED

✓ **Spinner** 

You can often solve a probability problem by simulating it. You can use a model, collect data based on the model, and then use the data to solve the problem.

> Sam delivers newspapers to many of his neighbors, including Mrs. Smith. Sam delivers Mrs. Smith's newspaper between 6:30 A.M. and 7:30 A.M. Mrs. Smith leaves for work between 7:00 A.M. and 8:00 A.M. What is the probability that Mrs. Smith gets her newspaper before she leaves for work?

READ

Read and understand the given information. Summarize the problem.

1. Will Mrs. Smith get the newspaper before she leaves for work if Sam delivers it at each time?
   a. before 7:00 A.M. **b.** after 7:00 A.M.
2. How much of the time does Sam deliver Mrs. Smith's newspaper before 7:00 A.M.? after 7:00 A.M.?
3. If Sam always wants Mrs. Smith to receive her newspaper before she leaves for work, during what time interval should he deliver her newspaper?
4. If Mrs. Smith always wants to get her newspaper before she leaves for work, during what time interval should she leave?
5. Two times are important in this problem: the time at which Sam delivers Mrs. Smith's newspaper, and the time at which Mrs. Smith leaves for work. Do the two times depend on each other or are they independent?

PLAN

Decide on a strategy to solve the problem.

Instead of collecting data on Sam and Mrs. Smith themselves, you can represent their situation with a model. Ways of using a model to simulate the problem include drawing cubes, tossing coins, spinning spinners, rolling dice, and using random numbers.

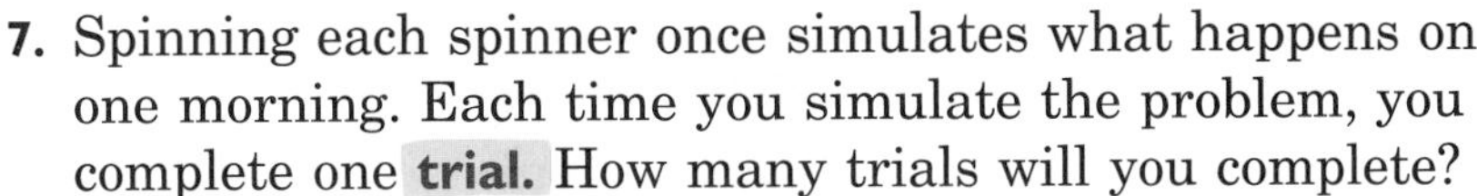

6. The spinner at the right represents the times at which Sam delivers newspapers. Draw a spinner to represent the times that Mrs. Smith leaves for work.

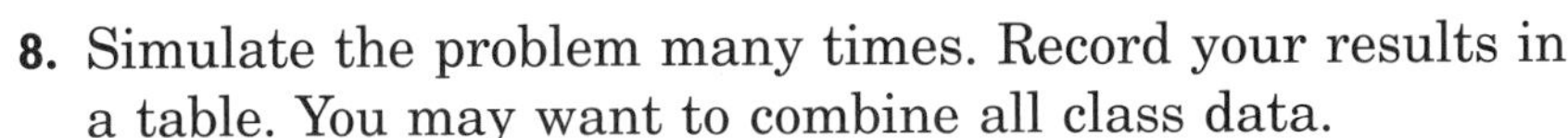

7. Spinning each spinner once simulates what happens on one morning. Each time you simulate the problem, you complete one **trial.** How many trials will you complete?

SOLVE

Try out the strategy.

8. Simulate the problem many times. Record your results in a table. You may want to combine all class data.

9. Use the data to find the experimental probability that Mrs. Smith will get her newspaper before she leaves for work in the morning. What does this tell you?

LOOK BACK

Think about how you solved this problem.

10. **Discussion** Does your answer seem reasonable? Is this the only possible answer?

11. **Discussion** Can you think of another way to simulate or solve this problem?

TRY THESE

Simulate and solve each problem. Show all your work.

12. You practice the piano 15 min every weekday between 4:00 P.M. and 5:00 P.M. Your father gets home from work every weekday between 4:30 P.M. and 5:30 P.M. What is the experimental probability that your father gets home from work while you are practicing the piano?

13. **Sports** A professional basketball player makes 75% of his free throws. What is the experimental probability that he will make two free throws in a row?

ON YOUR OWN

Use any strategy to solve each problem. Show all your work.

14. Suppose your class plans an end-of-the-year picnic. Each student gets one sandwich and one juice box. Three juice boxes cost $1.29. Sandwiches cost $1.85 each. Estimate the cost for the picnic for *your* mathematics class.

Mixed REVIEW

Draw a model to find each quotient.

1. $0.2 \div 0.04$
2. $0.9 \div 0.03$
3. Sharon and Ashur played a game 30 times. Sharon won 18 times and Ashur won 12 times. Is this a fair game? Explain.
4. Suppose you roll a die 10 times and get a 3 every time. Is this a fair die? Explain.
5. I'm thinking of a number. If I multiply by 3 and then subtract 11, the result is 43. What is the number?

15. Elvin estimated the amount of time during one year that he spends *not* in school. The amounts are given below. Elvin said that he has almost no time for school. Why?

Time Spent Not in School			
Sleeping	**Eating**	**School vacations**	**Weekends**
$\frac{1}{4}$	$\frac{1}{8}$	$\frac{1}{4}$	$\frac{2}{7}$

16. What is the least number of people you could have in a group and still be sure that at least two of them have birthdays in the same month? What is the least number so that three of them have birthdays in the same month?

17. **Investigation (p. 410)** Find the average temperature and precipitation for the current month in your city or region. Use an almanac or newspapers to find this information. Compare with today's temperature and precipitation.

18. **Data File 10 (pp. 408–409)** Is San Francisco or Anza more likely to have an earthquake? Explain.

19. An 8-by-8 checkerboard has one pair of opposite corners missing. One domino covers two squares of the checkerboard. Can you cover the entire checkerboard with dominoes? If so, draw a diagram that shows your solution. If not, explain why it is impossible.

Jumping spiders hunt by stalking. They follow an insect, then jump to grab it. Before jumping, they secure a silk thread on which they can climb if they miss their prey!

Source: *Wild, Wild World of Animals, Insects and Spiders*

20. **Writing** Velmanette is getting new bedroom carpet. Write down all the information she needs to take to the carpet store so that she can order new carpet.

21. A gumball machine holds many giant gumballs in four flavors: grape, lime, raspberry, and banana. Madeleine wants one of each flavor. Each gumball costs 25¢. About how much money will Madeleine spend in order to get the four different flavors of gumballs?

22. **Biology** Some jumping spiders can jump 40 times their own length. About how far in centimeters could a 15 mm jumping spider jump?

TECHNOLOGY

10-3 Experimental Probability & Simulations

What's Ahead

- Using computers to explore experimental probability
- Using random digits to simulate probability problems

WHAT YOU'LL NEED

✓ Stack of pennies 

✓ Computer 

✓ Software with random number and graphing capabilities 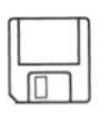

THINK AND DISCUSS

The coin spins upward from the referee's hand. Your coach has chosen you as the captain of the soccer team. You must call heads or tails to see which team gets the ball. In the first three games, the coin has landed heads.

1. Will you call heads or tails? Why?

2. You can act out the problem by tossing a coin.

a. You must first toss three heads in a row. What do these tosses represent?

b. You can then toss the coin a fourth time. What does this toss represent?

c. Why does acting out the problem take so long?

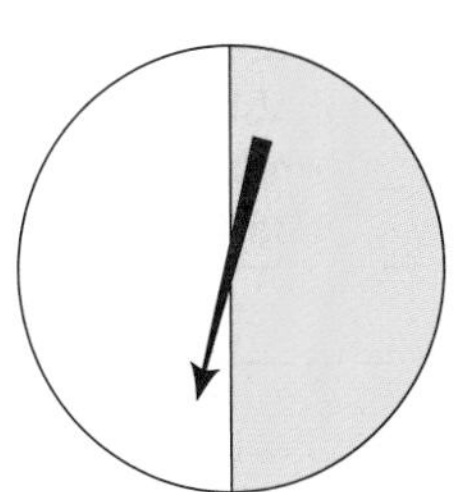

3. Can you use a spinner like the one at the left to simulate the problem? Would this method be faster than tossing a coin? Explain.

You can also use a computer to simulate the problem. A computer can quickly generate a list of *random digits.* Because they are random, all digits are equally likely to occur.

4. a. Suppose the digit 1 represents a coin toss landing heads. What series of digits would represent the coin tosses made by the referee in the first three games?

b. What is represented by the digits 1112? 1111?

List of Random 1's and 2's

1 1 2 1 2 1 2 2 2 1 1 2 2 1 2 1 2
1 1 1 1 2 1 2 1 2 1 2 1 2 2 2 1 2
2 2 1 2 1 1 1 1 2 1 2 1 2 2 2 2 1
1 2 1 2 1 1 2 2 1 1 1 1 2 2 2 1 2

5. Use the list of random digits at the left.

a. How many times does 1112 appear in the list?

b. How many times does 1111 appear in the list?

c. **Discussion** Do you think it is more likely that the referee will toss a heads or a tails at the start of the fourth game? Explain.

Number of times three heads were tossed, then another heads (1111)	■
Number of times three heads were tossed, then a tails (1112)	■

6. a. **Computer** Generate and print at least 500 random 1's and 2's digits.
   b. Complete the table at the left.
   c. Find Probability(fourth toss heads) and Probability(fourth toss tails).
   d. Now what do you think about your answer to Question 1? Explain.
   e. **Discussion** If you printed a list of 1,000 random digits, will you be more sure of your solution? Explain.

WORK TOGETHER

Work in pairs. Use the data you generated in Question 6 to simulate what happens with more and more tosses of a coin. Each pair of students should use a different section of the data and count the number of 1's and 2's.

7. Combine class data to complete the table below.

Number of tosses	Number of heads	Number of tails	Probability(heads) $= \frac{\text{number of heads}}{\text{number of tosses}}$
10	■	■	■
20	■	■	■
30	■	■	■
40	■	■	■
50	■	■	■
100	■	■	■
200	■	■	■
500	■	■	■
1,000	■	■	■

8. **Computer** Make a line graph to show what happens to Probability(heads) as the number of tosses increases.

9. **Writing** Do you see trends or patterns in the graph? Use the data or the graph to make at least one true statement.

10. **Critical Thinking** What do you think will happen to Probability(heads) if you simulate another 10,000 tosses?

Write two equal ratios.

1. 12 to 18 **2.** $\frac{15}{45}$

3. The Leopards played their first field hockey game Monday, September 20, and played a game every Monday thereafter. What was the date of their seventh game?

4. Brett makes 40% of his free throws. What is the probability that he will make three free throws in a row?

5. How many different ways can you make change for 31¢?

ON YOUR OWN

11. **Sports** Suppose your opponent tosses a dime to see who serves first in a tennis game. You must call heads or tails.

    a. The last nine tosses were tails. What will you call? Why?

    b. The last toss was heads. What will you call? Why?

12. a. How likely are "doubles" when you roll two dice? Simulate this by using the list. Use 2 digits at a time. Complete the table.

Number of doubles	▩
Number of times dice were rolled	▩
Probability(doubles)	▩

    b. Now analyze the problem by listing all possible outcomes. How likely are doubles? Show your solution.

13. A movie theater prints one digit 0–9 on each ticket. You collect tickets from movies you've seen. When you have each digit, you get a free ticket. How many movies will you have to see before you get a free ticket? Use the random digits at the right to simulate and solve this problem.

14. **Writing** A basketball player usually makes 50% of her free throws. Explain how to use a computer simulation to find the experimental probability that she makes 7 out of 10 free throws.

15. Here is a new game. Toss three coins. If you get exactly two heads or two tails, you win. Otherwise, your opponent wins. Is the game fair or unfair? Show your solution.

16. **Choose A, B, or C.** Suppose there is a 50% chance of rain for the next three days. Which method will *not* work to find out how likely it is to have three days of rain?

    A. Toss a coin. Let heads be "rain" and tails be "no rain."

    B. Use a computer to list random digits 0–9. Let even numbers be "rain" and let odd numbers be "no rain."

    C. Spin a spinner with three equal sections: one day of rain, two days of rain, and three days of rain.

List of Random Digits 1–6

2341632411 2534524
3514263523 2434644
2412336231 3264554
3631141342 4531415
2622

List of Random Digits 0–9

5820321984 5603216
6198723047 2822701
3639390265 8310886
8429750182 3954706

***While in prison** during World War II, John Kerrich tossed a coin 10,000 times. He tossed 5,067 heads. The experimental probability of tossing a head was 50.67%.*

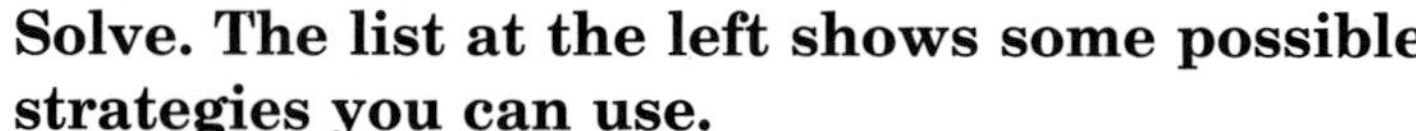

Problem Solving Practice

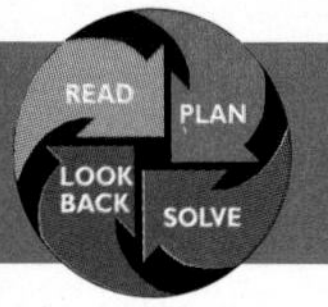

PROBLEM SOLVING STRATEGIES

Make a Table
Use Logical Reasoning
Solve a Simpler Problem
Too Much or Too Little Information
Look for a Pattern
Make a Model
Work Backward
Draw a Diagram
Guess and Test
Simulate a Problem
Use Multiple Strategies

Solve. The list at the left shows some possible strategies you can use.

1. Philip Astley, an Englishman, started the circus as we know it today. He presented trick riding shows to the public. Use the clues to find the year the circus began.
   - The sum of the digits equals 22.
   - The year is divisible by 4.
   - The American Revolution occurred in this century.

2. Did you know that a circus ring is a specific size? Philip Astley discovered that the ideal circle for bareback riding has a diameter of 42 ft. Find the area of this circle.

3. A survey reports that 73% of moviegoers buy popcorn at the movie theater. You own a theater with 360 seats. You sell containers of popcorn.
   a. If both movies sell out, how many containers of popcorn do you expect to sell each day?
   b. Each container of popcorn costs you 45¢ and sells for $1.50. What profit do you expect from popcorn each day?

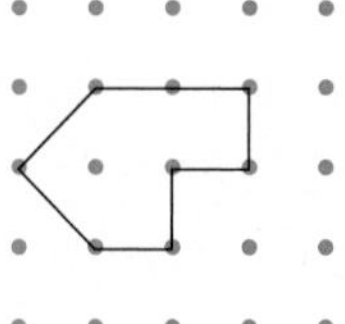

4. **Writing** Copy the polygon at the left onto dot paper. Find the area of each polygon. Notice that there is one dot inside the polygon. Also, there are 8 dots on the border of the polygon. Make five other polygons of this type. Find the area of each polygon. What do you observe?

5. A restaurant has 25 of each type of sticker: soup, sandwich, salad, and drink. One sticker is put on each menu. Each time you visit the restaurant, you receive a menu. The item listed on the sticker is free. How many times will you need to visit the restaurant to get each type of item free?

6. Suppose a planet has two hemispheres. In each hemisphere there are three continents. On each continent there are four countries. In each country there are five states. How many states are on the planet?

What's Ahead

- Determining the probability of an event

10-4 Probability

THINK AND DISCUSS

Think back to Game 3 on page 411. There were 3 red cubes and 1 blue cube in a bag.

In the hand game one player holds an unmarked object in one hand and a marked object in the other. An opponent wins by guessing which hand holds the unmarked object. ***What is the probability of choosing the correct hand?***

1. Suppose you draw 1 cube from the bag. Which is more likely, red or blue? How do you know?
2. Suppose you draw 1 cube from the bag and replace it 4 different times. How many times do you expect to get red? How many times do you expect to get blue?
3. Are all 4 cubes in the bag equally likely to be drawn?

Probability tells how likely it is that an event will happen. When all outcomes are equally likely, the probability that an event will occur is the ratio below. You can write this ratio as a fraction, a decimal, or a percent.

$$\text{Probability(event)} = \frac{\text{number of favorable outcomes}}{\text{number of possible outcomes}}$$

Example A bag contains 3 red cubes and 1 blue cube. What is the probability that a red cube is drawn?

- Find the probability that a cube drawn is red.

$$\frac{\text{number of favorable outcomes}}{\text{number of possible outcomes}} = \frac{\text{red cubes}}{\text{all cubes}} = \frac{3}{4}$$

$$\text{Probability(red)} = \frac{3}{4} = 0.75 = 75\%$$

4. Find the probability that a cube drawn is blue.
5. Design a spinner you could use to simulate this problem.
6. How many blue cubes could you add to the bag so that Probability(blue) = Probability(red)?
7. **Discussion** What does the word *favorable* mean in the formula for probability?

8. One marble is drawn from the bag at the left.
   a. How many possible outcomes are there? Are all outcomes equally likely?
   b. Find Probability(red). Write as a fraction, as a decimal, and as a percent. How many outcomes are favorable?
9. Suppose you roll a die once.
   a. List all the possible outcomes.
   b. What is the probability of rolling an even number?
   c. What is the probability of *not* rolling an even number? Describe this another way.
   d. Find the sum Probability(even) + Probability(not even). Are you surprised? Why or why not?

WORK TOGETHER

When the probability of an event is 1, the event is *certain* to happen. When the probability of an event is 0, the event is *impossible*.

10. Work with a partner to think of at least 3 examples of each type of event. Write down all your ideas.
    a. certain b. impossible c. possible but uncertain
11. Find the probability of each example you gave. Write each probability as a fraction, a decimal, and a percent.

Low High

12. Draw a number line to display the range of numbers used to describe probability. Label it with commonly used fractions, decimals, and percents. On the number line, write these words at appropriate places:

    certain, impossible, very likely, little chance, happens about half of the time

TRY THESE

13. Suppose your teacher writes the name of each student in your class on a card. To select a winner, your teacher draws one card from a box. Use your class data to find Probability(you win). Find Probability(you do not win).

A computer generates random digits 0–9. Find each probability. Write as a fraction, decimal, and percent.

14. Probability(6)

15. Probability(even number)

16. Probability(not 6)

17. Probability(1 or 2 or 3)

18. Do you agree or disagree with the following statement? An event with probability of 0 will never happen, and an event with probability of 1 will always happen.

19. **Activity** Work with a group to design a spinner with Probability(A) = 50%, Probability(B) = 10%, Probability(C) = 0%, and Probability(D) = 40%.

Mixed REVIEW

1. The radius of a circle is 15 m. What is the diameter?

2. The diameter of a circle is 22 ft. What is the radius?

3. You program a computer to list random 6's, 7's, and 8's. It lists four 6's in a row. Is it more likely to list a 6, a 7, or an 8 next? Explain.

4. Could the pattern be folded along the dashed lines to make a cube?

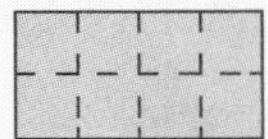

ON YOUR OWN

A die is rolled once. Find each probability. Write as a fraction, decimal, and percent.

20. Probability(4)

21. Probability(9)

22. Probability(not 5)

23. Probability(1 or 3 or 6)

24. Find Probability(red) and Probability(blue) for the spinner at the right.

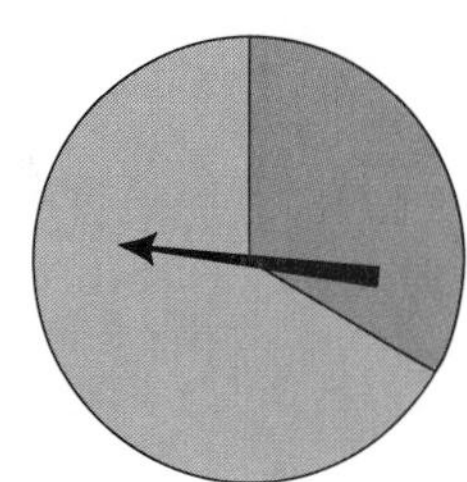

25. **Critical Thinking** An icosahedron is a die with 20 faces. All outcomes are equally likely. Each face is colored red, blue, yellow, or green. You know Probability(yellow) = Probability(blue) = Probability(green) = Probability(red). How many faces are colored red?

26. One thousand raffle tickets are sold. You buy two of them. One winning ticket is drawn.

a. What is the probability that you win?

b. What is the probability that you do not win?

27. **Investigation** **(p. 410)** Find the chance of precipitation for your region tonight and tomorrow.

a. Does the media report the probability as a fraction, a decimal, a percent, or with words?

b. **Writing** Write a sentence about your investigation.

The probability *of seeing a whale during a whale watch boat ride increases with the area of ocean, the season, the time of day, and the knowledge of the guide.*

28. **Writing** Does it make more sense to you to think of probability as a fraction, a decimal, or a percent? Why?

29. Order the following events from most likely to least likely.

A. The sun rises tomorrow.

B. You have a homework assignment tonight.

C. The next coin you toss comes up heads.

D. It snows somewhere in your state this week.

E. You complete a homework assignment tonight.

F. You live to be 195 years old.

G. You make a basket next time you play basketball.

30. A bag contains only red and green cubes. Probability(red) $= \frac{3}{8}$. You select one cube without looking.

a. Find Probability(green).

b. Draw a spinner you could use to simulate this problem.

c. How many of each color cube might the bag contain?

CHECKPOINT

1. A computer generates random digits 1–5. Find each probability. Write as a fraction, decimal, and percent.

a. Probability(3) **b.** Probability(odd number)

c. Probability(2 or 3) **d.** Probability(not 5)

Game Results	
Earline wins	14
Lei-Li wins	16
Times played	30

2. Lei-Li and Earline played a game and completed the table at the left.

a. Find the experimental probability that Earline wins.

b. Find the experimental probability that Lei-Li wins.

c. Is the game fair? Explain.

3. **Choose A, B, C, or D.** Which event is most likely?

A. "tails" when you toss a coin

B. "consonant" when you randomly choose a letter A–Z

C. "9" when a computer lists random digits 0–9

D. "not 3" when you roll a number cube

What's Ahead

- Displaying and counting all possible outcomes
- Finding probabilities using tree diagrams and the counting principle

10-5 Tree Diagrams & the Counting Principle

THINK AND DISCUSS

Students in a physical education class can choose what activity to do for a ten-week period. The choices are volleyball, soccer, and baseball. After the ten weeks are over, students choose again for the next ten-week period. They can choose the same activity.

1. How many choices do students have for the first activity?

A **tree diagram** displays all possible choices. Each branch of the tree diagram shows one choice. You use a tree diagram when all outcomes are equally likely to occur and when an event has two or more stages.

Example 1 Draw a tree diagram for the physical education activities. How many different ways can students choose?

Use the letter V for volleyball, S for soccer, and B for baseball.

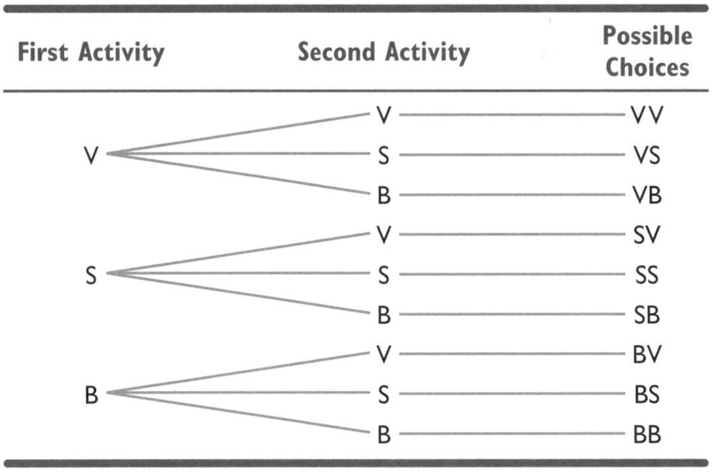

First Activity	Second Activity	Possible Choices
V	V	VV
	S	VS
	B	VB
S	V	SV
	S	SS
	B	SB
B	V	BV
	S	BS
	B	BB

There are 9 different ways to choose activities.

On September 4, 1993, Jim Abbott of the New York Yankees pitched a no-hitter against the Cleveland Indians.

2. Draw a tree diagram that shows all possible outcomes when you toss 3 coins.

You can use a tree diagram to find the probability of an event.

Example 2 Use the tree diagram in Example 1. Suppose a student chooses randomly. What is the probability she plays soccer during the second period?

- Count all possible outcomes: 9.
- Find the number of favorable outcomes: 3.

  Favorable outcomes are volleyball/soccer, soccer/soccer, and baseball/soccer.

Probability(soccer in second period) $= \frac{3}{9} = \frac{1}{3}$

3. **Critical Thinking** Is there a relationship among the number of first-period activities, the number of second-period activities, and the number of possible choices? If so, what is it?

4. Do you see a way to count all possible outcomes without using a tree diagram or a grid? Explain.

Another way to find the number of possible outcomes is to use *the counting principle.*

The Counting Principle

The number of outcomes for an event with two or more distinct stages is the product of the number of outcomes at each stage.

Example 3 You and your friends want to buy a pizza. You have only enough money for a medium size with one topping. How many different types of pizza can you buy?

Use the counting principle.

Topping (6 choices)		Crust (2 choices)		Types of pizza
6	×	2	=	12

You can buy 12 different types of pizza.

5. Pizza Palace decides to offer one more topping. How many more types of pizza can you and your friends buy?

6. **Discussion** What information do you get with a tree diagram that you do not get with the counting principle?

You can also use the counting principle to find the probability of an event.

Example 4 Use the information from Example 3. Suppose you and your friends choose a pizza at random. What is the probability that you choose a mushroom pizza with a thin crust?

- Count all possible outcomes: 12.
- Find the number of favorable outcomes: 1.

Probability(mushroom, thin crust) $= \frac{1}{12}$

7. Find the probability of choosing each type of pizza.

   a. a thick crust b. a pepperoni pizza

TRY THESE

8. a. Suppose you roll two dice. Use the counting principle to find the number of possible outcomes.

   b. Why would using the counting principle be easier than drawing a tree diagram?

   c. What is the probability of rolling two 5's?

9. **Cars** When you order a car, you choose the exterior and interior colors. A dealership offers a new car in 10 exterior colors: black, silver, teal, white, navy, royal blue, red, burgundy, forest green, and brown. Each exterior color has 3 different interior colors. How many different color combinations are there?

10. **Cars** A navy car is available with a gray, blue, or black interior. A silver car is available with a gray, blue, black, or red interior. Draw a tree diagram to show all possible color combinations.

Car dealerships predict that more people will order the car they want to buy rather than choose a car from the lot. It has become too expensive for car dealerships to stock all the different cars that are available. Consumers are happier because they get the cars they want!

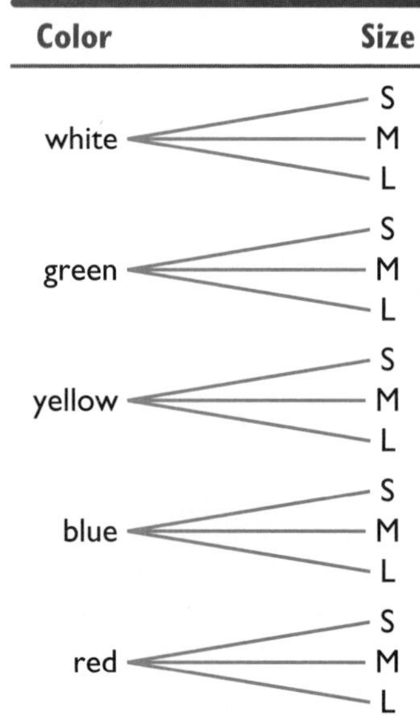

ON YOUR OWN

11. Small and large blocks in a special set come in five shapes: cube, pyramid, cone, cylinder, and triangular prism. List all the different types of blocks in the set.

12. **Travel** Four airlines fly nonstop from Washington to Columbus. Five airlines fly nonstop from Columbus to Seattle. How many different pairs of airlines can you use to fly from Washington to Seattle through Columbus?

13. **Writing** Write a problem that can be solved using the tree diagram at the left. Solve your problem.

14. **Consumer Issues** The table below gives some of the choices available when you buy a computer. Suppose you choose one keyboard, one monitor, and one printer.

Keyboards	Monitors	Printers
Standard $105	Monochrome $329	Laser $819
Extended $185	Color 14-in. $539	Stylewriter $339
Adjustable $195	Color 16-in. $1,459	Dot-matrix $439

a. How many outcomes are possible?

b. You want a color monitor but you do not want an adjustable keyboard. How many outcomes are left?

c. Which computer costs the least? Which computer costs the most? Write the range of costs for these computers.

15. A cafeteria serves the same three main courses and three desserts at lunch each day. You choose a different meal each day, but you always take one main course and one dessert. After how many days will you run out of choices?

16. To play a board game, you spin a spinner and take a card. The spinner has sections that tell you to move 1, 2, 3, or 4 spaces. The cards state Free Turn, Lose a Turn, or No Change. What is the probability you move 3 spaces and lose a turn?

17. **Cars** When you order a car, you must choose from 8 exterior colors and either cloth or leather interior. Cloth is available in 3 different colors. Leather is available in dark or light. How many different types of car are possible?

Mixed REVIEW

Use Napier's rods to find each product.

1. 297×5
2. $3{,}429 \times 7$

Find the probability of each event.

3. a month chosen at random has exactly 30 days
4. a letter chosen at random from the word SCIENCE is a vowel

5. Find the sum of the even whole numbers from 10 through 48.

What's Ahead

- Determining the probability of two independent events
- Deciding whether or not events are independent

WHAT YOU'LL NEED

✓ Red or blue cubes (or other objects of two colors) 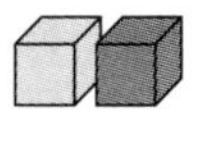

✓ Bag or container 

10-6 Independent Events

WORK TOGETHER

Work with a partner. Let's look at Game 3 from page 411 again!

1. Recall your results for Game 3. Is Game 3 fair or unfair? If necessary, play the game or draw a diagram to consider all possible outcomes again.

2. Now change Game 3 to Game 3A. Instead of drawing 2 cubes at a time, draw 1 cube at a time. Play Game 3A at least 20 times. Is Game 3A fair or unfair? Explain.

Game 3A Place 3 red cubes and 1 blue cube in a bag. Draw a cube from the bag without looking. Record the color, put the cube back into the bag, and again draw a cube. If the 2 cubes are the same color, player A wins. If not, player B wins.

THINK AND DISCUSS

		Outcomes
R	R	RR
	R	RR
	R	RR
	B	RB
R	R	RR
	R	RR
	R	RR
	B	RB
R	R	RR
	R	RR
	R	RR
	B	RB
B	R	BR
	R	BR
	R	BR
	B	BB

The tree diagram at the left shows 16 equally likely outcomes.

3. Is the tree diagram for Game 3, Game 3A, or both games?

4. **Discussion** Use the tree diagram to decide whether this game is fair or unfair. Make sure you all agree.

5. In Game 3A, are all 4 cubes equally likely to be drawn on the first draw? on the second draw? Does the second cube drawn depend on the first cube drawn?

6. In Game 3, does the second cube drawn depend on the first cube drawn? Why or why not?

If the outcome of one event does not depend on the outcome of another event, the events are **independent.**

7. Does Game 3 or Game 3A have independent events?

8. Are the two events independent? Why or why not?

   a. A card is drawn from a deck and is not replaced. Another card is drawn from the deck.

   b. Cleotha studies mathematics 30 min every evening. Cleotha gets an A on her next mathematics quiz.

   c. It snows in Washington, D.C. A new President of the United States is elected.

   d. At a soccer game, a coin is tossed and comes up heads. At the next game, the coin comes up tails.

   e. Faraj runs 6 mi every day. Faraj placed first in a cross country race.

9. **Critical Thinking** List some events that are independent and some that are not. Think of events that are not already described in this chapter.

10. When you toss a coin, what is the probability of tossing three tails in a row? Draw a tree diagram to show all possible outcomes. Are these independent events?

Another way to find the probability of independent events is to multiply the probabilities.

Probability(A and B) = Probability(A) × Probability(B)

11. Use multiplication to find the probability of tossing 3 tails in a row. Complete: Probability(tails, tails, tails) = Probability(tails) × Probability(tails) × Probability(tails) = ■ × ■ × ■ = ■. Compare with Question 10.

12. Mei-Ling has 3 sweaters: pink, white, blue. She has 2 pairs of jeans: white, blue. She has 5 pairs of socks: 3 white, 1 blue, 1 pink. She randomly selects 1 sweater, 1 pair of jeans, and 1 pair of socks. What is the probability that she selects all blue?

   a. Use the counting principle to find the number of possible outcomes. Then find the probability.

   b. Use multiplication to find the probability.

   c. Compare your answers for parts (a) and (b). Which method do you prefer for finding the probability? Why?

   d. Explain why you might not want to use a tree diagram to find this probability.

Use a protractor to draw an angle with each measure.

1. 45° 2. 130°

3. Draw a tree diagram to show all possible outcomes when you toss a coin and roll a die.

4. What is the probability of getting a heads and an even number in Exercise 3?

Use the Venn diagram.

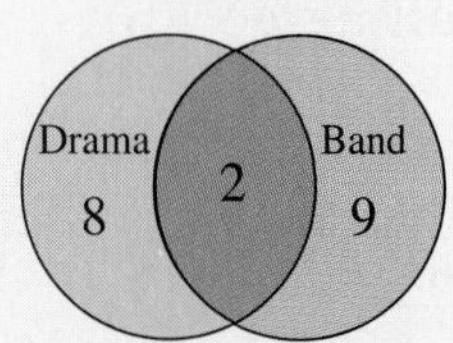

5. How many students are members of the drama club?

6. How many students are in the band and members of the drama club?

ON YOUR OWN

Use the spinner for Exercises 13–15. It is spun twice.

13. Are the two spins independent events? Explain.

14. Use multiplication to find the probability that the first spin is blue and the second spin is red.

15. Draw a tree diagram to show all possible outcomes. Find the probability that the two spins are the same color.

Use the two boxes at the right for Exercises 16–18. Box 1 contains 4 cards, and Box 2 contains 5 cards.

16. A card is drawn from Box 1. Find Probability(M).

17. A card is drawn from Box 1. Then a card is drawn from Box 2. Find Probability(ME).

18. A card is drawn from Box 1 and put back. Then another card is drawn. Find Probability(HA).

19. In a game you toss a coin and roll two dice. How many possible outcomes are there for each of the following?

a. one coin **b.** one die

c. one coin and one die **d.** the game

20. **Writing** Use your own words to explain to a friend what independent events are. Give some examples.

21. **Choose A, B, or C.** Which events are not independent?

A. Your computer randomly lists a 1 and then a 2.

B. You draw two colored cards at one time from a deck and get one red and one blue.

C. You roll a die twice and get 6 both times.

22. **Biology** Assume that "boy" and "girl" are equally likely outcomes for a baby. What is the probability that someone has five baby girls in a row? Show your solution in at least two different ways.

23. **Biology** Diana thinks that having two babies of the same gender is as likely as having two babies of different genders. Do you agree or disagree? Show your solution.

What's Ahead

- Determining the number of arrangements of a group of items

10-7 Exploring Arrangements

WORK TOGETHER

Work in groups of four students.

1. Make a prediction and write it down for this question: How many different ways can you arrange your group members in a line?

Suppose only 3 people are in line. How many different ways can the 3 people form a line?

2. Stand up and form one line of all your group members. Then form as many different lines as you can. How many different lines can you form?

3. Simulate this problem. Represent each member with an object, such as a pencil or a book. Arrange the objects in as many different lines as you can. Did you get the same number of possible arrangements?

4. Use a letter or a number to represent each group member. Make an organized list of all possible arrangements.
   a. How many arrangements are in your list?
   b. Compare this number with your prediction and your answers to Questions 2 and 3.

THINK AND DISCUSS

You can use several different methods to find the number of arrangements of a set of objects.

5. **Discussion** In the activity above, you used several methods to find the number of different arrangements of your group members. Name each method. What did you like or dislike about each method?

6. **Discussion** As a class, agree on the number of possible arrangements for groups with 3 members, 4 members, and 5 members.

You can draw a tree diagram or make an organized list. Then count all the possible arrangements.

7. The tree diagram at the right shows all possible arrangements of the numbers 1, 2, and 3. Draw a tree diagram that shows all possible arrangements of the numbers 1, 2, 3, and 4.

8. To count the number of arrangements of A, B, C, and D, Veronica started to make the list at the right. Complete the list. Would you organize the list this way?

9. Discussion Which method do you prefer, drawing a tree diagram or making a list? Do they give the same results?

			Outcomes
1	2	3	123
	3	2	132
2	1	3	213
	3	1	231
3	1	2	312
	2	1	321

Veronica's List
ABCD BCDA CDAB ...
ABDC
ACBD
⋮

You can also use the counting principle. For example, to find the number of arrangements of four students, think about each place in a line.

First place in line		Second place in line		Third place in line		Fourth place in line		
4	×	3	×	2	×	1	=	24

10. Discussion Why are there 4 choices for the first place in line, but only 3 choices for the second place in line?

11. Discussion Does this method make sense to you? When might this method be the most practical one to use?

12. Sports A coach must decide on a batting order for nine baseball players. Use the counting principle to find the number of choices the coach has for a batting order.

Problem Solving Hint

Write the product you need to find. Then use a calculator to find the product.

ON YOUR OWN

13. Make an organized list of all possible arrangements of the letters in the word SING. How many are English words?

14. Many daily newspapers have a feature called "Scramble." Imagine that you write this feature. How many different ways can you scramble the letters in the word RANDOM?

15. The school choir will sing five songs for an assembly. How many different ways can the director order the songs?

WHO? The Jamaican bobsled team was the subject of a 1993 movie called "Cool Runnings."

16. **Sports** Bobsled teams like to be one of the first down the track because the track becomes slower with use. Draw a tree diagram to show all the different arrangements of bobsled teams from Switzerland, Germany, and Italy.

17. **Literature** A library received a seven-volume set of books by C.S. Lewis called *The Chronicles of Narnia.*

    a. How many ways can the books be arranged in a row on a shelf?

    b. The seven books are placed in a random order on a shelf in the library. What is the probability that the books are in the correct order from left to right?

18. **Music** A radio disc jockey has ten songs to play in the next hour. How many different ways can he arrange the songs?

19. **Critical Thinking** Tanya said that her phone number has every digit from 3 to 9. Kenna decides to try every possible phone number until she reaches Tanya. Suppose Kenna is as unlucky as possible. How many different phone numbers will Kenna try before she reaches Tanya?

20. **Writing** Write a problem that can be solved by using the tree diagram. Solve the problem another way.

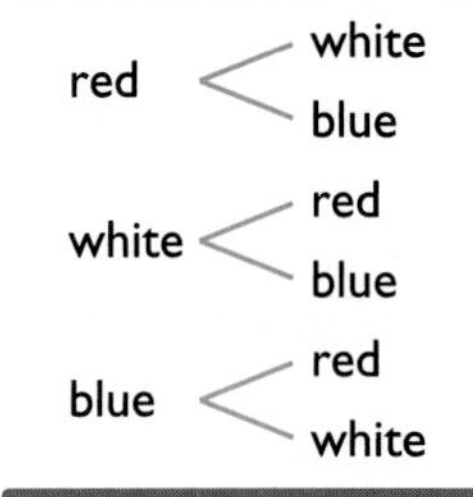

CHECKPOINT

1. A blue, red, or yellow chip is selected, and a coin is tossed.

    a. Draw a tree diagram to show all possible outcomes.

    b. Find Probability(yellow, then tails).

2. When ordering the luncheon special, you can choose from 3 entrees, 2 soups, and 2 desserts. Use the counting principle to find the number of possible combinations.

3. A bag contains 3 green cubes and 4 red cubes. A cube is drawn and replaced. Another cube is drawn. What is the probability that 2 red cubes are drawn?

4. How many different ways can 6 students be lined up shoulder-to-shoulder for a photograph?

Mixed REVIEW

Simplify.

1. $15 + 6 \div 3$
2. $8 \times 2^2 - 4 \div 2$

A die is rolled twice. Find the probability of each event.

3. 3, then odd
4. 5, then 5

5. Two numbers have a product of 364 and a difference of 15. What are the two numbers?

Practice

1. Is Game 4 fair or unfair?
   Game 4: Place 3 red cubes and 3 blue cubes in a bag. Draw 2 cubes from the bag without looking. If they are the same color, player A wins. If they are not the same color, player B wins.

2. **Sports** Solve by simulation.
   A batting average is the ratio of the number of hits to the number of times at bat. Andre's batting average is 0.250. Find the probability that he gets 2 hits the next 2 times at bat.

3. Kaylee tossed a coin 20 times with these results: 12 heads, 8 tails. Use her data to find the experimental probability of getting heads.

4. Explain how you can use random digits to simulate the probability of heads when you toss a coin. Discuss the number of trials you would do.

A die with 12 faces numbered 1–12 is rolled. All outcomes are equally likely. Find each probability.

5. Probability(even)
6. Probability(13)
7. Probability(not 1)
8. Probability(7 or 8)
9. Probability(number less than 10)

10. Suppose you read in the newspaper that the probability of precipitation is 10%. Write this probability two other ways and describe it using words.

11. Describe one event that is certain, one event that is impossible, and one event that may or may not happen. What is the probability of each event?

12. Sweatshirts are available in green, gray, black, blue, and orange. The sizes are small, medium, and large. Draw a tree diagram to show all possible outcomes for a sweatshirt.

13. Sweatshirts at another store are available in 10 different colors, 3 different styles, and 4 different sizes. Use the counting principle to find the number of possible outcomes.

Are the two events independent? Why or why not?

14. It snows overnight. You decide to go sledding the next day.

15. You reach into a bag with red and blue cubes and draw 2 red cubes.

16. You toss a coin twice.

17. A computer randomly lists 1, then 2.

18. What is the probability of getting two 6's when you roll two dice?

19. **Calculator** How many different ways can you arrange 11 books on a shelf?

MATH AND SURVEYS

What's Ahead

- Making predictions about a population based on a sample

10-8 Making Predictions

WHAT YOU'LL NEED

✓ A number of beans, chips, cubes, or other objects that differ only in color 

Polling is merely an instrument for gauging public opinion. When a president or any other leader pays attention to poll results, he is in effect, paying attention to the views of the people.
—George H. Gallup (1901–1984)

THINK AND DISCUSS

For the 1936 presidential election, *Literary Digest* did a survey to predict the results of the election. They mailed questionnaires to 10 million people. They used names and addresses from telephone books to select who would receive questionnaires. Only 2.4 million people sent questionnaires back. Here are the survey and election results.

	Survey Results	Actual Election Results
Franklin Roosevelt	43%	62%
Alfred Landon	57%	38%

1. Which candidate won the *Literary Digest* survey? Which candidate won the election? Were the survey results accurate?

A **population** is a group of people or other objects about whom you want information. A **sample** is the part of the population you use to make predictions about the population. In order to make accurate predictions, the sample must be *representative* of the whole population. With a *random* sample, each member of the population has the same chance of being in the sample. A random sample usually results in a representative sample.

2. For the *Literary Digest* survey, what is the population? What is the sample?

3. Two major problems with the *Literary Digest* survey led to poor predictions.
   a. **Discussion** Not everyone is listed in the telephone book! In fact, many Democrats who voted for Roosevelt did not have telephones. Was the sample representative? Was the sample random? Explain your answers.
   b. **Discussion** Only 2.4 million people sent their questionnaires back. Why is this a problem?

For the 1948 presidential election, three different surveys predicted that the Republican candidate Dewey would win. Instead, Truman won! All the surveys did personal interviews to collect data. Each interviewer asked a certain number of people from specific categories for whom they would vote. Here are the results.

	Crossley Predictions	Gallup Predictions	Roper Predictions	Election Results
Harry Truman	45%	44%	38%	50%
Thomas Dewey	50%	50%	53%	45%

***Harry Truman** was elected President, even though 3 surveys predicted that he would lose!*

4. **Discussion** The problem was that interviewers chose whom to interview within each category. So they visited affluent neighborhoods where mainly Republicans lived. How and why did this lead to poor predictions?

WORK TOGETHER

Work in teams to experiment with random samples. Take turns being Team 1 and Team 2. Then answer the questions.

Team 1: Create a population of objects that are the same except for color. For example, use red, white, and blue cubes. Use 2–4 different colors. Write down the number of each color in the population. Tell Team 2 only the number of objects in your population and the number of different colors you used.

Team 2: Take a random sample of the population. Then predict the distribution of colors within the population. For example, if the population contains 400 white and red cubes, you might predict that there are 100 white cubes and 300 red cubes.

5. How did you make sure that the samples were random?
6. How many objects did you use for a sample? Why?
7. How well did your sample represent the population?
8. How accurate were your predictions? Are you surprised?
9. **Discussion** Why take a random sample instead of counting or surveying the whole population?

Mixed REVIEW

Evaluate.

1. $2x + 5$ for $x = 9$
2. $b^2 + 4b$ for $b = 3$

3. A recruiter needs to schedule 7 people for interviews. How many different ways can the recruiter arrange the interviews?
4. In how many different ways can 4 people be seated in a row of 4 seats?
5. How many squares are there in the figure below?

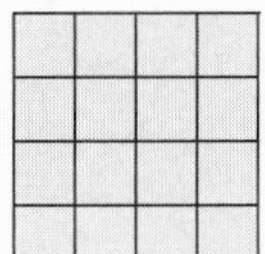

What Do You Think?

Call the number below to give your opinion on the following questions. Each call costs 75¢. Use only a touch-tone phone. Press 1 for YES. Press 3 for NO. After you answer the questions, enter your age. This opinion poll lasts only until midnight EST on Tuesday, May 15. This magazine will publish the results in a future issue.

ON YOUR OWN

The partial news article was distributed nationally.

10. Identify the population and sample for this survey.

11. Give at least three reasons why the data collected from the survey will not be representative of the population.

Is each sample random? representative? Explain.

12. A company wants to know the opinions of sixth graders in a certain town. The name of every sixth grader in town is placed in a revolving bin, and 30 names are drawn.

13. To find the cost to rent a two-bedroom apartment in the United States, 100 two-bedroom apartment dwellers in New York City are questioned.

14. To determine the most popular car in your city, data is collected on all the cars in the high school parking lot.

15. To taste a bowl of soup, you take a spoonful.

16. **Critical Thinking** Is it possible to have a sample that is representative but not random? random but not representative? Use examples to explain your answer.

GREAT EXPECTATIONS

Farmer

When I grow up I want to be a farmer. I think being a farmer would involve a lot of math. A farmer has to calculate where to place the seeds. I am not sure how I would calculate this. Maybe I could make a sketch. Does it take a lot of work and time just to figure out how many seeds to buy and where to plant them?

A farmer also has to calculate how much fertilizer to buy. I will have to know about crop rotation so I always have rich soil. I think this is how I will use math if I am a farmer.

Carri Chan

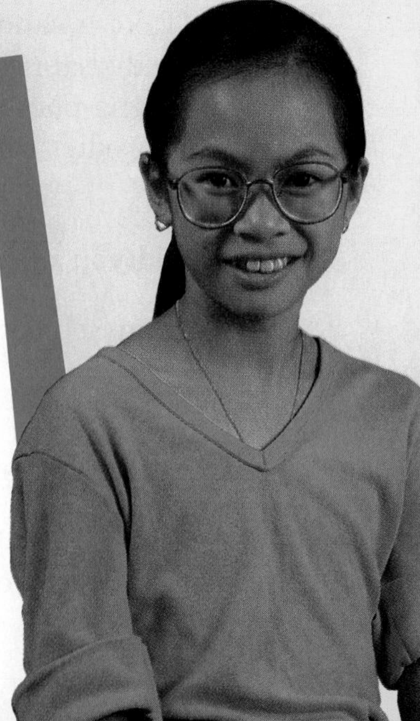

17. A UFO is an "unidentified flying object." Two surveys asked a random sample of Americans if UFOs were real or just in people's imaginations.

a. Estimate the probability that a person you meet tomorrow will believe that UFOs are real.

b. If you tell 300 people that UFOs are in people's imaginations, how many do you think will agree?

c. Why do you think the data changed from 1978 to 1990?

UFO Survey Results

	1978	1990
Real	57%	47%
Imagination	27%	31%
Not sure	16%	22%

18. **Data File I (pp. 2–3)** Data is given for the number of hours that people watch TV in a week. Can you tell if the sample is random or representative? Do you think the predictions are accurate?

19. **Writing** Find an article in a newspaper or magazine that includes data collected from a survey. Write a letter to the editor. Ask the editor about the sample, the population, and the methods they used. Send your letter!

20. **Investigation (p. 410)** Collect data on the daily weather for your region from the last two weeks. Look for patterns or trends. Predict the weather in your region for tomorrow. Explain how you made the prediction. Why might your prediction not be accurate?

Dear Carri,

Congratulations on having a career goal of being a farmer. Farmers are very important people. They produce a high-quality food supply for our country and other countries.

Math is very important in running a farm business. The farmer must calculate the number of dollars needed to plant crops and feed the animals. Farmers develop budgets, calculate interest, account for expense and income, understand profit and loss, and balance their record books.

Farmers must work with nature to produce the highest quality food. They keep charts and records of the rainfall and temperature to make decisions for growing plants and animals.

Farmers use percent to balance the feed rations for animals and fertilizer mixes for plants.

Best wishes for a successful farming career.

Larry D. Case

CHAPTER 10

Wrap Up

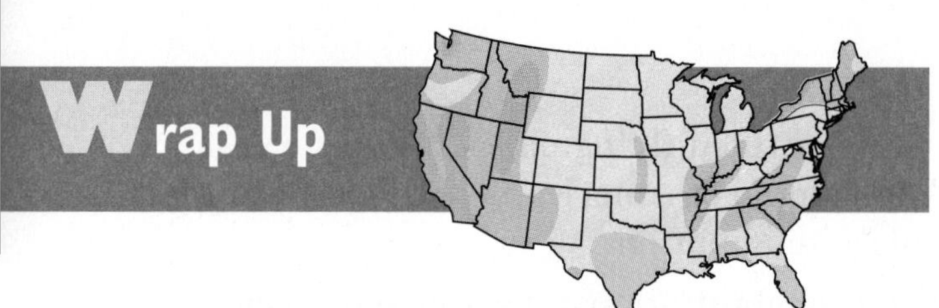

Fair and Unfair Games 10-1

A game is ***fair*** if each player has the same chance of winning.

One way to decide if a game is fair or unfair is to consider all the possible outcomes of the game.

1. Players take turns tossing two number cubes. If the sum of the numbers on the two cubes is even, Player A scores a point. If the sum is odd, Player B scores a point. The player with the most points at the end of 10 rounds wins.
   a. List all possible outcomes.
   b. Writing Is the game fair or unfair? Explain.

Experimental Probability and Simulations 10-1, 10-2, 10-3

You can also use experimental probability to determine if a game is fair or unfair. ***Experimental probability*** is a ratio that shows the fraction of the time a player wins a game.

A situation can be represented with a ***model.*** You can ***simulate*** a problem using a model or random digits.

2. Results of a game are shown below.

A wins	|||
B wins	~~||||~~ ||
Times played	~~||||~~ ~~||||~~

   a. Find Probability(A wins) and Probability(B wins).
   b. Is the game fair or unfair? Explain.

3. You take your dog for a 20 min walk every weekday any time between 5:00 P.M. and 6:00 P.M. Your mother gets home from work every weekday any time between 5:30 P.M. and 6:30 P.M. What is the probability that your mother gets home from work while you are walking your dog?

4. How likely are "consecutive numbers" when you toss two dice? Use the list of random digits at the right to simulate this problem.

List of Random Digits 1–6

23	41	63	24	11	25	34	52	22	51	42	63
52	32	43	41	11	24	12	33	62	31	32	64
55	43	63	11	41	34	24	51	14	15	26	32

Probability 10-4

You can describe the ***probability*** of an event occurring as the ratio of the number of favorable outcomes to the number of possible outcomes.

5. A bag contains the letters of the word MATHEMATICS. Find each probability.
   a. selecting the letter M
   b. selecting the letter R
   c. selecting a vowel

Tree Diagrams, the Counting Principle, and Independent Events 10-5, 10-6

You can use a ***tree diagram*** or the ***counting principle*** to find the number of possible outcomes.

If the outcome of one event does not depend on the outcome of another event, the events are ***independent.***

6. A company makes 5 car styles. Each car comes in 6 colors. Each car can have 4 interior styles and automatic or standard transmission. Harold wants one of each kind of car for his lot. How many cars must he order?

7. Suppose you play a game using the spinner at the right. Find the probability that the first spin is yellow and the second spin is green.

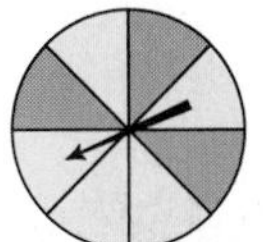

Arrangements and Making Predictions 10-7, 10-8

You can find the number of arrangements of a set of objects by making a list, drawing a tree diagram, using the counting principle, or simulating the problem.

A sample is *random* if each member of a population has an equal chance of being in the sample.

8. Zalika will play 5 songs for her piano recital. In how many ways can Zalika order the songs?

9. To find the favorite sport of boys in your school, you survey all boys who play on the soccer team. Is the sample random? Explain.

GETTING READY FOR CHAPTER 11

Would you represent each situation by a positive or a negative number?

1. a debt of $12
2. a gain of 10 yd
3. 100 ft below sea level
4. 3 steps forward

PUTTING IT ALL TOGETHER

Follow Up

How's the Weather?

Butterflies have been fluttering their wings all over the world since you began this chapter. Nevertheless, you should have a better idea now of how to predict the weather. To demonstrate your new expertise, prepare a 30-day long-range weather forecast for your city. Predict temperatures, precipitation, unusual weather events, and any other information you consider important. The following are ways you might present your predictions.

- ✓ a written report
- ✓ a newspaper article
- ✓ an oral "TV weatherperson" presentation

The problems preceded by the magnifying glass (p. 416, # 17; p. 423, # 27; and p. 439, # 20) will help you prepare your presentation.

The ability to predict the weather accurately is of critical importance to a nation, affecting everything from crop production to military campaigns. We have made great advances in weather forecasting in recent years. Because of all those butterflies, however, no one expects we will ever achieve 100% accuracy.

Excursion: Find out what effect, if any, weather or other natural events have on the price of home insurance in your city.

Who to Talk To:

- an insurance agent

That's the Way the Spinner Spins

Try this with your group.

This table shows the results of 60 spins on a spinner divided into 6 sections.

Use the data in the table to determine how many sections of each color were on the spinner. Then make a copy of the spinner.

Purple	⁄⁄⁄⁄ ⁄⁄⁄⁄ ⁄⁄⁄⁄ IIII	19/60
Green	⁄⁄⁄⁄ ⁄⁄⁄⁄	10/60
Blue	⁄⁄⁄⁄ ⁄⁄⁄⁄ ⁄⁄⁄⁄ ⁄⁄⁄⁄	20/60
Orange	⁄⁄⁄⁄ ⁄⁄⁄⁄ I	11/60

You can make a spinner with a pencil and paper clip. Hold the pencil upright with the point inside one of the ends of the paper clip. Use your thumb and forefinger to tap the paper clip to make it spin. Spin the spinner 60 times. Keep a tally and compare your results with the results shown in the table.

HEXAMANIA

Play this game with a friend. Copy the game shown.

- Each player chooses a mark such as an X or O. Players take turns placing their marks on a side of a hexagon.
- Players score the point value in the hexagon when they have a mark on four sides.
- The winner is the first player to score 62 or more points.
- Play several times and write a summary of a winning strategy.

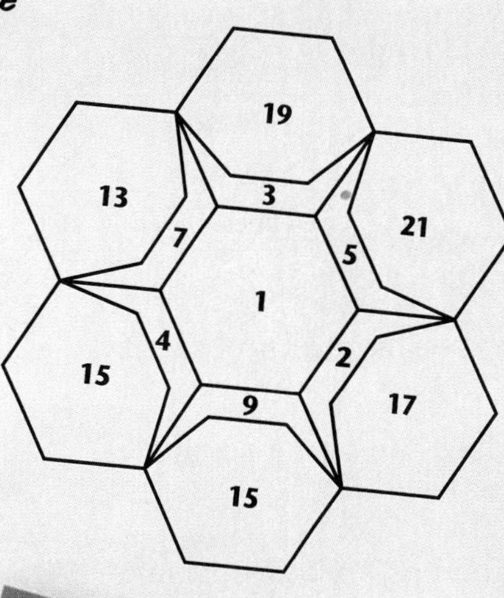

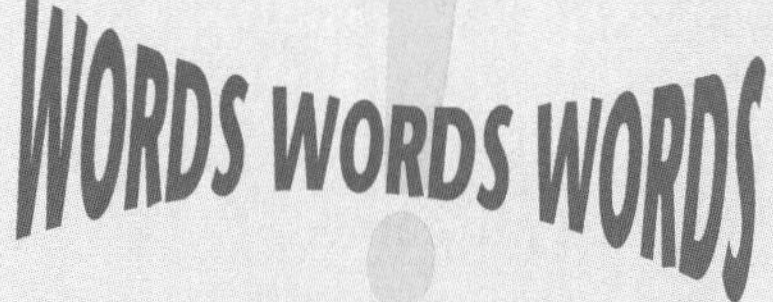

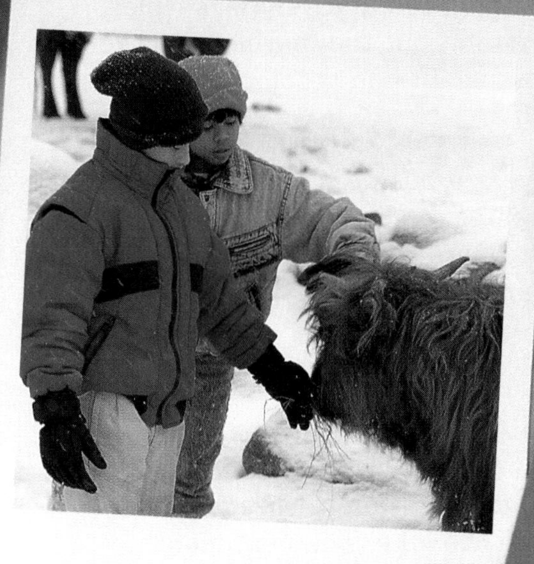

Do this with your group.

- Each group member selects a 50-word passage from a different source. (Try textbooks, newspapers or magazines, or a novel for example.)
- Using these passages, make a line plot of the letters of the alphabet. What mode(s) do you find?
- If you picked a word at random, what letter would it most likely contain?

Excursion: Investigate the letters in the game of Scrabble™. Is there a relationship between the number of a certain letter in the game and the letter's frequency in printed text? Is there a relationship between the frequency of letters in printed text and their point values?

Assessment

1. Sal and Matt played a game of chance.

Game Results	
Sal wins	7
Matt wins	13
Times played	20

   a. What is the experimental probability that Sal wins?

   b. Find the experimental probability that Matt wins.

   c. **Writing** Does the game seem fair? Explain.

2. A number cube has six sides numbered 1 through 6. The number cube is rolled twice. What is the probability of getting a 2 on the first roll and a 5 on the second roll?

3. Use the counting principle to find the number of possible outcomes.

   a. selecting a meal from 5 entrees, 4 soups, and 3 desserts

   b. tossing a coin four times

   c. number of possible groups of three letters for a monogram

4. **Choose A, B, C, or D.** The probability of a certain event is ■.

   A. 0 **B.** 1 **C.** $\frac{1}{2}$ **D.** $\frac{1}{4}$

5. The spinner is spun three times.

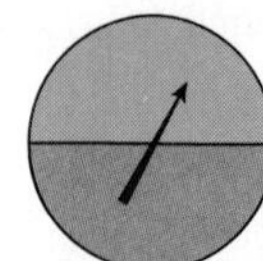

   a. Make a tree diagram to show all possible outcomes.

   b. Find Probability(green, red, green).

   c. Find Probability(all red).

6. A bag contains blue and green chips. The probability of drawing a blue chip is $\frac{5}{12}$.

   a. Find Probability(green).

   b. Draw a spinner you could use to simulate this problem.

7. Find the probability that a digit selected at random from the number 216,394 is a multiple of 3.

8. Determine if the events are independent.

   a. Two dice are thrown. One die shows a 3. The other displays a 1.

   b. You choose a red marble from a bag containing red and yellow marbles. You do not put the marble back. You choose again and get another red marble.

9. Every year a business gives 3 equal scholarships to eligible high school seniors. There are 7 seniors eligible this year to receive these scholarships. In how many ways can 3 seniors out of 7 be selected for the scholarships?

10. **Choose A, B, C, or D.** A marine biologist catches 75 fish from a lake, tags them, and then releases them back into the lake. The next month she catches 75 fish and finds that 5 of them are tagged. Estimate the fish population of the lake.

    A. about 80 **B.** about 325

    C. about 1,125 **D.** about 28,125

Cumulative Review

Choose A, B, C, or D.

1. What is the reciprocal of $4\frac{2}{5}$?

   A. $6\frac{1}{5}$ **B.** $\frac{5}{2}$ **C.** $\frac{5}{22}$ **D.** $\frac{1}{4}$

2. Find the next two terms in the number pattern 2, 6, 12, 20, . . .

   A. 28, 36 **B.** 30, 42
   C. 24, 32 **D.** 32, 44

3. You and a friend play the game "Rock, paper, scissors" by putting one hand behind your backs and, on the count of three, showing your hands in one of the positions. What is the probability that you each show "paper"?

   A. $\frac{1}{3}$ **B.** $\frac{1}{2}$ **C.** $\frac{1}{6}$ **D.** $\frac{1}{9}$

4. What is the value of m if $\frac{2m}{21} = \frac{8}{35}$?

   A. 7 **B.** $\frac{5}{12}$ **C.** 12 **D.** 2.4

5. Estimate the solution to the equation $x - 17.16 = 33.4$.

   A. About 16 **B.** About 50
   C. About 2 **D.** About 0.5

6. Which event is least likely to occur?

   A. You roll a die once and get a 6.
   B. You toss a coin twice and get two heads.
   C. You draw a card from a standard 52-card deck and get an ace.
   D. One of the next 7 days is Saturday.

7. Which value of d will make the sum $\frac{8}{1} + \frac{3}{d}$ greatest?

   A. 4 **B.** 5
   C. 6 **D.** 7

8. How many different three-digit numbers can you make using the digits 1, 3, 5, and 7? (Use each digit at most once.)

   A. $4 \times 3 \times 2$
   B. $7 \times 5 \times 3$
   C. $3 \times 2 \times 1$
   D. $4 \times 4 \times 4$

9. Which is the best buy?

   A. a half-dozen muffins, if a dozen costs $6.59
   B. a half-dozen muffins for $3.19
   C. a half-dozen muffins if each costs $.59
   D. a half-dozen muffins if muffins cost $1.19 for 2

10. You want to draw a map of your neighborhood on a piece of paper that is $8\frac{1}{2}$ in. by 11 in. What scale should you use to map an area 1,000 yd by 750 yd?

    A. 1 in. = 75 yd
    B. 1 in. = 80 yd
    C. 1 in. = 85 yd
    D. 1 in. = 90 yd

CHAPTER 11

Integers and Coordinate Graphing

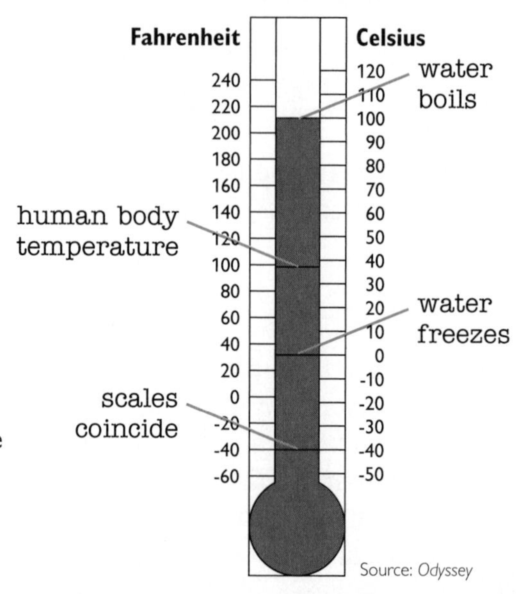

Source: *Odyssey*

Here is the formula to change from degrees *Celsius* (°C) to degrees *Fahrenheit* (°F):

$\frac{9}{5}(°C) + 32 = °F$

Highest Recorded Temperatures in Each of the Seven Continents

Africa	58°C	Al' Aziziyah, Libya
Antarctica	15°C	Bahia, Esperanza
Asia	54°C	Tirat Tsvi, Israel
Australia	53°C	Cloncurry, Queensland
Europe	50°C	Seville, Spain
N. America	57°C	Death Valley, California
S. America	49°C	Rivadavia, Argentina

Lowest Recorded Temperatures in Each of the Seven Continents

Africa	-24°C	Ifrane, Morocco
Antarctica	-89°C	Vostok
Asia	-68°C	Oimekon, Russian Federation
Australia	-22°C	Charlotte Pass, NSW
Europe	-59°C	Ust'Schugor, Russian Federation
N. America	-63°C	Snag, Yukon
S. America	-33°C	Colonia, Sarmiento, Argentina

Source: *Encyclopedia Britannica*

OCEAN FLOOR PROFILE ALONG THE EQUATOR

Elevation and depth (m)

6,000
4,000
2,000
Sea Level
2,000
4,000
6,000

Andes Mountains
Galapogos Islands
Pacific Ocean
South America

Data File 11

WHAT YOU WILL LEARN

- how to model addition and subtraction with integers
- how to create and use a coordinate system
- how to use technology to explore translations and reflections
- how to use multiple strategies to solve problems

The World's Climate Regions

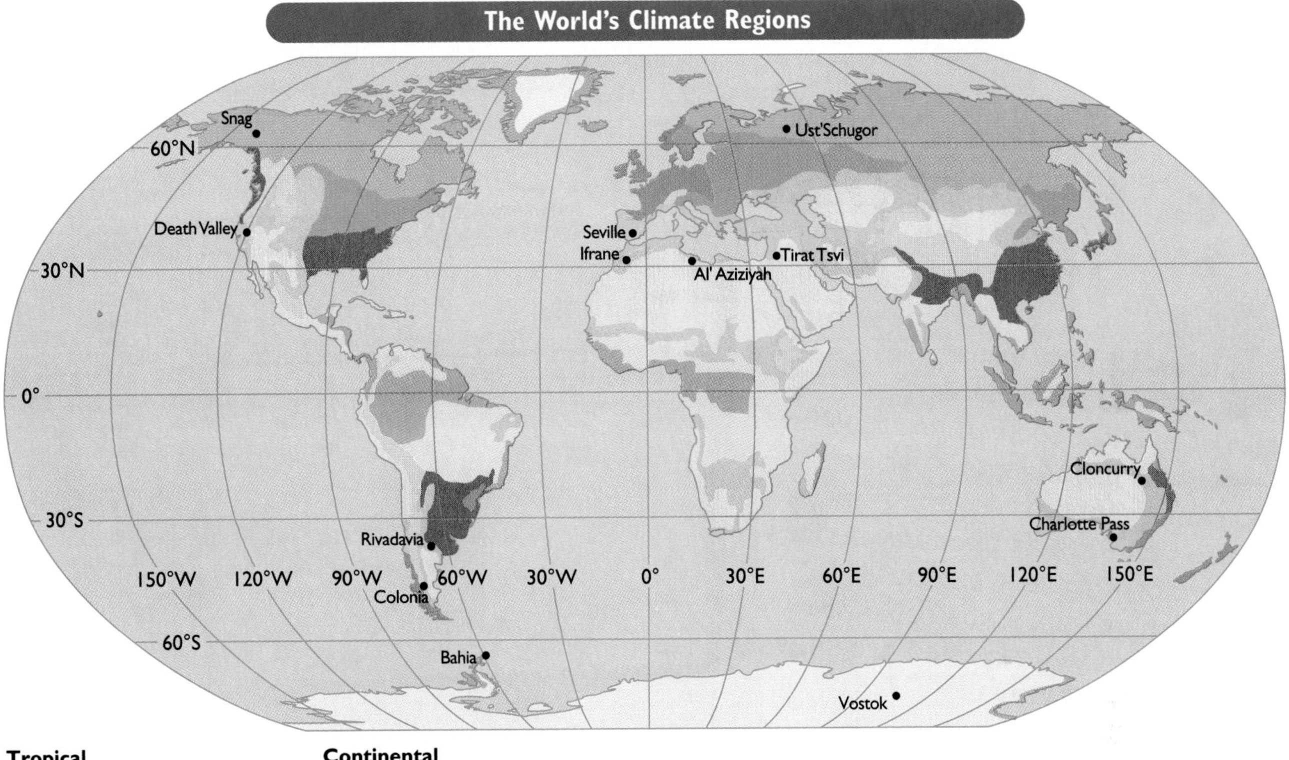

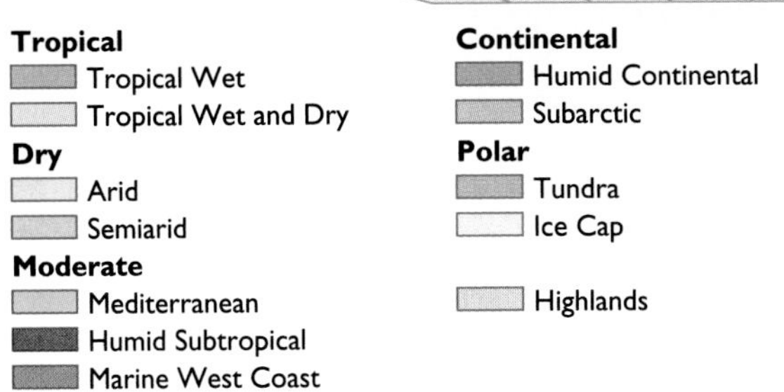

Hawaii is moving *toward* Japan at a rate of over 4 in. per year. North America and Europe are moving *apart* at a rate of about 1 in. per year.

Zaire Basin
Mt. Kenya
Maldives
Sumatra
Borneo
Celebes
Gilbert Islands
Africa
Indian Ocean
Pacific Ocean
Atlantic Ocean

investigation

Project File

Memo

A **timeline** is a visual representation of the dates of a series of events. You can use timelines to represent past events, such as important events in history. You can also use timelines as planning devices to show how future events may unfold. For example, you could draw a timeline to show expected progress in a fund-raising drive.

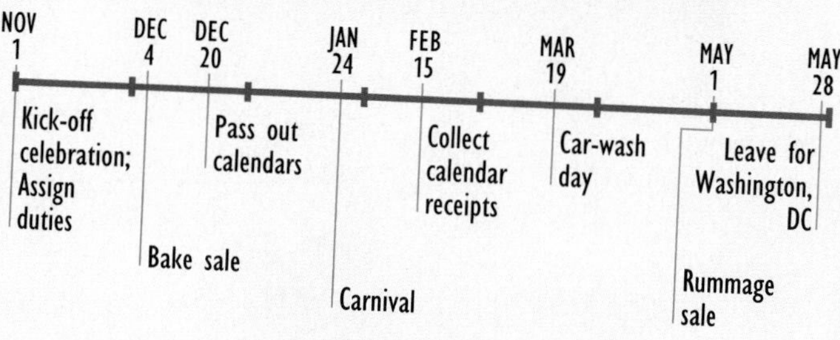

Mission: Create a timeline of important events that have occurred at your school. Begin your timeline at "Year 0," your first year in the school (or your first year as a member of your group). Your timeline should include descriptions of events and dates of events, numbered from zero, along with any other information you consider important.

Leads to Follow

✓ How can you decide whether an event is important enough to include on your timeline?

✓ Should you number your timeline by years, months, weeks, or by some other interval?

What's Ahead

- Graphing integers on a number line
- Comparing and ordering integers

11-1 Using a Number Line

THINK AND DISCUSS

In a football game, a receiver caught the football and gained 4 yd. Later a running back gained −3 yd, which means he lost 3 yd. In the second half the quarterback was sacked and gained −6 yd. Here's how you read the numbers of yards gained.

+4: *positive 4* −3: *negative 3* −6: *negative 6*

FLASHBACK

To graph a number on a number line, draw a point at that number.

To keep track of the yardage, you can graph the gains on a number line. Extend the number line to the left of 0 to show negative numbers.

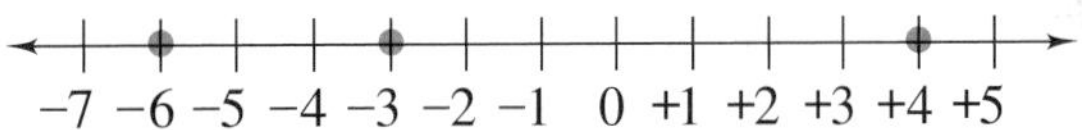

1. Another football player lost four yards on a carry. Write this amount as a number and graph it on a number line.
2. Graph the numbers −1, 5, and 0 on a number line.

The numbers . . . −3, −2, −1, 0, +1, + 2, +3, . . . are **integers.** The numbers +1, +2, +3, . . . are **positive integers.** The numbers −1, −2, −3, . . . are **negative integers.** The number 0 is neither positive nor negative. You can write positive numbers with or without a "+" sign. For example, +2 = 2.

Two numbers that are the same distance from 0 on a number line, but in different directions, are **opposites.**

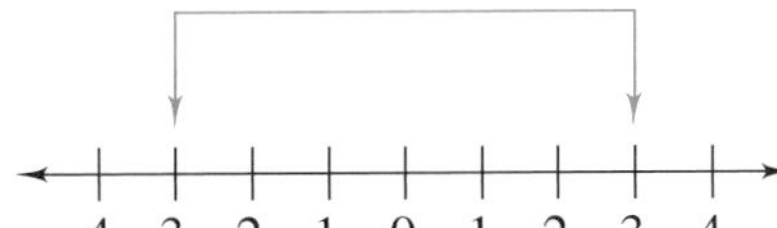

3 and −3 are three units from 0.
3 and −3 are opposites.

3. Name the opposite of each integer.
   a. 4 **b.** −6 **c.** 15 **d.** 0
4. Name two integers that are opposites. How far from 0 is each integer?

The longest field goal recorded is 63 yd. Tom Dempsey kicked the record-breaking field goal for the New Orleans Saints in 1970.

Source: *The Guinness Book of Records*

Nancy Lopez won the Rail Charity Golf Classic tournament in 1992 with a score of −17.

Source: *Sports Illustrated Sports Almanac.*

5. a. What is the opposite of gaining nine yards in football?
   b. Write the gain and its opposite as integers.

You can use the [+/-] key to write the opposite of a number.

5 [+/-] → −5   5 [+/-] [+/-] → 5

6. A calculator displays −12. If you press the [+/-] key, what does the calculator display?

7. Why is the [+/-] key called the "change-sign" key?

Golfers keep score by counting how many times they hit the golf ball. Then they compare that number to an accepted standard for the hole or course. A score of −2 means that you hit the ball two less times than the standard. In golf, the lowest score is the best.

Stoneham Golf Course	
Eugenio	−1
Mwita	−5

Example 1 Who had a lower score, Eugenio or Mwita?

- Graph each score on a number line.

−5 −4 −3 −2 −1 0 1

−5 is to the left of −1.
−5 < −1 or −1 > −5

Mwita had a lower score than Eugenio.

8. Compare using <, >, or =.
   a. 10 ■ 6 b. −7 ■ 0 c. 3 ■ −4 d. −13 ■ −11

FLASHBACK
Numbers on a number line increase in value from left to right.

9. **Critical Thinking** Complete with *always, sometimes,* or *never.*
   a. 0 is ■ greater than a negative integer.
   b. 0 is ■ greater than a positive integer.
   c. A negative integer is ■ less than another negative integer.

Golf Scores	
2	Ilana
0	Dwayne
−4	Luisa
3	Shani
−2	William

Example 2 List the scores in order from least to greatest.

- Graph each score on a number line.

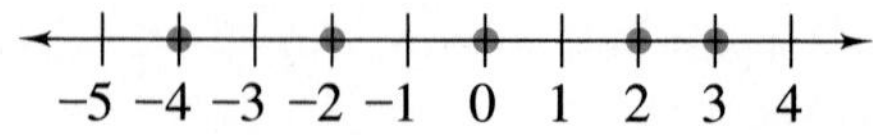

- Write the scores from left to right.

In order, the scores are −4, −2, 0, 2, and 3.

10. Which two players had opposite scores?

11. List in order from least to greatest: 7, −4, 11, 0, −8.

TRY THESE

12. Graph these integers on a number line: 6, −9, 7, −1, 0, 3.

Name the integer that is represented by each point.

13. *M*

14. *N*

15. *P*

16. *Q*

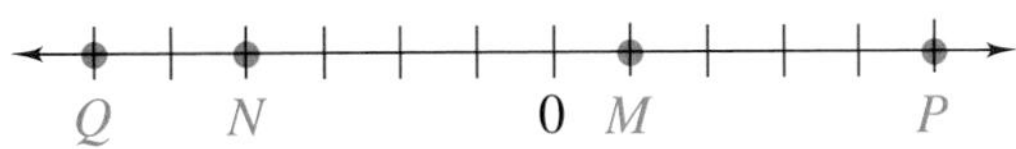

Write an integer to represent each situation.

17. earnings of $25

18. 14 degrees below zero

19. **Geography** Carlsbad Caverns in New Mexico are the deepest caves in the United States at 1,565 ft deep.

20. **Geography** Mt. Whitney in California has an elevation of 4,418 m.

Compare using <, >, or =.

21. −7 ■ 2

22. −12 ■ −9

23. −17 ■ −23

ON YOUR OWN

Use the bar graph at the right.

24. **Estimation** Estimate the change in the number of farmers by the year 2005.

25. **Estimation** Estimate the change in the number of lawyers by the year 2005.

26. Will bank tellers or typists lose more jobs? Explain.

27. a. List the jobs in order from the most gained to the most lost.

    b. Redraw the graph with the jobs in that order.

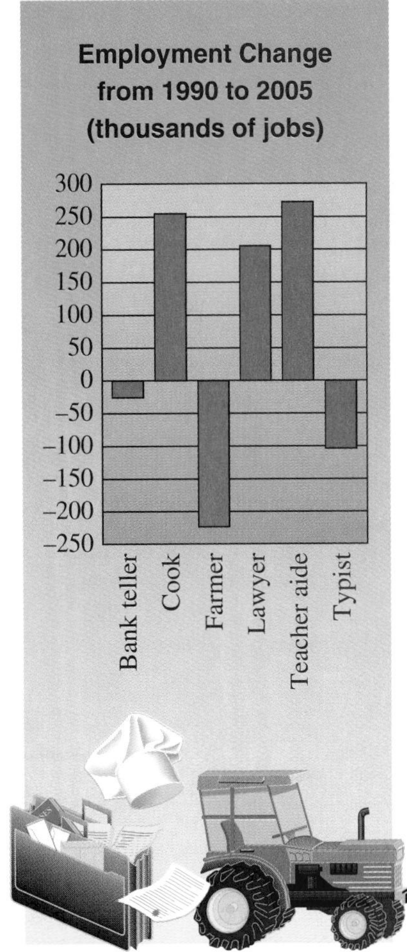

Mixed REVIEW

Find each sum or difference.

1. $5\frac{2}{3} + 3\frac{1}{6}$
2. $2\frac{7}{8} - 1\frac{2}{3}$
3. Explain why a sample should be chosen randomly.
4. A poll of voters found that 43% favored an increase in taxes. What is the probability that another voter, when asked, would favor an increase in taxes?
5. What is the sum of the first 10 even integers?

At age 14 Sarah Billmeier from Vermont won three skiing events at the 1992 Paralympics in France.

28. **Data File 11 (pp. 446–447)** Estimate the depth of the Indian Ocean. Write the amount as an integer compared to sea level.

Write an integer between the given integers.

29. $-7, 3$ 30. $0, -6$ 31. $-5, -13$

Name the opposite of each integer.

32. 13 33. -8 34. 150 35. -212

36. Name three pairs of situations that are opposites. For example, walk up two stairs; walk down two stairs.

Write an integer that makes each statement true.

37. $-5 <$ ■ 38. ■ < 6 39. opposite of ■ > 0

40. **Weather** List the temperatures from least to greatest.
    - Normal body temperature is about 37°C.
    - An average winter day on the polar ice cap is -25°C.
    - The warmest day in Canada was 45°C.
    - Water freezes at 0°C. Ski resorts can make artificial snow at this temperature.
    - The coldest day in Alaska was -62°C.

41. **Data File 11 (pp. 446–447)** List the lowest recorded temperatures from least to greatest.

42. **Writing** Explain what integers are and describe opposites. Include number lines in your descriptions.

Calculator Name the integer that results from each calculator key sequence.

43. 8 [+⇄-] 44. 9 [+⇄-] [+⇄-] 45. 6 [+⇄-]  

46. **Investigation (p. 448)**
    a. How is a time line similar to a number line? How is it different?
    b. What type of points on your time line represents events that happened before you entered school? after you entered school?

What's Ahead

- Representing positive integers, negative integers, and zero using models.

WHAT YOU'LL NEED

✓ Algebra tiles 

11-2 Modeling Integers

THINK AND DISCUSS

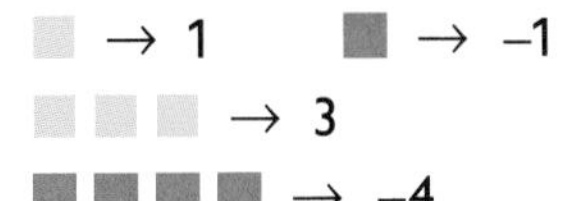

You can use colored tiles to model integers. Yellow tiles represent positive integers. Red tiles represent negative integers.

1. What integer is represented by the tiles?

   a. b.

   c. d.

2. Which integers in Question 1 are opposites?

3. **Critical Thinking** What do you notice about the sets of tiles that represent a number and its opposite?

4. Use tiles to represent each integer and its opposite.

   a. 4 b. −3 c. 2 d. −8

Suppose you earned \$1 and then spent \$1. Then represents the \$1 that you earned and represents the \$1 that you spent. You have *no more* or *no less* money than before.

5. Suppose you have seven positive tiles. How many negative tiles do you need to represent zero?

6. Suppose you have ten negative tiles. How many positive tiles do you need to represent zero?

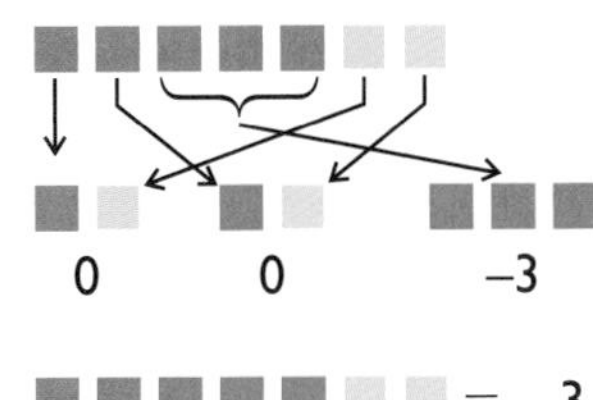

You can use zero pairs of tiles to write integers when you have tiles of both colors together.

- Group the pairs of tiles that represent zero.
- Remove the pairs from the other tiles.
- Write the integer that the remaining tiles represent.

7. Write the integer that is represented by the tiles.

   a. b. c.

8. a. What integer is represented by ■ ■ ▫ ▫ ▫ ▫?
   b. What integer is represented by ▫ ▫ ▫ ▫ ▫ ■ ■ ■?
   c. How do the answers to parts (a) and (b) compare?
   d. Critical Thinking How many ways are there to represent an integer with tiles? Explain.

WORK TOGETHER

Work with a partner. Repeat this activity four times.

- State a real world situation that can be represented by an integer. Have your partner name the integer and represent it with tiles.
- Have your partner describe the opposite real world situation. You name this opposite and represent it with tiles.

ON YOUR OWN

Mixed REVIEW

Find the value of x.

1. $\frac{20}{21} = \frac{x}{63}$
2. $\frac{4}{28} = \frac{8}{x}$

Write the opposite of each integer.

3. -4
4. 21

5. Draw a pair of triangles that are similar but not congruent.

9. **Writing** Explain how you can use tiles to represent integers. Include examples and diagrams.

Use tiles to represent each integer in two ways.

10. 1
11. -7
12. 0
13. 5

Write the integer that is represented by the tiles.

14. 

15. 

16. 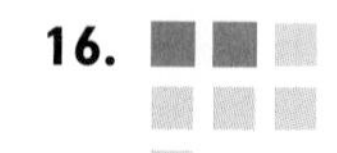

17. What integer is represented by 13 negative tiles and 7 positive tiles?

18. a. Think of two integers. Model them with tiles.
    b. Use a different number of tiles to represent the opposite of each integer.

19. **Critical Thinking** Suppose you had 6 tiles and didn't know the colors of the tiles.
    a. How many different ways can you color the tiles?
    b. List all the integers that the tiles can represent.

What's Ahead

- Adding integers using models

11-3 Modeling Addition of Integers

WHAT YOU'LL NEED

✓ Algebra tiles 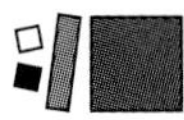

✓ Paper bag 

Toadstool's Practice Jumps

Attempt	First Jump	Second Jump
1	3 ft	7 ft
2	−5 ft	−2 ft
3	6 ft	−4 ft
4	−7 ft	3 ft
5	4 ft	−4 ft

THINK AND DISCUSS

People in Frogville train frogs for the Annual Frog Jumping Festival. The main event is the Double Jump, in which the distances for two leaps are combined. Last year's champion Toadstool is giving his owner Pamela a little trouble. Sometimes he jumps backward! Pamela kept track of Toadstool's practice jumps for the Double Jump.

You can model the lengths of Toadstool's jumps with tiles to find the sum of his jumps. To find the sum of his first attempt, write this number sentence.

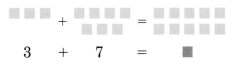

$3 + 7 = ■$

1. Complete the number sentence above. How many total feet did Toadstool jump in his first attempt?

2. Show how tiles can be used to find the sum $9 + 4$.

3. Complete: Adding two positive integers always results in a ■ integer.

Example 1 What was the sum of Toadstool's jumps in his second attempt?

- Model each integer with tiles. Then count the tiles.

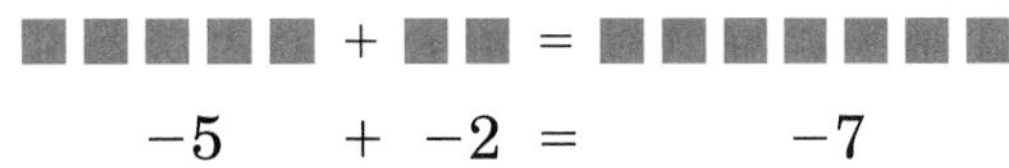

$-5 + -2 = -7$

He jumped a total of −7 ft.

The United States record for a jumping frog is 21 ft $5\frac{1}{2}$ in. total for 3 jumps and occurred at the Calaveras County, CA, Jumping Frog Jubilee.

Source: *The Guinness Book of Records*

4. Use tiles to find each sum.
   a. $-8 + (-1)$
   b. $-3 + (-6)$
   c. $-12 + (-9)$
   d. $-7 + (-8)$

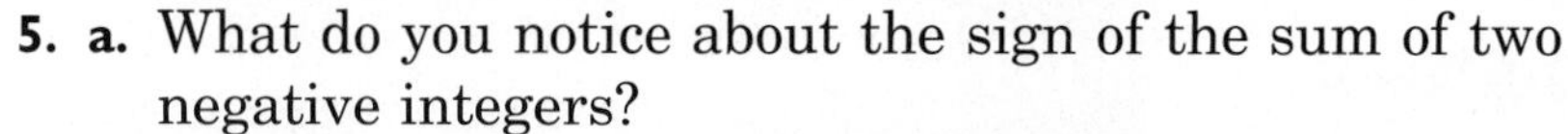

5. a. What do you notice about the sign of the sum of two negative integers?

   b. Complete: Adding two negative integers always results in a ■ integer.

Africa contains the largest frog in the world. A goliath frog found in Cameroon measured 14.5 in. long and weighed 8 lb 1 oz. The smallest frog in the world is in Cuba and is less than $\frac{1}{2}$ in. long!

Source: *The Guinness Book of Records*

Example 2 Use the table on page 455. What was the sum of Toadstool's jumps in his third attempt?

- Model each integer with tiles. Combine tiles to make zero pairs. Write the integer that the remaining tiles represent.

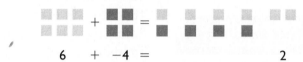

$6 \quad + \quad -4 \quad = \quad 2$

He jumped a total of 2 ft.

6. Use tiles to find each sum.

   a. $-5 + 9$ b. $-8 + 3$ c. $7 + (-7)$

7. What do you notice about the sign of the sum of a positive integer and a negative integer?

8. **Critical Thinking** What is the sum of a number and its opposite? Give examples to justify your answer.

WORK TOGETHER

Work with a partner. Place 20 yellow and 20 red algebra tiles in a paper bag. Make a scorecard like the sample at the left.

- Remove 1 tile from the bag. Write the integer that the tile represents. Replace the tile.
- Have your partner remove 1 tile, write the integer, and then replace the tile.
- Continue removing tiles and writing integers. During each round, increase the number of tiles you remove by 1.
- At the end of 8 rounds, find your score. Cross out any 0's or zero pairs. Model the remaining integers with tiles. Your score is the integer that these tiles represent.
- Compare your scores. Who had the greater score?

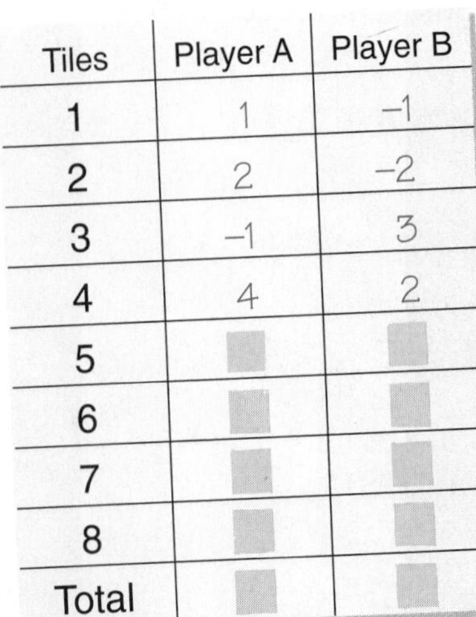

Tiles	Player A	Player B
1	1	−1
2	2	−2
3	−1	3
4	4	2
5	■	■
6	■	■
7	■	■
8	■	■
Total	■	■

TRY THESE

Write a numerical expression for each model. Find the sum.

9. ■■■ + ■■■ (tile model)
   ■■■   ■■

10. ■■ + ■■■■
         ■■■■

Use tiles to find each sum.

11. $-1 + (-5)$
12. $10 + (-10)$
13. $-11 + 4$

Mental Math **State whether the sum is positive or negative.**

14. $16 + 14$
15. $-16 + (-14)$
16. $-16 + 18$

Work with a partner. Write an addition exercise involving a positive integer and a negative integer so that you can get each type of answer.

17. negative
18. 0
19. positive

ON YOUR OWN

Use tiles to find each sum.

20. $9 + (-4)$
21. $-8 + (-7)$
22. $-15 + 6$
23. $-11 + 11$
24. $0 + (-8)$
25. $-6 + 11$

Compare. Write $<$, $>$, or $=$.

26. $-7 + (-3)$ ■ $7 + 3$
27. $5 + (-5)$ ■ $-1 + 1$
28. $-2 + 8$ ■ $-8 + 2$
29. $6 + (-3) + (-4)$ ■ $6 + (-7)$

30. **Weather** What was the temperature in Spearfish, SD, at 7:32 A.M. on January 22, 1943?

31. Use the table on page 456. Did Player A or Player B have the greater score after 4 rounds? Explain why.

32. **Money** On Saturday Tyrell earned \$12 running errands for the elderly center. On Monday he spent \$8 on a cassette. On Friday he earned \$7 baby-sitting. How much money did Tyrell have at the end of the week?

At 7:30 A.M. on January 22, 1943, the temperature was −4°F in Spearfish, SD. Two minutes later the temperature had risen an amazing 49°F!

Source: *Guinness Book of World Records*

33. **Sports** A football team gained 6 yd on one play. On the next play the team lost 11 yd. Write the total gain or loss of yards as an integer.

34. The mailroom of a large company is on the 15th floor. Linda delivers mail by first going up 5 floors in the elevator. She next goes down 3 floors. Then she goes down 4 floors. Where is she in relation to the mailroom?

35. **Investigation (p. 448)** Research events that happened at your school before you entered. Assign a negative time line date to each event. Explain the time line dates.

Magic Integer Square

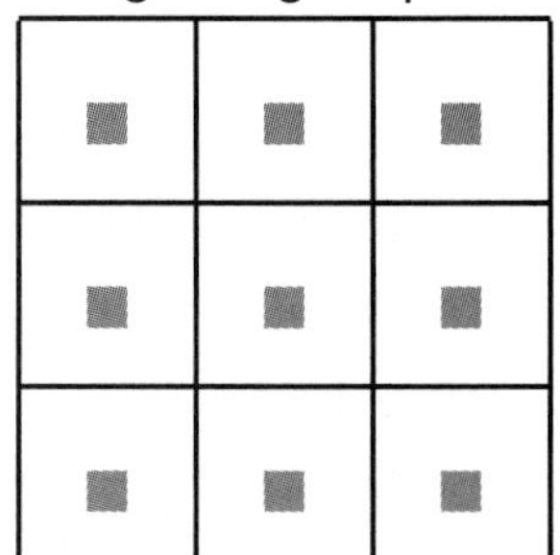

Mental Math Group opposites to get a sum of 0. Add the remaining integers.

36. $-4 + 7 + 4 + (-2)$

37. $6 + (-3) + (-8) + 3$

38. $8 + (-9) + (-8) + 9$

39. $-7 + 5 + (-1) + 7 + (-7)$

40. Copy the Magic Integer Square. Arrange the integers -4, -3, -2, -1, 0, 1, 2, 3, 4 so they add up to zero in all eight directions (vertically, horizontally, and on the diagonal).

41. **Writing** Summarize what you know about adding 2 positive integers, 2 negative integers, and a positive integer and a negative integer.

Mixed REVIEW

Write the integer that is represented by the tiles.

1. ■ ■ ■

2. ■ ■ ■ ■ ■

3. The length of a room in a blueprint is 4 in. The actual length is 20 ft. Find the scale of the blueprint.

4. A rectangle is 20 in. long. Its width is 4 in. What are its area and perimeter?

5. Find all combinations of 5 whole numbers that you can add to get a sum of 10.

CHECKPOINT

Compare using <, >, or =.

1. 2 ■ 5

2. -4 ■ -8

3. -3 ■ 0

4. Graph on a number line: 2, -5, 3, 1, -7, -2.

5. What integer is represented by ■ ■ ■ ■ ■ ■ ■?

Use tiles to represent each integer and its opposite.

6. 6

7. -5

8. -2

9. 8

Use tiles to find each sum.

10. $-2 + (-3)$

11. $7 + (-5)$

12. $-9 + 9$

What's Ahead

- Subtracting integers using models

WHAT YOU'LL NEED

✓ Algebra tiles

✓ Two dice of different colors

11-4 Modeling Subtraction of Integers

THINK AND DISCUSS

Suppose you have \$5 and want to spend \$2. How much will you have left? You subtract to find the answer. Here's how you can use algebra tiles to subtract $5 - 2$.

Start with 5 positive tiles.

Take away 2 positive tiles.

Three positive tiles remain. You have \$3 left.

1. Show how to use tiles to find the difference $10 - 6$.

Example 1 Use tiles to subtract $-8 - (-6)$.

- Start with 8 negative tiles.

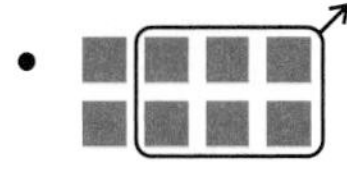

- Take away 6 negative tiles.
- There are 2 negative tiles.

$-8 - (-6) = -2$

2. Use tiles to find each difference.

a. $12 - 4$ **b.** $-10 - (-3)$ **c.** $-15 - (-9)$

Example 2 Use tiles to subtract $4 - (-3)$.

- There are not enough negative tiles to take 3 away. Add 3 zero pairs.

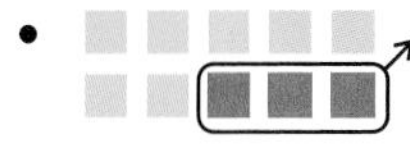

- Take away 3 negative tiles. There are 7 positive tiles left.

$4 - (-3) = 7$

3. a. What is the total value of the 3 zero pairs? Explain.

b. Did adding 3 zero pairs affect the value of -4? Explain.

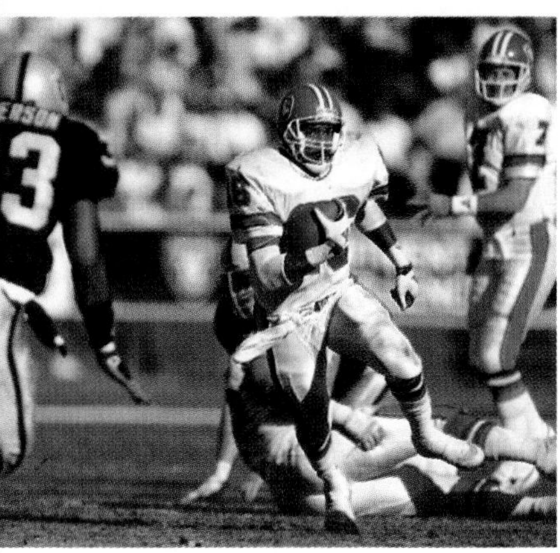

In the first half of a game against the L.A. Raiders, the Denver Broncos ran for 79 yd and passed for −6 yd. ***For how many more yards did the Broncos run than pass?***

Example 3 On January 15, the high temperature was 5°C. By midnight the temperature had dropped 9°C. What was the temperature at midnight?

- Use tiles to subtract $5 - 9$.
- Start with 5 positive tiles.
- 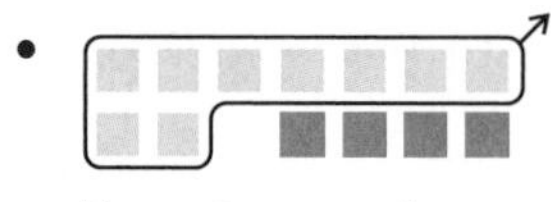 There are not enough positive tiles to take 9 away. Add 4 zero pairs.
- Take away 9 positive tiles. There are 4 negative tiles left.
- $5 - 9 = -4$

The temperature was $-4°$ C at midnight.

4. Critical Thinking

a. Could 3 zero pairs have been added in the Example? Why or why not?

b. If 5 zero pairs had been added in the Example, would the answer be the same? Why or why not?

5. Use tiles to find each difference.

a. $-5 - (-11)$ **b.** $-10 - 5$ **c.** $12 - 19$

How wonderful it is that nobody need wait a single moment before starting to improve the world.
—Anne Frank (1929–1945)

WORK TOGETHER

Work in groups of three. Start with 3 positive and 3 negative tiles each. Put the remaining tiles in a pile.

- Play the Great Integer Game. The object of the game is to be the first player to give away all his or her tiles.
- Decide which color die will be subtracted from the other. (For example, subtract a red die from a green die.)

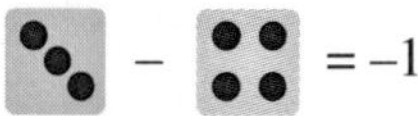

- Roll the dice. Put the resulting number of tiles in the pile.
- If you don't have enough tiles to put in the pot, you have to take zero pairs from the pile in order to make your number!
- The game is over when one player has no more tiles.

TRY THESE

Write a numerical expression for each model. Find the difference.

6. 

7. 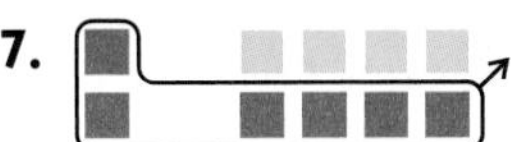

Use tiles to find each difference.

8. $7 - 12$
9. $-8 - 4$
10. $-1 - (-5)$

Model each situation with tiles. Give the result.

11. The temperature increases 9°F and then drops 17°F.
12. Elevator goes down 7 floors and then down 6 more floors.
13. **Sports** Tasheka finished a golf game at 4 strokes over par (+4). Carmen scored 5 under par (−5). How many more golf strokes did Tasheka make than Carmen?
14. **Weather** One winter day the temperature rose from a low of −8° C to a high of 9° C. What was the temperature range for the day?

Mixed REVIEW

State whether the sum is positive or negative.

1. $2 + 5$
2. $-2 + 5$

Find the prime factorization using a factor tree.

3. 60
4. 1,240

5. I'm thinking of a number. If I multiply by 4 and add 7, the result is 51. What is the number?

ON YOUR OWN

Use tiles to find each sum or difference.

15. $1 - 6$
16. $-13 - 8$
17. $-4 - (-15)$
18. $-9 + 7$
19. $12 + (-3)$
20. $0 - 10$

Compare. Write <, >, or =.

21. $-1 - 5$ ■ $-5 - 1$
22. $6 - 11$ ■ $11 - 6$
23. $-4 - (-9)$ ■ $-4 + 9$
24. $8 - (-8)$ ■ $-8 + 8$

Weather **Find each average for the data at the right.**

25. median
26. mode(s)
27. range

Average Low Temperatures (°C) for Boston, MA

Month	Temp.	Month	Temp.
Jan.	−6	July	18
Feb.	−6	Aug.	18
March	−1	Sept.	13
April	4	Oct.	8
May	9	Nov.	3
June	14	Dec.	−3

Critical Thinking **Find the next three integers in each pattern.**

28. 12, 7, 2, −3, ■, ■, ■
29. 19, 13, 7, 1, ■, ■, ■

30. **Writing** Describe how to use tiles to subtract integers. Include examples with both positive and negative integers.

31. **Investigation** Name several pairs of events that happened at your school. In each pair, one event should occur before and one after you entered school. What are the time-line dates of the events? Find the amount of time that elapsed between the two events in each pair.

Evaluate each expression when $a = -6$, $b = -1$, and $c = 9$.

32. $7 - a$ 33. $b - c$ 34. $-12 - b$ 35. $b - 11 - a$

Geography The map shows the time zones for North America. The starting point is a time zone through England, Spain, and Africa. The numbers indicate the time (in hours) compared to the starting zone's time.

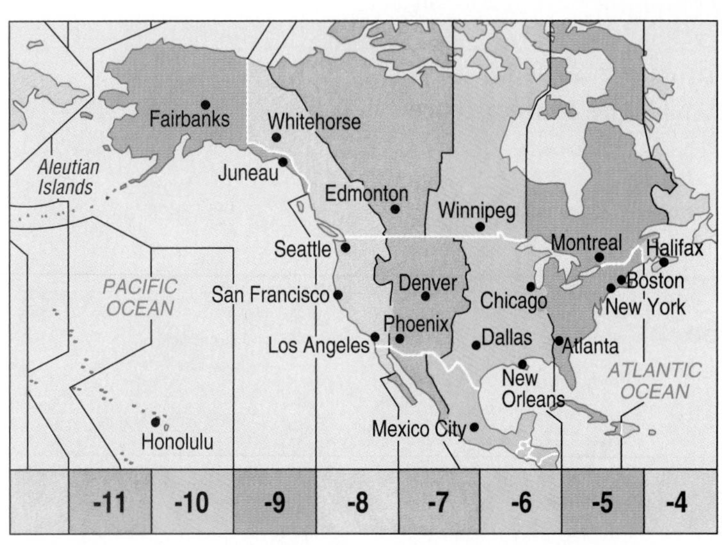

36. Complete with *add* or *subtract:* As you travel west, you ■ 1 h. As you travel east, you ■ 1 h.

37. It's 2:30 P.M. in the starting zone. What is the time in Denver?

38. It's 8:15 A.M. in San Francisco. What time is it in Dallas?

39. Times Square in New York is celebrating at midnight on New Year's Eve. What time is it in Los Angeles?

40. How does the time in New Orleans compare to Honolulu?

41. a. **Research** Find the names of the time zones on the map above.
    b. In what time zone do you live?
    c. Let t = the time at the starting zone. Write a variable expression to indicate the time in your time zone.

WHEN?

In 1884 an international conference established worldwide time zones. Before that, each place set its own time.

Source: *The World Book Encyclopedia*

Critical Thinking Use positive and negative integers to write two different subtraction sentences.

42. ■ − ■ = 0 43. ■ − ■ = 8 44. ■ − ■ = −5

Practice

Graph each integer on a number line.

1. -9 **2.** 4 **3.** -1 **4.** 7 **5.** 0

List the integers in order from least to greatest.

6. $-3, 0, -8, 2$ **7.** $5, -12, 1, -7$ **8.** $-9, 6, -4, 0, -2$ **9.** $-72, -76, 72, -73, 71$

Name the opposite of each integer.

10. 5 **11.** -3 **12.** 0 **13.** 6 **14.** -6

Compare using <, >, or =.

15. -1 ■ -3 **16.** 0 ■ -8 **17.** 3 ■ 2 **18.** -4 ■ -15

Write the integer represented by the tiles.

19. ■ □ ■ □ / ■ ■ □ □

20. ■ ■ ■ / □ ■

21. □ □ ■ ■ ■ □ □ □ □ / □ ■ ■ □ □ □

Use tiles to represent each integer in two ways.

22. 0 **23.** -2 **24.** -1 **25.** 4

Use tiles to find each sum or difference.

26. $-7 + (-3)$ **27.** $-2 + (-5)$ **28.** $-4 + 7$ **29.** $8 + (-8)$

30. $2 - 5$ **31.** $-12 - 9$ **32.** $-3 - (-10)$ **33.** $0 - 6$

Compare using <, >, or =.

34. $-5 + (-3)$ ■ $5 + 3$ **35.** $-7 + 10$ ■ $-10 + 7$ **36.** $-3 + 3$ ■ $1 + (-1)$

37. $-2 - 4$ ■ $-4 - 2$ **38.** $5 - (-5)$ ■ $-5 + 5$ **39.** $3 - 7$ ■ $7 - 3$

Model each situation with tiles. Give the result.

40. The temperature was 2°F below zero. The temperature then rose 9°F.

41. Chim ran 8 yd on a football play. On the next play he lost 13 yd.

What's Ahead

- Solving problems using multiple strategies

PROBLEM SOLVING

11-5 Use Multiple Strategies

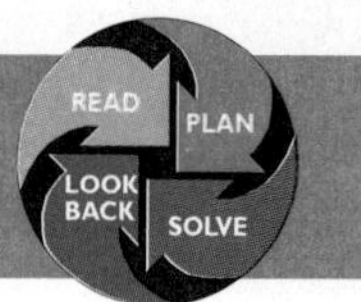

Sometimes you need to use more than one strategy to solve a problem.

> Shamika finished first in the flying ring contest at the football field. The field had scoring zones worth 1, 3, 5, 7, and 9 points. Each zone was shaped like a semicircle. Shamika scored on all five of her throws. Which of these scores could be Shamika's total score: 4 24 37 47?

READ

Read and understand the given information. Summarize the problem.

1. How many times did Shamika throw the ring?
2. What scores are possible on each throw?
3. Is 0 a possible score for one of Shamika's throws?

PLAN

Decide on a strategy to solve the problem.

First *draw a diagram* of the field to have a visual idea of the contest. Next *use logical reasoning* to eliminate as impossible some of the scores in the list above. Then *make a table* to keep track of the remaining throws and scores.

SOLVE

Try out the strategy.

A diagram of the field shows the scoring sections as semicircles. Each section has a label showing the points received when a flying ring lands in that section.

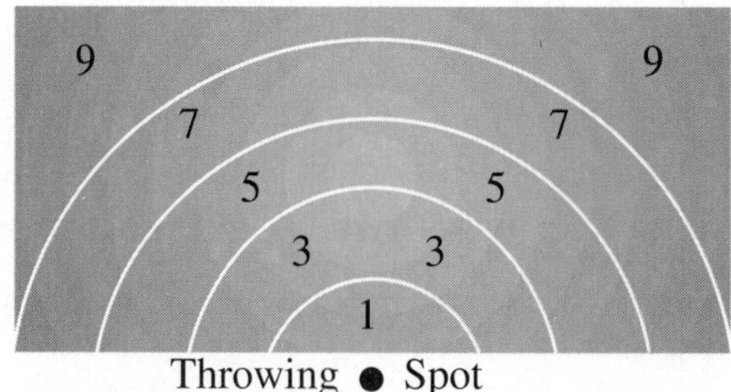

The only possible scores for a throw are 1, 3, 5, 7, or 9 points. Think logically about the possible scores that Shamika can get altogether for her 5 throws.

4. What is the highest total score Shamika could get?

5. What is the lowest total score she could get?

6. Which two scores in the list can you now eliminate?

A table can help you to see if Shamika could get the remaining scores of 24 or 37. The table shows an example in which a player got 3 points on each of 2 throws, 5 points on 1 throw, 7 points on 1 throw, and 9 points on 1 throw.

	Points for Each Throw					Total Score
	1	3	5	7	9	
Number of Throws	0	2	1	1	1	$(0 \times 1) + (2 \times 3) + (1 \times 5) + (1 \times 7) + (1 \times 9) = \mathbf{27}$
	■	■	■	■	■	■
	■	■	■	■	■	■

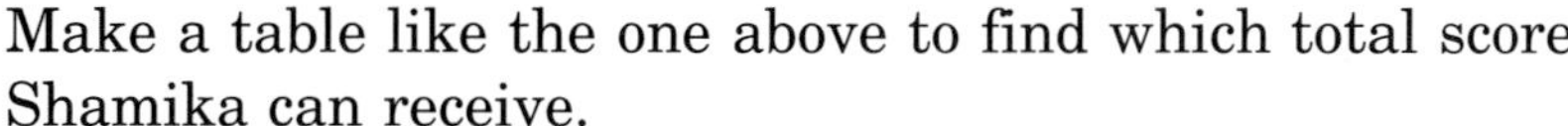

Make a table like the one above to find which total score Shamika can receive.

7. Experiment with possible ways to get the total score. Which problem solving strategy did you use?

8. Which remaining score is impossible? Why?

9. Which is the only possible total score?

10. Find three ways Shamika's 5 throws could have landed to get the only possible score.

***Scott Zimmerman** holds the world's record for throwing a flying ring. He threw a ring 1,257 ft across Niagara Falls from Canada to the United States.*

Source: *Guinness Book of Records*

LOOK BACK

Think about how you solved this problem.

TRY THESE

Use any strategy to solve each problem. Show all your work.

11. The old clock tower loses 10 minutes every 2 days. The town residents have decided that eventually it will get back to the correct time on its own. Suppose that today is May 1st. On what date will the clock show the correct time again?

12. A gardener wants to fence in the greatest possible area using 200 ft of fencing. What should be the length and the width of the garden?

ON YOUR OWN

Use any strategy to solve each problem. Show all your work.

Thor Heyerdahl and five companions sailed a wooden raft named "Kon-Tiki" from South America to the Polynesian islands. The trip covered over 4,000 miles and lasted $3\frac{1}{2}$ months.

13. Suppose you launched a raft on the Ohio River at Three Rivers Stadium in Pittsburgh, PA. Your raft drifted at a steady 3 mi/h for 9 hours less than exactly 2 weeks. When your raft landed in Cairo, IL, you had traveled the entire length of the Ohio River. How long is the Ohio River?

14. There are 48 students in the band. Of these students, 10 are left-handed and 19 have pierced ears. There are 27 students who are *not* left-handed and do *not* have pierced ears. How many students are left-handed and have pierced ears?

15. A couple who won the lottery gave their children half of the money. They gave their grandchildren half of the remaining money and kept \$3.8 million for themselves. How much did the couple win?

16. **Consumer Issues** Suppose a customer will accept no more than 6 one-dollar bills in change. In how many different ways can you give the customer change from a \$100 bill for a \$79 purchase?

17. Find the sum of all the odd whole numbers from 1 to 99.

18. A young man jogs in the park every other day. His sister jogs every third day. They both jogged on July 1. How many more days in July can they jog together if they keep to this schedule?

19. Suppose the average blink takes $\frac{1}{5}$ of a second and a person blinks 25 times per minute. You traveled at an average speed of 50 mi/h for 12 hours. How many miles would you have traveled with your eyes closed?

20. A student spent $\frac{1}{2}$ of her money for a movie and then \$3 on a snack for the movie. After the movie, she spent $\frac{1}{2}$ of her remaining money for a bus home. She then had \$2. How much money did she have before the movie?

21. You have a stick 4 cm long and a stick 8 cm long. What are the possible whole-number lengths (in cm) of a third stick you could use with these sticks to form a triangle?

Mixed REVIEW

Use tiles to find each difference.

1. $5 - (-2)$
2. $-3 - (-5)$

Write each as a percent.

3. 18 boards out of 100 boards are warped
4. 86 seats out of 100 seats are occupied
5. Two numbers have a sum of 34 and a product of 273. What are the two numbers?

What's Ahead

- Using a coordinate plane to graph points
- Naming the coordinates of points on a coordinate plane

WHAT YOU'LL NEED

✓ **Geoboard** 

✓ **Rubber bands**

11-6 Graphing on the Coordinate Plane

WORK TOGETHER

Work with a partner. Agree on a system for locating points on a geoboard.

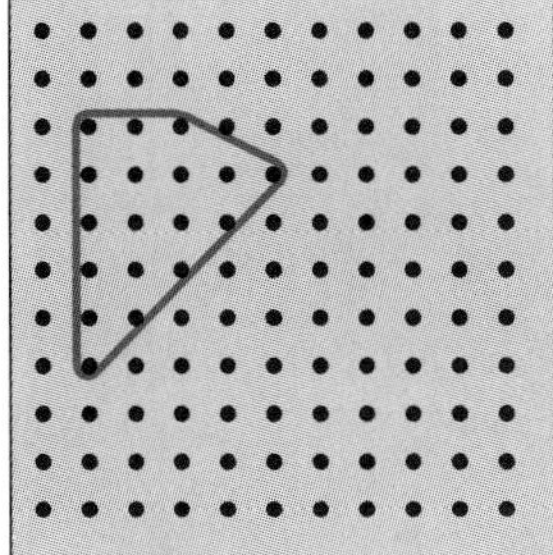

- Create a shape on a geoboard with a rubber band. An example is at the left. Don't let your partner see your shape!
- Have your partner ask questions about the lines in your shape. Some topics might be the starting point, direction, distance, changes in direction, position, etc. Answer the questions using your location system.
- Your partner should use your answers to guess your shape and make a copy of it on his or her geoboard. Compare your partner's guess to your original shape.
- Switch roles and repeat the activity.

THINK AND DISCUSS

y
y-axis
3
2
1
O
−4 −3 −2 −1 1 2 3 4 x
origin
−2
−3
−4
x-axis

In mathematics you identify points by using a *coordinate plane.* The **coordinate plane** is formed by the intersection of two number lines. The horizontal number line is the **x-axis.** The vertical number line is the **y-axis.** The point where the 2 axes intersect is the **origin.**

You can graph points on a coordinate plane. Each point has 2 *coordinates,* which form an **ordered pair.** The *first coordinate* tells how far to move along the x-axis. The *second coordinate* tells how far to move along the y-axis.

1. What are the coordinates of the origin?
2. Do you move *left* or *right* from the origin to graph a point with a negative first coordinate? Explain.
3. Do you move *up* or *down* from the origin to graph a point with a positive second coordinate? Explain.

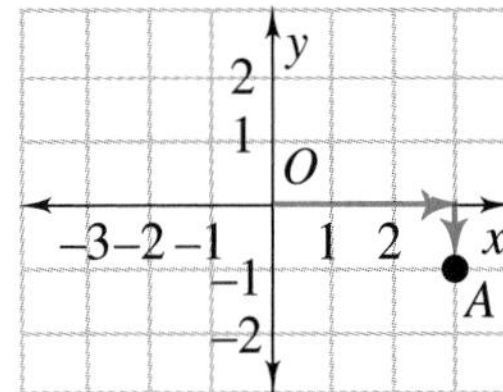

Example 1 Graph point A with coordinates $(3, -1)$.

- Move 3 units to the right from the origin.
- Move 1 unit down from the x-axis.
- Plot a point and label it A.

You can use a similar method to name the coordinates of points that are already graphed.

Example 2 Find the coordinates of point B.

- Start at the origin.
- Move 2 units to the left. The first coordinate is -2.
- Then move 3 units up from the x-axis. The second coordinate is 3.

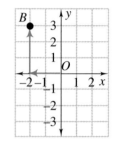

The coordinates of point B are $(-2, 3)$.

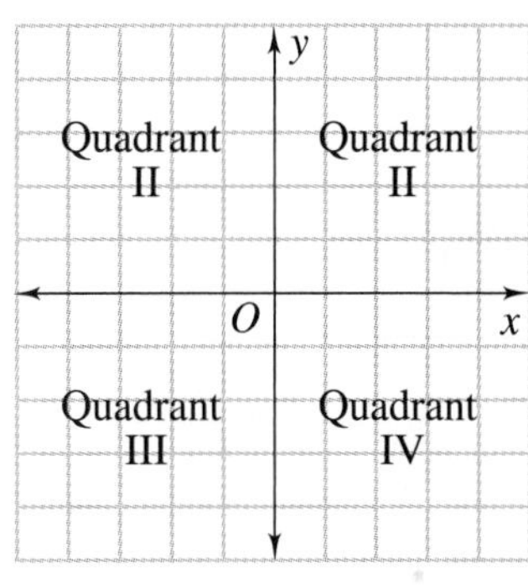

The axes separate the coordinate plane into four *quadrants.*

4. In which quadrant is the point $M(-2, 5)$ located?

5. In which quadrants are the first coordinates of the points positive numbers?

6. In which quadrants are the second coordinates of the points negative numbers?

TRY THESE

Name the point with the given coordinates.

7. (1, 2) **8.** (−2, −6) **9.** (3, −3) **10.** (0, −5) **11.** (3, 0)

Write the coordinates of each point.

12. C **13.** D **14.** K **15.** Q **16.** N

17. Point M is at (6, 4). What point has opposite coordinates?

18. What are the signs of the first and second coordinates of all the points in the second quadrant?

19. In which quadrant are all coordinates positive?

20. Three corners of a square have coordinates (4, 2), (4, 7), and (−3, 2). Find the coordinates of the fourth corner.

ON YOUR OWN

Identify the quadrant in which each point lies.

21. (3, 2) 22. (−17, 2) 23. (−6, −40) 24. (9, −11)

25. a. Graph the points $M(-5, -3)$, $N(2, -4)$, and $P(0, 1)$ on a coordinate plane.
  b. Connect the points in order. What shape do you see?

26. a. Graph the points $A(4, 3)$, $B(-1, 3)$, $C(-4, 0)$, and $D(1, 0)$.
  b. Connect the points in order. What shape do you see?
  c. **Critical Thinking** What is the most specific name you can use to describe figure *ABCD*? Explain.

Where on Earth Are You?

How can you tell someone else where you are on Earth?

Scientists have put a coordinate system on Earth so that locations can be described easily. The equator is the "horizontal axis." The prime meridian is the "vertical axis" and runs from the North Pole to the South Pole through Greenwich, England.

Degrees are used to indicate distances from these axes. Degrees north or south of the equator are *degrees of latitude.* Degrees east or west of the prime meridian are *degrees of longitude.* You identify a place by the degrees. For example, New York City is at 41°N 74°W. Los Angeles is at 34°N 118°W.

27. **Data File 11 (pp. 446–447)** Estimate the location of each city using latitude and longitude.
  a. Rivadavia, Argentina b. Cloncurry, Australia

28. **Research** Find a map of your state in an atlas or encyclopedia. Locate your town to the nearest degree of latitude and longitude.

Mixed REVIEW

1. Payat bought 3 shirts for \$14 each and a pair of pants for \$23. How much of his clothing budget does Payat have left?

2. The temperature is 70°F at 10:00 A.M. It increases 2°F every hour. What will the temperature be at 4:00 P.M.?

3. Write 45% as a decimal and as a fraction in simplest form.

4. Write $\frac{3}{8}$ as a decimal and as a percent.

5. A basketball player makes 80% of his foul shots. What is the probability that he makes two foul shots in a row?

29. a. **Research** Use a map to find the longitude and latitude of your birthplace to the nearest degree.

b. Compare these to your current town's location, which you found in Exercise 28.

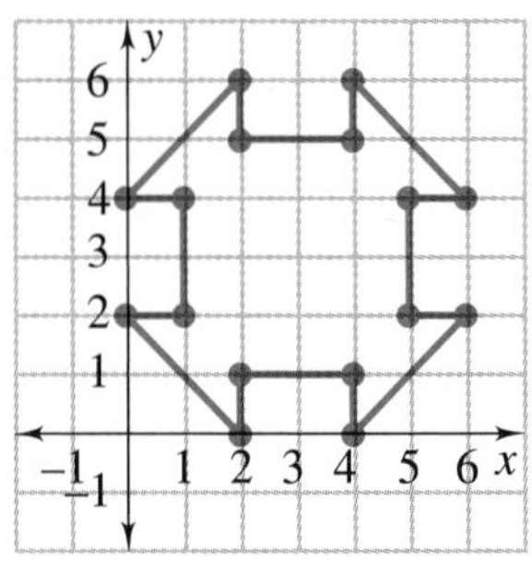

Crafts **Some quilt makers use coordinate grids to plan their patterns before they stitch the quilt.**

30. The Monkey Wrench pattern is from an African-American story quilt. Find the coordinates of the pattern points.

31. Create your own quilt pattern. Draw the pattern on a grid and name the coordinates of the points.

Geography **Mapmakers use a coordinate system so that people can locate places on a map. Coordinates on a map refer to a section of the map, not a point on the map.**

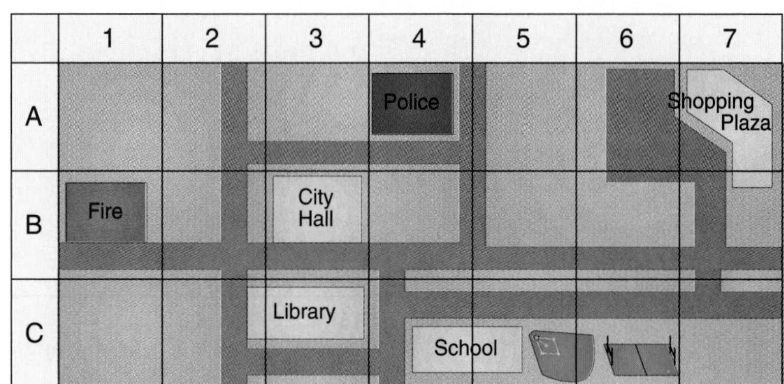

32. What do the letters A–C identify? the numbers 1–7?

33. What is located in section B3?

34. What are the coordinates of the school and its fields?

35. **Writing** How are a map and the coordinate plane alike? How are they different?

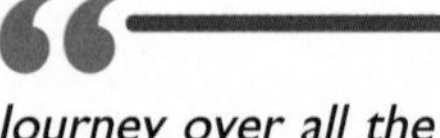

Journey over all the universe in a map, without the expense and fatigue of traveling.

—Miguel de Cervantes (1547–1616)

36. a. **Computer** Print out a blank spreadsheet. How are the rows, columns, and cells of a spreadsheet like a map?

b. **Activity** Choose any town or create a place of your own. Draw a map of this place on the spreadsheet. Include names of places or items on the map.

c. Make a table listing the places or items on the map and their map coordinates.

Problem Solving Practice

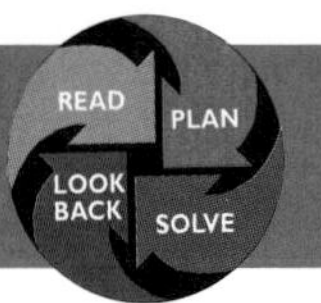

PROBLEM SOLVING STRATEGIES

- Make a Table
- Use Logical Reasoning
- Solve a Simpler Problem
- Too Much or Too Little Information
- Look for a Pattern
- Make a Model
- Work Backward
- Draw a Diagram
- Guess and Test
- Simulate a Problem
- Use Multiple Strategies

Solve. The list at the left shows some possible strategies you can use.

1. Larry and Shamir want to build identical houses. They bought a rectangular piece of land and divided it into two identical squares. Each square piece of land has an area of 2500 m^2. What is the perimeter of the original rectangle?

2. A positive number is a *Perfect Square* whenever it is the square of a whole number. The first three perfect squares are 1, 4, and 9. What is the 100th perfect square?

3. After 5 tests, Pedro's average was 80%. Pedro thought he had a "B" wrapped up for his report card. He took the final exam and his final average dropped to 76% which is a "C." What must Pedro have scored on the final exam?

4. Yoko and four friends divided a cake evenly among themselves. Yoko then shared her piece evenly with her four sisters. Yoko's youngest sister, Hoshi, gave half of her piece to her kitty, Leo. What percentage of the original cake did Leo get?

5. **Travel** Walter started his U.S. tour with \$250 to spend. Walter spent 5 times as much in Philadelphia as in New York. He spent \$9.59 more in Washington, D.C. as in Philadelphia. In Boston, Walter spent \$74.97. He spent 3¢ less in Boston than he did in Philadelphia. How much money did he have left?

6. **Weather** On an unusual winter trip Mina Blackhawk left Helena, Montana, and watched the thermometer on the side of her plane rise 100°F as she stopped in Houston, Texas. She went on to Marshall, Minnesota, where she saw a −71°F drop in temperature. When she reached Portland, Maine, it was 12°F, a full 14°F warmer than Marshall. What was the temperature in Helena that morning?

TECHNOLOGY

11-7 Translations and Reflections

What's Ahead

- Exploring translations and reflections on a coordinate plane using computers

WHAT YOU'LL NEED

✓ Computer 

✓ Software 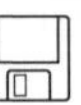

THINK AND DISCUSS

Band members march in step during half-time. Jets fly overhead in precise patterns. Tall ships sail in unison. On ground, in air, or on water, each formation moves as one, as though joined by invisible bonds.

The Valley Middle School marching band made a V on the football field at half-time of a game. They marched down the field and played the school song while keeping the V formation.

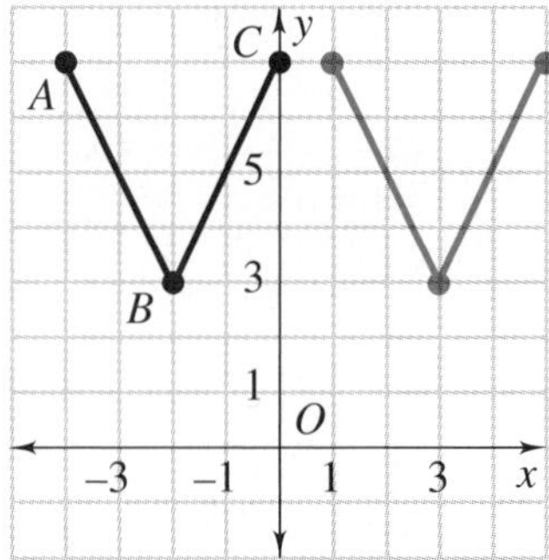

1. What are the coordinates of the vertices of the original V?
2. The V moved to the right. How many units did the V move?
3. What are the coordinates of the vertices of the new V?
4. Compare the size and shape of the new V to the original V.

You can say that the V was *translated* to the right. A **translation** is moving a figure so that every point moves in the same direction and the same distance. Each new point is called the **image** of the original point.

5. **Discussion** Why is a translation also called a *slide*?
6. **a.** Copy and complete the table for the translation above.

	original x	new x	change in x	original y	new y	change in y
A	−4	1	+5	7	7	0
B	■	■	■	■	■	■
C	■	■	■	■	■	■

The largest marching band *played at Dodger Stadium and consisted of 4,524 students from 52 schools in the Los Angeles area.*

Source: *Guinness Book of Records*

b. What patterns do you notice for the changes in x and the changes in y?

7. Suppose part of the band also made an M with coordinates $(-1, -2)$, $(-1, 2)$, $(1, 0)$, $(3, 2)$, and $(3, -2)$. The M formation moved at the same time as the original V.

a. What would the M's coordinates be after the translation? Explain.

b. Draw a diagram to show the translation.

Another way of moving a figure is to *reflect* it. A **reflection** is flipping a figure across a line. The new figure is a mirror image of the original.

8. At an air show, five fighter airplanes travel parallel to the grandstand. Their formation $DEFGH$ changes as shown.

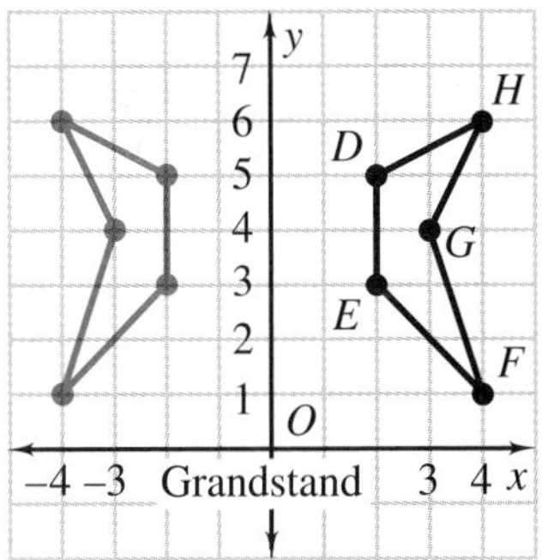

a. During the change, do all four airplanes move the same distance? Explain.

b. What happens to the shape of the formation?

c. Copy the diagram and fold along the center line. What do you notice about the original points and the image points?

d. **Discussion** Describe how the airplanes were reflected across the y-axis.

9. Copy the original formation of the airplanes. Draw the formation after a reflection across the x-axis.

WORK TOGETHER

10. a. **Computer** Draw a figure with three or more vertices to represent a formation of ships. Draw the reflection of the figure across the x-axis.

b. Make a table like the one in Question 6.

c. **Writing** Make a conjecture about how the coordinates of the points on a figure change when the figure is reflected across the x-axis.

d. **Critical Thinking** How would you test your conjecture?

e. Repeat parts (a)–(c) for a reflection across the y-axis.

The Navy's demonstration flying team, The Blue Angels, fly in the F/A-18 Hornet, which has a top speed of Mach 2. The Air Force's Thunderbirds fly in the F-16 Fighting Falcon, which has a top speed of Mach 2.3.

Source: *The Kids' World Almanac of Transportation*

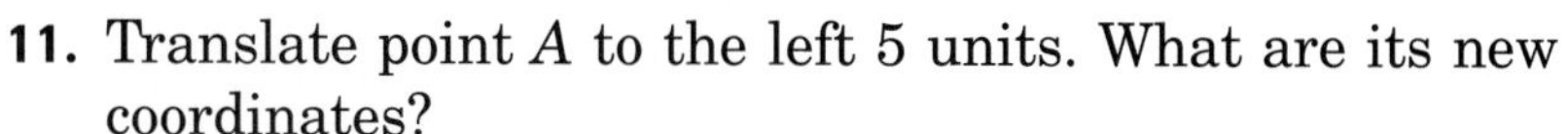

ON YOUR OWN

Use the graph at the left.

11. Translate point A to the left 5 units. What are its new coordinates?

12. Translate point B down 3 units and to the right 2 units. What are its new coordinates?

13. Point C is translated to point D. How far and in which directions has point C moved?

14. Reflect point E across the x-axis. What are its new coordinates?

15. Reflect point F across the x-axis and across the y-axis. What are its new coordinates?

Tell whether the graph shows a translation or a reflection. Describe the movement of the points.

16.

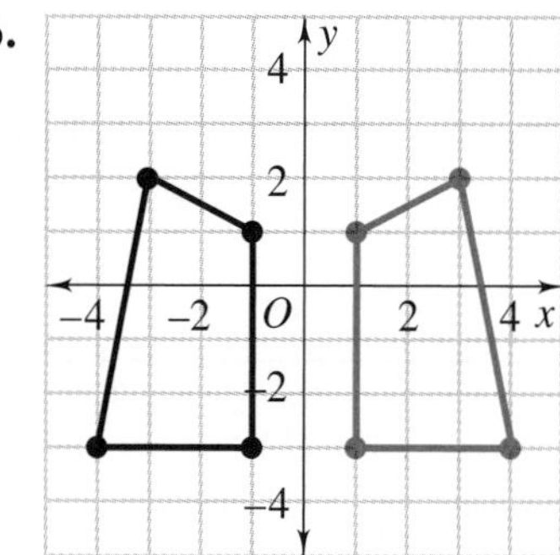

17.

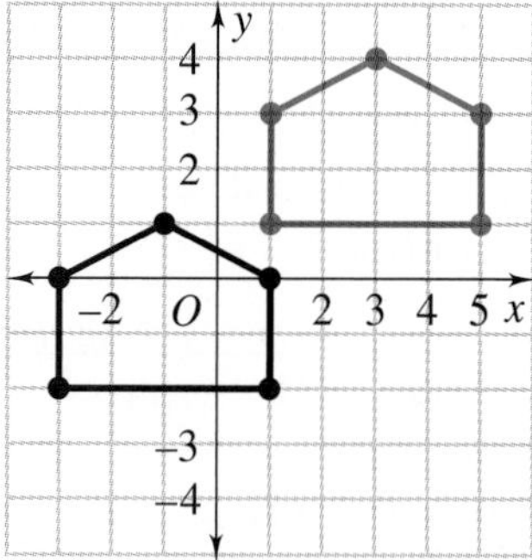

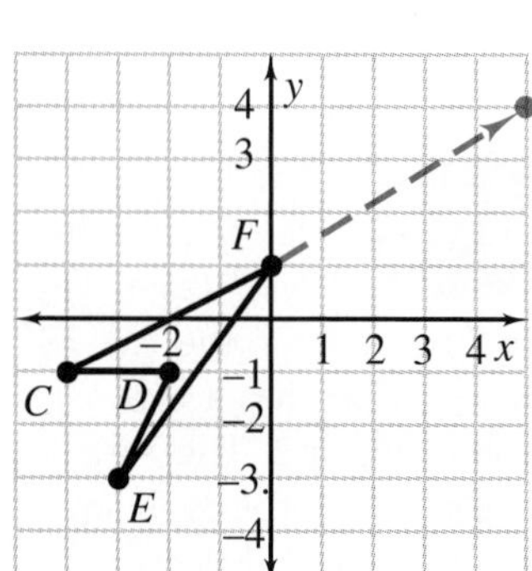

18. Four speed boats made an arrow formation. They moved in the same direction and the same distance as ship F.

a. How far and in which directions did the boats move?

b. **Computer** Graph the original and the new positions of each boat. Connect each set of points.

c. List the coordinates of the original positions of the boats and of the new positions.

19. **Writing** Describe how translations and reflections are alike and how they are different. Include examples.

20. **Investigation (p. 448)** Draw a vertical line through year 0 on your time line. Explain how you could use your time line to show school enrollment through the years.

21. a. **Computer** Graph the points $(2, -6)$, $(8, -6)$, and $(4, -1)$.

b. Connect the points. What geometric figure have you drawn?

c. **Computer** Reflect the figure across the x-axis. What are the new coordinates?

d. What is the area of the original figure? the new figure?

e. Make a conjecture about what happens to the area of a figure after a reflection.

22. **Computer** Create your own show. Choose any kind of vehicles or performers for your formation. Your show must include at least 1 translation and 1 reflection.

a. Graph the original position and shape of the formation. Label the coordinates of each object in the formation.

b. Draw the formation after each translation or reflection. Describe how the formation moves after each translation or reflection.

c. Write the coordinates of each point after each change.

Mixed REVIEW

1. In which quadrant would you find the point $(7, -8)$?

2. In which quadrant are both coordinates of a point positive?

Estimate a 5% sales tax for each item.

3. game: $8.99

4. bicycle: $135.95

5. Kendra has 20 dimes and nickels altogether. The total value of the coins is $1.35. How many dimes does Kendra have?

CHECKPOINT

1. Rachel numbered 235 tickets by hand starting with the number 1. How many digits did she write?

Name the point with the given coordinates.

2. $(-1, -3)$ 3. $(0, 2)$ 4. $(2, -2)$ 5. $(-4, 1)$

Write the coordinates of each point.

6. J 7. M 8. C 9. F

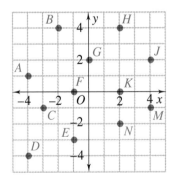

10. **Choose A, B, C, or D.** The vertices of $\triangle ABC$ are $A(-4, 2)$, $B(-3, 4)$, and $C(-2, 2)$. This triangle is translated. The new coordinates for point A are $(2, 2)$ and for point B are $(3, 4)$. What are the new coordinates for point C?

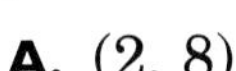

A. $(2, 8)$ **B.** $(4, 2)$ **C.** $(-2, 8)$ **D.** $(-8, 2)$

Use a calculator to find each sum or difference.

11. $-215 + 343$ 12. $451 - (-134)$ 13. $-1035 - 961$

MATH AND BUDGETS

11-8 Applying Integers and Graphs

What's Ahead

- Using a balance sheet to determine profit or loss
- Drawing and interpreting graphs involving integers

WHAT YOU'LL NEED

✓ Calculator 

THINK AND DISCUSS

Businesses keep track of not only the money they receive (income), but also any money they spend (expenses). The *balance* is the profit or loss that a company makes. A *balance sheet* is a table that helps keep track of income and expenses. Income is listed as a positive number. Expenses are listed as negative numbers. To find the balance, you add the income and expenses together.

positive balance → profit   negative balance → loss

1. **Discussion** What are some expenses that a business might have?

2. Some expenses stay the same every month. Some vary every month. List some expenses of each type.

3. List several different businesses. Describe the type of income each company would expect.

You can use a calculator to find balances. Remember that pressing [+/-] will change the sign of a number.

Balance Sheet for Video Mania

Month	Income	Expenses
Jan.	$11,917	–$14,803
Feb.	$12,739	–$9,482
March	$11,775	–$10,954
April	$13,620	–$15,149

Example 1 Find the balance for the month of February for Video Mania. Did the company make a profit or a loss during February?

- Add the income and the expenses.

  12,739 [+] 9,482 [+/-] [=] 3257

- The balance is positive. So, there is a profit.

Video Mania made a profit of $3,257 during February.

4. Find the balance for each month. Tell whether Video Mania made a profit or a loss during that month.
   - **a.** January
   - **b.** March
   - **c.** April

After businesses calculate their monthly balances, they often make a line graph to look at trends. You can use what you know about coordinate grids to make line graphs showing data of balances, income, and expenses. Use the first and fourth quadrants to graph these types of data.

Balance Sheet for Hobby & Toy Town	
Month	Balance (Profit/Loss)
January	–$1,917
February	–$682
March	$303
April	$781
May	–$150
June	$250
July	$933
August	$1,110
September	–$417
October	–$824
November	$1,566
December	$1,945

Example 2 Draw a line graph of the monthly balances for the Hobby & Toy Town store.

- Put the months on the horizontal axis. Put the dollar amounts on the vertical axis.
- The data goes from $-1{,}917$ to 1,945. Make a scale from $-2{,}000$ to 2,000. Use intervals of 500.
- Graph the data and connect the points.

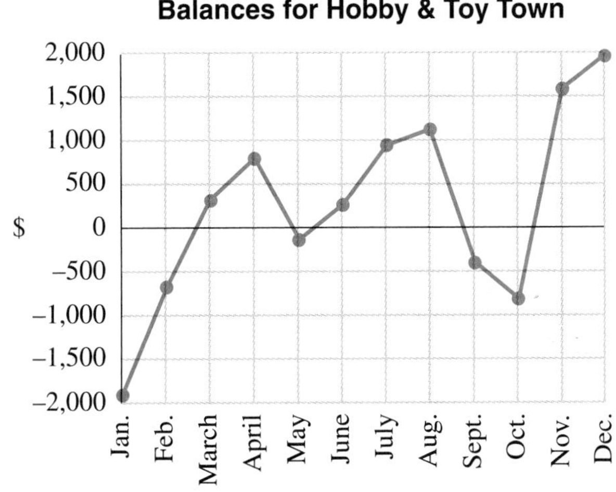

5. In which months was there a profit?

6. In which month did the greatest loss occur?

7. In which two months did the balance stay about the same?

8. Which month showed the greatest change in the balance?

9. Find the range of the balances.

TRY THESE

Calculator **Use a calculator to find each sum or difference.**

10. $-435 + 628$ **11.** $581 - (-57)$ **12.** $-2044 - (-1806)$

What scale and intervals would you use to graph the data set?

13. $-2, 3, 2, 4, -4, 1, -1, 3$

14. $1, 7, -3, -4, 0, 9, -8, 0, -9$

15. $-34, 98, 12, -71, 53, -95$

16. $4, 68, 50, 41, -13, -18, 27$

ON YOUR OWN

Choose **Use a calculator, mental math, or paper and pencil.**

17. $-12 + 5$

18. $38 - 64$

19. $-245 + 245$

20. $1342 + (-672)$

21. $29 - (-18)$

22. $-86 + (-96)$

23. **a.** Use the data at the left. Find the balance for each day.
    b. Draw a line graph to display the balances.

Day	Expenses	Income
Mon.	–$85	$94
Tues.	–$60	$78
Wed.	–$22	$13
Thurs.	–$73	$90
Fri.	–$49	$37
Sat.	–$16	$15
Sun.	–$36	$19

24. Writing Describe a business that you would like to start. (You could sell some item or you could perform a service such as tutoring.) List all the expenses you would have.

GREAT EXPECTATIONS

Video Game Producer

I would like to be a video game creator. I like challenging video games that you can play time after time and always try to beat your score from before. I think you would use math in this job. For example you would need to know how big the screen is to make the characters fit on the screen. If the characters took up the whole screen, there would be no room for background. If I made a game with many characters, I would need room for all of them to fit.

I have a few questions. After you think of your idea for a game, what do you do? Do you draw a diagram? How do you create one game and then put it at different levels? Where do you get your ideas?

Janna Mendoza

Computer **Set up a spreadsheet like the one below.**

	A	B	C	D
1	Week	Income	Expenses	Balance
2	2/1–2/7	\$4,257	−\$6,513	■
3	2/8–2/14	\$3,840	−\$2,856	■
4	2/15–2/21	\$4,109	−\$3,915	■
5	2/22–2/28	\$3,725	−\$4,921	■
6	Totals	■	■	■

25. What formulas would you put in cells D2–D5?

26. What formula goes in cell B6? Explain.

27. Fill in the formulas to find the unknown values.

28. Did any weeks show a profit? Explain.

29. What was the final balance for the month? Was it a loss or profit?

Mixed REVIEW

Find the number with the given prime factorization.

1. $2 \times 2 \times 3 \times 7 \times 13$
2. $2 \times 3 \times 3 \times 5 \times 23$

The coordinates of the vertices of $\triangle ABC$ are $A(-4, 1)$, $B(3, 5)$, and $C(3, 1)$. For each translation, give the new coordinates of each vertex.

3. up 4 units
4. right 6 units

5. Write a word problem with too little information.

Dear Janna,

A great video game usually starts with one person's idea. However, most creators work with groups of people. They prepare diagrams, animate people, objects, and animals, try ideas, solve problems, and write and test the game software.

When you finish college, computers will be quite different. Today's computer displays are colorful, but they are small and two-dimensional, and the computers used in games are slow. In ten years, creators will probably use three-dimensional (perhaps even holographic) displays. The software will animate figures realistically. Virtual reality may even make you part of the game.

To make games look life-like and operate realistically, creators should understand perspective, anatomy, structure, color, and lighting. To accomplish what they want their programs to do, math is important. Simple arithmetic is used everywhere in a game, but really good programmers also use trigonometry and advanced math.

Steven L. Cool

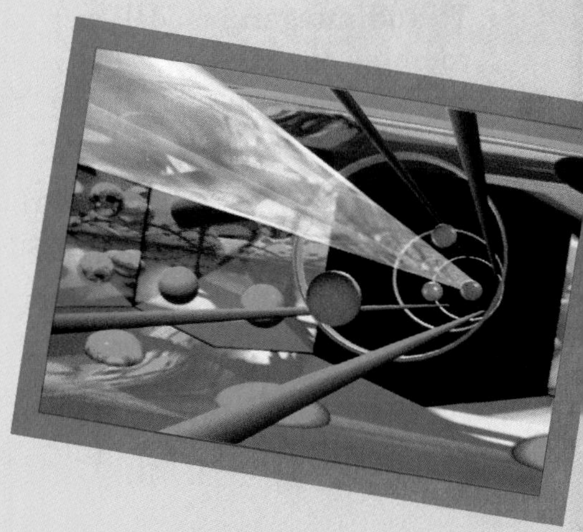

CHAPTER 11

Wrap Up

Integers and Opposites 11-1, 11-2

Opposites are two numbers that are the same distance from 0 on the number line, but in opposite directions. The set of ***integers*** is the set of whole numbers and their opposites.

To compare integers, think of the number line. The integer farther to the right is the greater integer.

1. What integer represents 7°F below zero?

2. Name the opposite of each integer.
   a. -7 **b.** 1 **c.** -8 **d.** -14

3. Write three numbers that are between -4 and -5. Are these numbers integers? Why or why not?

4. Explain how to order the following integers from least to greatest: 3, -1, -13, 5, 0.

Compare using <, >, or =.

5. -9 ■ -11 6. 4 ■ -13 7. -21 ■ 16 8. 0 ■ 9 9. 6 ■ 11

Write the integer represented by each set of tiles.

10. 11. 12. 13.

Modeling Addition and Subtraction of Integers 11-3, 11-4

To add integers, model each integer with tiles. If possible, combine the tiles to make zero pairs and remove as many zero pairs as possible. Write the integer that the remaining tiles represent.

To subtract integers, model the first integer with tiles. Take away the second number of tiles. (You may need to add zero pairs to do this.) Write the integer that the remaining tiles represent.

Use tiles to find the sum or difference.

14. $9 + (-4)$ 15. $-13 + 6$ 16. $1 - (-7)$ 17. $-2 - 8$

Graphing on the Coordinate Plane 11-6

The ***coordinate plane*** is formed by the intersection of the *x-axis* and the *y-axis*. Every point on the plane can be described by an ***ordered pair*** of numbers (x, y). These *coordinates* tell how far a point is from the origin, (0, 0).

Name the point with the given coordinates.

18. (0, 4) **19.** (3, 1) **20.** (−3, 3)

21. (2, 3) **22.** (−4, −3) **23.** (1, 1)

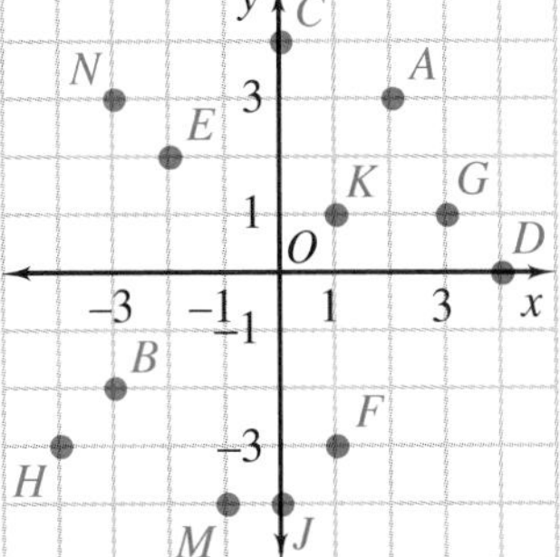

Write the coordinates of each point.

24. *B* **25.** *F* **26.** *J*

27. *E* **28.** *D* **29.** *M*

Translations and Reflections 11-7

You can move figures in a coordinate plane by a ***translation*** or flip figures by a ***reflection.***

30. a. The vertices of triangle *ABC* are $A(-4, -3)$, $B(1, 4)$, and $C(1, -3)$. Find the coordinates of the vertices of the triangle after it has been translated 4 units up.

b. What can you say about the two triangles?

Strategies and Applications 11-5, 11-8

You can use multiple strategies to solve problems.

A *balance sheet* is a table that helps keep track of income and expenses. *Income* is listed as a positive number and *expenses* are listed as negative numbers.

31. a. Find the balance for each month. Was there a profit or a loss?

b. What scale and intervals would you use to graph the balances?

c. Draw a line graph to display the balances.

Balance Sheet for Royale Bakery

Month	Income	Expenses
Jan.	\$1,314	−\$828
Feb.	\$2,120	−\$120
March	\$1,019	−\$1,285
April	\$1,438	−\$765

32. Two people live 36 mi apart. They leave their homes on bicycles at 10:00 A.M. riding toward each other. The first person averages 8 mi/h and the second person averages 10 mi/h. At what time will they meet?

PUTTING IT ALL TOGETHER

Follow Up

Lining Up Time

At the beginning of the chapter you created a timeline that began with year zero, your first year in the school (or your first year as a member of your group). Now extend your timeline into the past (before year zero) based on your study of the chapter.

Convey as much information as possible on your timeline. You may wish to use negative numbers or a vertical axis to accomplish this. The problems preceded by the magnifying glass (p. 452, # 46; p. 458, # 35, p. 462, # 31; and p. 474, # 20) will help you complete your timeline.

Excursion: Suppose you decided to create a timeline of mathematics history that included the years of your birth, of Albert Einstein's death, and of the Greek mathematician Pythagoras's death. What difficulties would you encounter?

Where to Look:

- an encyclopedia

Battle Grids

Try this with a partner. You will need graph paper.

- *Each player makes 2 grids on graph paper. Each grid must have a vertical y axis numbered 0-10 and a horizontal x axis numbered 0-10. Players keep the grids from their opponent's view.*
- *On the first grid, form a letter of the alphabet by placing Xs where the lines of the grid intersect. Use the other grid to guess your opponent's letter.*
- *Player A calls out to Player B an ordered pair of numbers. Player B tells whether or not the point plotted by the ordered pair is part of his or her letter. If so, Player A places an X on that spot on the blank grid. If not, an O is placed on that spot. Player B now takes a turn.*

The first player to correctly name the other player's letter wins.

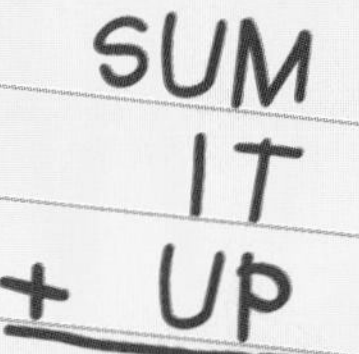

Rules:

- Play with two or more players.
- Make two number cubes.
  On one number cube write positive numbers from 1-6. On the other number cube write negative numbers from 7-12.
- Players take turns rolling the number cubes and adding the numbers shown on them. If a player correctly adds the numbers, the sum is the players score. If a player incorrectly adds the numbers, the player receives no score. After an equal number of rounds, the player with the lowest score wins.

Excursion: Subtract or multiply the numbers instead of adding. Make a third number cube with an equal amount of + signs, - signs, and x signs. Roll all the cubes at the same time. The sign on the number cube will tell you whether you should add, subtract, or multiply.

Do this with your group.

Each member of the group cuts different geometric shapes from heavy paper. Shapes should be no larger than 2 in. by 2 in. Place the shapes into a paper bag. Group members take turns reaching into the bag and pulling out a shape.

Group members use their shapes to trace a design on a sheet of paper. The designs must be either a slide image or a flip image of the shape. Try to fill up as much of the paper as possible.

Four, Three, Two, One, Zero

Do this with a partner.

Moving vertically or horizontally, add your way through the grid below so that your path results in a sum of 0. You can enter at any outside square and exit through any outside square.

Excursion: Make your own maze, using a 6 by 6 grid. Exchange grids with a partner and solve.

-2	-13	7	1	-15
-11	8	-3	-2	7
9	4	6	5	-3
-3	2	12	-7	4
-4	14	-10	6	13

CHAPTER 11

Assessment

1. Compare using <, >, or =.
   a. 18 ■ −24 b. −15 ■ −9
2. Write the integer that is represented by the tiles.
   a. ▫▫▫■ b. ■■■■▫
3. Use tiles to represent each integer and its opposite.
   a. −1 b. 6 c. −2 d. −9
4. Compare using <, >, or =.
   a. −13 + 4 ■ 13 + −4
   b. 7 + (−8) + (−1) ■ 7 + (−9)
5. The temperature was 4°F below zero at midnight. By 6:00 A.M. it had risen 22°F. What was the temperature at 6:00 A.M.?
6. Use tiles to find each sum or difference.
   a. −11 + (−4) b. −12 − 4
   c. 6 − (−3) d. −5 + 5
7. Evaluate each expression when $x = 4$, $y = -3$, and $z = -12$.
   a. $9 - y$ b. $x + y + z$
   c. $z - y - x$ d. $-8 + y - x$
8. a. Graph the points (−4, 1), (1, 6), (−4, 6), and (1, 1). What do you notice about these four points?
   b. Add 2 to the x-coordinate of all the vertices. Graph the new vertices.
   c. **Writing** How do these two graphs compare?
9. **Choose A, B, C, or D.** On his corrected math quiz Emilio had −2 points on the first question, −1 on the second, −3 on the third, −2 on the fourth, and −1 on the fifth. The quiz was worth 50 points. How many points did Emilio get on the quiz?
   A. 50 **B.** 41 **C.** 32 **D.** 12
10. Fai bought 3 birthday cards for $1.50 each and 2 posters for $2.75 each. How much did he spend in all?
11. Use a calculator to find each sum or difference.
    a. −85 + 54 b. −112 − (−792)
    c. 384 + (−556) d. 3077 − (−1902)
12. Identify the quadrant in which each point lies.
    a. (4, 2) b. (−6, −5)
    c. (9, −15) d. (−8, 3)
13. The data below shows the balance sheet for Balloons Galore.

Month	Balance
January	−$985
February	$10,241
March	−$209
April	$17,239

    a. Find the total balance for the four months ending with April for Balloons Galore.
    b. **Writing** Did the company make a profit or loss? Explain.

Cumulative Review

Choose A, B, C, or D.

1. Find the perimeter of a square with sides 5 m.

   A. 20 m B. 25 m
   C. 10 m D. 125 m

2. Which could be a net for a rectangular prism?

   A. 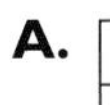
   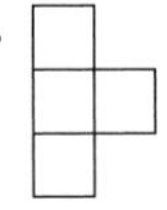
   B. 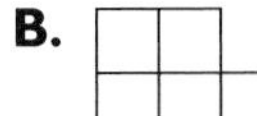
   C. 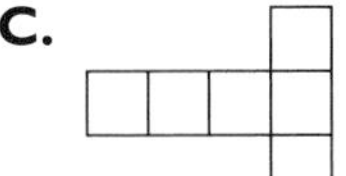
   D. 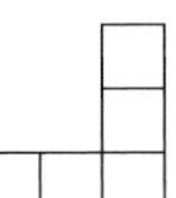

3. Find the best estimate for 43% of 87.

   A. 50 B. 36
   C. 30 D. 25

4. Which statement is false?

   A. A square is always a rectangle.
   B. Some rectangles are rhombuses.
   C. All quadrilaterals are parallelograms.
   D. Parallelograms can be divided into two congruent triangles.

5. Rehema bought 9 apples, 6 oranges, 12 pears, and 8 plums. What was the ratio of number of plums bought to number of pears bought?

   A. $\frac{2}{3}$ B. 9 to 12
   C. 12:8 D. 4:2

6. You roll a number cube three times. Find the probability of getting either a 3 or a 4 all three times.

   A. 1 B. $\frac{1}{8}$
   C. $\frac{1}{216}$ D. $\frac{1}{27}$

7. Evaluate the expression $b - a - 8$ when $a = -7$ and $b = -4$.

   A. -19 B. -11
   C. -5 D. 11

8. Write the numerical expression that is represented by the set of tiles. Then find the sum.

   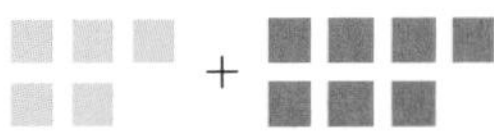

   A. $-5 + 7; -2$ B. $5 + (-7); -2$
   C. $5 + 7; 12$ D. $-5 + (-7); -12$

9. Four students are chosen at random. Find the probability that all four were born on a Monday.

   A. $\frac{4}{365}$ B. $\frac{1}{343}$
   C. $\frac{1}{2401}$ D. $\frac{1}{7}$

10. How many different six-digit numbers can be formed using the digits 1, 2, 3, 4, 5, and 6 if no digit is repeated in a number?

    A. 5040 B. 36
    C. 21 D. 720

Chapter 1

Extra Practice

The table at the right shows the number of books Lee read each month for 1 year.

Number of books Lee read					
3	1	4	2	4	1
3	2	4	4	2	1

1. a. Make a line plot.
   b. Find the median and mode.

Make a frequency table and find the mean, median, and mode.

2. 23, 26, 22, 25, 22, 28, 22, 10, 11
3. 102, 202, 102, 302, 102, 402, 102, 402, 201

Name the type of graph most appropriate for each situation.

4. amount of rainfall in Costa Rica each month for 1 year
5. cost of six different cars
6. number of students from each grade who play soccer
7. Data File 1 (pp. 2–3) Using the most appropriate type of graph, represent the data given in the chart "How Much TV Do We Watch?"
8. a. Data File 8 (pp. 316–317) Using the most appropriate type of graph, show the number of different types of medals won by Cuba in 1992.
   b. How will increasing the scale in your graph affect the appearance of the data?
9. Data File 1 (pp. 2–3) Draw 2 different line graphs using the data in "Persons Viewing in Prime Time." Draw the first graph using the scale shown. Draw a second graph using a scale of 5, starting at 80 and ending at 110. How does the change in scale affect each representation?
10. Mr. Yee deposited $710 into his account. He gave the teller twice as many $5's as $1's and three times as many $10's as $5's. Find the number of $1, $5, and $10 bills Mr. Yee deposited.
11. Data File 3 (pp. 92–93) Find the number of old Bolivian stamps a person must use to cover one side of a 3 in. $\times$ 5 in. postcard.

Chapter 2

Extra Practice

Use the figure at the right for Exercises 1–9. Name each of the following.

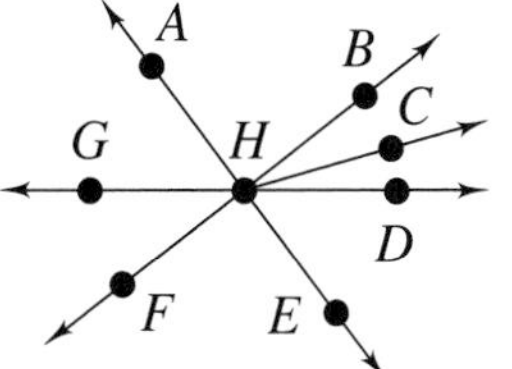

1. 3 acute angles
2. 4 obtuse angles
3. 3 noncollinear points
4. 6 rays

Use a protractor to find the measure of each angle.

5. $\angle BHF$
6. $\angle FHC$
7. $\angle FHG$
8. $\angle CHD$
9. $\angle AHC$

10. Draw a segment $\overline{RS}$. Construct a segment three times as long as $\overline{RS}$.

11. Draw an acute $\angle F$. Construct an angle congruent to $\angle F$.

Classify the triangle with the given side lengths as scalene, isosceles, or equilateral.

12. 7 cm, 9 cm, 7 cm
13. 3 m, 3 m, 3 m
14. 18 in., 16 in., 5 in.

Classify the triangle with the given angle measures as acute, obtuse, or right.

15. 2°, 176°, 2°
16. 30°, 60°, 90°
17. 45°, 65°, 70°

18. Find the number of lines of symmetry in this octagon.

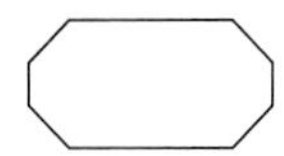

19. Draw a circle with a chord, central angle, and diameter.

20. In October, 65 middle school students visited the science museum. Of these students, 24 viewed an Omni theatre movie, 29 went to the planetarium, and 12 walked around the dinosaur exhibit. No students signed up for two choices. How many must have signed up for all three?

21. Tickets at the Highview theatre cost \$2 for children and \$5 for adults. One afternoon, the theatre took in \$100 for one showing. List the possible combinations of ticket sales involving children and/or adults. Describe the pattern you see.

Extra Practice

Draw a model for each decimal.

1. 0.8 **2.** 0.35 **3.** 1.2 **4.** three tenths **5.** seven hundredths

Write each decimal in words.

6. 0.10 **7.** 0.8 **8.** 0.51 **9.** 0.30 **10.** 3.25 **11.** 33.05

Write each number in standard form.

12. four tenths **13.** fifty-seven hundredths **14.** sixty-six and seven hundredths

15. one hundred forty-two thousandths **16.** two hundred twenty-two thousandths

Find the value of the digit 9 in each number.

17. 0.9 **18.** 1.009 **19.** 52.39 **20.** 0.4829 **21.** 351.09

Compare. Use >, <, or =.

22. 1.11 ■ 1.09 **23.** 0.2357 ■ 0.23 **24.** 11.521 ■ 11.53 **25.** 13.10 ■ 13.1

Round to the nearest whole number. Estimate the sum or difference.

26. 0.8 + 3.5 **27.** 6.2 − 0.625 **28.** 5.001 − 0.67 **29.** 13.41 + 7.61

30. 1.14 + 9.3 **31.** 9 − 3.5 **32.** 4.11 − 2.621 **33.** 3.541 + 1.333

34. Measure each side of the triangle in millimeters and find its perimeter.

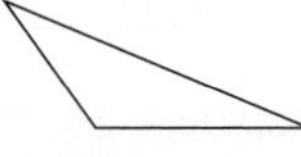

35. What metric unit would you use to measure each item?

a. height of a house **b.** length of a pencil **c.** length of a river

36. In one month, Rachel wants to buy a new pair of $170 in-line skates. She works 10 h a week for $5/h. She also spends $15 a week. Can Rachel buy the skates in one month?

37. Judith found a picture of her mother at 3 years of age dated 1960. Judith was 12 years old in 1993. In what year will she be half her mother's age?

Chapter 4

Extra Practice

Round each factor to the nearest whole number to estimate the product.

1. 3.7×6.8
2. 4.8×3.2
3. 11.69×8.49

Use compatible numbers to estimate.

4. $3{,}126.38 \div 26.01$
5. 21.49×3.76
6. 2.68×4.59

Use order of operations to evaluate.

7. $7 + 5 \times 6 \div 3$
8. $(17 + 1) \div 3 \times 2$
9. $6 \div 2 + 5 \times 3$
10. $(3 \times 5) \times (6 \div 2)$
11. $26 - 6 \div 3 \times (3 + 5)$
12. $8 \div (1.25 + 0.75)$

Use the distributive property to evaluate.

13. $3 \times (10 + 5)$
14. $4 \times (50 - 5)$
15. $5 \times (7 - 5)$
16. $6 \times (8 + 5)$

Use the distributive property to rewrite and evaluate.

17. 7×78
18. 8×503
19. 6×66
20. 9×12

Find each product.

21. 0.35×0.07
22. 100×0.069
23. 7.9×0.03
24. 9.9×1.2

Draw a model to find each quotient.

25. $0.6 \div 0.05$
26. $1.5 \div 3$
27. $0.24 \div 6$
28. $1.8 \div 0.09$

Find each quotient.

29. $6.72 \div 4.2$
30. $6.2\overline{)0.5952}$
31. $7.5\overline{)64.5}$
32. $21.12 \div 4.4$

33. What information is missing or given but not needed?

    Symphony tickets cost \$12 for orchestra seats or \$7 for balcony seats. Programs cost \$3. Madeline bought two tickets. How much did she spend?

34. Hameen bought two shirts on sale for a total of \$28.50. Earlier in the week the store offered the shirts for \$18.99 apiece. Find how much money Hameen saved by buying the shirts on sale.

Chapter 5

Extra Practice

Find the next three terms in each number pattern. Write a rule to describe each number pattern.

1. 1, 4, 16, 64
2. 0, 3, 6, 9
3. 0.3, 2.3, 4.3, 6.3

Name the base and the exponent.

4. 2^{16}
5. 4^7
6. 4^2
7. 7^4
8. 1^0

Choose **Use a calculator, mental math, or paper and pencil to evaluate.**

9. $(8^2 - 4) \div 10$
10. $6(5 + 5)$
11. $5^8 \div 2$
12. $144 + 56 \div 4$

Mental Math **Evaluate each expression for the given values of the variables.**

13. $7x$ for $x = 7$
14. $a + 0.30$ for $a = 1.70$
15. $b^2 - 24$ for $b = 8$

Write a variable expression for each word phrase.

16. one less than b
17. twice as many p
18. four greater than b

Solve each equation.

19. $3b = 21$
20. $20 = y + 1$
21. $27 + a = 163$
22. $n - 35 = 75$
23. $178 = 10d$
24. $b \div 7 = 7$
25. $25 = p - 4.2$
26. $1.5t = 6$
27. $40 = k \div 5$
28. Sunscreen carries an SPF number. To find how long you can sunbathe while wearing sunscreen, you multiply the SPF number by the number of minutes you can safely stay in the sun *without* sunscreen. Suppose you can be in the sun safely without sunscreen for n min. Write a variable expression for the amount of time you can sunbathe while wearing a 15 SPF sunscreen.
29. In 1990, the population of Hillsboro was 25,000. The population increases by 5,000 people every 5 years. What will be the population in the year 2005?

Chapter 6

Extra Practice

Find the area of each figure. Use 3.14 for π.

1. 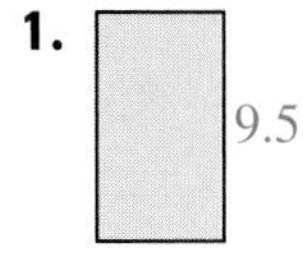

2. 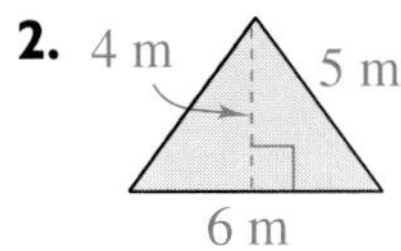

3. 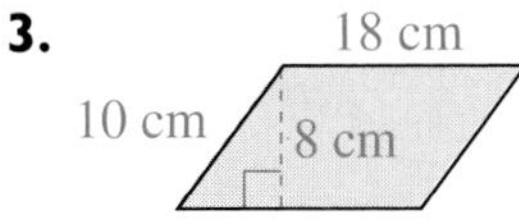

4. 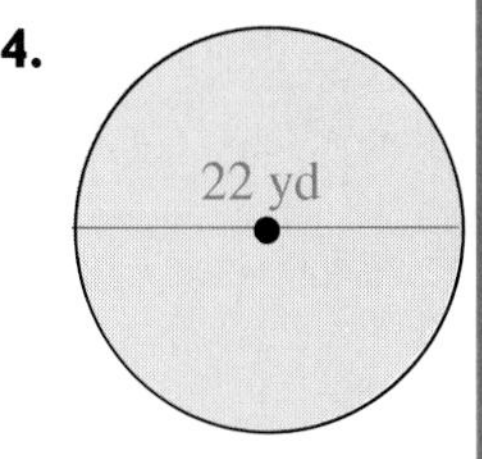

5. The area of a triangle equals 36 cm^2. The base equals 12 cm. Find the height of the triangle.

6. The area of a rectangle equals 64 cm^2. The height equals 4 cm. Find the width.

Find the circumference and area of a circle with the given radius or diameter. First estimate using 3 for π, then use a calculator.

7. $d = 26$
8. $d = 10.6$
9. $r = 30$
10. $r = 11$

11. a. Identify the figure below.
    b. Find the number of faces, edges, and vertices.

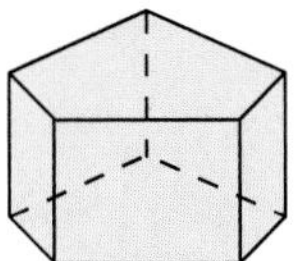

12. Find the volume and surface area of the rectangular prism below.

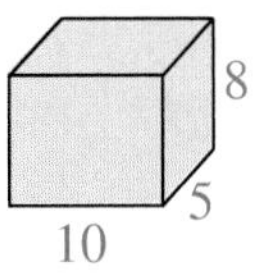

13. Identify the figure formed by the net at the right. Then find its surface area.

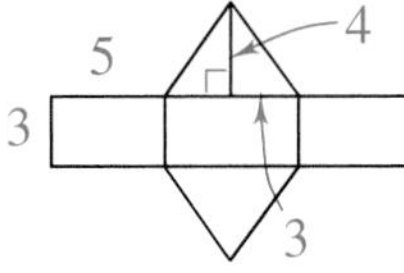

14. Martin wants to tack a rectangular poster onto his bulletin board. The board measures 90 cm by 150 cm. The poster's perimeter equals 466 cm. How many posters with this perimeter will fit on the board.

15. Triangles are worth 9 points, quadrilaterals 16 points, and pentagons 25 points. Find the total number of points contained in the figure below. Use only convex shapes.

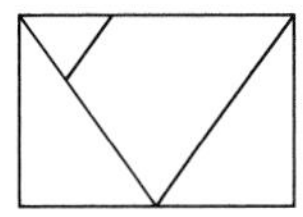

Chapter 7

Extra Practice

Mental Math **Decide whether each number is divisible by 1, 2, 3, 5, 9, or 10.**

1. 324 **2.** 2685 **3.** 540 **4.** 114 **5.** 31 **6.** 981

Tell whether each number is prime or composite.

7. 24 **8.** 49 **9.** 7 **10.** 81 **11.** 37 **12.** 23

Use prime factorization to find the GCF of each set of numbers.

13. 16, 36 **14.** 25, 75 **15.** 16, 24, 8 **16.** 54, 63 **17.** 15, 25, 30 **18.** 17, 23

Write two fractions equivalent to each fraction. Then write each fraction as a decimal.

19. $\frac{2}{3}$ **20.** $\frac{3}{4}$ **21.** $\frac{2}{5}$ **22.** $\frac{1}{4}$ **23.** $\frac{1}{2}$ **24.** $\frac{3}{5}$

Find the GCF of each numerator and denominator. Then simplify each fraction.

25. $\frac{30}{35}$ **26.** $\frac{27}{36}$ **27.** $\frac{40}{50}$ **28.** $\frac{32}{48}$ **29.** $\frac{6}{60}$

Write each improper fraction as a mixed number.

30. $\frac{25}{7}$ **31.** $\frac{39}{12}$ **32.** $\frac{12}{5}$ **33.** $\frac{10}{7}$ **34.** $\frac{7}{2}$

Write each mixed number as an improper fraction.

35. $1\frac{7}{8}$ **36.** $2\frac{3}{5}$ **37.** $11\frac{1}{9}$ **38.** $5\frac{6}{8}$ **39.** $10\frac{1}{8}$

40. I am thinking of a two-digit prime number. The product of the digits in the number equals 12. Find the number.

41. Complete the number below with the digits 5, 3, and 1 so that the number is divisible by 6. How many different ways can you do this? If you completed the number with any other digits from 0 to 9, will the number still be divisible by 2? 3 ■ 6 ■ 2 ■ 1 2 4

Chapter 8

Extra Practice

Find each sum or difference.

1. $\frac{1}{2} + \frac{1}{3}$
2. $\frac{1}{6} - \frac{1}{8}$
3. $\frac{3}{4} - \frac{1}{3}$
4. $\frac{7}{10} + \frac{3}{10}$
5. $\frac{7}{8} + \frac{1}{7}$
6. $\frac{3}{5} - \frac{1}{2}$
7. $6\frac{2}{3} + 1\frac{1}{2}$
8. $3\frac{2}{3} - 3\frac{2}{7}$
9. $7\frac{4}{5} + 1\frac{2}{3}$
10. $11\frac{15}{16} - 2\frac{3}{4}$
11. $7\frac{5}{6} - 2\frac{1}{12}$
12. $4\frac{2}{3} + 4\frac{1}{5}$

Estimate **Then find the product and simplify.**

13. $\frac{1}{2} \times \frac{2}{3}$
14. $4\frac{1}{4} \times 3\frac{5}{6}$
15. $6\frac{1}{3} \times 7\frac{1}{5}$
16. $5\frac{7}{8} \times 2\frac{3}{4}$
17. $8 \times \frac{1}{4}$
18. $\frac{1}{20} \times 100$
19. $\frac{8}{7} \times \frac{4}{9}$
20. $4\frac{7}{6} \times 2\frac{2}{3}$

Divide. Write each answer in simplest form.

21. $\frac{4}{5} \div 2$
22. $\frac{6}{7} \div \frac{2}{5}$
23. $2\frac{1}{7} \div \frac{2}{3}$
24. $4\frac{1}{2} \div 3\frac{1}{4}$
25. $\frac{2}{5} \div \frac{2}{25}$
26. $\frac{13}{16} \div \frac{1}{16}$
27. $\frac{5}{6} \div \frac{5}{6}$
28. $\frac{1}{4} \div \frac{4}{4}$

Draw a model for each equation.

29. $\frac{6}{7} - \frac{1}{14} = \frac{11}{14}$
30. $\frac{1}{4} + \frac{1}{2} = \frac{3}{4}$
31. $\frac{1}{3} - \frac{1}{5} = \frac{2}{15}$
32. $\frac{2}{5} + \frac{1}{2} = \frac{9}{10}$

Write the reciprocal of each number.

33. $\frac{3}{4}$
34. 5
35. $\frac{3}{9}$
36. $\frac{1}{3}$
37. $4\frac{1}{3}$
38. $5\frac{3}{4}$

39. Complete the table at the right. Then add another row and describe the pattern.

Expression	Sum
$\frac{1}{2}$	$\frac{1}{2}$
$\frac{1}{2} + \frac{2}{4}$	■
$\frac{1}{2} + \frac{2}{4} + \frac{3}{6}$	■

40. Maria wants to plant a row of pine trees to form a hedge. Her yard measures 44 ft long. Trees must be 4 ft apart. Draw a diagram to find the number of trees she can plant.

41. Jules Verne wrote the classic tale *20,000 Leagues Under the Sea.* One league equals 3 miles. How many miles equals 20,000 leagues?

Chapter 9

Extra Practice

Write each ratio as a fraction in simplest form.

1. 30 to 60
2. 5 : 15
3. 13 to 52
4. 7 : 77
5. 18 : 72

Find the value of *n*.

6. $\frac{n}{30} = \frac{3}{15}$
7. $\frac{64}{n} = \frac{5}{10}$
8. $\frac{13}{3} = \frac{n}{6}$
9. $\frac{5}{225} = \frac{2}{n}$
10. $\frac{9}{12} = \frac{12}{n}$
11. $\frac{n}{50} = \frac{3}{75}$
12. $\frac{18}{n} = \frac{3}{10}$
13. $\frac{51}{17} = \frac{n}{3}$
14. $\frac{2}{16} = \frac{n}{24}$
15. $\frac{3}{45} = \frac{4}{n}$

Write each as a percent.

16. 0.77
17. $\frac{10}{25}$
18. 0.06
19. 0.9
20. $\frac{13}{50}$
21. $\frac{18}{60}$
22. 0.03
23. $\frac{3}{50}$
24. 0.39
25. 0.17
26. $\frac{12}{75}$
27. $\frac{4}{5}$

Write each as a fraction in lowest terms.

28. 42%
29. 0.66
30. 96%
31. 0.24
32. 80%
33. 0.56

Express each as a decimal.

34. 1%
35. $\frac{7}{10}$
36. 87%
37. $\frac{8}{40}$
38. 88%
39. $\frac{15}{25}$

Find each percent.

40. 48% of 200
41. 5% of 80
42. 62% of 150
43. 35% of 50
44. 20% of 80
45. 15% of $17.50
46. 50% of 86
47. 90% of 100

48. A diorama of Minute Man National Historic Park in Concord, MA, shows the road from the Old North Bridge to the visitor center as 12 in. long. One inch on the model represents $\frac{1}{16}$ mi. How far is the bridge from the center?

49. Data File 5 (pp. 182–183) Compare the average number of hours pigs sleep to the average number of hours two-toed sloths sleep. Write the comparison as a fraction, as a percent, and as a decimal.

Chapter 10

Extra Practice

1. Harvey rolls a number cube. If he rolls an even number, he wins. If he rolls an odd number, his sister wins. Is this a fair game? Explain.

2. Solve by simulation. Suppose you take a four-question true-false test. You guess all the answers. What is the probability you will get 3 out of 4 correct?

3. Nina took a true-false test. She did not know any of the answers but got 4 correct and 6 incorrect. Use this data to find the experimental probability of getting a question right.

4. Use the number 3,486,335,206 to find the following probabilities. Write the probabilities as a percent and fraction.
   a. probability that a digit selected at random is a 3
   b. probability that a digit selected at random is a 2
   c. probability that a digit selected at random is a multiple of 2

5. Make a tree diagram to show all possible sandwich combinations. Assume you choose one in each category.

Sandwiches	
Meats:	Turkey, Roast Beef
Breads:	Bagel, Whole Wheat, White
Toppings:	Lettuce, Tomatoes, Onions

Is each sample random? representative? Explain.

6. A school district wants to find out what fruits to sell in its school cafeterias. They survey all the students in one school.

7. A teacher wants to know the opinions of all her students on the upcoming elections. She places each student's name in a box and draws 15 names.

Extra Practice

List the integers in order from least to greatest.

1. $-7, -6, 7, 6$ **2.** $0, -14, -15, -13$ **3.** $15, -7, 71, 1$ **4.** $5, -4, -1, 1$

Compare using <, >, =.

5. -3 ■ -1 **6.** 5 ■ 7 **7.** -5 ■ -7 **8.** -6 ■ 0

9. $-3 - 1$ ■ $-3 + (-1)$ **10.** $4 - 8$ ■ $8 - 4$ **11.** $-5 - (-2)$ ■ $-5 - 2$

Use the graph at the right for Exercises 12–23. Name the coordinates of each point.

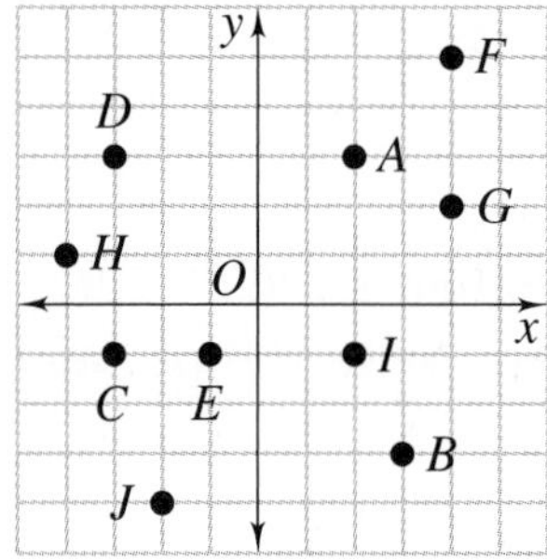

12. *A* **13.** *B* **14.** *C* **15.** *D* **16.** *E*

Name the point with the given coordinates.

17. $(4, 2)$ **18.** $(4, 5)$ **19.** $(2, -1)$ **20.** $(-4, 1)$

21. In which quadrant are points *C*, *E*, and *J*?

22. Translate point *G* to the left 4 units and down 2 units. What are its new coordinates?

23. Reflect point *D* across the *y*-axis. What are its new coordinates?

24. Graph the points $X(-3, 2)$, $Y(5, -4)$, and $Z(0, 5)$.

Use any method to evaluate.

25. $-14 + 28$ **26.** $31 - (-52)$ **27.** $-72 + (-53)$ **28.** $-217 - (-217)$

What scale and intervals would you use to graph the data set?

29. $0, -35, 25, 15, -17, 5, -4.1$

30. $-12, 0, 12, -7, -6, 3, -8, 6$

31. Mars travels around the Sun in 687 days. Earth journeys around the Sun in 365 days. About how many times will Mars and Earth travel around the Sun in twenty years?

32. **Data File 4 (pp. 138–139)** Bernie and Bernice are twins. They turn twelve in two months. Each is 140 cm tall. Estimate each twin's adult height.

Tables

Table 1 Measures

Metric

Length
10 millimeters (mm) = 1 centimeter (cm)
100 cm = 1 meter (m)
1,000 m = 1 kilometer (km)

Area
100 square millimeters (mm^2) = 1 square centimeter (cm^2)
10,000 cm^2 = 1 square meter (m^2)

Volume
1,000 cubic millimeters (mm^3) = 1 cubic centimeter (cm^3)
1,000,000 cm^3 = 1 cubic meter (m^3)

Mass
1,000 milligrams (mg) = 1 gram (g)
1,000 g = 1 kilogram (kg)

Capacity
1,000 milliliters (mL) = 1 liter (L)

United States Customary

Length
12 inches (in.) = 1 foot (ft)
3 feet = 1 yard (yd)
36 in. = 1 yd
5,280 ft = 1 mile (mi)
1,760 yd = 1 mi

Area
144 square inches ($in.^2$) = 1 square foot (ft^2)
9 ft^2 = 1 square yard (yd^2)
4,840 yd^2 = 1 acre

Volume
1,728 cubic inches ($in.^3$) = 1 cubic foot (ft^3)
27 ft^3 = 1 cubic yard (yd^3)

Weight
16 ounces (oz) = 1 pound (lb)
2,000 lb = 1 ton (T)

Capacity
8 fluid ounces (fl oz) = 1 cup (c)
2 c = 1 pint (pt)
2 pt = 1 quart (qt)
4 qt = 1 gallon (gal)

Time
1 minute (min) = 60 seconds (s)
1 hour (h) = 60 min
1 day (da) = 24 h
1 year (y) = 365 da

Table 2 Formulas

Circumference of a circle
$C = \pi d$ or $C = 2\pi r$

Area

parallelogram:	$A = bh$
rectangle:	$A = bh$
triangle:	$A = \frac{1}{2}bh$
circle:	$A = \pi r^2$

Volume rectangular prism: $V = lwh$

Table 3 Symbols

$>$	is greater than
$<$	is less than
$=$	is equal to
$^\circ$	degrees
%	percent
$a : b$	*ratio of* a to b, $\frac{a}{b}$
$\lvert a \rvert$	absolute value of a
$P(E)$	probability of an event E
π	pi
$\approx$	is approximately equal to
$\overline{AB}$	segment AB
$\overrightarrow{AB}$	ray AB
$\overleftrightarrow{AB}$	line AB
$\angle ABC$	angle ABC
AB	length of segment AB
mi/h	miles per hour

A

Acute angle (p. 46) An acute angle is any angle that measures less than 90°.

Example $0° < m\angle 1 < 90°$

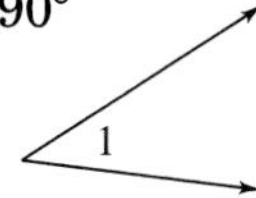

Acute triangle (p. 54) A triangle that contains all acute angles is an acute triangle.

Example $m\angle 1, m\angle 2, m\angle 3 < 90°$

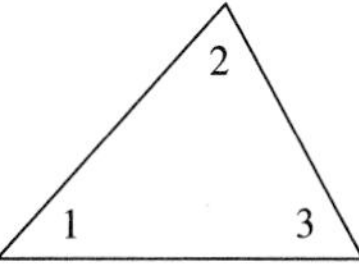

Angle (p. 45) An angle is made up of two rays with a common endpoint.

Example

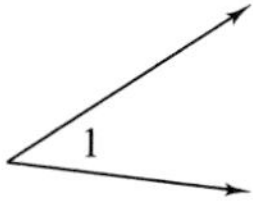

Area (p. 229) The number of square units inside a figure is the area.

Example $l = 6$ ft, and $w = 4$ ft, so the area is 24 ft^2.

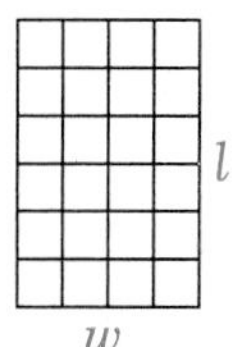

Each square equals 1 ft^2.

B

Bar graph (p. 20) A bar graph compares amounts.

Example This bar graph represents class sizes for grades 6, 7, and 8.

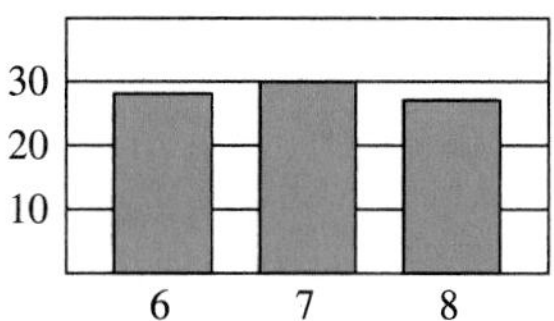

Base (p. 192) When a number is written in exponential form the number that is used as a factor is the base.

Example $5^4 = 5 \times 5 \times 5 \times 5$

↑ base

C

Chord (p. 78)

A chord is a segment with endpoints on a circle.

Example $\overline{BC}$ is a chord of circle O.

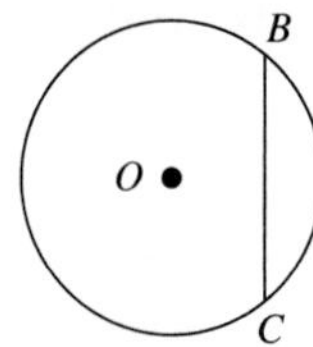

Circle (p. 78)

A circle is a set of points on a plane that are all the same distance from a given point, called the center.

Example Circle O

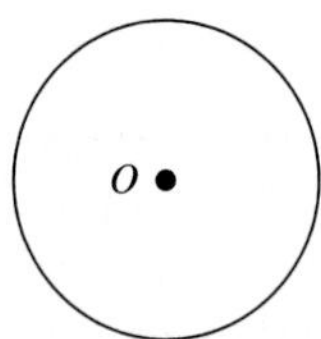

Circle graphs (pp. 21, 399)

The entire circle represents the whole. Each wedge in the circle graph represents a part of the whole.

Example The circle graph represents the different types of plays William Shakespeare wrote.

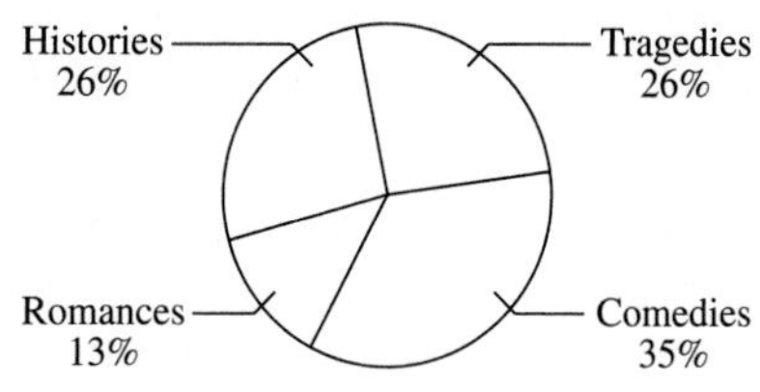

Circumference (p. 206)

Circumference is the distance around a circle. You calculate the circumference of a circle by multiplying the diameter by pi (π) ($C = \pi \times D$). Pi is approximately equal to 3.14.

Example The circumference of a circle with a diameter of 10 cm is approximately 31.4 cm.

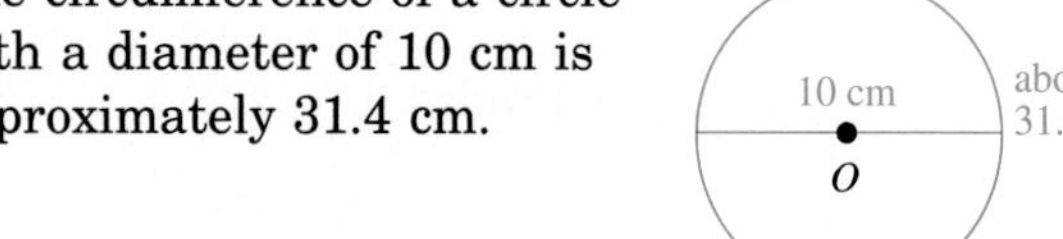

Collinear points (p. 42)

If there is a line that goes through a set of points, the points are collinear.

Example Points B, C, R and S are collinear.

B C R S

Compass (p. 51) A compass is a tool that is used to draw circles or parts of circles called arcs.

Example

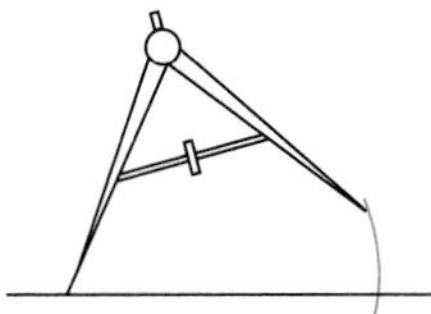

Compatible numbers (p. 141) Estimating products or quotients is easier when you use compatible numbers. Compatible numbers are numbers close in value to the numbers you want to estimate. Choose numbers that are easy to multiply or divide mentally.

Example Estimate the quotient $151 \div 14.6$.

$151 \approx 150$
$14.6 \approx 15$
$150 \div 15 = 10$

Composite number (p. 278) A number that has more than two factors is called a composite number.

Example 24 is a composite number that has 1, 2, 3, 4, 6, 8, 12, and 24 as factors.

Congruent figures (p. 70) Figures that have the same size and shape are congruent.

Example $AB = QS$, $CB = RS$, and $AC = QR$. $m\angle A = m\angle Q$, $m\angle C = m\angle R$, and $m\angle B = m\angle S$. Triangles ABC and QSR are congruent.

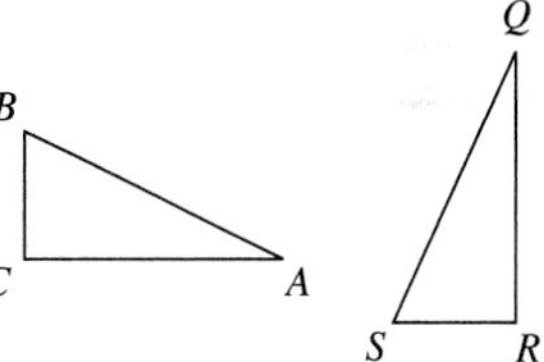

Congruent angles (p. 52) Congruent angles are angles that have the same measure.

Example $\angle C$ and $\angle B$ are both 60° so $\angle C$ is congruent to $\angle B$.

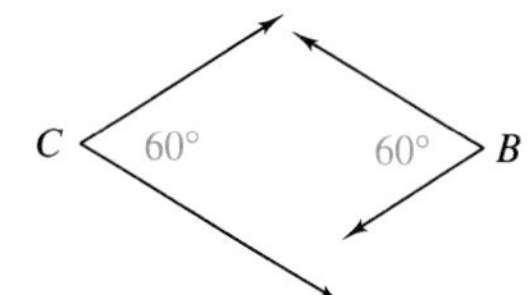

Student Study Guide

Congruent polygons (p. 70) Polygons whose corresponding parts (sides and angles) are congruent are congruent polygons.

Example triangle *HOT* is congruent to triangle *PIE*

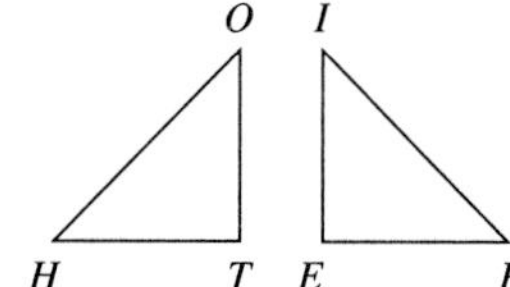

Congruent segments (p. 51) Congruent segments are segments that have the same length.

Example $\overline{AB}$ is congruent to $\overline{WX}$

Coordinate plane (p. 467) A coordinate plane is formed by the intersection of a horizontal number line, called the *x*-axis, and a vertical number line, called the *y*-axis.

Example

Coordinates (p. 467) Each point on the coordinate plane is identified by a unique ordered pair of numbers called its coordinates. The first coordinate tells you how to move from the origin along the *x*-axis. The second coordinate tells you how to move from the origin along the *y*-axis.

Example The ordered pair of coordinates $(-2, 1)$ describes the point that is two units to the left of, and one unit above the origin.

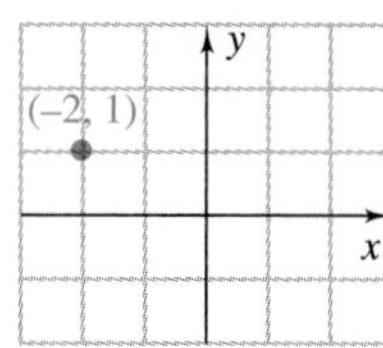

Counting principle (p. 426) The number of outcomes for an event with two or more stages is the product of the number of outcomes at each stage.

Example Flip a coin and roll a number cube. The total number of possible outcomes $= 2 \times 6 = 12$.

Cross products (p. 369) The cross products of the proportion $\frac{a}{b} = \frac{c}{d}$ are $a \times d$ and $b \times c$.

Example The cross products of the proportion $\frac{2}{15} = \frac{6}{45}$ are 2×45 and 15×6.

Cube (p. 252) A cube is a rectangular prism with six congruent faces.

Example

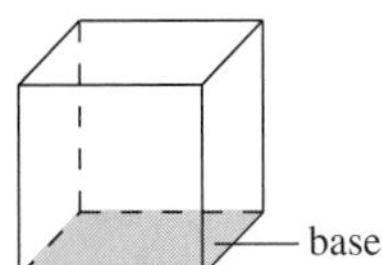

D

Diameter (p. 78) A diameter is a segment that passes through the center of a circle and has both endpoints on the circle.

Example $\overline{RS}$ is a diameter of circle O.

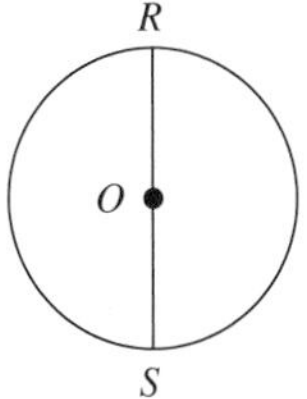

Distributive Property (p. 152) Each term inside a set of parentheses can be multiplied by a factor outside the parentheses.

Example $a \times (b + c) = a \times b + a \times c$.
Likewise, $a \times (b - c) = a \times b - a \times c$.

Divisibility (p. 275) Divisibility is the ability of one number to divide into another with no remainder.

Example 15 and 20 are both divisible by 5.

E

Equal ratios (p. 365) Ratios that make the same comparison or describe the same rate are equal ratios.

Example $\frac{2}{3} = \frac{4}{6} = \frac{24}{36}$ are equal ratios.

Equation (p. 212) A mathematical sentence that contains an equal sign, =, is an equation.

Example $2(6 + 17) = 46$

Equilateral triangle (p. 54) An equilateral triangle is a triangle with three congruent sides.

Example $\overline{SL} \cong \overline{LW} \cong \overline{WS}$

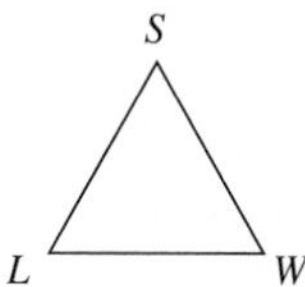

Equivalent fractions (p. 286) Fractions that are equal to each other are equivalent fractions.

Example $\frac{1}{2} = \frac{25}{50}$

Evaluate an expression (p. 197) To evaluate an expression, replace each variable with a number. Then compute, following the order of operations.

Example Evaluate the expression $2^3 + (y - 5)$ for $y = 17$.
$2^3 + (17 - 5) = 8 + 12 = 20$

Expanded form (p. 98) Expanded form shows the place and value of each digit.

Example 0.85 can be written in expanded form as 0.8 + 0.05.

Exponent (p. 192) An exponent expresses how many times a base is used as a factor.

Example $3^4 = 3 \times 3 \times 3 \times 3$ (exponent)

F

Factor (p. 278) One number is a factor of another if it divides that number with no remainder.

Example 1, 2, 3, 4, 6, 9, 12, and 36 are factors of 36.

Factor tree (p. 278) A factor tree is used to find a number's prime factors.

Example

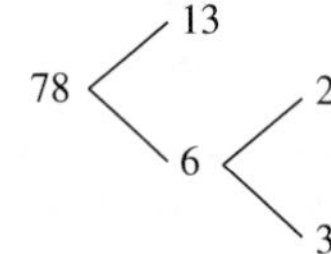

Fair game (p. 411) A game is fair if each player has the same chance of winning.

Example Predicting whether a coin will land "heads" or "tails" is a game where each player has the same chance of winning, so it is a fair game.

Frequency table (p. 5)

A frequency table lists items together with the number of times, or frequency, they occur.

Example

Phones	Tally	Frequency
1	~~||||~~ |||	8
2	~~				~~		6
3						4

Front-end estimation (p. 112)

To use front-end estimation to estimate sums, first, add the front-end digits. Then, adjust by estimating the sum of the remaining digits. Add the two values.

Example Estimate \$3.49 + \$2.29.

$3 + 2 = 5$

$0.49 + 0.29 \approx 1$

$5 + 1 = 6$

Function (p. 209)

A function is a relationship in which each member of one set is paired with exactly one member of another set.

Example

No. of nickels	Value in cents
0	0
1	5
2	10
3	15

G

Gram (p. 260)

A gram is the basic unit of mass, or weight, in the metric system.

Example A paper clip weighs about 1 g.

Greatest common factor (p. 282)

The greatest common factor (GCF) of two or more numbers is the greatest number that is a factor of all the numbers.

Example 12 and 30 have a GCF of 6.

I

Image (p. 472) A point, line, or figure that is transformed to a new set of coordinates is the image of the original point, line, or figure.

Example Rectangle $A'B'C'D'$ is the image of rectangle $ABCD$.

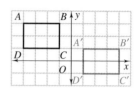

Improper fraction (p. 294) A fraction whose numerator is greater than its denominator is called an improper fraction.

Example $\frac{73}{16}$ is an improper fraction.

Independent events (p. 429) Two events are independent if the outcome of one event has no effect on the outcome of the other.

Example Rolling a number cube and tossing a coin are independent events.

Integers (p. 449) Integers are the set of whole numbers and their opposites.

Example $\ldots -3, -2, -1, 0, 1, 2, 3, \ldots$ are integers.

Isosceles triangle (p. 54) An isosceles triangle is a triangle with at least two congruent sides.

Example $\overline{LM} \cong \overline{LB}$

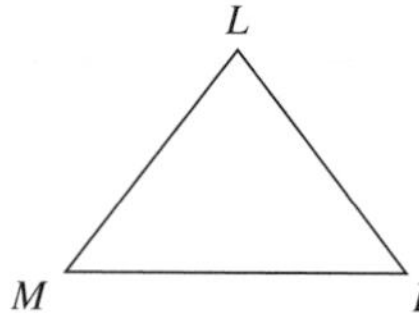

L

Least common denominator (p. 301) The least common denominator (LCD) of two or more fractions is the least common multiple (LCM) of their denominators.

Example The LCD for the fractions $\frac{3}{8}$ and $\frac{7}{10}$ is 40.

Least common multiple (p. 297) The smallest number that is a common multiple of two or more numbers is the least common multiple (LCM).

Example The LCM of 15 and 6 is 30.

Line (p. 41) A line continues without end in opposite directions.

Example $\overleftrightarrow{AB}$ represents a line.

Line graph (p. 21)

A line graph shows how an amount changes over time.

Example: This line graph represents seasonal snow blower sales (in thousands) for a large chain of department stores.

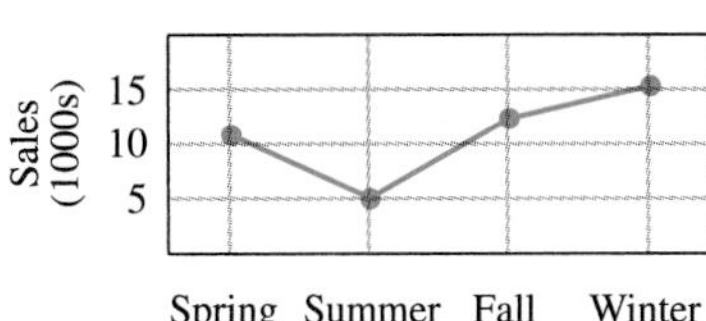

Line plot (p. 5)

A line plot displays data on a horizontal line.

Example: This line plot shows the frequency of video game scores during sessions of play.

```
                    ×
                ×   ×
            ×   ×   ×   ×
×   ×   ×   ×   ×   ×
-------------------------
45  46  47  48  49  50
```

Line symmetry (p. 74)

A figure has line symmetry if a line can be drawn through the figure so that one side is a mirror image of the other.

Example: The figure shown has one line of symmetry, l.

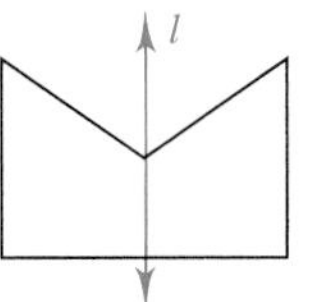

Liter (p. 262)

A liter is the basic unit of capacity, or volume, in the metric system.

Example: A pitcher holds about 2 L of juice.

M

Mean (p. 11)

The mean of a set of data is the sum of the data divided by the number of pieces of data.

Example: The mean temperature (°F) for the set of temperatures, 44, 52, 48, 55, 60, 67, and 58, is approximately 54.86°F.

Median (p. 124)

The median is the middle number in a set of data when the data are arranged in numerical order.

Example: Temperatures (°F) for one week arranged in numerical order are 44, 48, 52, 55, 58, 60, and 67. 55 is the median temperature because it is the middle number in the set of data.

Meter (p. 124) — A meter is the basic unit of length in the metric system.

Example A doorknob is about 1 m from the floor.

Mixed number (p. 294) — A mixed number shows the sum of a whole number and a fraction.

Example $3\frac{11}{16}$ is a mixed number; $3\frac{11}{16} = 3 + \frac{11}{16}$

Mode (p. 12) — The mode is the data item that appears most often.

Example The mode of the set of wages \$2.50, \$3.75, \$3.60, \$2.75, \$2.75, \$3.70, is \$2.75.

Multiple (p. 297) — A multiple of a number is the product of that number and any whole number.

Example The number 39 is a multiple of 3 and 13.

N

Net (p. 253) — The pattern that you cut out and fold to form a three-dimensional figure is called a net.

Example This net can be folded to make a cube.

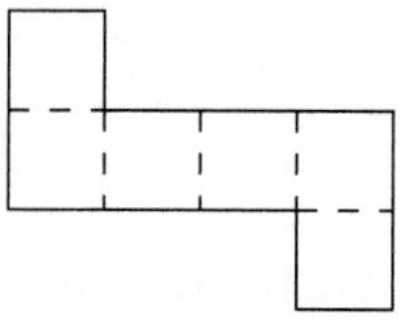

Noncollinear points (p. 42) — If there is no line that goes through all the points in a set, the points are noncollinear.

Example Points S, Q, R, and T are noncollinear.

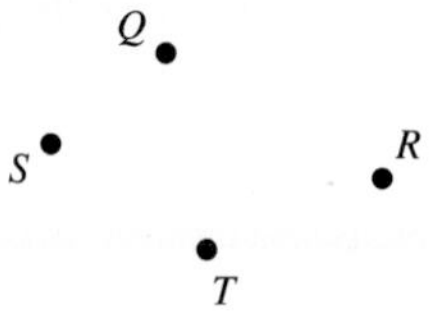

Numerical expression (p. 196) — An expression that contains only numbers and mathematical symbols is a numerical expression.

Example 2 (5 + 7) − 14 is a numerical expression.

O

Obtuse angle (p. 47)

An obtuse angle is any angle that measures greater than 90° and less than 180°.

Example

Order of operations (p. 148)

1. Do all operations within parentheses.
2. Do all work with exponents.
3. Multiply and divide from left to right.
4. Add and subtract from left to right.

Example $2^3(7 - 4) = 2^3 \cdot 3 = 8 \cdot 3 = 24$

Ordered pair (p. 467)

An ordered pair is a pair of numbers that describe the location of a point on a coordinate plane. The first value is the x-coordinate and the second value is the y-coordinate.

Example $(-2, 1)$. The x-coordinate is -2; the y-coordinate is 1.

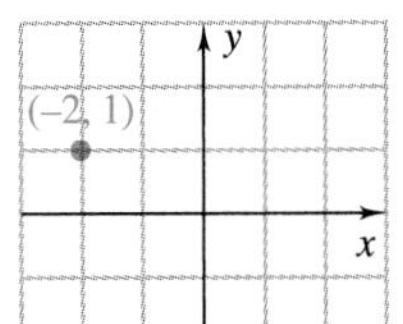

Origin (p. 467)

The origin is the point of intersection of the x- and y-axes on a coordinate plane.

Example The ordered pair that describes the origin is (0, 0).

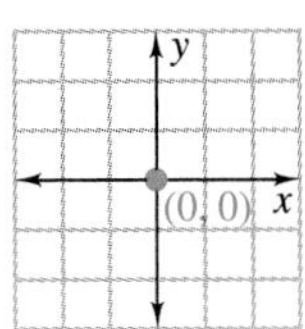

P

Parallel lines (p. 43)

Parallel lines are lines on the same plane that do not intersect.

Example $\overleftrightarrow{EF} \parallel \overleftrightarrow{HI}$

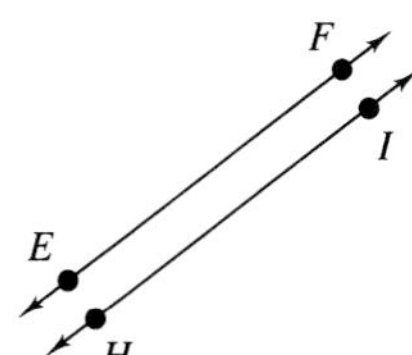

Parallelogram (p. 62) A parallelogram has both pairs of opposite sides parallel.

Example $\overline{KV}$ is parallel to $\overline{AD}$ and $\overline{AK}$ is parallel to $\overline{DV}$.

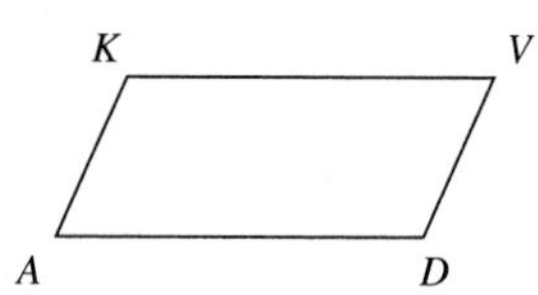

Percent (p. 384) A percent is a ratio that compares a number to 100. The symbol for percent is %.

Example The ratio 50 to 100 is a percent because 50 is compared to 100.
$\frac{50}{100} = 50\%$

Perimeter (p. 233) The perimeter of a figure is the distance around it.

Example The perimeter of $ABCD =$
2 ft + 4 ft + 2 ft + 4 ft = 12 ft.

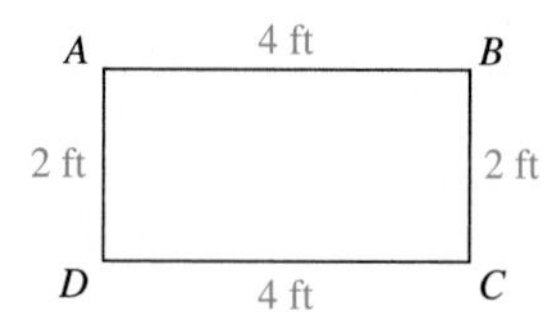

Perpendicular lines (p. 47) Perpendicular lines are lines that intersect to form right angles.

Example $\overleftrightarrow{DE} \perp \overleftrightarrow{RS}$

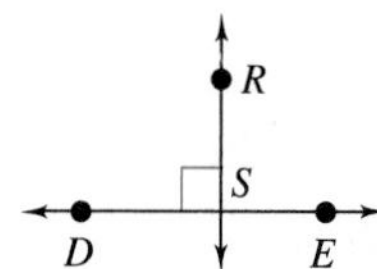

Point (p. 41) A point is a position in space. It has no size, only location.

Example *D*, *B*, and *N* represent points.

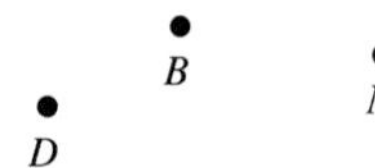

Polygon (p. 58) A polygon is a closed plane figure formed by three or more line segments.

Example The figure *CDEFG* is a convex polygon. The figure *VWXYZ* is not convex.

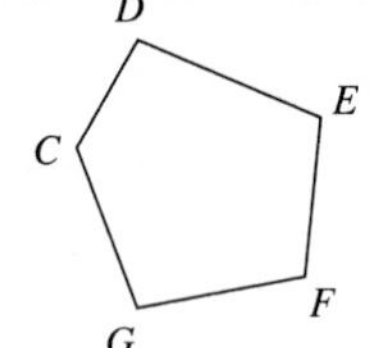

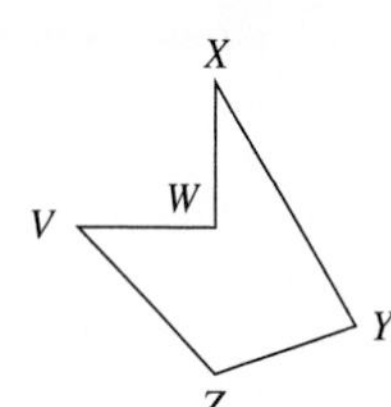

Population (p. 436)	A population is a group of people or objects about whom information is gathered.
Example	A quality control inspector examines a sample of the population, which is the output of a factory.
Power (p. 192)	The number that is expressed using an exponent is called a power.
Example	2^4 is two to the fourth power; $2^4 = 2 \times 2 \times 2 \times 2$
Prime factorization (p. 279)	Writing a composite number as the product of its prime factors is called prime factorization.
Example	The prime factorization of 30 is $2 \times 3 \times 5$.
Prime number (p. 278)	A number that has exactly two factors, 1 and the number itself, is a prime number.
Example	13 is a prime number because its only factors are 1 and 13.
Probability (p. 421)	Probability is used to describe how likely it is that an event will happen. The ratio for probability, P (E), is: $P(E) = \frac{\text{number of favorable outcomes}}{\text{number of possible outcomes.}}$
Example	The probability of spinning the number 4 is $\frac{1}{8}$.
Proportion (p. 369)	A proportion is an equation stating that two ratios are equal. The cross products of a proportion are always equal.
Example	The equation $\frac{3}{12} = \frac{12}{48}$ is a proportion because $3 \times 48 = 12 \times 12$.
Protractor (p. 45)	A protractor is a tool used to measure and draw angles.
Example	$m\angle A = 40°$
Pyramid (p. 252)	Pyramids are three-dimensional figures with only one base. The base is a polygon and the other three faces are triangles. A pyramid is named by the shape of its base.
Example	The figure shown is a rectangular pyramid.

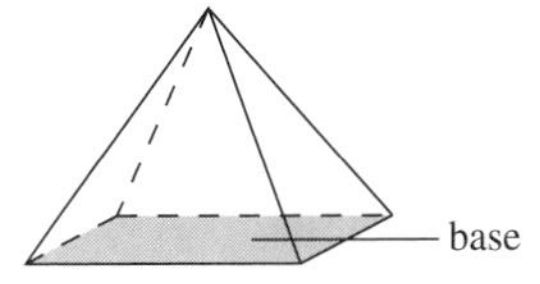

Student Study Guide

Q

Quadrant (p. 468)

The x- and y-axes divide the coordinate plane into four regions, called quadrants.

Example

R

Radius (p. 78)

A radius is a segment that has one endpoint at the center and the other endpoint on the circle.

Example $\overline{OA}$ is a radius of circle O.

Range (p. 6)

The range of a set of data is the difference between the greatest and the least values in the set.

Example Data set: 62, 109, 234, 35, 96, 49, 201
Range: $234 - 35 = 199$

Rate (p. 366)

A rate is a ratio that compares two quantities measured in two different units.

Example A student typed an 1,100 word essay in 50 min, or 22 words/min.

Ratio (p. 363)

A ratio is a comparison of two numbers.

Example A ratio can be written in three different ways: 72 to 100, 72 : 100, and $\frac{72}{100}$.

Ray (p. 42)

A ray is a part of a line. It consists of one endpoint and all the points of the line on one side of the endpoint.

Example $\overrightarrow{SW}$ represents a ray.

Reciprocal (p. 347)

Two numbers are reciprocals if their product is 1. Dividing by a number is the same as multiplying by the reciprocal of that number.

Example The numbers 5 and $\frac{1}{5}$ are reciprocals because $5 \times \frac{1}{5} = 1$.

Rectangle (p. 62) A rectangle is a parallelogram with four right angles.

Example

Reflection (p. 473) A reflection flips a figure across a line.

Example $K'L'M'N'$ is a reflection of $KLMN$ over the y-axis.

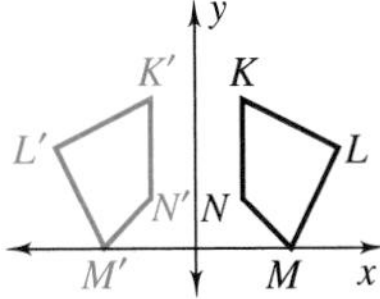

Repeating decimal (p. 304) A decimal whose digits repeat without end is a repeating decimal. A bar indicates the digits that repeat.

Example $0.6666\ldots$ or $0.\overline{6}$

Rhombus (p. 62) A rhombus is a parallelogram with four congruent sides.

Example

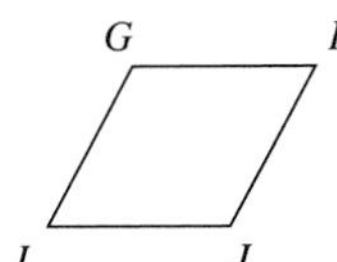

Right angle (p. 46) A right angle is an angle with a measure of 90°.

Example $m\angle D = 90°$.

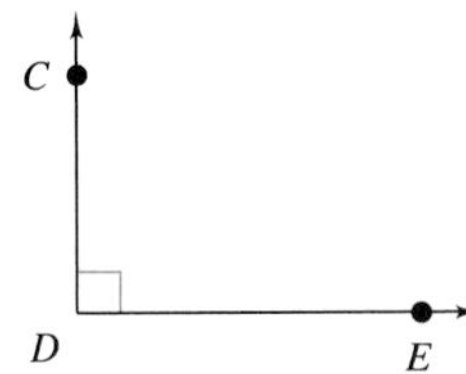

Right triangle (p. 54) A right triangle is a triangle with a right angle.

Example $m\angle B = 90°$.

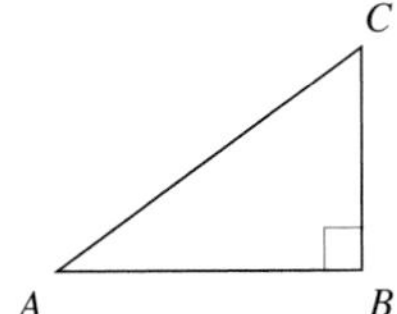

Student Study Guide

S

Sample (p. 436)

A sample of a group is a smaller subgroup selected from within the group. A representative sample of a group is a subgroup that has the same characteristics as the larger group. A random sample of a group is a subgroup selected at random from the group.

Example A representative sample of last week's math quizzes would include quizzes from each of several math classes. A random sample could be obtained by shuffling all the quizzes together and selecting a certain number of them without looking at them.

Scalene triangle (p. 54)

A scalene triangle is a triangle with no congruent sides.

Example

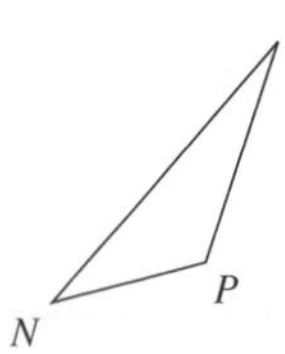

Segment (p. 41)

A segment is part of a line. It consists of two points and all the points on the line that are between the two points.

Example $\overline{CB}$ represents a segment.

Similar (p. 71)

Figures that have the same shape are similar.

Example $\triangle ABC \sim \triangle RTS$.

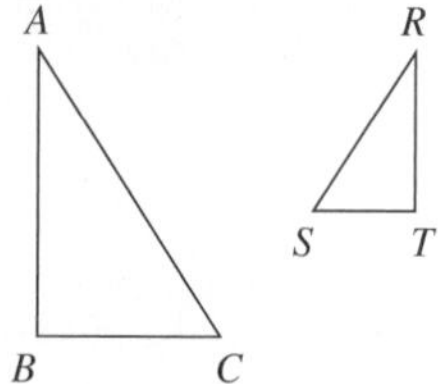

Simplest form of a fraction (p. 289)

A fraction is in simplest form when the GCF of the numerator and denominator is 1.

Example The fraction $\frac{3}{7}$ is in simplest form because the GCF of 3 and 7 is 1.

Simulation (p. 414)

A simulation is a model of a real-world situation.

Example A baseball team has an equal chance of winning or losing the next game. You can toss a coin to simulate the outcome.

Solution of an equation (p. 213)

A value of the variable that makes the equation true is called a solution of the equation.

Example 4 is the solution of $x + 5 = 9$.

Spreadsheet (p. 16)

A spreadsheet is a tool used for organizing and analyzing data. Spreadsheets are arranged in rows and columns. A cell is the box on a spreadsheet where a row and a column meet. The names of the row and column determine the name of the cell. A cell may contain data values, labels, or formulas.

Example In the spreadsheet shown, column C and row 2 meet at the shaded box, cell C2. The value of cell C2 is 2.75.

	A	B	C	D	E
1	0.50	0.70	0.60	0.50	2.30
2	1.50	0.50	2.75	2.50	7.25

Square (p. 62)

A square is a parallelogram with four right angles and four congruent sides.

Example

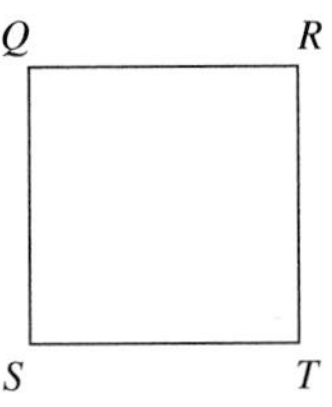

Straight angle (p. 47)

An angle that measures 180° is called a straight angle.

Example $m\angle TPL = 180°$

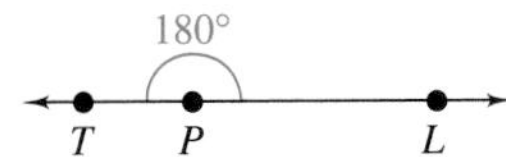

Straightedge (p. 51)

A straightedge is a tool used to draw lines, rays, and segments. It is similar to a ruler, but does not have marks to indicate measure.

Example A ruler, if you ignore the markings, can be used as a straightedge.

Surface area of a rectangular prism (p. 256)

The surface area of a rectangular prism is the sum of the areas of the faces.

Example Surface area $= 4 \times 12 + 2 \times 9 = 66$ in^2.

Each square = 1 in.^{2}

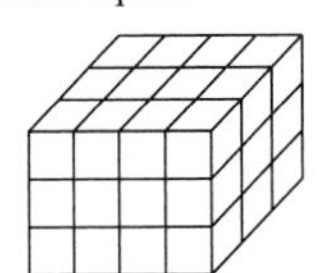

T

Terminating decimal (p. 304)

A terminating decimal is a decimal that stops or terminates.

Example Both 0.6 and 0.7265 are terminating decimals.

Tessellations (p. 82) Tessellations are repeated geometric designs that cover a plane with no gaps and no overlaps.

Example

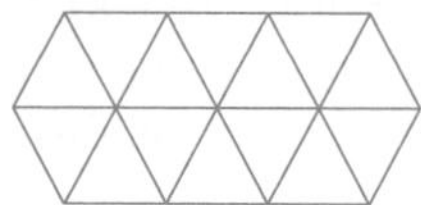

Translation (p. 472) A transformation that slides points, lines, or figures on a coordinate plane is a translation.

Example Rectangle *ABCD* has been translated to rectangle *A′B′C′D′*.

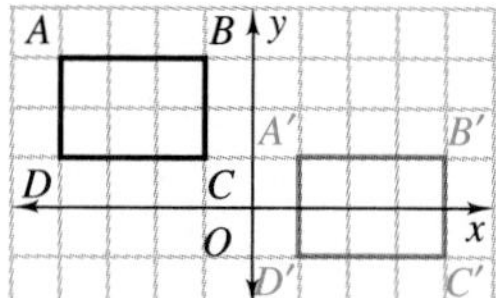

Trapezoid (p. 62) A trapezoid has exactly one pair of parallel sides.

Example

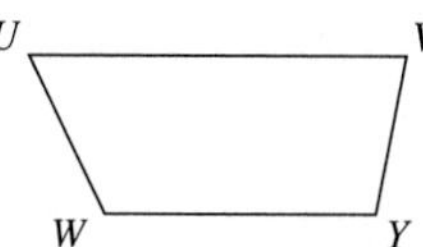

Tree diagram (p. 425) A tree diagram displays all the possible outcomes of an event.

Example There are for 4 possible outcomes for tossing 2 coins: (H,H), (H,T), (T,H), (T,T).

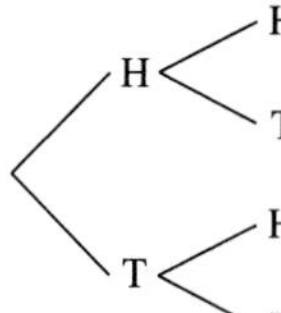

U

Unit rate (p. 366) A unit rate compares a quantity to a unit of one.

Example Miles per hour is a unit rate that compares distance traveled, in miles, to one unit of time, one hour.

V

Variable (p. 196) A variable is a symbol, usually a letter, that stands for a number.

Example x is a variable in the equation $9 - x = 3$.

Variable expression (p. 196) A variable expression is an expression that contains at least one variable.

Example $7 + x$

Vertex of a polygon (p. 237) A vertex of a polygon is any point where two sides of the polygon meet.

Example C, D, E, F, and G are all vertices of the pentagon shown.

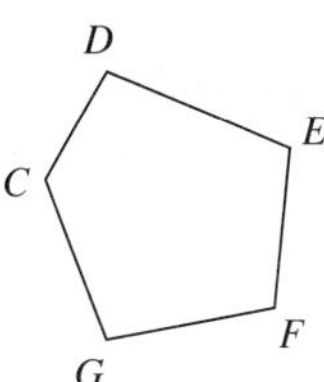

Volume (p. 259) The volume of a three-dimensional figure is the number of cubic units needed to fill the space inside the figure.

Example The volume of the rectangular prism is 36 in.^{3}.

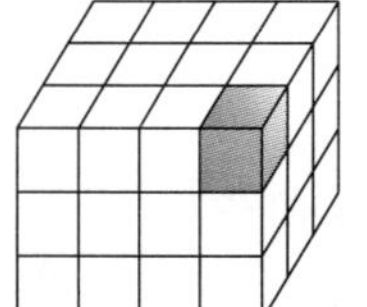

X

x-axis (p. 467) The x-axis is the horizontal number line that, together with the y-axis, forms the coordinate plane.

Example

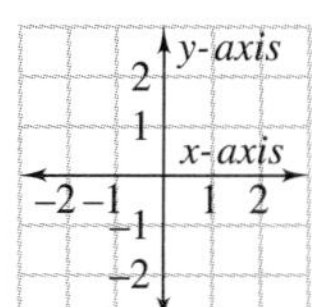

Y

y-axis (p. 467) The y-axis is the vertical number line that, together with the x-axis, forms the coordinate plane.

Example

Z

Zero pairs (p. 453) Zero pairs are pairs of tiles that represent the number zero.

Example 

Index

Index

Selected Answers

CHAPTER 1

1-1 pages 5–7

On Your Own **7. a.** 1, 3, 6, 0 **9.** 17.5 in. **13. b.** VA, MA, NY, OH **c.** No; the data are not numerical

Mixed Review **1.** 1,139 **2.** 218 **3.** 18,629 **4.** 174 **5.** 1 quarter, 2 dimes, 1 nickel, and 2 pennies

1-2 pages 8–10

On Your Own **15.** Carla **17.** 16 triangles **19.** 65 numbered pages **21.** 1:10 P.M.

Mixed Review **3.** 8 in **4.** 4,096 members

1-3 pages 11–14

On Your Own **9. a.** 11 songs; 12 songs **b.** mode; it is the most frequent number of songs appearing on CDs.

Mixed Review **1.** 764 **2.** 1,488 **3.** 1,368 **4.** 31 **5.** 7,600 ft

Checkpoint

1.

grams fat	tally	freq
0	𝍸|||	8
1	𝍸||||	9
2	𝍸	5
3					3

2.

```
   ×
×  ×
×  ×
×  ×
×  ×  ×
×  ×  ×
×  ×  ×  ×
×  ×  ×  ×
×  ×  ×  ×
0  1  2  3
```

3. 8.6 players **4.** 9 players **5.** 11 players

Problem Solving Practice page 15

1. \$2 **3.** 6 y and 9 y **5.** 7

1-4 pages 16–19

On Your Own **9.** Subtract the value in cell B2 from the value in cell C2; multiply the value in cell D2 by 6. **11. a.** No; it would calculate Tamara working a negative ten hours instead of the three hours she worked. **13.** B2 + C2 + D2; B3 + C3 + D3; B4 + C4 + D4; B5 + C5 + D5; B6 + C6 + D6 **15.** No; she could have added the scores for each group and divided by 3. **17. b.** yellow **c.** green **d.** yellow; they had the highest mean score.

Mixed Review **1.** 26 **2.** 17 **3.** 15. **4.** 11 **5.** 49°F

1-5 pages 20–23

On Your Own **17.** the number of balloons in the Fiesta has increased over the past 20 y. **19.** 1980 to 1981 **21.** 5 teachers **23.** circle graph; two parts are being compared to a whole. **25.** bar graph; several life spans are being compared.

Mixed Review **1.** spreadsheet **2.** cell **3.** formula **4.** Yes; the mean of the test scores is 85.

Practice page 24

1.

```
 ×
 ×    ×                  ×
 ×    ×    ×    ×    ×    ×
196  197  199  202  205  210
```

3. 14 mi/h **7.** 3,523; 3,662; no mode **9.** line graph **11.** ME; RI **13.** >

1-6 pages 25–28

On Your Own **7.** Answers may vary. Sample: intervals of 200 **9.** The population declined from 1950 to 1990 **11. c.** Both the cost of a public college education and a private college education are increasing.

Mixed Review **1.** bar graph **2.** bar graph **3.** line graph **4.** 21 and 22

Checkpoint **1.** c **2.**

Scores: 100, 80, 60, 40, 20, 0; J E N

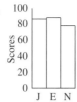

3. Army **4.** 238 medals of honor

Mixed Review **2.** 20 h

Wrap Up pages 32–33

1.

vowel	tally	freq
a	||||/ ||||/ ||||/	15
e	||||/ ||||/ |||	13
i	||||/ ||	7
o	||||/ ||||	9
u	|||	3

2.

×	×	× × × ×	
the	and	a	are

3. 9 ways **4.** 6 ways **5.** 45; 49; 50 **6.** 6 in.; 7 in.; 9 in. **7.** The number of string sales on 9/10/93 **8.** B2 + C2 + D2 **9.** $940.00 **10.** bar graph **11.** line graph **12.** circle graph

Getting Ready for Chapter 2 **1.** triangle **2.** rhombus, parallelogram, square, rectangle **3.** rectangle, parallelogram **4.** circle **5.** Sample: tip of an Indian arrowhead. **6.** Sample: tile **7.** Sample: pizza **8.** Sample: photograph

Cumulative Review page 37

1. A **2.** A **3.** C **4.** C **5.** C **6.** D **7.** B **8.** C

CHAPTER 2

2-1 pages 41–44

On Your Own **21.** A, B, and C **23.** Sample: $\overline{AC}$, $\overline{BD}$, $\overline{DE}$ **25.** Sample: $\overleftrightarrow{AC}$ and $\overleftrightarrow{DE}$ **27.** $\overline{XY}$ and $\overline{WZ}$ **29.** • • • • • A B C D E **31.** always **33.** sometimes **35.** never

Mixed Review **1.** 120 **2.** 20 **3.** 52 **4.** 50 **5.** 12

2-2 pages 45–49

On Your Own **11. a.** $\overrightarrow{LK}$, $\overrightarrow{LM}$, $\overrightarrow{LN}$ **b.** $\angle MLN$: acute; $\angle KLM$: right; $\angle KLN$: obtuse

13.

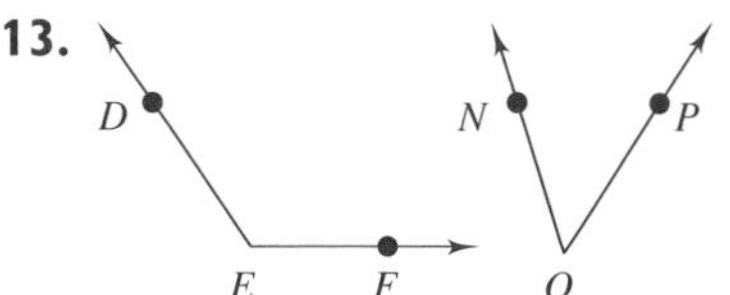

15. Samples: 90°, 180° You need only a straight edge to draw a straight angle; a corner to draw a right angle. **17.** 60° **19.** 150° **21.** about 120°; obtuse **27.** 45° **29.** A **31. a.** 180° **b.** 70° **c.** 120° **d.** 90° **e.** $\angle AGE$, $\angle BGE$, $\angle BGF$, $\angle CGF$ **f.** $\angle AGD$, $\angle DGF$, $\angle CGE$ **g.** $\angle AGF$

Mixed Review **1.** 997 **2.** 1,494 **3.** mode **4.** Sample: A, B, C **5.** Sample $\overrightarrow{BC}$, $\overrightarrow{CB}$ **6.** 12 books

Problem Solving Practice page 50

1. C; E **3.** 7 days

2-3 pages 51–53

On Your Own **7., 9.** Answers may vary.

Mixed Review **1.** < **2.** =

3.

data	tally	freq
0	||	2
1	||	2
2	||	2
3	||	2
4	||	2

4. 4 **5.** $\angle 1$

6. 145° **7.** 10,880 ft.

2-4 pages 54–57

On Your Own **13.** isosceles **15.** equilateral **17.** acute **19.** Yes; it has at least two congruent sides; no; it may only have two congruent sides

21. **27.**

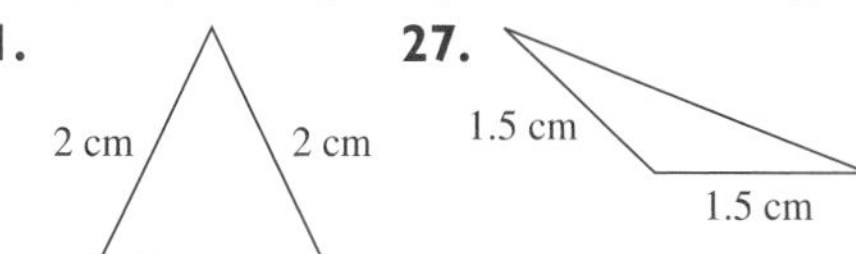

29. Not possible; an acute △ has three acute angles.

Selected Answers

Mixed Review **1.** 4,527; 3,201; 3,097; 2,852; 2,684; 978 **2.** about 88 million **3.** compass **4.** congruent **5.** 6

Checkpoint **1.** $\overleftrightarrow{LM}$, $\overleftrightarrow{KN}$ **2.** Sample: $\overrightarrow{JK}$, $\overrightarrow{JL}$, $\overrightarrow{JP}$ **3.** Sample: $\overline{LM}$, $\overline{JP}$, $\overline{JN}$ **4.** Sample: $\angle LJK$ **5.** Sample $\angle KJM$ **6.** Sample $\angle LJP$ **7.** Sample $\angle LJM$ **8.** Sample: L, J, M **9.** Sample: J, P, M **10.** 47° **13.** B **14.** Answers may vary. Sample: quilt designs, tile floors, sails

2-5 pages 58–61

On Your Own **7.** hexagon **9.** decagon **11.** octagon **13. a.** 3 congruent sides and 3 congruent angles **b.** 4 congruent sides and 4 congruent angles **c.** 5 congruent sides and 5 congruent angles **d.** equal sides and equal angles **15.** Sample: quadruplet, quadrant, quadriceps **19.** D

Mixed Review **1.** 230 **2.** 15 **3.** acute **4.** obtuse **5.** 12 packages

2-6 pages 62–65

On Your Own **13.** **15.**

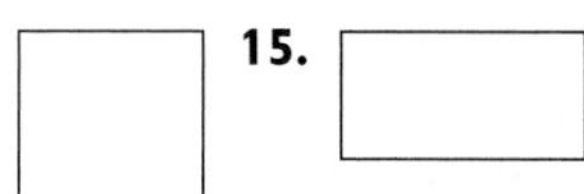

17. **19.** parallelogram, (rectangle)

23. a. congruent **b.** isosceles **c.** Isosceles trapezoid because two of its sides are congruent. **25.** parallelogram, rectangle, rhombus, square, trapezoid **27.** rectangle, rhombus, square **29.** Some **31.** All **33.** Some

Mixed Review **1.** 29 **2.** 25,000 **3.** octagon **4.** pentagon **5.** 15°

2-7 pages 66–68

On Your Own **11. a.** 17 **b.** 4 **13.** 17 pennies; 12 pennies, 1 nickel; 7 pennies, 1 dime; 7 pennies, 2 nickels; 2 pennies, 1 dime, 1 nickel; 2 pennies, 3 nickels

Mixed Review **1.** 630 **2.** 380 **3.** 11 **4.** 9 **5.** trapezoid **6.** parallelogram **7.** 82

Practice page 69

1. S, R, P **3.** $\overline{RQ}$, $\overline{SR}$, $\overline{PR}$ **5.** $\angle QRP$ **7.** 50° **9.** 140° **11.** 40° **17.** isosceles **19.** right **21.** acute **25.** true **27.** true

2-8 pages 70–73

On Your Own **7.** a, d **9.** similar **11.** congruent, similar **15.** Congruent; The window must be the same size and shape to fit in the window opening. **17. b.** No; Rhombuses can be different shapes. **c.** Yes; They are always the same shape. **19.** They appear to be similar.

Mixed Review **1.** = **2.** = **3.** circle graph **4.** 38 **5.** 18

2-9 pages 74–77

On Your Own

7. **9.**

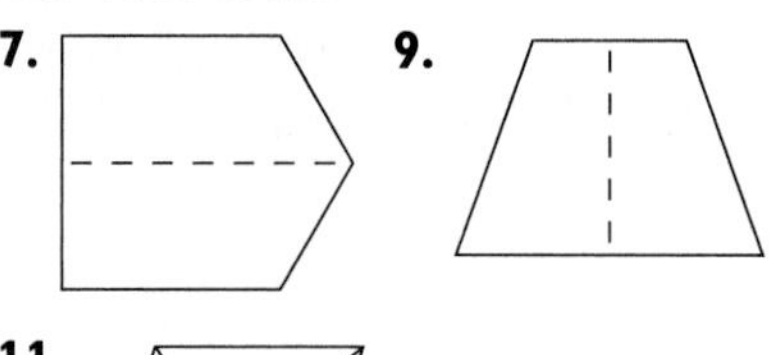

11.

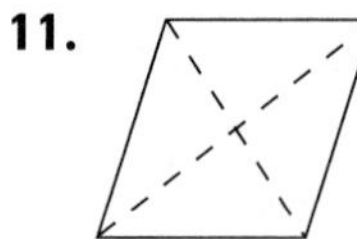

13.

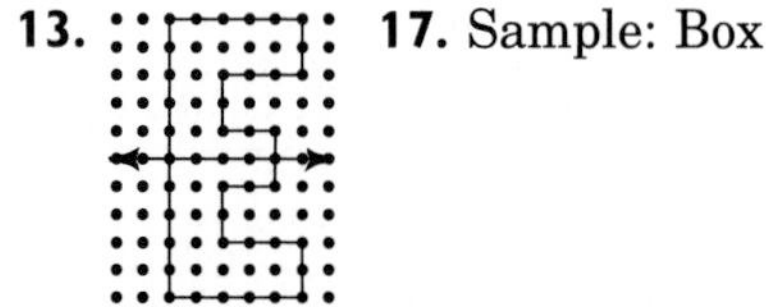

17. Sample: Box

Mixed Review **1.** 332 **2.** 332 **3.** equilateral **4.** scalene **5.** c, b **6.** a, b, c **7.** 5 and 7

Checkpoint **1.** 10 **2.** 8 **3.** 4 **5. a.** 6 **b.** 21 **6. a.** A, B, E **b.** A, B, D, E **7.** A

2-10 pages 78–81

On Your Own **11.** $\overline{RT}$ **13.** $\overline{RT}$, $\overline{ST}$ **15.** 5 in **19.** 125 ft **21.** 360 ÷ no. of cars **23.** $\angle ACB$ is always a right angle.

Mixed Review **1.** $=$ **2.** $>$ **3.** 0 **4.** 1 **5.** 16 **6.** 8

2-11 pages 82–85

On Your Own **7.** yes **9.** yes **13.** D

Mixed Review **1.** 37,442 **2.** 7,079 **3.** 4 **4.** 7 **5.** twice **6.** diameter

Wrap Up pages 86–87

1. A C B **2.** J M K N **3.** 3; 6; 1 **4.** straight **5.** acute **6.** obtuse **7.** Sample: $\overline{OX}$, $\overline{OY}$, $\overline{OV}$ **8.** $\overline{XV}$ **9.** $\angle XOY$, $\angle VOY$ **10.** $\overline{VW}$, $\overline{WY}$, $\overline{VX}$ **13.** B **14.** similar **15.** neither **16.** 2 **18.** 5

Getting Ready for Chapter 3 **1.** hundreds **2.** 6

Cumulative Review page 91

1. A **2.** C **3.** B **4.** D **5.** D **6.** A **7.** A **8.** B **9.** C **10.** C

CHAPTER 3

3-1 pages 95–97

On Your Own **13.** eight hundredths **15.** fifty-six hundredths **19.** 0.4 **21.** 0.6 **23.** 0.8 **25.** about 0.25

Mixed Review **1.** 2 **2.** 95 **3.** yes **4.** no **5.** 4,250 lb

3-2 pages 98–100

On Your Own **19. a.** 0.22 **b.** 2 tenths; 2 hundredths; 0.2 + 0.02 **21.** $.06 **23.** $.75 **25.** 5 tenths **27.** 5 millionths
35. 0.2 + 0.04 + 0.009 + 0.0008 **37.** Every 4 years a day is added. These years are called leap years. **39.** 4.7 pt **41.** 0.001 s

Mixed Review **1.** acute **2.** acute **3.** 0.9 **4.** 1.05 **5.** thirty-five hundredths **6.** two and thirty-three hundredths **7.** $19.50

3-3 pages 101–104

On Your Own **13.** $>$ **15.** $>$ **17.** $>$ **21.** No, the number of decimals between 0.4 and 0.5 is unlimited. Other decimal places can be added to 0.4 such as thousandths, ten thousandths, etc. **23.** 0.4; 0.8; 1.1 **25.** 4.28, 4.37, 8.7, 11.09, 11.4 **27.** Light year is the distance light travels in one year; i.e., approx. 6 million miles. This unit enables astronomers to measure vast solar distances with smaller, more understandable numbers.

Mixed Review **1.** 68° **2.** 31° **3.** 3 tenths **4.** 3 tens **5.** 25 lb

Checkpoint **1.** nine tenths **2.** one hundredth **3.** seventy-three hundredths **4.** sixty hundredths **5.** 0.3 **6.** 0.02 **7.** 0.92 **8.** 6 tenths **9.** 7 hundredths **10.** 8 ones **11.** 3 thousandths **12.** $<$ **13.** $=$ **14.** $>$

3-4 pages 105–107

On Your Own **9.** No; 1,320 people will get in **11.** About 2.97 qt **13.** $14.77

Mixed Review **1.** 78° **2.** 25° **3.** $<$ **4.** $>$ **5.** 243 passengers

3-5 pages 108–110

On Your Own **11.** 0.95 **13.** 47, 4, 7 **15.** 11 **17.** 0.7 **19.** 0.3 **21.** 1.09 **23.** 1.55 **25.** 2.00 **27.** 1.76

Mixed Review **1.** yes **2.** no **3.** false **4.** true **5.** 61 times

3-6 pages 111–114

On Your Own **19.** 0.1 **21.** 2,7084 **23.** $14.00 **25.** $45.00 **27. a.** about 1.8 oz; about 5.20 oz **b.** about 0.2 oz **c.** about 3.7 oz **29.** about $118 **31.** Answers may vary. Sample: Two adults, one child—about $34 more **33.** B **35. a.** 3.158 and 6.8 **b.** 13.228 and 6.8 **37.** higher; all numbers have been rounded up. **39.** $226,000 more

Mixed Review **1.** $\overleftrightarrow{ST}$, $\overleftrightarrow{SU}$, $\overleftrightarrow{SV}$ **2.** $\overrightarrow{TS}$, $\overrightarrow{TU}$, $\overrightarrow{UV}$ **3.** 2.6 **4.** 0.1 **5.** 60 books

Problem Solving Practice page 115

1. 7,282 mi **3.** Steve, Sara, Sam, Sue **7.** Yes; the total cost of the tickets is $28. The estimated discount total is $3.50. $28 − $3.50 = $24.50

3-7 pages 116–119

On Your Own **15.** 6; 5.1 **17.** 9; 8.561 **19.** 3; 2.7 **21.** 14; 13.87 **23.** 0.27 **27.** gas and firewood/charcoal **29.** 0 **31.** $4.25 **33.** C **35.** Charges based on the dollar amount of the order are less.

Mixed Review **1.** True **2.** False **3.** 1.949 **4.** 23.0 **5.** $269.50

3-8 pages 120–122

On Your Own **15. a.** Answers may vary. Sample: Data is organized into cells. **b.** Put In; Took Out; End of Day **c.** $24.50 **d.** less; Start of Day equaled $20 **e.** $24.50 **f.** Start of Day: 20.00, 24.50, 19.49, 23.99, 33.24; Took Out: 7.00; End of Day: 17.50, 19.49, 23.99, 33.24, 8.24

Mixed Review **1.** 45.25 **2.** 4.6 **3.** 22.35 **4.** 4.16 **5.** $70

Practice page 123

7. five tenths **9.** seventy hundredths **11.** seventy-five and three hundredths **13.** 0.45 **15.** 7 tenths **17.** 7 tens **19.** 7 hundredths **21.** 100.051 **23.** 30 + 8 + 0.8 + 0.001 + 0.0005 **25.** > **27.** < **31.** 6.188 **33.** 95.36 **35.** 3 **37.** $9.00 **39.** $1.00 **41.** 3; 3.0 **43.** 8; 8.461 **45.** 11; 11.53 **47.** 5; 5.909

3-9 pages 124–127

On Your Own **13.** 28 mm **15.** 92 mm **17.** 110 mm **19.** 18 m **21.** no; 30 m **23.** no; 18 cm **27.** centimeter **29.** kilometer

Mixed Review **1.** 82° **2.** 136° **3.** False **4.** True **5.** $99.63

Checkpoint **1–4.** Samples given. **1.** 7; 7.32 **2.** 8; 8.26 **3.** 19; 18.19 **4.** 29; 29.2 **5.** 12.04 **6.** 2 **7.** 9.066 **8.** 53.9 **9.** C

3-10 pages 128–131

On Your Own **9. a.** 25 min **13.** Captain EO, Red Baron

Mixed Review **1.** right **2.** acute **3.** 6 mm **4.** meter **5.** 6:00 P.M.

Wrap Up pages 132–133

1. 0.5 **2.** 0.48 **3.** 9.0008 **4.** > **5.** > **6.** = **7.** > **8.** 5.698 **9.** 0.88 **10.** 9.236 **11.** 4.0 **12.** 44 **13.** 0.7 **14.** 1.68 **15.** 0.931 **16.** 53.642 **17.** 357.48 **18.** 85.62 **19.** 65.62 **20.** 0.40 **21.** meter **22.** centimeter **23.** meter **24.** yes; 8:40 P.M. **25.** 1,440 times

Getting Ready for Chapter 4 **1.** about 8 **2.** about 54 **3.** about 1,190 **4.** about 9 **5.** about 8 **6.** about 10 **7.** about 33 **8.** about 231 **9.** about 1,920 **10.** about 3 **11.** about 210 **12.** about 3

Cumulative Review page 137

1. B **2.** C **3.** B **4.** D **5.** A **6.** A **7.** C **8.** D **9.** B **10.** A

CHAPTER 4

4-1 pages 141–143

On Your Own **19.** about 36 **21.** about 0 **23.** about 93 **25.** about 5 **27.** about 8 **29.** about 6 **31.** about 60 ft/s **33.** about 64 g **35. a.** about $300 **b.** about $9 **37.** B **39.** about 60 km

Mixed Review **1.** 1:32 P.M. **2.** 0.54 **3.** 18,000 **4.** 40 **5.** Feb. and Mar.

4-2 pages 145–147

On Your Own **9. a.** Coin, Composition, Condition, Cost **b.** 5 **c.** Answers may vary **e.** $86.75

Mixed Review **1.** about 200 **2.** about 28 **4.** 0.65 **5.** 3.016 **6.** yes

4-3 pages 148–150

On Your Own **9.** subtraction **11.** multiplication **13.** 12 **15.** 7.9 **17.** 60 **19.** S **21.** 1.5 **25.** $>$ **27.** $<$ **29.** When the subtraction is in parentheses. **31.** $14 \div (2 + 5) - 1 = 1$ **33.** $(11 - 7) \div 2 = 2$ **35.** no parentheses needed **37.** 28 **39.** 8 **41.** $\div, +, +$ **43.** $-, \times, \div$ or $-, \times, \times$

Mixed Review **1.** $240 **2.** 28 **3.** about 120 **4.** about 1000 **5.** about 10 **6.** 176 lockers

4-4 pages 151–154

On Your Own **23.** $(3 \times 6) + (3 \times 2)$; $3 \times (6 + 2)$; 24 **25.** 8; 3 **27.** 336 **29.** 560 **31.** 80 **33.** 77

Mixed Review **1.** 15 **2.** 3 **3.** 0 **6.** 4.12; 12; 9 **5.** 8.6; 8.5; 7.4; 8.5

Checkpoint **1.** about 18 **2.** about 52 **3.** about 60 **4.** about 80 **5.** about 36 **6.** about 1500 **7.** -19 **8.** 6 **9.** 8 **10.** C

Problem Solving Practice page 155

1. 10 calls **3.** 19 rows **5.** May 7 **7.** 204

4-5 pages 156–157

On Your Own **7.** $0.6 \times 0.9 = 0.54$ **9.** $0.5 \times 0.5 = 0.25$ **11.** 0.6 **13.** 1.8 **15.** **17.** 0.6 **19.** 0.72 **21.** One and five-tenths times one tenth equals fifteen hundredths.

Mixed Review **1.** $>$ **2.** $<$ **4.** 120 **5.** 2,574 **6.** 82.6

4-6 pages 158–161

On Your Own **21.** 14.72 **23.** 15.857 **25.** 62 **27.** 3500 **29.** 24.78 **31.** 0.124 **33.** 4.5 **35.** 0.1152 **37.** Yes; answers may vary.

39. False; Sample: $2 \times 3 = 6$, $3 \times 2 = 6$ **43.** 5 cm **45.** 105 calories **47.** 196 calories; more

Mixed Review **1.** 544 **2.** 380 **3.**

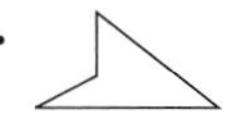

4. **5.** 4.97 L **6.** 8 h 27 min

4-7 pages 162–164

On Your Own **9.** The amount she was charged is needed to solve the problem **11.** about 19.5 bands **13.** The number of stores is needed to solve the problem **17.** Not enough information; The tidal range is 39.4. The water level at low tide is needed.

Mixed Review **1.** 1.52 **2.** 5.7 **3.** 8 **4.** 4 and 24 **5.** 0.05, 0.505, 0.55, 5.55 **6.** 9.004, 9.04, 90.4, 900.4 **7.** 11

Practice page 165

1. about 32 **3.** about 3 **5.** about 5 **7.** about 100 **9.** about 4 **11.** 20 **13.** 1 **15.** 9 **17.** $\div, -$ **19.** $-, \times$ **21.** 6, 4 **23.** 33 **25.** 14 **27.** 60 **29.** 228 **31.** 801 **33.** 0.636 **35.** 6.916 **37.** 0.492 **39.** 0.0252

4-8 pages 166–167

On Your Own **9.** 10 **11.** 0.25 **13.** 1.6 **15.** 16 **17.** 4 **19.** 2 **21.** 3

Mixed Review **1.** 2.714 **2.** 0.0072 **3.** 0.06 **4.** Pool record needed. **5.**

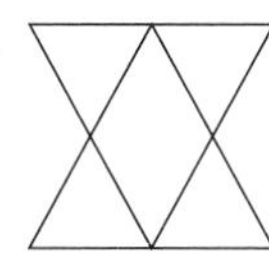

4-9 pages 168–171

On Your Own **23.** 2.5 **25.** 0.003 **27.** 0.02 **29.** 0.05 **31.** 0.073 **33.** 38 **35.** 6,450 **37.** 32 **39.** 0.079 in **43.** **a.** 5 **b.** greater than both 3.5 and 0.7

Checkpoint **1.** 9; 8 **2.** 5; 6; 2 **3.** 32.76 **4.** 1.9598 **5.** $48.75 **6.** 4.25 **7.** $14.20 **8.** 16.4

4-10 pages 172–175

On Your Own **5. a.** two times greater **b.** \$24.40 **c.** about 2.8 or 3 times greater **c.** Today: Answers may vary. 1985: \$4.45 **9. a.** \$.63 **b.** about 6

Mixed Review **1.** 0.39 **2.** 1.91 **3.** 0.0082 **4.** RF **5.** $\angle M$

Wrap Up pages 176–177

1. 125 **2.** 30 **3.** 7 **4.** 4 **6.** 72 **7.** 19.7 **8.** 105 **9.** 360 **10.** A **11.** 9; 45 **12.** 30; 216 **13.** $0.3 \times 0.1 = 0.03$ **14.** $0.5 \div 0.1 = 5$ **15.** 0.1286 **16.** 46.08 **17.** 0.75 **18.** 30 **23.** The number of students riding the bus is needed **24.** 153.5 cm tall

Getting Ready for Chapter 5 **2.** x; y; z

Cumulative Review page 181

1. A **2.** C **3.** A **4.** D **5.** D **6.** B **7.** C **8.** D **9.** C **10.** C

CHAPTER 5

5-1 pages 185–187

On Your Own **9.** 35, 42, 49 **11.** 1, 1.25, 1.5 **13.** $\frac{1}{16}, \frac{1}{32}, \frac{1}{64}$ **15.** 1, 1.5, 2.25, 3.375, 5.0625

Mixed Review **1.** 44.7 **2.** 8.1 **3.** \$8 **4.** \$223.11 **5.** seventy-three hundredths **6.** three hundred eighty-six and nine hundred eight thousandths. **7.** \$77

5-2 pages 188–191

On Your Own **13.** 301 **15.** 3,632 **17.** 256,758 **19.** 261,992 **21.** 140 min

Mixed Review **1.** 3.2 **2.** 19.52 **3.** 256; 1,024; 4,096 **4.** 1.1, 1.4, 1.7 **5.** 7 **6.** 12 **7.** 5, 12

5-3 pages 192–195

On Your Own **19.** 7, 9 **21.** 10, 3 **23.** 4^6 **25.** 35 **27.** 183 **29.** 82 **31.** 500 **33.** 2^3 **35. a.** 10,000; 10^5; 100,000 **c.** 100,000,000; 10,000,000,000; 1,000,000,000,000

Mixed Review **1.** 10,000 **2.** 2,400 **3.** 8, 10, 12 **4.** 24, 30, 36 **5.** 5 blocks

Checkpoint **1.** 4, 8, 16, 32, 64 **2.** 10^6 **3.** 4,782,969 **4.** 468 **5.** 6 **6.** 4 **7.** 14

5-4 pages 196–199

On Your Own **19.** 8 **21.** 193 **23.** 3 **25.** 216 **27.** 4 **29.** $r = 8$, $s = 11$, $t = 10$ **31.** $x = 10$; 14, 28, 42, 56 **33.** A **35.** 110 + 630

Mixed Review **1.** 15 **2.** 16 **3.** 5^4 **4.** 9^3 **5.** 2, 9, 16, 23, 30 **6.** 95 people

5-5 pages 200–202

On Your Own **13.** 7 h **15.** yes; no; yes **17.** 7 and 9 **19.** 24 and 25

21.

	hat	coat
Anita	Althea	Beth
Cheryl	Anita	Althea
Beth	Cheryl	Anita
Althea	Beth	Cheryl

Mixed Review **1.** 52.27 **2.** 2.689 **3.** n **4.** f **5.** 45 **6.** 38 **7.** 6 outfits

Practice page 203

1. 10, 12, 14 **3.** 3.2, 4.2, 5.2 **5.** 7, 4 **7.** 2, 8 **9.** 24^2 **11.** 6 **13.** 14,348,907 **15.** 4 **17.** 468 **19.** 2r + 4 **21.** 2s + 3 **23.** 5 **25.** 21 **27.** 12 **29.** 30

5-6 pages 204–206

On Your Own **17.** h less than 18, 18 minus h **19.** quotient of 21 and m, 21 divided by m. **21.** $K - 22$ **23.** $3m$ **25.** $3b$ **27.** $a + 3$ **29. a.** 37; 43 **b.** 57 **c.** $n + 10$, $n - 10$, $n - 2$, $n + 2$ **31. a.** $x - 3$ **b.** $x + 10$ **c.** $x - t$ **d.** $x + t$ **33. a.** $15t$ **b.** $15t \div 60$

Mixed Review **1.** 144.72 **2.** 5.176 **3.** = **4.** > **5.** 32 pieces

Problem Solving Practice Page 207

1. 6 days **3.** Joe: 2.5 km; Frank: 1.25 km; Steve: 2.25 km **5.** 15 push pins **7.** 16 s

5-7 pages 208-211

On Your Own 7. a. 11, 14, 17; 6, 10, 14 **b.** $3n + 5$; $4n - 2$ **c.** Yes; the price increases at a constant rate. **d.** No; you would not order zero tees.

Mixed Review 1. false **2.** false **3.** x divided by 5 **4.** 14 more than s **5.** $t - 3$ **6.** $n + 8$ **7.** 7 games

5-8 pages 212–216

On Your Own 19. True **21.** True **23.** yes **25.** yes **27.** no **29.** 88 **31.** 48 **33.** 26.6 **35.** 389 **37.** 74.578

41. a. $1 + 3 + 5 + 7 + 9 = 25$ or 5^2
$1 + 3 + 5 + 7 + 9 + 11 = 36$ or 6^2
$1 + 3 + 5 + 7 + 9 + 11 + 13 = 49$ or 7^2
b. The number of addends is equal to the base of the power. **c.** Use 10 as the base of the power; 10^2 or 100 **d.** 20^2 or 400
43. $p + 1{,}200 = 2{,}250$; 1,050 mi

Mixed Review 1. hexagon **2.** decagon **5.** ninth stop

Checkpoint 1. 13 **2.** $y + 12$ **3.** $b + 5$ **4.** $6 - w$ **5.** $22 - r$ **6.** 50 **7.** 385 **8.** 2

5-9 pages 217–219

On Your Own 13. no **15.** no **17.** 125 **19.** 18 **21.** 51,772 **23.** 1.65 **25.** 162.5 **29. a.** 1.28 g = 16 **b.** 12.5 gal **31.** 1,188; 1,287; 1,386; 1,485; $99 \times 16 = 1{,}584$; $99 \times 17 = 1{,}683$

Mixed Review 1. 26 cm **2.** 116 m **3.** 6 **4.** 17 **5.** 18 numbers

Wrap Up pages 220–221

1. 162; 486; 1,458; start with the number 2 and multiply by 3 repeatedly **2.** 9 **3.** 89 **4.** 16 **5.** 1.25 **6.** $x - 5$ **7.** $y \div p$ **8.** D **9.** $.39 **11.** subtraction; 5 **12.** addition; 23 **13.** division; 8 **14.** multiplication; 128 **15.** D

Getting Ready for Chapter 6 1. Perimeter: add the lengths of the sides. Area: multiply the length and width. **2.** 15.6 **3.** 289 **4.** 120

Cumulative Review page 225

1. C **2.** C **3.** D **4.** A **5.** B **6.** B **7.** B **8.** B **9.** D **10.** A **11.** C

CHAPTER 6

6-1 pages 229–232

On Your Own 7. 8 cm^2 **9.** sample given: about 21 in.^{2} **11.** Sample given: about 56 cm^2 **15.** B; A **17.** Sample given: about 52 in.^{2}

Mixed Review 1. 100 **2.** 9 **3.** 153 **4.** 16 **5.** 25 **6.** $9 \times 7{,}531$

6-2 pages 233–236

On Your Own 13. 7 cm; 3 cm^2 **15. a.** 200 in.^{2} **b.** 60 in. **17.** 9 in.^{2} **19.** 7 ft **21. a.** 2 m **b.** 0.25 m^2 **23. a.** 5 m **b.** 1 m^2 **25.** D **27.** 4 by 1, 3 by 2

Mixed Review 1. 368 **2.** 8,199 **3.** about 11 square units **4. a.** 3.6 **b.** $70.15

6-3 pages 237–240

On Your Own 11. 54 cm; 90 cm^2 **13.** 9 square units **15.** 16 square units **17. a.** 30 square units **b.** 25.8 square units **c.** 21 square units **d.** As the measure of $\angle B$ decreases, so does the area of the parallelogram. **19. a.** 12 cm^2

Checkpoint 1. 175 in.^{2}; 80 in. **2.** 240 in. **3.** 38 units; 84 square units **4.** 34 units; 72.25 square units.

Problem Solving Practice page 241
1. 8 **3.** 1 by 17, 2 by 16, 3 by 15, 4 by 14, 5 by 13, 6 by 12, 7 by 11, 8 by 10, 9 by 9 **5.** 4, 5, 25; 9, 10, 15; 9, 12, 13 **7.** 64 in.; 64 in.

6-4 pages 242–245
On Your Own **11.** about 33 m. **13.** about 18 m **15.** 157 m **17.** 402 m **19.** 55 ft **21.** 1 m **23.** 27 cm **25.** 18 m **27.** 22 cm **29.** 6 m **31.** Yes **33. a.** Neither; Every point on the stage turns simultaneously **b.** The keyboard player; She is on a circle with greater diameter. **c.** 94.2 ft **d.** yes; $2 \times 3.14 \times 30 = 2 \times 2 \times 3.14 \times 15$

6-5 pages 246–249
On Your Own **11.** 254.5 cm^2 **13.** 1,963.5 m^2 **15.** 15.4 units; 14.1 square units **17.** about 3 m^2 **21.** 74 m^2 **23.** 19 m^2 **27.** 52 y

Mixed Review **1.** 3.96 **2.** 345 **3.** about 3.14 m **4.** about 100.5 in. **5.** 16

Practice page 250
1. Sample 50 cm^2 **3.** 50 cm^2 **5.** 245 m^2; 63 m **7.** 24 ft^2; 24 ft **9.** 48 in. **11.** 30 cm; 75 cm^2 **13.** 12 cm; 12 cm^2 **15.** 65.97 in.; 346.36 $in.^2$ **17.** 452.39 m; 16,286.02 m^2 **19.** 452.16 cm^2 **21.** 5941.62 yd^2

6-6 pages 251–255
On Your Own **17.** cylinder **19.** cone **25.** rectangular prism **27.** triangular prism

Mixed Review **1.** 1.68 **2.** 2.05 **3.** 254.34 ft^2 **4.** 153.86 m^2 **5.** 45 **6.** 45 **7.** $1.92

6-7 pages 256–258
On Your Own **5.** 406 $in.^2$ **7.** 1,440 cm^2 **9.** 3,150 mm^2 **11.** 80 m^2 **15. a.** 240 ft^2 **b.** 207 ft^2 **c.** 447 ft^2 **d.** 2

Mixed Review **1.** 50 **2.** 4 **3.** sphere **4.** rectangular prism **5.** 1,260 **6.** 83.325 **7.** the square pizza

6-8 pages 259–262
On Your Own **9.** 600 $in.^3$ **11.** 180 mm^3 **13.** 42 ft^3 **15.** l = 5 cm **17. a.** 125 cm^3 **19.** C **21.** 1 by 1 by 32, 2 by 1 by 16, 2 by 2 by 8, 2 by 4 by 4, 4 by 1 by 8 **23. a.** about 960 m^3 **b.** about 960,000 L **c.** at least 24 m by 16 m

Mixed Review **3. a.** rectangular prism **b.** 64 $in.^2$ **4.** Jerry; 15¢

6-9 pages 263–265
On Your Own **9. a.** Answers may vary. Sample: 8, 16, 32 **11.** about 8.5 square units **13.** 1 by 1 by 12 **15. a.** 6 **b.** 27 **c.** 1

Mixed Review **1.** 6^4 **2.** 22^3 **3.** 56 cm^3 **4.** 105 ft^3 **5.** makes $7

Wrap Up pages 266–267
1. about 7 m^2 **2.** 13.5 cm^2; 22 cm **3.** 34 m **4.** 45.6 cm^2 **5.** 37.7 in.; 113.0 $in.^2$ **6.** 23.9 m; 45.3 m^2 **7.** 76.9 cm; 471.2 cm^2 **8.** 118.1 ft; 1,109.8 ft^2 **9.** 31.4 cm; 78.5 cm^2 **10.** 40.8 m; 132.7 m^2 **11.** 29.5 m; 69.4 m^2 **12. a.** rectangular pyramid **b.** 5, 8, 5 **14.** 64 m^2; 28 m^3 **15.** B **16.** 26 **17.** The dimensions of the box are 8 in. by 8 in. by 4 in.

Getting Ready for Chapter 7 **1.** 2 **2.** 2, 5, 10 **3.** no **4.** 5 **5.** 2, 5, 10 **6.** no

Cumulative Review page 271
1. C **2.** C **3.** B **4.** A **5.** A **6.** C **7.** D **8.** A **9.** D

CHAPTER 7

7-1 pages 275-277
On Your Own **11.** 1, 3, 5 **13.** 1, 2, 3, 5, 10 **15.** 1, 2 **17.** 1, 2, 3, 9 **19.** 7 **21.** 4 **23.** Sample: 330 **25.** Sample: 1,200,000,000 **27.** C **29. a.** 78; 8,010; 21,822 **b.** 78; 8,010; 21,822 **c.** A number is divisible by 6 if it is divisible by both 2 and 3.

Mixed Review **1.** 9 **2.** 24 **3.** 1 **4.** 30 **5.** 16 **6.** 18 **7.** 270

7-2 pages 278–281

On Your Own **27.** 1, 3; prime **29.** 1, 3, 7, 21; composite **31.** prime **33.** composite **35.** prime **37.** composite **39.** prime **41.** composite **43.** 34; 2; 17 **45.** $2 \times 5 \times 5$ **47.** $3 \times 3 \times 5$ **49.** 11×13 **51.** $2 \times 2 \times 3 \times 3 \times 3$ **53.** 692,733 **55.** 3, 5; 5, 7; 11, 13; 17, 19; 29, 31; 41, 43; 59, 61; 71, 73

Mixed Review **1.** 3, 9 **2.** 3, 5, 9 **3.** 3, 5, 9 **4.** 3 **5.** 24 m^2 **6.** 5.76 cm^2 **7.** 975

7-3 pages 282–284

On Your Own **13.** 7 **15.** 3 **17.** 1 **19.** 2 **21.** 3 **23.** 17

Mixed Review **1.** $2 \times 2 \times 3 \times 3 \times 3 \times 3$ **2.** $2 \times 2 \times 2 \times 3 \times 5 \times 5$ **5.** 153.86 m^2 **6.** 200.96 $in.^2$ **7.** 12 h 11 min

Checkpoint **1.** 1, 2, 3, 5, 10 **2.** 1, 3, 9 **3.** 1, 2, 3, 5, 10 **4.** 1, 2, 3, 5, 10 **5.** $2 \times 2 \times 2 \times 2 \times 2 \times 2 \times 3 \times 5$ **6.** $3 \times 3 \times 3 \times 3 \times 3$ **7.** $2 \times 3 \times 5 \times 7 \times 11$ **8.** $2 \times 3 \times 5 \times 13 \times 13$ **9.** 8 **10.** 6 **11.** 150

Problem Solving Practice page 285

1. 3 times **3.** 8 students **5.** \$8 **9.** 5:50 P.M.

7-4 pages 286–287

On Your Own **11.** $\frac{3}{4}$ **13.** $\frac{2}{4}, \frac{3}{6}, \frac{4}{8}, \frac{5}{10}$, or $\frac{6}{12}$ **15.** $\frac{4}{6}, \frac{6}{9}$, or $\frac{8}{12}$

Mixed Review **1.** 6 **2.** 15 **3.** 4 **4.** $n - 10$ **5.** $2n + 5$ **6.** $6n$ **7.** $12m \times 4m$

7-5 pages 288–290

On Your Own **15.** $\frac{47}{64}$ **17.** $\frac{2}{6}, \frac{1}{3}$; yes **19.** $\frac{5}{5}$ **21.** Sample: $\frac{1}{2}, \frac{2}{4}$ **23.** Sample: $\frac{1}{3}, \frac{2}{6}$ **25.** no; $\frac{3}{7}$ **27.** no; $\frac{1}{6}$ **29.** no; $\frac{1}{3}$ **31.** no; $\frac{2}{13}$ **35.** $\frac{2}{6}, \frac{4}{12}; \frac{2}{4}, \frac{6}{12}$

Mixed Review **1.** 1 **2.** 0 **3.** $\frac{1}{2}$ **4.** 600 cm^2 **5.** 148 $in.^2$ **6.** 12 people

Practice page 291

1. 1, 2 **3.** 1, 2, 3, 5, 10 **5.** 1, 2, 3 **7.** composite **9.** composite **11.** 5×7 **13.** $3 \times 7 \times 13$ **15.** $2 \times 2 \times 2 \times 2 \times 3 \times 3$ **17.** 5 **19.** 7 **21.** $\frac{2}{4}$ **23.** $\frac{1}{3}$ **25.** $\frac{6}{8}, \frac{9}{12}$ **27.** $\frac{4}{10}$ **29.** $\frac{2}{12}, \frac{3}{18}$ **31.** $\frac{1}{4}, \frac{6}{24}$ **33.** $\frac{22}{24}, \frac{33}{36}$ **35.** $\frac{3}{6}, \frac{2}{4}$; yes **37.** $\frac{2}{3}$ **39.** $\frac{1}{6}$ **41.** $\frac{3}{7}$

7-6 pages 292–293

On Your Own **13.** $\frac{4}{13}$ **15.** $\frac{2}{5}$ **17.** $\frac{5}{8}$ **19.** $\frac{1}{3}$

Mixed Review **1.** $\neq$ **2.** = **3.** 20 **4.** 4 **5.** 1 **6.** 50 **7.** 11th floor

7-7 pages 294–296

On Your Own **15.** B **17.** $1\frac{6}{7}$ **19.** $3\frac{1}{12}$ **21.** $\frac{33}{5}$ **23.** $\frac{9}{2}$ **25.** $\frac{9}{5}$; $1\frac{4}{5}$

Mixed Review **1.** $\frac{3}{4}$ **2.** $\frac{9}{16}$ **3.** 1,728 cm^3 **4.** 180 cm^3 **5.** $\times$, +

Checkpoint **1.** $\frac{3}{4}$ **2.** $\frac{2}{3}$ **3.** $\frac{7}{9}$ **4.** $\frac{1}{6}$ **5.** $\frac{1}{2}$ **6.** $9\frac{4}{5}$ **7.** $2\frac{5}{8}$ **8.** $8\frac{1}{6}$ **9.** $4\frac{1}{4}$ **10.** $2\frac{1}{2}$ **11.** $\frac{17}{3}$ **12.** $\frac{51}{4}$ **13.** $\frac{53}{6}$ **14.** $\frac{21}{2}$

7-8 pages 297–299

On Your Own **5.** 660 **7.** 60 **9.** 462 **11.** in 48 day **13.** D

Mixed Review **1.** $2\frac{1}{2}$ **2.** $7\frac{7}{8}$ **3.** $6\frac{3}{4}$ **4.** 14 **5.** A = 11.52 cm^2; P = 14.4 cm **6.** A = 225 m^2; P = 60 m **7.** about 1256 ft^2

7-9 pages 300–302

On Your Own **13.** < **15.** > **17.** Timothy **19.** $\frac{8}{15}, \frac{23}{40}, \frac{7}{12}, \frac{19}{30}$ **23.** B

Mixed Review **1.** 24 **2.** 30 **3.** 90 **4.** 360 **5.** 686 **6.** 424 **7.** π

7-10 pages 303–306

On Your Own **17.** $\frac{113}{200}$ **19.** $\frac{7}{100}$ **21.** $1.\overline{1}$ **23.** $0.4\overline{6}$ **25.** $0.208\overline{3}$ **27.** $3.\overline{36}$ **29.** 0.25 **31.** $\frac{11}{20}$ **33. a.** 0.34, $0.\overline{3}$, 0.32, $0.34\overline{6}$ **b.** $\frac{8}{25}, \frac{1}{3}, \frac{17}{50}, \frac{26}{75}$

Mixed Review **1.** $\frac{2}{3}, \frac{7}{10}, \frac{3}{4}$ **2.** $\frac{1}{6}, \frac{1}{5}, \frac{3}{10}$ **3.** $\frac{32}{10}, 3\frac{3}{8}, \frac{7}{2}$ **4.** $\frac{18}{20}, \frac{27}{30}, \frac{36}{40}$ **5.** $\frac{6}{8}, \frac{9}{12}, \frac{12}{16}$ **6.** Jan \$2.00; Leah \$3.25

Checkpoint **1.** 96 **2.** 504 **3.** 360 **4.** 0.4 **5.** 0.07 **6.** 0.375 **7.** $0.1\overline{6}$ **8.** $\frac{13}{25}$ **9.** $\frac{1}{25}$ **10.** $\frac{3}{4}$ **11.** $15\frac{1}{40}$ **12.** D

7-11 pages 307–309

On Your Own **11.** 8 **13.** 18 muffins **15.** Saturday **23.** 1 h 54 min

Mixed Review **1.** 0.85 **2.** 0.12 **3.** $\frac{12}{25}$ **4.** $\frac{3}{50}$ **5.** $\frac{19}{20}$ **6.** $\frac{19}{125}$ **7.** 1 tricycle, 3 bicycles, 3 unicycles

Wrap Up pages 312–313

1. 1, 3 **2.** 1, 2 **3.** 1, 3, 9 **4.** 1, 3, 5, 9 **5.** 1, 2 **6.** 1, 2, 3, 5, 10 **7.** B **8.** $2 \times 2 \times 2 \times 3 \times 3$ **9.** $2 \times 2 \times 2 \times 3 \times 5$ **10.** 3×11 **11.** $2 \times 2 \times 2 \times 2 \times 5$ **12.** $2 \times 3 \times 3 \times 13$ **13.** $3 \times 5 \times 23$ **14.** 20; 280 **15.** 1; 294 **16.** 3; 72 **17.** 5; 75 **18.** 6; 1260 **19.** 2; 240 **20.** $\frac{8}{9}$ **21.** $\frac{2}{5}$ **22.** $\frac{3}{10}$ **23.** $\frac{3}{8}$ **24.** $\frac{4}{11}$ **25.** $\frac{2}{7}$ **26.** Sample: $\frac{2}{16}, \frac{3}{24}$ **27.** Sample: $\frac{1}{5}, \frac{4}{20}$ **28.** Sample: $\frac{1}{5}, \frac{10}{50}$ **29.** Sample: $\frac{6}{10}, \frac{9}{15}$ **30.** Sample: $\frac{1}{2}, \frac{2}{4}$ **31.** Sample: $\frac{3}{5}, \frac{6}{10}$ **32.** $\frac{19}{4}$ **33.** $4\frac{2}{5}$ **34.** $8\frac{1}{7}$ **35.** $\frac{17}{7}$ **36.** $2\frac{2}{14}$ **37.** $\frac{57}{11}$ **38.** $\frac{35}{36}, 1\frac{3}{4}, 1\frac{7}{9}, 1\frac{5}{6}$ **39.** $\frac{19}{50}$ **40.** $3\frac{7}{8}$ **41.** $2\frac{7}{50}$ **42.** 0.425 **43.** $0.\overline{8}$ **44.** $0.\overline{54}$ **45.** \$39

Getting Ready for Chapter 8 **1.** $\frac{1}{2}$ **2.** 1 **3.** 0 **4.** 0 **5.** $\frac{1}{2}$ **6.** $\frac{1}{2}$

Cumulative Review page 315

1. B **2.** A **3.** B **4.** C **5.** B **6.** C **7.** D **8.** C **9.** C **10.** A **11.** D

CHAPTER 8

8-1 pages 319–321

On Your Own **13.** 10 **15.** $100\frac{1}{2}$ **17.** 4 innings **19.** $\frac{1}{2}$ **21.** 1 ft **23.** $1\frac{1}{2}$ **25.** 3 **27.** 13 **29.** Answers will vary. Sample: $\frac{1}{10}, \frac{2}{10}, \frac{8}{10}$ **33.** 24 ft

Mixed Review **1.** 0.1 **2.** 5.618 **3.** Saturday **4.** 24 **5.** The cost of each juice.

8-2 pages 322–325

On Your Own **17.** $\frac{1}{5} + \frac{3}{5} = \frac{4}{5}$ **19.** $\frac{2}{6} + \frac{3}{6} = \frac{5}{6}$ **21.** $\frac{4}{6} - \frac{1}{6} = \frac{3}{6}$ **23.** $\frac{8}{10}$ **25. a.** $\frac{2}{4}$ tablespoon **b.** $\frac{1}{4}$ cup **27.** no; $\frac{2}{5}$ **29.** no; $\frac{4}{9}$ **31.** no; $\frac{2}{3}$ **33.** yes; $\frac{1}{3}$ **39.** $\frac{5}{10}$ **41.** $\frac{7}{8}$ **43.** $\frac{2}{3}$

Mixed Review **1.** triangular prism; 4; 6; 4 **2.** cube; 6; 12; 8 **3.** 2 **4.** 4 **5.** \$42

8-3 pages 326–329

On Your Own **27.** $\frac{1}{3} - \frac{1}{6} = \frac{1}{6}$ **29.** > **31.** $1\frac{9}{24}$ or $1\frac{3}{8}$ **33.** $\frac{9}{10}$ **35.** $\frac{5}{6}$ **39.** $\frac{1}{10}$ **41.** $\frac{3}{8}$ **43.** no

Mixed Review **1.** $\frac{2}{3}$ **2.** $\frac{1}{9}$ **3.** 3 **4.** 1.91

Problem Solving Practice page 330

1. 19 boxes **3.** 6,000 m **5.** 8:45 A.M.

8-4 pages 331–333

On Your Own **21.** $\frac{5}{16}$; $\frac{21}{64}$; $\frac{1}{4}+\frac{1}{16}+\frac{1}{64}+\frac{1}{256}$; $\frac{85}{256}$ **25.** D; In the eleventh minute, you would receive more than $1\frac{1}{2}$ oz.

Mixed Review **1.** $1\frac{11}{15}$ **2.** $\frac{11}{48}$ **3.** $\overline{CA}$ **4.** $\overline{OB}$, $\overline{OA}$, or $\overline{OC}$ **5.** 47 min 50 s

Checkpoint **1.** $\frac{5}{12}$; $\frac{1}{2}$ **2.** $\frac{4}{5}$; 1 **3.** $\frac{6}{7}$ **4.** $\frac{4}{8}$; $\frac{1}{2}$ **5.** $\frac{3}{9}$; $\frac{1}{3}$ **6.** $\frac{1}{12}$ **7.** $\frac{38}{45}$ **8.** $\frac{9}{8}$ or $1\frac{1}{8}$ **9.** $\frac{9}{20}$ **10.** $\frac{8}{39}$ **11. a.** $\frac{6}{25}$; $\frac{31}{125}$ **b.** $\frac{1}{5}+\frac{1}{25}+\frac{1}{125}+\frac{1}{625}$; $\frac{156}{625}$

8-5 pages 334–337

On Your Own **19.** coyote; $\frac{1}{4}$ in. **21.** 4 **23.** $4\frac{2}{3}$ **25.** Black, Red, White, Norway **27.** White and Red; Red and Black **29.** $3\frac{1}{8}$ **31.** $4\frac{7}{15}$ **33.** $3\frac{1}{4}$ **35.** $13\frac{7}{12}$ **37.** \$77.50 **39.** $10\frac{1}{4}$ in. **41.** $3\frac{1}{2}$; $2\frac{1}{3}$

Mixed Review **1.** $\frac{7}{5}$; $\frac{9}{5}$; $\frac{11}{5}$ **2.** $\frac{7}{10}$; $\frac{3}{5}$; $\frac{1}{2}$ **3.** equilateral **4.** isosceles **5.** \$7.25

8-6 pages 338–340

On Your Own **15.** 80 gifts **17.** yes **19.** 30 s **21.** 230 ft

Mixed Review **1.** $6\frac{9}{14}$ **2.** $2\frac{1}{2}$

3.

```
x       x
x   x   x
x   x   x   x   x
A   B   C   D   F
```

4. 8 students **5.** 28 handshakes

Practice page 341

1. $1\frac{1}{2}$ **3.** $\frac{1}{2}$ **5.** 8 in. **7.** $3\frac{1}{2}$ in. **9.** 10 in. **11.** $\frac{4}{8}$; $\frac{1}{2}$ **13.** $\frac{2}{4}$; $\frac{1}{2}$ **15.** $\frac{1}{10}$ **17.** $\frac{73}{168}$ **19.** $\frac{17}{60}$ **21.** $1\frac{1}{10}$ **23.** $8\frac{1}{6}$ **25.** $2\frac{11}{12}$ **27.** $9\frac{1}{16}$ **29.** $15\frac{1}{8}$ **31.** $1\frac{1}{2}$ mi

8-7 pages 342–345

On Your Own **25.** 18 **27.** 60 **29.** $119\frac{3}{4}$ in. **33.** 10 **35.** 4 **37.** $13\frac{7}{8}$ **39.** $\frac{1}{15}$ **41.** 90 out of 191 million **43.** $1\frac{4}{15}$ million; about $\frac{3}{50}$

Mixed Review **1.** 26 **2.** 18 **3.** 4 **5.** 744 times

8-8 pages 346–349

On Your Own **27.** 6 pieces **29.** $1\frac{7}{10}$ mi **31.** McKinley **33.** 2 **35.** $1\frac{1}{8}$ **37.** $1\frac{1}{2}$ **39.** $\frac{2}{15}$ **41.** 12 **43.** 24 **47.** 16 **49.** 24 pieces **51.** $6\frac{2}{3}$ **53.** $2\frac{5}{7}$ **55.** $\frac{2}{5}$ **57.** $1\frac{5}{7}$

Mixed Review **1.** 0.05 **2.** 0.047 **3.** $11\frac{1}{5}$ **4.** 28 **5.** 3 students

Checkpoint **1.** 8 pieces **2.** $\frac{8}{7}$; $\frac{1}{4}$; 3; $\frac{6}{13}$ **3.** $\frac{112}{125}$ **4.** $\frac{20}{27}$ **5.** $2\frac{1}{4}$ **6.** 6 **7.** $\frac{1}{9}$ **8.** $1\frac{5}{9}$ **9.** $16\frac{2}{3}$ **10.** $1\frac{11}{15}$ **11.** C

8-9 pages 350–352

On Your Own **15.** 9,240 **17.** $1\frac{1}{2}$ **19.** 34 **21.** yes **23.** > **25.** < **27.** $6{,}665\frac{1}{8}$ in. **29. a.** 45,000,000 gallons **b.** 3,000 T **31.** 3 yd 2 ft

Mixed Review **1.** 9 **2.** 12 **3.** $3\frac{1}{2}$ **4.** $\frac{15}{49}$ **5.** \$17

Wrap Up pages 176–177

1. $\frac{1}{2}$ **2.** $1\frac{1}{2}$ **3.** $4\frac{1}{2}$ **4.** 6 **5.** $\frac{1}{5} + \frac{1}{2} = \frac{7}{10}$

6. $\frac{5}{6} - \frac{2}{6} = \frac{3}{6} = \frac{1}{2}$ **7.** $\frac{5}{9}$ **8.** $2\frac{1}{2}$ **9.** $1\frac{1}{12}$ **10.** $1\frac{2}{7}$

11. $\frac{11}{16}$ **12.** $3\frac{13}{20}$ **13.** $5\frac{1}{24}$ **14.** $\frac{1}{15}$

15.

$\frac{1}{3}$	$\frac{1}{3}$
$\frac{1}{3} + \frac{1}{6}$	$\frac{3}{6}$
$\frac{1}{3} + \frac{1}{6} + \frac{1}{12}$	$\frac{7}{12}$
$\frac{1}{3} + \frac{1}{6} + \frac{1}{12} + \frac{1}{24}$	$\frac{15}{24}$

The denominator is multiplied by 2 each time. The numerator increases by 2^n.

16. $\frac{1}{2}$ **17.** $\frac{1}{12}$ **18.** $8\frac{1}{8}$ **19.** $\frac{19}{20}$ **20.** 1 **21.** $24\frac{6}{7}$

22. 6 **23.** $2\frac{1}{2}$ **24. b.** living room: 8 ft × 10 ft, dining room: 8 ft × 8 ft **c.** living room: 80 ft^2, dining room: 64 ft^2, hallway: 72 ft^2, total area: 216 ft^2 **25.** 20 yd **26.** 96 pancakes

Getting Ready for Chapter 9 **1.** 7 **2.** 6 **3.** 18 **4.** 2

Cumulative Review page 359

1. A **2.** D **3.** A **4.** C **5.** B **6.** B **7.** D **8.** C **9.** C **10.** A **11.** D **12.** D **13.** A

CHAPTER 9

9-1 pages 363–364

On Your Own **9.** 2 to 1, 2 : 1, $\frac{2}{1}$ **11.** 3 to 2, 3 : 2, $\frac{3}{2}$ **13.** 5 : 7 **21.** hexagon to triangle **23.** triangle to trapezoid or rhombus to hexagon

Mixed Review **1.** About 25.12 cm **2.** About 50.24 cm^2 **3.** 2 ft 4 in. **4.** 1 ft **5.** Answers may vary. Samples: $\frac{4}{6}, \frac{6}{9}$ **6.** Answers may vary. Samples: $\frac{6}{10}, \frac{9}{15}$ **7.** 5 birds and 3 squirrels

9-2 pages 365–368

On Your Own **15.** $\frac{1}{2}, \frac{5}{10}, \frac{100}{200}$ **17.** 4 : 7, 16 : 28, 24 : 42 **19.** 10 **21.** 2 **23.** 21 **27.** $\frac{2}{3}$ **29.** 0 **31.** 25 mi/da **33.** 2 pears/child **35.** 12 players/team **37.** $\frac{2}{5}$ **39.** $\frac{3}{4}$

Mixed Review **1.** $\frac{6}{15}$ **2.** $3\frac{9}{16}$ **3. a.** 3 : 1 **b.** 1 : 6 **4.** 2 dimes, 1 nickel

9-3 pages 369–372

On Your Own **15.** yes **17.** yes **19.** 112.5 **21.** 9 **23.** Sample answer: $\frac{2}{6} = \frac{5}{15}$ **27.** 27 coaches **29.** about 112 people

Mixed Review **1.** 9 **2.** 26 **3.** 28 **4.** 28 : 70, 42 : 105 **5.** $\frac{3}{4}, \frac{12}{16}$ **6.** 2 to 5, 16 to 40 **7.** Julio: roast beef, Stella: chicken, Ted: tuna

Checkpoint **1.** C **2.** $\frac{2}{3}, \frac{20}{30}$ **3.** 10 to 17, 40 to 68 **4.** 9 : 20, 36 : 80 **5.** $\frac{46}{88}, \frac{69}{132}$ **6.** $\frac{14}{19}$ **7.** 11 : 30 **8.** $\frac{1}{3}$ **9.** 9 : 19 **10.** \$.89/taco **11.** \$.35/battery **12.** no **13.** yes **14.** no **15.** no **16.** 108 in.

9-4 pages 373–375

On Your Own **9.** 80 adult tickets **11.** Bob **13.** Sums and placement of digits may vary. **15.** 24 **17.** 13 **19.** 14 **21.** ↑← or ←↑ **23.** 30

Mixed Review **1.** 55 **2.** 27 **3.** F **4.** T **5.** T **6.** F **7.** 6:58 A.M.

Problem Solving Practice page 376

1. 111, 112 **3.** \$4.89 **5.** $M = 1, F = 9, A = 0$ **7.** Marla, Jon, Noel, Dana **9.** 75 cm

9-5 pages 377–379

Mixed Review **1.** 22 ft **2.** 28 ft **3.** 60 **4.** 125 **5.** 8, 13

9-6 pages 380–383

On Your Own **9.** 12 m **11.** 120 cm

Mixed Review **1.** $>$ **2.** $<$ **3.** $\angle D, \angle E, \angle F$ **4.** EF **5.** $\frac{27}{100}$ **6.** $\frac{56}{100}$ **7.** 140.8 ft/sec

9-7 pages 384–386

On Your Own **15.** 31% **17.** 11% **19.** 4% **21.** 33% **23.** 25% **25.** 1% **27.** \$0.05; \$0.50 **29.** 25%

Mixed Review **1.** $1\frac{5}{16}$ **2.** $\frac{3}{8}$ **3.** 2 m × 5 m **4.** 2.4 m **5.** 0.25 **6.** 0.5625 **7.** 13 students

9-8 pages 387–389

On Your Own **11.** $\frac{11}{50}$; 0.22 **13.** 0.88; 88% **15.** 0.8; 80% **17.** D **19. a.** 25%; 34%; 44%, 55%; 69%, 77% **c.** Sample answer: about 87%

Mixed Review **1.** 2197 **2.** 729 **3.** 40% **4.** 92% **5.** \$10.50

Practice page 390

1. $\frac{5}{34}$, 5 : 34, 5 to 34 **3.** $\frac{5}{3}$, 5 : 3, 5 to 3 **5.** $\frac{1}{4}$ **7.** $\frac{3}{7}$ **9.** $\frac{1}{3}$ **11.** Answers may vary. **13.** 21 **15.** 5 **17.** 60 **19.** 1.3 m **21.** 55%, $\frac{11}{20}$, 0.55 **23.** 25%, $\frac{1}{4}$, 0.25 **25.** 20%, $\frac{1}{5}$, 0.2

9-9 pages 391–394

On Your Own **25.** Sample answers: **a.** \$70 **b.** \$1105 **c.** \$262.50 **27.** c **a.** \$.63 **b.** \$.48 **c.** \$.72 **37.** rounding to \$16, \$9.20 each

Mixed Review **1.** $\frac{11}{15}$ **2.** $\frac{5}{24}$ **3.** 25% **4.** 75% **5.** $\frac{2}{5}$ **6.** $\frac{17}{20}$ **7.** 69, sample method: truncate $1{,}000 \div 13 \approx 76$, and subtract the no. of 2-digit numbers, $76 - 7 = 69$

9-10 pages 395–398

On Your Own **5.** 393 **7.** 5.6 **9.** 51.8 **11.** 8.64 **13.** 65.34 **15.** \$380 **17.** about 39 **19.** about 7 **21.** Answers may vary. Consonants also occur. **23.** 647 children and teenagers **25.** males—about 220; females—about 319

Mixed Review **1.** $<$ **2.** $<$ **3.** Sample answer: \$.60 **4.** Sample answer: \$2.33 **5.** 120 **6.** 135 **7.** 60 singers

Checkpoint **1.** 8, 9, 10 **2.** $x = 10$ **3.** 262.5 km **8.** 75% **9.** 45% **10.** 67% **11.** 60% **12.** C **13.** 41.76 **14.** 35.26 **15.** 3.2

9-11 pages 399–401

Mixed Review **1.** $\frac{15}{16}$ **2.** $\frac{12}{15}$ **3.** 212.3 **4.** 19.14 **5.** Answers may vary.

Wrap Up pages 402–403

1. 45 to 100, $\frac{45}{100}$, 45 : 100 **2.** three tapes: \$1.99, two tapes: \$1.88; The tape in the package of three. **3.** 21 **4.** 27 **5.** 3 **6.** 16 **7.** 3 **8.** 9 **10.** 24 ft **11.** 1.5 m **12.** 0.65, $\frac{13}{20}$ **13.** about \$70 **14.** C **15.** 30 **16.** 4.37 **17.** 48 **18.** 23.5 **19.** \$.80 **21.** 11 small feeders

Getting Ready for Chapter 10 **1.** 100

Cumulative Review page 407

1. B **2.** C **3.** B **4.** C **5.** D **6.** A **7.** B **8.** C **9.** A **10.** D

CHAPTER 10

10-1 pages 411–413

On Your Own **15.** the game seems fair **17.** unfair; There are 15 possible prime sums and 21 possible composite sums.

Mixed Review **1.** $1\frac{23}{170}$ **2.** $1\frac{7}{20}$ **3.**

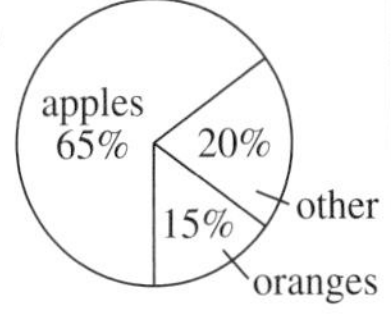

4. 16, 22, 29 **5.** 1.95, 2.25, 2.55

10-2 pages 414–416

On Your Own **19.** No; two non-adjacent squares would always be left uncovered **21.** Use a simulation. Answers may vary.

Mixed Review

1. 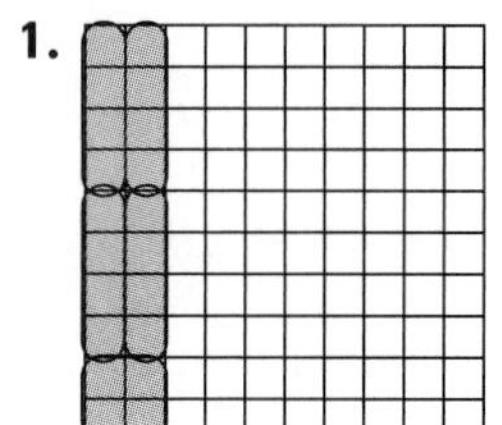 **2.** 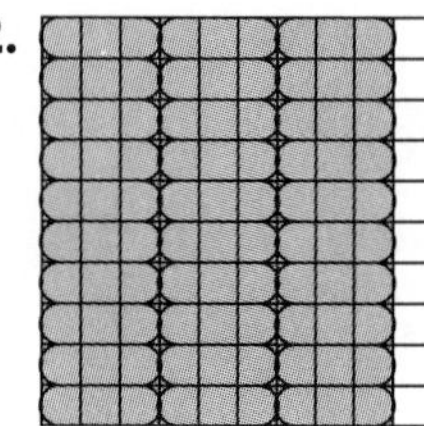

5. 18

10-3 pages 417–419

On Your Own **13.** about 17 **15.** unfair

Mixed Review **1.** $\frac{2}{3}, \frac{4}{6}$ **2.** $\frac{1}{3}, \frac{2}{6}$ **3.** Nov. 1 **4.** $\frac{8}{125}$ **5.** 14

Problem Solving Practice page 420

1. 1768 **2.** about 1,384.74 sq ft **3. a.** about 525 **b.** $551.25 **6.** 120

10-4 pages 421–424

On Your Own **21.** 0, 0.0, 0% **23.** $\frac{1}{2}$, 0.5, 50% **25.** 5 **29.** Answers may vary. Sample: A, B, E, G, C, D, F

Mixed Review **1.** 30 m. **2.** 11 ft **3.** They all have an equal chance. **4.** no

Checkpoint **1. a.** $\frac{1}{5}$, 0.2, 20% **b.** $\frac{3}{5}$, 0.6, 60% **c.** $\frac{2}{5}$, 0.4, 40% **d.** $\frac{4}{5}$, 0.8, 80% **2. a.** $\frac{7}{15}$ **b.** $\frac{8}{15}$ **3.** D

10-5 pages 425–428

On Your Own **15.** 9 **17.** 40

Mixed Review **1.** 1,485 **2.** 24,003 **3.** $\frac{1}{3}$ **4.** $\frac{3}{7}$ **5.** 580

10-6 pages 429–431

On Your Own **13.** Yes; The second spin is independent of the first spin. **17.** $\frac{1}{10}$ **19. a.** 2 **b.** 6 **c.** 12 **d.** 72 **21.** B

Mixed Review **1.** 45° **2.** 130°

4. $\frac{1}{4}$ **5.** 10 **6.** 2

10-7 pages 432–434

On Your Own **15.** 120 **17. a.** 5040 **b.** $\frac{1}{5{,}040}$ **19.** 5,040

Mixed Review **1.** 17 **2.** 24 **3.** $\frac{1}{12}$ **4.** $\frac{1}{36}$ **5.** 28, 13

Checkpoint **1. a.**

B < H, T
R < H, T
Y < H, T

b. $\frac{1}{6}$ **2.** 12 **3.** $\frac{16}{49}$ **4.** 720

Practice page 435

1. unfair **3.** $\frac{3}{5}$ **5.** $\frac{1}{2}$ **7.** $\frac{11}{12}$ **9.** $\frac{3}{4}$ **13.** 120 **15.** no **17.** yes **19.** 39,916,800

10-8 pages 436–439

On Your Own **13.** no; no **15.** yes; possibly **17. a.** 47% **b.** about 93

Mixed Review **1.** 23 **2.** 21 **3.** 5,040 **4.** 24 **5.** 30

Wrap Up pages 440–441

1. a.

	1	2	3	4	5	6
1	2	3	4	5	6	7
2	3	4	5	6	7	8
3	4	5	6	7	8	9
4	5	6	7	8	9	10
5	6	7	8	9	10	11
6	7	8	9	10	11	12

2. a. $\frac{3}{10}$; $\frac{7}{10}$ **b.** unfair **4.** $\frac{2}{9}$ **5. a.** $\frac{2}{11}$ **b.** 0 **c.** $\frac{4}{11}$ **6.** 240 cars **7.** $\frac{13}{64}$ **8.** 120 **9.** no; no

Getting Ready for Chapter 11 **1.** negative **2.** positive **3.** negative **4.** positive

Cumulative Review page 443

1. C **2.** B **3.** D **4.** D **5.** B **6.** C **7.** A **8.** A **9.** B **10.** D

CHAPTER 11

11-1 pages 449–452

On Your Own **25.** Answers may vary. Sample: +210,000 **27. a.** teacher aide, cook, lawyer, bank teller, typist, farmer **29.** −3 **31.** −8 **33.** 8 **35.** 212 **37.** −2 **39.** −7 **41.** −89°C, −68°C, −63°C, −59°C, −33°C, −24°C, −22°C **43.** −8 **45.** −6

Mixed Review **1.** $8\frac{5}{6}$ **2.** $1\frac{5}{24}$ **4.** 43% **5.** 110

11-2 pages 453–454

On Your Own

11. Sample:

15. −2 **17.** −6 **19. a.** 64 ways **b.** −6, −5, −4, −3, −2, 1, 0, 1, 2, 3, 4, 5, 6

Mixed Review **1.** 60 **2.** 56 **3.** 4 **4.** −21

11-3 pages 455–458

On Your Own **21.** −15 **23.** 0 **25.** 5 **27.** = **29.** = **31.** A **33.** −5 yd **37.** −2 **39.** −3

Mixed Review **1.** −3 **2.** 5 **3.** 4 in.; 20 ft **4.** 80 in^2; 48 in.

Checkpoint

43. > **45.** −7 −6 −5 −4 −3 −2 −1 0 1 2 3 4 5

47. 6, −6 **49.** −2, 2 **51.** −5 **53.** 0

11-4 pages 459–462

On Your Own **15.** −5 **17.** 11 **19.** 9 **21.** = **23.** = **25.** 6°C **27.** 24°C **29.** −5, −11, −17 **33.** −10 **35.** −6 **37.** 7:30 A.M. **39.** 9:00 P.M.

Mixed Review **1.** positive **2.** positive **3.** 2 × 2 × 3 × 5 **4.** 2 × 2 × 2 × 5 × 31 **5.** 11

Practice page 463

7. −12, −7, 1, 5 **9.** −76, −73, −72, 71, 72 **11.** 3 **13.** −6 **15.** > **17.** > **19.** 0 **21.** 5 **23.** Answers may vary. **25.** Answers may vary. **27.** −7 **29.** 0 **31.** −21 **33.** −6 **35.** > **37.** = **39.** < **41.** −5 yd

11-5 pages 464–466

On Your Own **13.** 981 mi **15.** $15.2 million **17.** 2500 **19.** 50 mi **21.** 61

Mixed Review **1.** 7 **2.** 2 **3.** 18% **4.** 86% **5.** 13 and 21

11-6 pages 467–470

On Your Own **21.** I **23.** III **27. a.** Estimates may vary. about 30°N, 65°W **b.** about 20°S, 140°E **33.** City Hall

Mixed Review **1.** not enough information to solve **2.** 82°F **3.** 0.45; $\frac{9}{20}$ **4.** 0.375; 37.5% **5.** $\frac{16}{25}$

Problem Solving Practice page 471

1. 300 m **3.** 56% **5.** $.44

11-7 pages 472–475

On Your Own **11.** (−2, 4) **13.** 3 units to the left and 7 units up **15.** (4, −3) **17.** translation, 4 units right, 3 units up **21. b.** triangle **c.** (2, 6), (8, 6), (4, 1) **d.** 15 sq. units; 15 sq. units

Mixed Review **1.** IV **2.** I **3.** $.45 **4.** $6.80 **5.** 7

Checkpoint **23.** 597 **25.** G **27.** A **29.** (4, −1) **31.** (−1, 0) **33.** 128 **35.** 1996

11-8 pages 476–479

On Your Own **17.** −7 **19.** 0 **21.** 47 **23. a.** Mon.: $9; Tues.: $18; Wed.: −$9; Thurs.: $17; Fri.: −$12; Sat.: −$1; Sun.: −$17 **25.** B2 + C2 = D2; B3 + C3 = D3; B4 + C4 = D4; B5 + C5 = D5 **27.** Balances 2: −$12,256; 3: $984; 4: $194; 5: −$1196 Totals Income: $15,931; Expenses: −$18,205; Balance: −$2,274

Mixed Review **1.** 1092 **2.** 2070 **3.** A(−4, 5) B(3, 9) C(3, 5) **4.** A(2, 1) B(9, 5) C(9, 1)

Wrap Up pages 480–481

1. −7 **2. a.** −7 **b.** −1 **c.** 8 **d.** 14 **5.** > **6.** > **7.** < **8.** < **9.** < **10.** −1 **11.** 3 **12.** 1 **13.** 2 **14.** 5 **15.** −7 **16.** 8 **17.** −10 **18.** *C* **19.** *G* **20.** *N* **21.** *A* **22.** *H*23. *K* **24.** (−3, −2) **25.** (1, −3) **26.** (0, −4) **27.** (−2, 2) **28.** (4, 0) **29.** (−1, −4) **30. a.** (−4, 1); (1, 8); (1, 1) **b.** They are congruent. **31. a.** Jan.: $486, profit; Feb.: $2,000, profit; March: −$266, loss; April: $673, profit **b.** scale from 0 to 2,000; intervals of 500.

Cumulative Review page 485

1. A **2.** C **3.** B **4.** C **5.** A **6.** D **7.** C **8.** B **9.** C **10.** D

Extra Practice 1 page 486

1. a.

x	x		x
x	x	x	x
x	x	x	x
1	2	3	4

b. 2.5; 4

3.

num	tally	total
100	||||	4
200	||	2
300	|	1
400	||	2

mean: 213
median: 201
mode: 102

5. bar graph **7.** circle graph
11. about 131

Extra Practice 2 page 487

1. Answers may vary. Sample: ∠*BHC*, ∠*BHD*, ∠*CHD* **3.** Sample: *E, D, C* **5.** 180° **7.** 38° **9.** 111° **13.** equilateral **15.** obtuse **17.** acute
19.

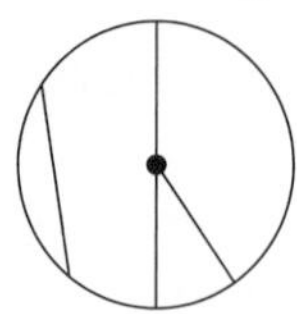

Extra Practice 3 page 488

1. **5.**

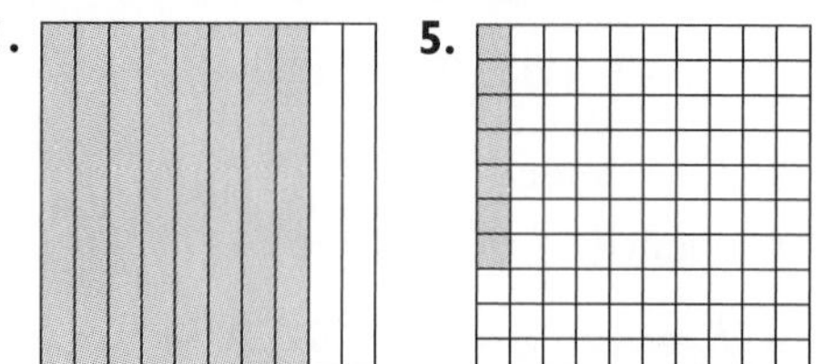

7. eight tenths **9.** thirty hundredths **11.** thirty-three and five hundredths **13.** 0.57 **15.** 0.142 **17.** 9 tenths **19.** 9 hundredths **21.** 9 hundredths **23.** > **25.** = **27.** 5 **29.** 21 **31.** 5 **33.** 5 **35. a.** m **b.** cm **c.** km **37.** 2005

Extra Practice 4 page 489

1. 28 **3.** 96 **5.** 7 **7.** 17 **9.** 18 **11.** 10 **13.** 45 **15.** 10 **17.** 546 **19.** 396 **21.** 0.0245 **23.** 0.237 **25.** 12 **27.** 0.04 **29.** 1.6 **31.** 8.6 **33.** Cannot tell which type of ticket she bought. Do not need to know how much programs cost.

Extra Practice 5 page 490

1. 256, 1024, 4096; Begin with 1 and multiply by 4. **3.** 8.3, 10.3, 12.3; Begin with 0.3 and add 2 to each preceding number. **5.** 4, 7 **7.** 7, 4 **9.** 6 **11.** 195,312.5 **13.** 49 **15.** 40 **17.** 2*p* **19.** 7 **21.** 136 **23.** 17.8 **25.** 29.2 **27.** 200 **29.** 40,000

Extra Practice 6 page 491

1. 52.25 $in.^2$ **3.** 144 cm^2 **5.** 6 cm **7.** $C = 78$; 81.68; $A = 507$; 530.93 **9.** $C = 180$; 188.5; $A = 2700$; 2827.43 **11. a.** pentagonal prism **b.** 7, 15, 10 **13.** triangular prism; 66 sq. units **15.** 4 triangles, 4 quadrilaterals, 1 pentagon; 125 points

Extra Practice 7 page 492

1. 1, 2, 3, 9 **3.** 1, 2, 3, 5, 9, 10 **5.** 1 **7.** composite **9.** prime **11.** prime **13.** 4 **15.** 8 **17.** 5 **19.** $\frac{4}{6}, \frac{6}{9}$; $0.\overline{6}$ **21.** $\frac{4}{10}, \frac{6}{15}$; 0.4 **23.** $\frac{2}{4}, \frac{3}{6}$; 0.5

25. 5, $\frac{6}{7}$ **27.** 10, $\frac{4}{5}$ **29.** 6, $\frac{1}{10}$ **31.** $3\frac{1}{4}$ **33.** $1\frac{3}{7}$

35. $\frac{15}{7}$ **37.** $\frac{100}{9}$ **39.** $\frac{81}{8}$ **41.** 6; 531, 135, 351, 513, 153, 315; yes

Extra Practice 8 page 493

1. $\frac{5}{6}$ **3.** $\frac{5}{12}$ **5.** $\frac{57}{56}$ or $1\frac{1}{56}$ **7.** $\frac{49}{6}$ or $8\frac{1}{6}$ **9.** $\frac{142}{15}$ or $9\frac{7}{15}$

11. $\frac{147}{16}$ or $9\frac{3}{16}$ **13.** $\frac{1}{3}$ **15.** $\frac{228}{5}$ or $45\frac{3}{5}$ **17.** 2 **19.** $\frac{32}{63}$

21. $\frac{2}{5}$ **23.** $\frac{45}{14}$ or $3\frac{3}{14}$ **25.** 5 **27.** 1 **33.** $\frac{4}{3}$ **35.** 3

37. $\frac{3}{13}$ **41.** 60,000 mi

Extra Practice 9 page 494

1. $\frac{1}{2}$ **3.** $\frac{1}{4}$ **5.** $\frac{1}{4}$ **7.** 128 **9.** 90 **11.** 2 **13.** 9 **15.** 60

17. 40% **19.** 90% **21.** 30% **23.** 6% **25.** 17%

27. 80% **29.** $\frac{33}{50}$ **31.** $\frac{6}{25}$ **33.** $\frac{14}{25}$ **35.** 0.7 **37.** 0.2

39. 0.6 **41.** 4 **43.** 17.5 **45.** $2.63 **47.** 90

49. $\frac{13}{20}$, 65%, 0.65

Extra Practice 10 page 495

1. Yes, it is fair **3.** 0.4

5.

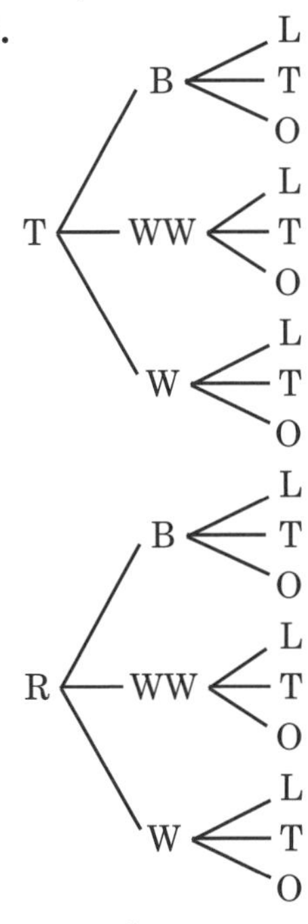

7. random

Extra Practice 11 page 496

1. −7, −6, 6, 7 **3.** −7, 1, 15, 71 **5.** $<$ **7.** $>$

9. $=$ **11.** $>$ **13.** (3, −3) **15.** (−3, 3) **17.** *G*

19. I **21.** 3rd quadrant **23.** (3, 3) **25.** 14

27. 125 **29.** scale: −35 to 25; intervals: 10

31. Mars: about $10\frac{1}{2}$ times; Earth: 20 times

Acknowledgments

Cover Design
Martucci Studio and L. Christopher Valente

Front Cover Photo Martucci Studio

Back Cover Photo Ken O'Donoghue

Book Design DECODE, Inc.

Technical Illustration ANCO/Outlook

Illustration

Anco/OUTLOOK: 15, 118, 119, 121, 122, 128, 129, 130, 133, 141, 142, 145, 162, 200, 230 T, 231, 264, 265, 277, 287, 301, 302, 319, 325, 331, 332, 333, 336, 352, 365, 376, 380, 382, 384, 412, 431, 433, 450, 456, 460, 464, 470, 476, 477, 478, 481, 484

Eliot Bergman: 195

Arnold Bombay: 28, 118, 172, 426, 451

DECODE, Inc.: vii TL, viii TL, ix TL, x TL, xi TL, xii TL, xiii TL, xiv TL, xv TL, xvi TL, xvii TL, 2 TL, 34 B, 35 BL, 35 C, 35 TL, 40, 88 C, 89 B, 89 C, 89 T, 92 TL, 134,B, 135 BR, 135 T, 135,BL, 138 TR, 178 B, 179 B, 179 TL, 179 TL, 182 TL, 222 B, 223 CL, 223 CR, 223 T, 226 TL, 228, 268 B, 269 B, 269 CR, 269 T, 272 TL, 312 BR, 313, 313 B, 313 C, 316 TL, 318, 356 B, 357 R, 357 TL, 360 TL, 380 TR, 404 B, 405 T, 405,BR, 408 TL, 442 B, 443 C, 443 T, 446 TL, 482 B, 483 B, 483 TL, 483 TR

Jim DeLapine: 41, 47, 54, 99, 279, 288

Donald Doyle: 384

Horizon Design/John Sanderson: 229, 230 B, 329, 462

Dave Joly: 455, 457

Rick Lovell: viii TR, 38–39, 126, 205

Scott MacNEILL: 21, 164, 174, 397, 398, 413, 461

Steve Moscowitz: 63, 73, 78, 275, 292, 338, 364, 400

Matthew Pippin: 242, 256, 259, 411, 422

Precision Graphics: vii TR, x TR, xi TR, xiii TR, xv TR, xvi TR, xvii TR, 2–3, 138 C, 139 L, 182-183, 272-273, 274, 317, 361, 408–409, 409 T, 446–447, 447 T

Pat Rossi: 25, 100, 186, 199, 212, 337

Schneck-DePippo Graphics: 59, 75, 82, 84, 208

Schneck-DePippo Graphics and Anco/OUTLOOK: 49, 59, 75, 185, 186, 187, 196, 201, 202, 210

Ned Shaw: xv B, 13, 105, 112, 113, 173, 200, 219, 241, 280, 289, 377, 378, 392

DAYS OF THUNDER™, 299; drawing courtesy of Paramount Parks. DAYS OF THUNDER is a trademark of Paramount Pictures

Photography

Front Matter: i, ii, iii, Martucci Studio; **iv–v,** Bill DeSimone Photography; **vii BL,** C.C. Lockwood/Cactus Productions; **viii TR,** Josef Beck/FPG; **ix TR,** PH Photo; **x L,** Lee Celano/Sipa Press; **xii L,** R. Ian Lloyd/Stock Market; **xii TR,** Steve Greenberg Photography; **xiv TR,** Mike Powell/Allsport; **xiv L,** William R. Sallaz/duomo; **xvi L,** PH Photo.

Chapter One: 4, Ken O'Donoghue; **7,** Courtesy, The Franklin D. Roosevelt Library; **9,** Museum of the American Indian; **12,** C.C. Lockwood/Cactus Clyde Productions; **16,** Dan McCoy/Rainbow; **17,** The Metropolitan Museum of Art, Rogers Fund, 1903, Photograph by Schecter Lee; **18,** Russ Lappa; **19,** Carol Halebian/The Gamma Liaison Network; **23,** Bob Burch/Bruce Coleman, Inc.; **30,** A. Tannenbaum/Sygma; **31,** Christopher Brown/Stock Boston; **35,** David Young-Wolf/PhotoEdit.

Chapter Two: 43, Steven E. Sutton/© duomo; **45,** Ken O'Donoghue; **46,** S. N. Nielsen/Bruce Coleman, Inc.; **50,** Courtesy, Jay E. Frick; **55,** Rob Crandall/Stock Boston; **57,** Ken O'Donoghue; **58 both,** The Granger Collection; **59,** Dr. Jeremy Burgess/Science Photo Library/Photo Researchers, Inc.; **60,** © Staller Studios; **61,** Raphael Gaillarde/Gamma Liaison; **65,** Josef Beck/FPG International; **70,** Bryce Flynn/Stock Boston; **71,** J. Messerschmidt/Bruce Coleman, Inc.; **74,** John Shaw/Bruce Coleman, Inc.; **75,** © Boltin Picture Library; **77,** Philippe Sion/The Image Bank; **81,** The Granger Collection; **82,** Reproduced with permission from *Geometry in Our World*; **85,** Courtesy, Roma Tile Company, Watertown, MA., photo by Ken O'Donoghue; **89,** Sybil Shackman/Monkmeyer Press.

Chapter Three: 92 BL, Annie Hunter; **92,** Courtesy, Prentice Hall; **94,** Ken O'Donoghue; **96,** Photo by Gary Gengozian, Fort Payne, AL.; **102,** Louis Goldman/Photo Researchers, Inc.; **107, 109,** The Granger Collection; **111,** © Jerry Jacka Photography; **114,** Courtesy, Paramount's Great America; **115,** The National Museum of Photography, Film & Television/The Science Museum; **116,** Ken Levine/Allsport; **117,** UPI/Bettmann; **120,** Paula Friedland; **122,** Robb Kendrick/National Geographic Society; **125,** Bob Daemmrich/The Image Works; **128,** Lawrence Migdale; **130,** Courtesy, Evin Demirel; **131,** © NASA (Dan McCoy)/Rainbow; **132,** Annie Hunter.

Chapter Four: 140, Mark Thayer; **143,** D. Mainzer Photography, Inc.; **144,** Richard Hutchings/Photo Researchers, Inc.; **146,** Willie Hill, Jr./Stock Boston; **148,** The Bettmann Archive; **150,** Arthur Grace/Stock Boston; **152,** The Granger Collection; **153,** Derek Berwin/The Image Bank; **155,** Richard J. Green/Photo Researchers, Inc.; **158,** Lee Celano/Sipa Press; **159,** Hans Reinhard/Bruce Coleman, Inc.; **161,** Bob Daemmrich/Stock Boston; **164,** Robert Maier/Animals Animals; **169,** Courtesy, Ringling Brothers, Barnum and Bailey; **171 L,** © M.M. Heaton; **171 R,** The Granger Collection; **174,** Courtesy, Justin Rankin; **175,** Ken O'Donoghue; **179,** Tony Freeman/PhotoEdit.

Chapter Five: **184,** David Young-Wolff/PhotoEdit; **186,** The Science Museum; **187,** ESA/Phototake; **188,** The Science Museum, London; **190,** Courtesy, Katherine Shell; **191 both,** Lee Boltin; **192,** Kindra Clineff; **193,** The Granger Collection; **198,** Mary Evans Picture Library; **199,** Wolfgang Kaehler; **204,** Peter Morenus/Cornell University Photo; **208,** Lon Photography/NFL Photos; **209,** Rosanne Olson; **214,** Association for Women in Mathematics; **216 both,** Mark Greenberg/Visions; **218,** UPI/Bettmann; **223,** Bob Daemmrich/The Image Works.

Chapter Six: **229,** Steve Greenberg; **232,** Solomon D. Butcher Collection/Nebraska State Historical Society; **233,** The Bettmann Archive; **234,** Comstock; **236,** R. Ian Lloyd/TSM; **238,** V. Wilkinson/Valan Photos; **239,** Abe Frajndlich/Sygma; **245,** Mary Evans Picture Library; **247,** Jock Montgomery/Bruce Coleman, Inc., **249,** Museo de Anthropologia, Mexica City, Mexico/Superstock; **251 L,** Hazel Hankin/Stock Boston; **251 R,** Kunio Owaki/The Stock Market; **252,** J. Messerschmidt/The Stock Market; **253 TL,** Gordon R. Gainer/The Stock Market; **253 TR,** Bill Gallery/Stock Boston; **253 BL,** Halle Flygare Photos LTD/Bruce Coleman, Inc.; **253 BR,** Peter Campbell/The Bettmann Archive; **254 T,** Rene Burri/Magnum Photos; **254 B,** Courtesy, Jane Broussard; **255,** Laurence Gould - Oxford Scientific Films/Earth Scenes; **258,** Debra P. Hershkowitz/Bruce Coleman, Inc.; **260,** Annie Hunter; **264,** Mike Moreland/Custom Medical Stock Photo; **268,** Lawrence Migdale/Stock Boston.

Chapter Seven: **275,** Norman Owen Tomalin/Bruce Coleman, Inc.; **276,** Scala/Art Resource; **282,** Ken O'Donoghue; **283,** E. Adams/Sygma; **286,** Kent Wood/Peter Arnold, Inc.; **290,** T. Campion/Sygma; **294,** Eddie Hironaka/The Image Bank; **297,** CNRI/Science Photo Library/Photo Researchers, Inc.; **298,** Courtesy, Stephen Horel; **305,** NASA; **308,** AP Photo/Wide World; **309,** Emerson/NARAS/Sygma; **312,** David R. Frazier/Photo Researchers, Inc.

Chapter Eight: **316,** Mike Powell/Allsport; **320,** Jim Gund/Allsport; **321,** Wendell Metzen/Bruce Coleman, Inc.; **323,** Ken O'Donoghue; **325,** Jean-Pierre/Sygma; **328,** E.R. Degginger/Bruce Coleman, Inc.; **330,** William R. Sallaz/© duomo; **335,** K&K Ammann/Bruce Coleman, Inc.; **336,** Lynne M. Stone/Bruce Coleman, Inc.; **339,** The Granger Collection; **344,** Bruce Roberts/Photo Reserachers, Inc.; **347,** © duomo; **348,** David pMadison/Bruce Coleman, Inc.; **351,** James P. McCoy Photography; **352,** Courtesy, Lisa Mollmann; **353,** Norvia Behling/Animals Animals; **354,** Mike Powell/Allsport; **357,** PhotoEdit.

Chapter Nine: **360,** Victah Sailer/Agence Shot; **366,** Mitchell Layton/© duomo; **367,** Darek Karp/Animals Animals; **369,** Mike James/Photo Researchers, Inc.; **370,** Ken O'Donoghue; **371,** The Granger Collection; **372,** Bjorn Bolstad/Photo Researchers, Inc.; **383,** George Goodwin/Monkmeyer Press; **387,** Tom McHugh/Photo Researchers, Inc.; **388,** Michael Simpson/FPG International; **395,** Ken O'Donoghue; **402,** Victah Sailer/Agence Shot; **405,** David Young-Wolf/PhotoEdit.

Chapter Ten: **410,** Keith Kent/Science Photo Library/Photo Researchers, Inc.; **416,** Mik Dakin/Bruce Coleman, Inc.; **419,** Fred Lyon/Photo Researchers, Inc.; **421,** Ken O'Donoghue; **424,** J. David Taylor/Bruce Coleman, Inc.; **425,** Kevin Larkin/AP/Wide World Photos; **427,** Tony Freeman/PhotoEdit; **432,** Rhoda Sidney/Stock Boston; **434,** David Madison/© duomo; **437,** UPI/Bettmann; **438,** Russ Lappa; **439,** Thomas Kitchin/Tom Stack & Associates; **443,** Jock Montgomery/Bruce Coleman, Inc.

Chapter Eleven: **449,** AP/Wide World Photos; **450,** Dan Helms/© duomo; **452,** David Madison/© duomo; **459,** Sportschrome East/West; **460,** The Granger Collection; **465,** Denis Cahill/The St. Catharines Standard; **466,** Courtesy, The Kon-Tiki Museum, Oslo; **469,** Courtesy, The First Church of Christ Scientist; **472,** C.V. Faint/The Image Bank; **478,** Courtesy, Janna Mendoza; **479,** Gregory MacNicol/Photo Researchers, Inc.; **482,** Mary Mate Denny/PhotoEdit.

Photo Research Toni Michaels

Contributing Author Paul Curtis, Hollis Public Schools, Hollis NH

Editorial, Design, and Electronic Prepress Production, for the Teaching Resources
The Wheetley Company

Editorial Services for the Teacher's Edition
Publishers Resource Group, Inc.